BEEF CATTLE

Frontispiece. The breeding of superior purebred beef cattle is one of the most interesting and constructive enterprises in which a farmer may engage.

BEEF CATTLE

ROSCOE R. SNAPP, Ph.D.

Professor of Animal Science, University of Illinois

With a chapter on

STERILITY

by HARRY HARDENBROOK, Jr., D.V.M., M.S.

Assistant Professor of Veterinary Clinical Medicine
University of Illinois

FOURTH EDITION

NEW YORK
JOHN WILEY & SONS, INC.

CHAPMAN & HALL, LTD.
LONDON

Library of Congress Catalog Card Number: 52–9366

PRINTED IN THE UNITED STATES OF AMERICA

TO MY FATHER
Who always believed that the breeding of
a good grade of livestock was the best business
in which a farmer could engage
this book is affectionately dedicated

Preface to
Fourth Edition

The wide use which has been made of this book by college students, farmers, and ranchers since the first edition in 1925 has caused the author to prepare frequent revisions in an attempt to keep it up to date. The increased interest in beef cattle and the sharp rise in cattle numbers which occurred during the 1940's were accompanied by a notable expansion of the beef cattle research programs of both state and federal experiment stations. Consequently, a great amount of new information on beef cattle feeding and management has become available since the third edition was published in 1939. In order that this new information might be presented in detail without the book's becoming too large to be used as a classroom text, the four chapters of introductory and background materials have been omitted in the present edition. Additional space also has been provided for new subject matter by condensing the treatment accorded a number of topics and omitting entirely some subjects that seemed rather too elementary for a textbook used principally by college students and experienced cattlemen.

Another change that will be noted by those familiar with former editions is the omission of the lists of references at the ends of the chapters. The references have been omitted partly to conserve space and partly to avoid the difficult task of deciding which references should be included. Since it was impossible to list all important references, it was decided to list none. Moreover, it is believed that most teachers will prefer to prepare their own lists of outside readings, in order to include only those references which are easily available to students.

Many of the results of recent feeding experiments are presented in the form of tables. Tables are an effective teaching device for presenting factual data to the student and forcing him to draw his own conclusions from them. Thus he obtains practice in thinking and in expressing himself, which he would not be called upon to do if the data were discussed and the conclusions stated in the text.

Undoubtedly the most important new feature of the fourth edition is a special chapter on sterility written by Dr. Harry Hardenbrook, Jr., of the College of Veterinary Medicine of the University of Illinois. I am deeply indebted to Dr. Hardenbrook for this clear, concise discussion of a subject about which up-to-date, factual information has long been urgently needed by beef cattle breeders. Since sterility usually is the result of a diseased condition, the chapter has been placed at the very end of the book after the chapter on diseases and parasites. However, some instructors may wish to assign this subject immediately after the chapters on reproduction, pregnancy, and parturition have been studied.

When *Beef Cattle* was initially written, it was expected that its use would be confined principally to the Corn Belt states. However, with each revision more and more material has been included about the beef industry of other regions. While the Corn Belt is still given major emphasis, there is perhaps no good reason to imply in the title that the book is of value only to readers who reside there. Indeed, its wide sale elsewhere is unmistakable evidence that it contains much information that is useful in practically all parts of the country, as well as abroad. Consequently, the subtitle "Their Feeding and Management in the Corn Belt States" has been omitted in the new edition.

I wish to acknowledge the generosity of the large number of station directors, professors, and research specialists who have so kindly granted permission to use their tables, charts, photographs, and other material in this new edition. Without such assistance this revision would have been quite impossible. An attempt has been made to cite the source of all such materials and to give credit to the appropriate persons or stations. Any failure to give recognition for help and materials received has been wholly unintentional and is deeply regretted.

ROSCOE R. SNAPP

Urbana, Illinois
September, 1952

Courses in animal feeding and management have been taught in agricultural schools and colleges for over thirty years. At the beginning the material available to the instructor was exceedingly meager, and the courses offered were little more than a description of the feeding methods followed by the successful stockmen of that period. At the present, however, an entirely different situation exists. Such a vast amount of knowledge has accumulated, largely through the work of the state and federal experiment stations that the teacher is at a loss to know what to use and what to reject.

The author himself has faced this dilemma throughout much of the time that he has been responsible for part of the instruction in beef cattle management at the University of Illinois. Finally, some three years ago, he set about to reorganize completely his lecture notes and class room material, retaining in his files only the data that applied directly to the principles and theories he sought to teach. The following pages are the outgrowth of this work.

In preparing the material for publication, the author has had in mind primarily the college student. Hence, some subject-matter has been included which may appear to the general reader and practical stockman to be somewhat irrelevant to the everyday problems of beef cattle production. The author's defense for this apparent digression from his subject is that, if courses in livestock production are to be retained in college curricula, they must be something more than a mere description of what are generally accepted as good feed-lot methods of management. Hence, a textbook on beef cattle designed for college students should be considerably more than a practical feeding manual. In particular, it should include a consideration of the broader aspects of beef production as well as a discussion of the more practical phases of cattle husbandry. These requirements have been ever before the author in the selection and presentation of the subject-matter.

In most cases the principles and theories presented are accompanied by the data on which the author's opinions are based. Hence, if the reader is inclined to disagree, he may draw his own conclusions without stopping to look up the particular bulletin or journal in which the original data appear. It is believed that teachers will also find these data useful in making up problems and exercises to be done outside the class room.

The author desires to acknowledge his great indebtedness to his former teacher and present co-worker, Professor H. P. Rusk, from whom he has obtained many of the ideas found on the following pages; also to Mr. J. H. Knox, for the valuable suggestions and criticisms given on many parts of the manuscript. He is likewise deeply grateful to the men in the various experiment stations and in the United States Department of Agriculture, who furnished him with many data not yet issued in bulletin form. He would also mention the kindness of the United States Department of Agriculture, The Breeder's Gazette, and various other publishing companies, as well as many individuals, who furnished or loaned illustrations or extended copyright privileges. In all such cases, the donors of the material used are named in accompanying footnotes.

ROSCOE R. SNAPP

Urbana, Illinois
September 1, 1925

Contents

PART 1. GENERAL ASPECTS OF THE BEEF-CATTLE INDUSTRY

1. Phases and Areas of Beef Production 3
2. The Relation of Beef Cattle to General Farming 19
3. The Relation of Beef Cattle to Soil Fertility 30

PART 2. THE BREEDING HERD

4. Advantages and Disadvantages of a Breeding Herd . . . 45
5. When to Start a Breeding Herd 49
6. The Selection of Breeding Stock 52
7. Reproduction and Mating 83
8. Pregnancy 102
9. Parturition 112
10. The Summer Management of the Breeding Herd 127
11. The Winter Management of the Breeding Herd 149
12. Weaning, Dehorning, Castration, and Marking of Calves . . 174
13. Feeding and Care of Young Cattle 188

PART 3. FATTENING CATTLE FOR MARKET

14. Fattening Cattle for Market 217
15. The Importance of Age in Growth and Fattening 228
16. The Importance of Grade and Sex in Feeder Cattle . . . 237
17. The Use of Grain in Fattening Cattle 262
18. Carbonaceous Concentrates and Their Use in the Fattening Ration 278
19. Protein Requirements and How to Supply Them 310
20. The Principal Nitrogenous Concentrates Used in Cattle Feeding . 329
21. Roughage and Its Use in the Fattening Ration 357
22. Common Roughages Used in Fattening 366
23. Corn Silage as a Feed for Fattening Cattle 386
24. A Comparison of Various Silages for Cattle 407
25. Grass as a Feed for Fattening Cattle 426
26. Miscellaneous Feeding Stuffs 459
27. The Preparation of Feeds for Beef Cattle 474
28. Methods of Feeding 497

PART 4. GENERAL PROBLEMS IN BEEF PRODUCTION

29. Baby-Beef Production 509
30. The Marketing of Cattle 527

31. The Financial Aspect of Beef Production 546
32. Fitting Cattle for Show and Sale   572
33. Buildings and Equipment for Beef Cattle 584
34. Diseases and Parasites Affecting Beef Cattle 596
35. Sterility (*by Dr. Harry Hardenbrook, Jr.*) 627
    Index   635

PART · 1

General Aspects of the Beef-Cattle Industry

1 —————————————————

The production of beef cattle differs from that of most other kinds of livestock in that the operation is frequently divided into several distinct steps or phases. It is possible to carry on all these phases on a single farm as successive steps of a continuous process. More often, however, one or two are carried on to the exclusion of the others, not only as regards individual farms, but also as regards agricultural regions. In addition, we have some two or three highly specialized forms of beef production that differ so much in methods of management from those commonly followed as to deserve special mention.

PHASES OF BEEF PRODUCTION

1. Breeding and Rearing Calves. Breeding calves and raising them to weaning age constitute the initial and most fundamental steps in the process of beef production. They provide, so to speak, the raw material out of which the finished bullocks will eventually be made. As the breeding herd needs but little grain or other expensive feeds, the rearing of beef calves is confined chiefly to those sections that possess an abundance of cheap grazing land. Hence, we find the important breeding centers located either in regions that are but sparsely settled or in hilly areas where the land is too rolling to be farmed to advantage. Climate also plays an important part in determining the location of the breeding industry. The southern and southwestern states have a decided advantage over those farther north, as the calves are born from 4 to 6 weeks earlier and are larger and heavier when marketed in the fall.

The raising of beef calves is carried on most successfully on comparatively large farms, as but little more labor is involved in caring for a herd of 50 to 80 cows than for one of 10 to 20. So long as there exist in the world extensive areas of free or very low-priced grazing lands where large herds are cared for at the rate of only 1 man for each 500 cows, so long will the farmer who operates a quarter section of high-priced land find it unprofitable to engage extensively in breeding beef calves for the open market. This statement should not be construed to mean that a breeding herd may not have a place on a great many Corn

3

Belt farms. What is meant is that the breeding of commercial cattle will necessarily be of secondary importance to some other enterprise that will utilize more efficiently the available land and labor. On such farms the breeding herd will be a sort of by-product plant in which the unmarketable products of the farm will be successfully utilized. The number of beef breeding cows has increased greatly in the Corn Belt states during the past ten years, partly because of existing high prices of beef cattle and partly because beef cattle have been needed to utilize the increased amounts of hay and pasture that have resulted from better rotations and the seeding down of fields that eroded seriously when plowed. Most of these cows are maintained throughout the year on pasture and unmarketable roughages, and thus interfere little with the production of grain.

Apart from the return realized from the utilization of otherwise waste feeds is the advantage of having one's own source of supply of calves to put into one's feed lots. While there appears to be no permanent shortage of good western-bred cattle for Corn Belt feeders, home-grown calves are in many respects superior. This point will be further discussed in connection with the production of "baby beef."

2. Growing of Stockers. By definition, a stocker is a young animal that is being fed and cared for in such a way that growth rather than an improvement in condition may be realized. Stock cattle are of two kinds, heifers that are intended for use in the breeding herd, and steers and heifers that are intended for the market. In either case the principal purpose in the mind of the owner is to effect as much economy in feeding and management as is consistent with normal growth and development. Necessarily, then, stockers are handled only by farmers who have much cheap feed, either in the form of cheap pasture or cheap harvested roughage such as hay, straw, fodder, and silage. Since stock heifers that are intended for breeding purposes will be in demand principally in the breeding centers where they have been produced, few animals of this class are to be found outside such areas. In general, their method of management is much like that of the breeding herd.

With stockers intended for the market, however, we have a somewhat different situation. Such cattle may be grown out in the region where they were bred and reared, by allowing them to graze cheap grass land of the same character as that used by their mothers; or they may be shipped soon after they are weaned, either to grazing areas that are not fully stocked with cows and young calves, or to grain-growing sections where they ultimately will be fattened. In grain sections their feed will consist mainly of the aftermath of meadows, legume pasture crops grown in the regular farm rotation, stalk fields, oat straw, legume hay, corn stover, and silage. Many cattle feeders of the Corn Belt make a practice of buying their cattle as calves or yearlings and carrying them on such feeds for six months or a year before putting them into the feed lot. In this way the by-products of grain farming are utilized; any undesirable or unthrifty cattle are weeded out before the use of expensive feeds is begun; and, what is probably most important of all, the cattle are purchased when market conditions are particularly favorable to the buyer.

Stock cattle may be put in at almost any time of year on a well-diversified farm. Hence, an order for their purchase may be placed in the hands of a commission firm with instructions to buy when the next "big bargain day" occurs. On the other hand, cattle that are to go directly into the feed lot must be purchased within a rather short period, unless the plans for feeding and marketing are to be disarranged. It often happens that feeder cattle are selling unusually high at the time the farmer wishes to start his feeding operations. Had he bought his animals from three to six months earlier, during a time of market depression, and carried them along on rough feed until he really needed them, he might have effected a saving in the cost price of $1 to $5 per hundredweight.

Stockers are seldom carried more than a year before they are placed in the feed lot or sold to some other cattleman for further development or fattening. A more common practice in the Corn Belt is to keep them only through the grazing season of summer and fall, or during the fall and winter months when stalk fields, corn stover, oat straw, silage, and other coarse roughages are available

3. Fattening for Market. In some sections of the country the grass is sufficiently abundant and nutritious to enable mature cattle to fatten on it without any additional feed. Most grazing areas, however, are so heavily stocked that they will furnish little more than a growing ration for the animals they carry, making it necessary to use liberal amounts of harvested feeds in finishing the cattle for market. The greatest production of such feeds is found in the Corn Belt, and it is here that we find the center of the cattle-fattening industry. Other important fattening sections are in the irrigated valleys of north central Colorado, where the cattle are fed large quantities of sugar beet by-products, and in the tobacco and truck growing sections of the eastern states where cattle feeding is carried on principally to obtain the manure needed to grow these high-profit crops successfully.

In those sections of the Corn Belt where the land is somewhat rolling and where considerable pasture is available, the common method of fattening cattle is to feed corn on grass during the summer and fall months. Such sections often produce a small percentage of their supply of feeders, the balance being purchased from the western states. In the Corn Belt proper, however, where most of the land is tillable, the cattle are finished almost entirely on harvested feeds and the feeding is confined mainly to the winter months. The common practice is to buy, in the fall, cattle that are ready to go directly into the feed lot. They are accustomed to a full feed of grain as soon as possible, and by April or May are usually carrying sufficient flesh to be satisfactory to the butcher. Cattle handled in this way interfere very little with the growing of crops. They arrive at the farm in the fall about the time the corn is harvested, and leave in the spring before the busy season begins. While many cattle fattened in the Corn Belt are carried well into the summer and fall, either in dry lot or on pasture, they are owned for the most part by large operators who have one or more men who do relatively little field work and devote most of their time to caring for the livestock on the farm.

The fattening of cattle for market has several important advantages in addition to the direct financial profit realized from the enterprise. One of the benefits is the fertility that remains on the farm in the manure. Farms on which cattle have been fed over a period of years are much more productive, as a rule, than adjoining farms where grain and hay have been sold. Cattle feeding offers an opportunity to utilize to advantage damaged grain and hay that would contribute very little to the farm income if sold for cash. Farmers located at a considerable distance from shipping points are able to reduce considerably their marketing expenses by marketing the products of their farms through cattle instead of in the form of hay and grain. Still another source of income from feeding cattle is the gain made by the hogs which are kept in the feed lot to utilize the grain that is not thoroughly masticated by the cattle and, hence, is only partially digested.

Cattle feeding, like other industries that derive their profits from buying raw materials and selling them several months later in the form of a finished product, involves some speculative risk. This risk is necessarily high where both cattle and feed are purchased, and the temptation is ever present to expand or contract operations according to the prospect of favorable or unfavorable prices for fat cattle in the future. However, in a regular, conservative feeding program that is adapted to marketing the feeds grown on a given farm, the risk is probably no greater than that connected with a number of other major farm enterprises.

4. Baby-Beef Production. Strictly fat, young cattle, varying in age from 10 to 15 months and weighing 650 to 850 pounds, are called "baby beeves." Baby beeves, like "hot house" lambs, represent a highly specialized form of livestock production, quite different in many respects from that commonly followed in producing the rank and file of market animals. In making them fat at so early an age, unstinted use must be made of palatable and highly nutritious feeding stuffs. Hence, it follows that baby-beef production is carried on almost wholly within the Corn Belt states, where an adequate supply of grain and other concentrates may be had at a reasonable cost.

Strictly speaking, the production of baby beef implies the breeding, rearing, and fattening of the calves on the same farm. As only calves of strictly beef type will exhibit a pronounced tendency to fatten at so early an age, the breeding herd itself must exhibit those characteristics that signify early maturity and a pronounced disposition to put on flesh. Since mother's milk is the best fattening feed that either nature or man has as yet devised, the cows should be chosen with an eye to their milking ability. Grain is placed before the calves as soon as they are old enough to eat, which is usually when they are from 4 to 6 weeks old. At no time during their short lives are they allowed to experience the feeling of hunger. Roughage occupies a minor place in the fattening ration, as the calves have little capacity for much roughage after consuming the desired amount of grain. However, the presence of the cow herd on the farm insures the utilization of all roughage materials. Thus, the cows and calves taken together furnish a means of marketing practically all the crops commonly grown on Corn Belt farms.

Buyers have shown an increasing interest, during recent years, in younger and lighter cattle, and baby beeves have for some time enjoyed an enviable market position. This has led a number of feeders who lack either the facilities or the aptitude for maintaining a breeding herd to attempt to produce baby beeves from western-bred calves bought on the market in the fall, soon after they are weaned. As a rule, however, such calves are inferior to home-bred calves, in that they suffer many hardships while en route to and from market and arrive at Corn Belt feed lots very tired and noticeably lacking in condition. Moreover, they are wholly unaccustomed to grain and must be fed very carefully for 5 to 8 weeks while being gradually got on to a full feed. Despite these handicaps western calves carrying considerable flesh and showing excellent breeding can be finished into baby beeves of a very acceptable type if carefully handled and fed for a period of 6 or 7 months. However, a majority of range-bred calves require from 8 to 10 months of feeding to make them sufficiently fat to grade "prime," at the end of which time they are 16 to 20 months of age and weigh 900 to 1050 pounds. On the market they are commonly referred to as "short yearlings" rather than "baby beeves."

5. Dual-Purpose Cattle. Despite the fact that milk production has received but little attention in the development of our modern type of beef cattle, it is nevertheless true that beef-bred cows are depended upon by a large number of farmers for the family's milk supply.[1] In not a few cases, cream is sold for buttermaking from farms where the cows show more beef than dairy breeding. From the standpoint of dairy products alone, such cows are not likely to be highly profitable. But for the general farmer who keeps cows largely to obtain the greatest possible diversification of enterprise and the full utilization of all farm products, dual-purpose cattle apparently fill a real economic need.

The value of a dual-purpose cow lies in her flexibility of management. She is like a double-barreled shotgun, in that if she doesn't strike a profit with one "shot" she probably will with the other. If dairy products are relatively high and there is sufficient labor to take care of them—a situation usually encountered during the fall and winter months—she can be hand-milked and her calf bucket-fed or sold for veal. If, on the other hand, dairy products sell for scarcely enough to cover the cost of production, or if a shortage of labor exist, she can be given an extra calf, besides her own, to raise, with fairly good assurance that their value at weaning time will cover all items of expense involved in their production.

Dual-purpose cows are especially well adapted to Corn Belt conditions. The size of the farms in this region often precludes the keeping of beef herds of sufficient size to be profitable. Dual-purpose herds, however, need not be so large, inasmuch as the returns per cow are much greater. Also, the labor requirements of dual-purpose cattle vary more or less directly with the number kept; whereas in the case of beef cattle they do not. Thus, a herd of 8 or 10 good dual-purpose cows will often return a fair wage for nearly full-time employment for 1 man during the fall and winter months. The same number of beef cows could be counted on for hardly more than an eighth or a tenth of the wages of their herdsman, inasmuch as a herd eight or ten times as large would require the full time of but 1 man.

Methods of Handling a Dual-Purpose Herd. Seldom are all the cows in a dual-purpose herd hand-milked. Beef being a product, as well as milk, some consideration must be given to the needs of the

[1] A survey made of the cattle of South Dakota in 1947 showed that approximately 70 per cent of all cows milked in that state were of Hereford breeding.

calves. While it is possible to put the calves on skim-milk after they are six or eight weeks old, a more common way is to allow them to suckle until old enough to wean. Some farmers follow the practice of allowing the calves to run with the cows during the day only, the cows being milked in the morning. Others will permit the calves to take only a portion of their mothers' milk, the remainder being taken for

Fig. 1. A trio of excellent dual-purpose cows. Cows of this type will produce both milk for the dairy and calves for the feed lot.

household and market purposes. Still another way is to milk only the best cows, allowing the calves to suckle the remainder. When the last method is used, a common practice is to put two calves apiece on most of the cows that are not milked.

Calves from dual-purpose cows are, as a rule, fed a good grain ration as soon as they are old enough to eat, and are pushed hard from the start. When so handled they can be marketed as baby beeves when around fifteen months of age. However, they are not so satisfactory for this purpose as the best beef-bred calves, because of their lack of that extreme beef type which insures early maturity and thick fleshing qualities.

6. **Breeding Purebred Cattle.** The breeding of purebred cattle is a highly specialized form of beef production, for which comparatively few men are well fitted. Because of the relatively large amount of capital required for animals and equipment, and because of the skill and sound judgment that must be possessed by the manager before

success is possible, this phase of cattle breeding is one better suited to men of considerable experience than to beginners. It should, however, be the ultimate goal of a large number of breeders, particularly if it is to be carried on in connection with the production of the highest type of cattle for the open market.

The opportunities offered the breeder of purebred cattle are almost unlimited. Honor, fame, and large financial rewards are all within the possibility of realization. The purebred cattle business in this country, large though it is, is still in its infancy. That great strides will be taken in its expansion during the immediate future is scarcely to be doubted.

Ranchers in the western states, where cattle are the principal source of income, have long recognized the value of purebred stock and have been willing to pay from $500 to $1500 apiece for young purebred bulls to produce grade calves and yearlings to sell on the market. Farmers in the Corn Belt, however, who maintain small breeding herds as a minor enterprise, have been slow to recognize the importance of superior breeding. Too often they have been unwilling to pay more for a herd bull than the amount received for a fat steer at the market. During the decade of the 1940's, however, Corn Belt farmers witnessed the outstanding value of hybrid corn and now realize that pedigrees may be very valuable in predicting the breeding ability of both plants and animals. Consequently, the time is ripe for a strong demand for bulls of proven merit from owners of grade beef herds.

Although purebred beef cattle have increased noticeably in the Corn Belt in recent years, they have not kept pace with the increase of grade beef cows in this area. When it is considered that probably not over 35 per cent of the grade beef cows of the Corn Belt are now bred to purebred bulls and that probably half of the purebred beef bulls now used in grade herds are of mediocre merit, the future market for young purebred bulls with production records or with progeny-tested sires appears unusually bright. Purebred herds in the western part of the Corn Belt are still the source of supply for many bulls for the Western Range, while the purebred breeders of Illinois, Indiana, and Ohio will be called upon more and more to supply large numbers of purebred males and females for the rapidly expanding beef cattle industry of the South.

AREAS OF BEEF PRODUCTION[2]

Four rather well-defined areas of beef production exist in the United States. Each differs from the others in the extent to which beef pro-

[2] U. S. D. A. Yearbook, 1921, p. 245.

duction is carried on and in the relative importance of the various phases of management that have just been discussed. Obviously, each of these areas may be divided into still smaller regions, each of which is noted for some particular phase of cattle raising or for some rather unusual method of handling its cattle. However, no attempt will be made to indicate these smaller subdivisions, inasmuch as interest in them is largely local.

1. The Western Range. The Western Range consists roughly of that area lying west of the one-hundredth meridian. This area may be further divided into the Great Plains region, the Rocky Mountain region, the Pacific Coast region, the American Desert region, and certain smaller sections of more or less local importance.[3]

In this area the breeding of calves and the growing out of young cattle on grass are the dominant phases of beef production. Owing to the great amount of cheap grazing land, some of which is still public domain, this region is particularly well suited for these extensive, rather than intensive, forms of cattle raising. Although some of the more mature steers have sufficient flesh, when removed from grass in the fall, to make them acceptable for immediate slaughter, the majority of the cattle are sold as feeders for further finishing.

Inasmuch as beef production is a major enterprise with a majority of the farmers of this area, we find the cattle well bred and handled according to modern methods of ranch management. According to figures gathered by the United States Department of Agriculture, over 77 per cent of the cattle of the Rocky Mountain states show a predominance of the blood of one of the three modern beef breeds.[4] This percentage is much higher than that for any other section of the country.

Formerly most of the purebred bulls used in improving the type and quality of the range cattle were purchased from Corn Belt breeders, but at the present time a large percentage of the bulls used in the range area are bred there. In fact, breeding good bulls for sale to commercial ranchers, as well as breeding superior young bulls and heifers to go into other purebred herds, is now a highly important phase of beef production in the Western Range states. This is especially true of the Hereford breed, which is the most popular breed in this area.

2. The Corn Belt. This area is noted for its broad stretches of prairie land and for its exceedingly fertile soil. Hence, it is a region

[3] See Fig. 2.

[4] Percentages by states are as follows: Wyoming, 82.7; Montana, 81.4; New Mexico, 81.1; Colorado, 78.5; Utah, 74.8; Arizona, 70.2; and Idaho, 64.1. U. S. D. A. Yearbook, 1920, p. 731.

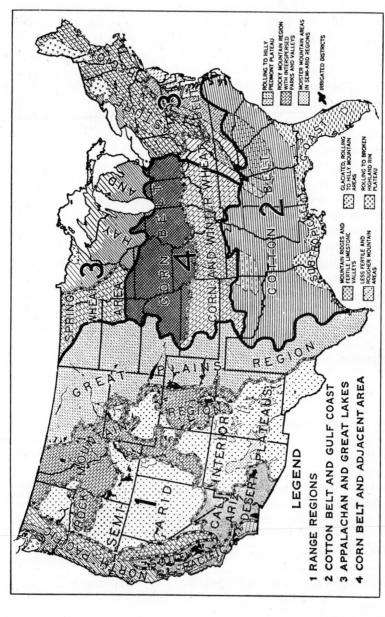

Fig. 2. The four important areas of beef production. The methods followed in each area are determined largely by the climate and the feed supply. (*Courtesy U.S.D.A.*)

devoted largely to the growing of crops.   Because of the high price of land, we find rather small to medium-sized farms, which are devoted largely to general farming but on which grain growing occupies the place of major importance.   Intensive rather than extensive methods of husbandry prevail.

Beef production, under such conditions, necessarily assumes quite a different rôle from that which it plays in the Western Range area,

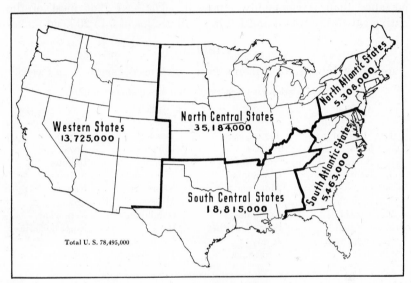

FIG. 3.   Total cattle and calves on farms and ranches, Jan. 1, 1949.   Nearly half of all cattle and calves were in the North Central states.
(*Swift and Co. Agr. Research Bull.* **15.**)

where land is plentiful and cheap.   It, too, is carried on according to intensive rather than extensive methods of management.   The fattening of western-grown cattle, either in dry lot or on a limited amount of pasture, represents the typical method of handling cattle in the Corn Belt.   As a rule, the cattle are bought in the fall at public stockyards, feeder cattle auctions, or direct from the range.   They are commonly allowed to run on pastures and stalk fields for 3 or 4 weeks while becoming accustomed to corn, at the end of which time they are confined in dry lots and given a full feed of grain.   Normally, 6 to 9 months are required to produce satisfactory market bullocks, though many feeders make no attempt to finish their cattle, shipping at the end of what is termed a "short feed" of 90 to 120 days.

Summer feeding on grass is the method commonly followed in sections that are somewhat rolling and, hence, have large areas in pasture. Because of the scarcity of thin cattle in the spring, steers that are to be fed on pasture are often bought in the fall and carried through the winter on such feeds as straw, stover, hay, and silage, which tend to produce growth rather than fat. Thus, two phases of beef production are represented in such a method of management.

Breeding operations in the Corn Belt, although smaller than they were at the beginning of the twentieth century, are still of more importance than is commonly supposed. The fact that most of the native calves are raised and fed in small groups of 5 to 20 head makes

TABLE 1

IMPORTANCE OF CORN BELT IN THE PRODUCTION OF PUREBRED BEEF CATTLE*

States in Which Largest Number of Calves were Registered in 1950

	Aberdeen Angus	Hereford	Polled Hereford	Shorthorn and Polled Shorthorn
1.	Missouri	Texas	Texas	Illinois
2.	Iowa	Kansas	Illinois	Iowa
3.	Illinois	Nebraska	Kansas	Indiana
4.	Kentucky	Oklahoma	Missouri	Missouri
5.	Kansas	Montana	Nebraska	Kansas
6.	Indiana	Missouri	Mississippi	Ohio
7.	Texas	Colorado	Oklahoma	Nebraska
8.	Virginia	South Dakota	Iowa	North Dakota
9.	Oklahoma	Iowa	California	Oklahoma
10.	Ohio	California	Tennessee	South Dakota

* Information from annual reports of breed secretaries.

the breeding industry less spectacular than the feeding of shipped-in cattle, which are frequently handled in droves of 50 to several hundred. Nevertheless, fully two-thirds of the cattle and calves normally slaughtered within the Corn Belt or shipped from there to central markets are native cattle which have been bred in this region. Whereas a considerable portion of these cattle are discarded dairy cows and veal calves, a large number are young cattle of beef and dual-purpose breeding which are marketed as fat yearlings or as baby beeves.

Another aspect of breeding operations in the Corn Belt is the raising of purebred cattle. This region, because of its abundant feed supply and its proximity to the Western Range and the Cotton Belt areas, enjoys particularly favorable conditions for the raising of purebred beef cattle. The former makes possible low costs of production, whereas the latter insures a broad market for all surplus breeding stock.

3. **The Appalachian and Great Lakes Region.** This region is noted for its rolling topography, which in places assumes a really mountainous character. Under such conditions, permanent pastures and woodlands naturally occupy a considerable portion of the total area. As always in broken regions, wide variations exist in the character and fertility of the soil. In certain sections there are extensive outcrops of limestone on which the best bluegrass of the country is found. Grass grown on such a soil is exceedingly nutritious and is valued highly by cattle grazers. Such areas are usually stocked with mature steers, which fatten satisfactorily during the summer on this grass alone. In other areas of this region the soil is very thin and produces but a scanty growth of grass and weeds of inferior feeding value. These areas are used mainly by breeding herds or by young stocker cattle that have been purchased in the West and South. At the end of the grazing season these cattle are either fattened on feeds grown on the bottom land or are held over for another summer, being wintered on hay, stover, and silage.

The presence of numerous towns and cities, together with good transportation facilities, makes the northeastern part of the United States an ideal place for the production of dairy products. This fact, coupled with the relatively small size of the none-too-productive farms, tends to bring about a condition particularly favorable for the production of dual-purpose cattle. Western Pennsylvania and the adjacent portions of Ohio and New York have established a national reputation as a breeding center of Milking Shorthorns. In the New England states both the Shorthorn and Devon breeds are valued for their dual-purpose qualities.

Despite the predominance of dairy and dual-purpose cattle in the Appalachian and Great Lakes region, beef cattle have increased noticeably in numbers there since the mid-1930's. Especially is this true in Michigan, Maryland, and the Virginias. Many farms and plantations in these states, which formerly produced principally truck, cash grain crops, or tobacco, are now largely in grass utilized by beef cattle. Many excellent purebred herds of beef cattle have been established in this area and are a source of improved breeding stock for the rapidly expanding beef industry of the Southeastern states. The Appalachian and Great Lakes states are better suited for the production of grass than for any other agricultural product because of the rolling topography. Hence it is a natural beef cattle area, and further increases in the beef cattle population may be expected as more and more land is taken out of cultivation and is used for pasture and hay.

4. The Cotton Belt. Except for the two states Texas and Oklahoma, the Cotton Belt has not been an important beef-producing region until recently. As a rule, but few cattle were found on each farm, and often these were noticeably lacking in type and quality. Some years ago, Jersey blood became widely disseminated over a great part of the South, which, together with the original Spanish ancestry, imparted "mealy" noses and yellow and brindle colors to a considerable percentage of the calves. Owing to poor breeding and unfavorable environment, such animals were small and underdeveloped, often being no larger at two years of age than the average western-bred yearling.

Several factors have served to handicap beef production in the South, chief of which has been the southern-fever tick. These ticks are the carriers of a protozoan which gains access to the blood stream of cattle upon their being bitten by the ticks. These organisms produce the disease known as southern, splenetic, or tick fever.[5] The disease is nearly always fatal to adult animals, but young calves as a rule recover and are thereafter immune. However, their growth is seriously retarded by the pain and annoyance caused by the ticks and by the loss of considerable quantities of blood, which the ticks consume.

Since tick fever is so fatal to adult animals, it was impossible to bring many purebred cattle into tick-infested regions to improve the native stock. Hence, the first step in the establishment of the beef industry in the South was the extermination of the ticks. This task, begun in 1906, has been virtually completed by the periodic dipping of all cattle in infested areas under the supervision of federal and state veterinarians. As the tick has been exterminated, improved blood has been brought in and the cattle of the South have increased greatly in both numbers and quality.

Other factors that have served to retard the development of beef production in the South have been an interest in cotton growing to the exclusion of other forms of husbandry, and a lack of pasture and forage crops possessing a high feeding value. Happily, both these hindrances are rapidly disappearing with the accelerated movement toward diversified farming. The one-crop farmer, who spent all his time and energy on a field or two of cotton, leaving his few cattle to eke out a miserable existence on the wild cane and wire grass that grew on those parts of the plantation unsuited for cotton growing, has been replaced to a great extent by one who grows a variety of crops, among which are both grains and forages for livestock. With its large amount

[5] This disease is commonly called Texas fever by northern cattlemen, because it has on a few occasions been carried into the North by Texas cattle.

of rolling land unsuited for cultivation, its short, mild winters and long grazing season, and the multitude of forage crops that can be successfully grown, the South is the logical place to look for that expansion in beef production which must occur if the growing demands of an ever-increasing population are to be met. That the cattle population of the South has been increasing at a faster rate than that of any other section of the country is shown by Table 2.

TABLE 2

RELATIVE GROWTH MADE IN TOTAL CATTLE NUMBERS IN DIFFERENT AREAS OF THE UNITED STATES*
(1930–1950)

Area	Total Cattle, 1930 (millions)	Total Cattle, 1950 (millions)	Per Cent Increase	Rank
New England	1,122	1,145	2	9
Middle Atlantic	3,595	4,242	18	8
East North Central	9,606	12,786	33	5
West North Central	17,877	22,958	28	7
South Atlantic	3,717	5,866	58	2
East South Central	3,532	6,074	72	1
West South Central	8,837	13,961	58	2
Mountain	6,574	8,544	30	6
Pacific	3,118	4,701	51	4
Total United States	57,978	80,277	38	

*Compiled from U.S.D.A. Agricultural Statistics, 1931 and 1950.

The Beef Cattle Cycle. A study of the fluctuations in the cattle population of the United States over a series of years discloses that these fluctuations have not been haphazard but have followed a rather regular order. Periods of large cattle numbers have occurred about every 14 to 16 years. Likewise, periods of unusually low numbers of cattle have been separated by about the same interval. (See Fig. 4.) As price is a function of supply, it follows that approximately the same time intervenes between periods of very high prices or between periods of very low prices, viz., about 15 years. This interval of time, which is termed "the cattle cycle," is much used by agricultural statisticians and market forecasters in predicting the supply and price of cattle in the immediate future. Having located our place on "the cycle" with reference to the last "peak" or "low spot," we have but to construct that part of the curve which represents the next 5 or 6 years to see what supply and price changes are likely to occur during that period. However, it should be pointed out that the price of cattle is not determined by the cattle population but by the number of cattle which are marketed and by the consumer demand for beef. Consequently, any event that will change either of these factors will have far more effect upon cattle prices than will the total number of cattle in the country. For example, the severe droughts that were experienced on the Range and in the Corn Belt during 1934 and 1936 resulted in a sharp reduction in the number of cattle after only 5 or 6 years of expansion instead of the usual 7 or 8. The decline in numbers was abnormally severe but was of short duration because of the advent of World War II.

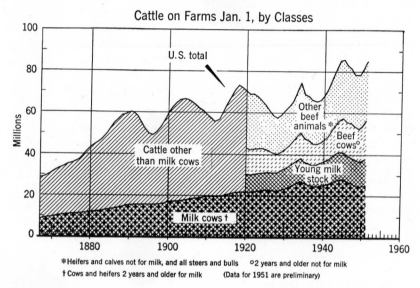

Cattle on Farms Jan. 1, by Classes

*Heifers and calves not for milk, and all steers and bulls   °2 years and older not for milk
† Cows and heifers 2 years and older for milk   (Data for 1951 are preliminary)

Fig. 4. Cycles in beef production, 1865–1951. It will be noted that "peaks" in the cattle population have occurred about every 15 or 16 years.
(*Courtesy U.S.D.A.*)

The heavy demand for beef by both military and civilian consumers during the war resulted in cattle numbers' and cattle prices' rising together, whereas, normally, when numbers increase, prices fall. Hence, the cattle cycle may be greatly disturbed by unforeseen abnormal conditions. For this reason it should not be followed blindly but should be regarded only as a very rough guide in planning a cattle enterprise on an individual farm.

2 ——————— The Relation of Beef Cattle to General Farming

For the farmer who makes a practice of growing a variety of crops and who divides his time between grain and animal production, beef cattle possess some advantages over other kinds of livestock. Some of these advantages are of sufficient importance to warrant their analysis and discussion. Attention should be called to the fact that some of the data cited in support of certain statements are based on all cattle—both beef and dairy. Unfortunately, available statistics do not permit an accurate separation of these two types for making some highly desirable studies. The advantages of beef cattle are briefly discussed below under six heads.

1. **Cattle Utilize Large Quantities of Roughage.** Any system of general farming produces a large quantity of coarse, low-grade roughages that have a very low market value. In the common Corn Belt rotation of corn, corn, oats, and clover, approximately 1¾ tons of

TABLE 3

SOURCE OF ALL FEED FED DIFFERENT CLASSES OF LIVESTOCK*
(Average 1942–1946)

	Per Cent of Total Feed Fed				
	Beef Cattle	Dairy Cattle	Hogs	Sheep	Poultry
Corn	12.8	8.1	69.2	2.6	39.2
Other grain	2.5	7.7	17.4	2.4	31.5
Commercial by-products	2.3	8.4	6.2	1.0	22.7
Seeds and skim milk	0.6	2.0	4.6	...	1.9
Hay	14.1	26.5	...	12.5	...
Silage and stover	7.5	9.9	...	3.1	...
Pasture	60.2	37.4	2.6	78.4	4.7
Total	100.0	100.0	100.0	100.0	100.0

* U.S.D.A. Circular 836, December, 1949.

roughage are produced for every ton of grain secured. Of this roughage, that resulting from the corn crop is practically unsalable, and the oat straw and clover hay are often hard to dispose of at remunera-

19

TABLE 4

ESTIMATED PRODUCTION OF CEREAL STRAW AND PERCENT USED, 1945*

Geographical Area	Estimated Production of Straw, 1945 (1000 tons)	Left in Field as Stubble, Chaff, and Short Straw from Combines (1000 tons)	Recoverable for Use on Farms or for Sale (1000 tons)	Recoverable Straw That Was: Used on Farm or Sold (Per cent)	Recoverable Straw That Was: Left in Field or Otherwise Not Used (Per cent)	Calculated Total Amount of Straw Left in Field Which Could Have Been Recovered if Cut with Binder and Threshed (1000 tons)	Approximate Number of Cows That Could Be Wintered on Waste Straw if Fed with Five Lbs. of Legume Hay per Head Daily[a]
Corn Belt	23,038	9,707	13,331	66.6	33.4	14,160	3,540,000
Lake	17,397	5,174	12,223	78.5	21.5	7,802	1,950,000
Great Plains	49,189	22,064	27,125	25.7	74.3	42,218	10,554,000
Oklahoma-Texas	11,131	5,754	5,377	15.8	84.2	10,281	2,570,000
United States	134,518	58,112	76,406	45.1	54.9	100,059	25,015,000

* U.S.D.A., Harvesting Small Grains and Utilization of the Straw, F. M. 66, June, 1947.

[a] Allowing 4 tons of straw per cow for feed and bedding.

tive prices, especially if damaged slightly by rain or by the presence of weeds. All these roughages, when properly fed, constitute good feed for beef cattle and will, on the average, return more to the farmer when fed than when sold on the market.

At the present time, large quantities of corn stover are allowed to go to waste, which if properly stored and fed, would support millions of beef cows and stocker cattle during the winter months. The annual production of both straws and stover in the United States is enormous, being nearly 175,000,000 tons. When this amount is compared with the total production of wild and tame hay, viz., 100,000,000 tons, the importance of the roughages that are by-products of grain production is realized. In the Corn Belt area, where a system of general farming is the rule, the percentage which stover and straw constitute of the total roughage supply is even more important than for the country as a whole. That but a comparatively small amount of this vast quantity of roughage is efficiently used in this area is indicated by Tables 4 and 5.

A more efficient utilization of all farm products is one of the important problems of the general farmer. With these coarse roughages beef cattle offer a solution that will usually be found satisfactory. Mature beef cows and stocker steers can be maintained satisfactorily on rations composed of roughage alone, whereas steers that are being fattened for the market consume from 50 to 300 per cent as much roughage as grain, depending on the degree to which their grain ration is limited. Professor Case,[1] summarizing the cost account data obtained from a typical cattle feeder in western Illinois over a period of seven years, states that the ratio of roughage to concentrates fed was 141 to 100.[2] Thus, it is seen that beef cattle are well adapted to utilize the surplus roughages that are produced under a system of general farming.

2. Cattle Utilize Pasture Crops. The importance of pasture crops in the Corn Belt states is often overlooked. Many people are prone to regard this area as being devoted almost entirely to the growing of grain. Instead, the Corn Belt, together with the Middle Atlantic States to the eastward, constitutes the general farming section of the country, and it is here that livestock farming, as well as grain production, reaches its highest state of development.

Such being the case, pastures necessarily occupy no small fraction of the total farm area. Contrary to the opinion held by some, permanent pastures have by no means disappeared in the Corn Belt, nor is it at all

[1] Illinois Bulletin 261, 1925.
[2] Including straw used for bedding.

TABLE 5

CORN HARVESTING METHODS AND UTILIZATION*

(1943 Crop)

Geographical Area	Corn Harvested in 1943 (1000 acres)	Harvested from Standing Stalks (per cent)	Cut and Shocked (per cent)	Hogged, Grazed, or Cut, and Fed Green (per cent)	Cut for Silage (per cent)	Average Yield of Grain per Acre[a] (bushel)	Estimated Stover Represented by Standing Stalks[b] (1000 tons)	Approximate Number of Cows That Could Be Wintered on the Stover Represented by Standing Stalks[c]
Appalachian	6,021	52.5	45.1	1.5	0.9	26	2,875	719,000
Corn Belt	31,420	83.2	12.2	2.6	2.0	49	44,830	11,207,000
Lake	9,252	50.4	24.8	4.0	20.8	43	7,020	1,755,000
Great Plains	16,667	79.4	6.8	10.9	2.9	26	12,045	3,011,000
United States	94,445	76.3	14.7	4.4	4.6	32.5	82,000	20,500,000

Total beef cows 2 years old and over in United States Jan. 1, 1944, 15,500,000[d]

* U.S.D.A. F. M. 49, Harvesting the Corn Crop, April, 1945.
[a] Computed from U.S.D.A. Agricultural Statistics, 1945.
[b] Assuming production of stover equal to weight of husked ears (70 pounds per bushel).
[c] Allowing 4 tons of corn stover per cow for 6-month period.
[d] From U.S.D.A. Agricultural Statistics, 1945.

TABLE 6

IMPORTANCE OF PASTURE IN GENERAL FARMING AREA*

	Average Pasture Acreage per Farm			Percentage of Total Farm Area in Pasture		
	Crop Land Used Only for Pasture (acres)	Woodland and Other Pasture (acres)	Total Pasture (acres)	Crop Land Used Only for Pasture (per cent)	Woodland and Other Pasture (per cent)	Total Pasture (per cent)
Illinois	11	27	38	7	18	25
Indiana	10	24	34	10	23	33
Iowa	7	40	47	4	25	29
Missouri	21	52	73	15	35	50
Ohio	8	28	36	9	28	37
Middle Atlantic states	4	29	33	4	29	33
East North Central states	10	30	40	8	25	33
West North Central states	10	101	111	4	37	41
United States	8	98	106	4	51	55

* Compiled from U. S. Census of Agriculture, 1945.

likely that they ever will, the reason being that, even in the Corn Belt, a by no means negligible area of land is better suited for pasturage than for anything else. Also, farmers have found that a certain area of

FIG. 5. Yearling steers on alfalfa pasture. Beef cattle are a strong incentive for a farmer to follow a good rotation, since cattle make good use of legume pastures and hay.

permanent grass land is almost indispensable to good animal management and, over a series of years, is likely to prove as profitable per acre as any other part of the farm. To this permanent pasture must be added the acreage of temporary pasture crops, such as timothy, red and sweet clover, and various mixtures of grasses and legumes, most of which are grown as a part of the regular farm rotation. Thus, it is not surprising that the total pasture area is considerable, even in the major Corn Belt states.

Just what percentage of this great area of pasture is grazed by beef cattle can only be estimated. In some sections, such as central Missouri, southwestern Wisconsin, and southern Iowa, beef cattle are by far the most important kind of livestock kept. Around Chicago, Omaha, Minneapolis, St. Paul, and other large cities dairy cattle predominate. Making due allowance for the pasture used by work horses, sheep, and cattle of dairy type, about 30 to 35 per cent of the total pasture area of the North Central states is utilized by beef cattle. This is equivalent to approximately 50,000,000 acres, or 14 per cent of the total area in farms.

3. Cattle Furnish a Home Market for Grain and Hay. Excepting wheat, comparatively little of the immense supplies of grain and hay produced in this country is used otherwise than as food for farm animals. The great bulk of these feed materials is used on the farms where it is produced, while of that sold, the larger portion is bought by feeders who do not raise enough to supply their own needs. Even in the heart of the Corn Belt considerably more than 60 per cent of the grain and hay is fed on the farms where it is grown.

That beef cattle constitute an important home market for these farm-grown feeding stuffs no one will deny. For the United States as a whole, beef cattle consume 11 per cent of the 3 billion bushel corn crop. For the Corn Belt section, this percentage is very much higher, since corn is the principal feed used in the extensive fattening operations carried on in this region. It has been estimated that over 25 per cent of the corn grown in the Corn Belt is fed to beef cattle.[3]

The demand for corn for cattle feeding exercises an effect on the corn market that can hardly be overestimated. It is far more important than the total demand for commercial uses and export combined. The steers that were put on grain feed in Illinois alone during the three years 1939–1941 consumed more corn than was exported during that period. Exports of corn during and since World War II have been so greatly affected by military and political conditions that a later comparison is of little value. For example, only 6,800,000 bushels of corn were exported during 1947, or less than that consumed by the 196,000 beef steers sold for slaughter in Chicago during April and May of that year.

Grain growers, instead of seeking new foreign outlets for corn or new uses for it in industry to increase demand and thus secure a higher price could, as a rule, use their efforts to better advantage by encouraging the feeding of more livestock. An increase of 20 per cent

[3] U. S. D. A. Yearbook, 1921, p. 260.

in the amount of corn fed to farm animals in 1945 would have resulted in a demand for 555,000,000 more bushels of corn that year, whereas the total amount of corn exported and used in industry in 1945 was only 250,000,000 bushels.[4]   Since such a large percentage of the grain

TABLE 7

PERCENTAGE OF FARM FEEDS CONSUMED BY DIFFERENT
CLASSES OF LIVESTOCK[1]
(Average 1942–1946)

	Corn, Including Corn In Silage	All Concentrates Hay and Pasture	All Roughage Including Silage and Pasture	All Feeds Including Pasture
Beef cattle	10.8	37.0	31.3	21.0
Dairy cattle	15.1	34.3	42.3	31.3
Sheep	0.8	16.5	12.3	7.1
Hogs	47.1	1.4	0.8	17.9
Poultry	17.1	1.6	1.0	11.4
Horses and mules	6.8	9.2	12.0	9.7
Other livestock	2.3	. . .	0.5	1.6
Total	100.0	100.0	100.0	100.0

[1] U.S.D.A. Circular 836, December, 1949.

grown in the United States is fed to livestock, its feeding must return a reasonable profit, even to the marginal feeder, if the price of grain is to be high enough to cover the costs of growing it.   For if the marginal feeders lose money on their cattle and hogs, a large number

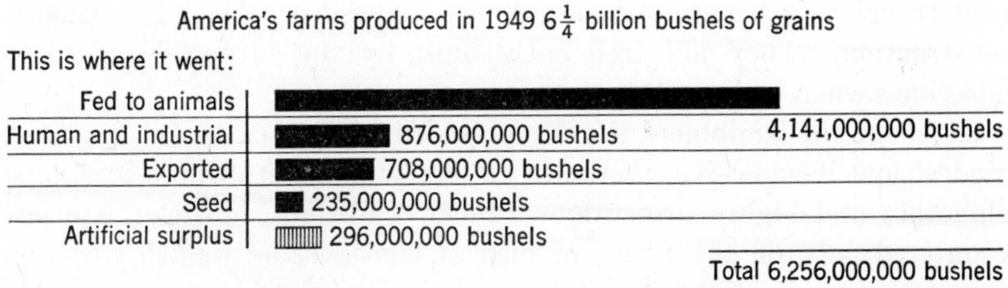

America's farms produced in 1949 $6\frac{1}{4}$ billion bushels of grains

This is where it went:

Fed to animals	4,141,000,000 bushels
Human and industrial	876,000,000 bushels
Exported	708,000,000 bushels
Seed	235,000,000 bushels
Artificial surplus	296,000,000 bushels

Total 6,256,000,000 bushels

FIG. 6.   More than two-thirds of the grain produced in the United States is fed to livestock.   Only about one-fourth of the acreage of grain now grown is needed to satisfy human, industrial, and export requirements.
(*Courtesy The Meat Institute.*)

will drop out and sell their corn with the result that corn prices will fall sharply the following year because of the increased supply and the decreased demand.   Thus, it happens that unsatisfactory prices of cattle and hogs for the livestock farmer quickly bring about unsatis-

[4] U. S. D. A. Agricultural Statistics, 1949, p. 50.

factory prices of corn for the cash grain farmer. This situation can always be expected as long as livestock furnishes the principal market for the grain farmers' product. When considered over a period of years, it is only when corn, oats, and hay can be fed with greater profit than can be realized from their sale that the production of these crops will be found profitable on Corn Belt farms. That corn fed to beef cattle usually returns substantially more than its current market price is shown in Table 258.

4. **Beef Cattle Require a Small Investment in Buildings and Equipment.** The average investment in buildings and equipment per hundred dollars invested in livestock is lower for beef cattle than for other farm animals. Investigations carried on in De Kalb County, Illinois, by the United States Department of Agriculture and the University of Illinois, over the five-year period 1919–1923 showed an annual equipment charge per steer of $3.94. This was only 6 per cent of the original cost of the animal when put into the feed lot and 3 per cent of its total value when finished for the market. Although new building costs have advanced greatly during the past few years, they have not advanced nearly so fast as the value of beef cattle. Moreover, many of the shelters and feed yards in use 30 or 40 years ago are still being used today and, therefore, no longer have a claim to an annual interest and depreciation charge.

The equipment charge made against the breeding herd is likewise low, amounting on many farms to less than $5 per cow per year. Equipment used in beef production consists mainly of shelter, fences, feed troughs, and water tanks. None of these need be of expensive construction. They are frequently built by the farmer himself, at odd times when he has little else to do.

Although the equipment usually provided for beef cattle is altogether modest and inexpensive, there are not a few instances where it is very elaborate and highly pretentious. Such conditions, however, are encountered only on the farms of men of considerable wealth who can afford to attract attention to their purebred cattle in this way. Although expensive barns, mechanical feed and litter handling equipment, extensive paddocks, and so forth are very convenient and quite desirable from a labor-saving standpoint, they are by no means indispensable. Some of the most noted feeders of market-topping steers, as well as the owners of some of the best purebred herds of beef cattle, use equipment no more expensive than that found on the average well-kept livestock farm.

5. **Beef Cattle Assist in Utilizing Man and Horse Labor.** Beef cattle require but little labor compared with dairy cattle and hogs, or

with cultivated crops occupying an equal area of land. Of the labor that is required, the larger part is needed during the winter and early spring when there is no demand for labor in the fields. Thus, beef cattle tend to distribute the labor requirements of the farm throughout the year by (1) utilizing labor that otherwise would be unemployed during the winter, and (2) lessening the summer demand for labor by

TABLE 8

EFFECT OF THE MAJOR FARM ENTERPRISE ON OPERATING
COSTS, RETURN ON INVESTMENT, ETC.*

	1949				1950			
	Beef Cattle Farms	Dairy Cattle Farms	Hog Farms	Grain Farms	Beef Cattle Farms	Dairy Cattle Farms	Hog Farms	Grain Farms
Number of farms	35	25	102	104	33	19	77	127
Average size of farms, acres	299	297	302	303	300	300	300	303
Tillable area, acres	252	234	251	277	252	236	246	274
Percentage of tillable land								
All hay and pasture	26	38	23	14	32.1	39.4	27.8	20.1
Deep-rooted legumes	19	26	13	7	21.7	30.1	16.1	10.3
Corn yield per acre, bushels	69	64	66	64	66.6	56.7	63.6	61.2
Total labor, months	26	25.6	24	22	26.6	25.4	23.7	20.9
Total returns per farm	$38,246	$25,306	$29,427	$19,990	$49,953	$32,397	$37,609	$25,636
Total farm input*a*	$33,143	$24,347	$26,326	$16,165	$36,773	$26,528	$27,601	$17,092
Returns to total farm for:								
Unpaid labor, capital, and management	11,781	6,493	8,740	9,283	19,635	11,325	15,456	13,785
Capital and management	9,595	4,299	6,555	7,098	17,446	9,142	13,293	11,755
Operator's labor and management	6,822	2,619	4,818	5,512	14,962	7,649	11,755	10,256

* Dept. of Ag. Ec., Univ. of Ill., the 1949 and 1950 Annual Reports of the Illinois Farm Bureau Farm Management Service.

a Comprises all expenses, including interest on invested capital, taxes, total labor, feed, etc.

using part of the tillable land for hay and pasture. A farm that would require the employment of an extra man during the spring and summer under a grain system is frequently operated by the owner alone under a livestock system in which beef cattle predominate. Moreover, the cattle furnish many hours of profitable employment for the owner and

TABLE 9

MONTHLY EXPENDITURE OF MAN AND HORSE LABOR IN FEEDING BEEF CATTLE*

	Man Labor Expended		Horse Labor Expended	
	For Cattle	For Total Farm	For Cattle	For Total Farm
	hrs.	hrs.	hrs.	hrs.
January.......	164	511	202	495
February......	144	496	178	428
March........	132	718	179	1,121
April.........	79	916	77	1,792
May..........	31	1,000	30	1,828
June.........	....	1,133	....	1,632
July..........	....	1,370	....	1,316
August.......	....	889	....	1,024
September.....	1	934	....	1,137
October.......	13	815	7	1,274
November.....	78	825	91	1,471
December.....	129	648	147	913
Total Labor per Year.....	771	10,255	911	14,431
Labor, Nov. 1 to April 1....	647	3,198	797	4,428
Per Cent of Labor coming in fall and winter.......	83.8	31.2	87.5	30.7

* Illinois Bulletin 261, 1925.

his team during the winter, which without cattle would be spent largely in idleness.

The attention of the reader is called to Table 9, which shows the average monthly expenditure of labor on a 295-acre Corn Belt farm where 40 to 79 cattle were fed annually over a 7-year period. Had cattle feeding not been included in the system of farming, it is likely that but a small fraction of the 647 hours of man labor and 797 hours of horse labor expended during the winter months would have gone into remunerative enterprises. The returns realized from this labor, therefore, may be counted as an almost clear gain to the farm income.

6. Beef Cattle Entail Little Death Risk. Beef cattle enjoy an advantage over most other forms of livestock in that they are subject to few ailments and diseases that are likely to have a fatal termination. Compared with sheep and hogs, beef cattle have an unusually low death rate. They are subject to no disease at all comparable with hog cholera in mortality, nor are they an easy prey to many internal parasites, as are sheep. Rarely do they meet with a serious accident, and any wounds sustained usually heal rapidly without becoming infected.

Losses among calves and yearlings are, of course, higher than for mature cattle, but even here they are far below those for young pigs and lambs. Investigations carried on by the United States Department of Agriculture in Illinois and Iowa in 1921 disclosed that the death losses among pigs, up to the time they were weaned, were 340 per 1000.[5] No figures are available on the losses among young calves and lambs, but no one who has had a wide experience with all classes of livestock will question for a moment that calves are outstanding in their ability to survive the hazards of parturition and the various afflictions to which youth of all forms is subject.

Beef cattle are not, as a rule, seriously injured by improper methods of feeding. They do not go off feed easily, and usually show rapid recovery from the effects of improper rations or poor methods of management. These advantages should be carefully considered by the ambitious young farmer who has had little experience with livestock.

[5] U. S. D. A. Yearbook, 1922, p. 224.

3 ———————— The Relation of Beef Cattle to Soil Fertility

It is generally recognized that one of the important advantages enjoyed by the farmer who markets his crops through animals is the conservation of the fertility of his soil. Animals retain in their bodies but a small part of the plant food elements contained in the feeds consumed, returning the greater part to the soil in the manure produced. As a result, the livestock farmer is able to maintain his land in a high state of fertility with the purchase of a smaller amount of fertilizers than is needed by the farmer who sells his grain.

Fig. 7. A valuable compost pile in the making. Under such conditions nearly all the fertility value of the feeds fed is recovered in the manure.
(*Courtesy Illinois Experiment Station.*)

It has been estimated that one billion tons of manure are produced annually by the livestock on the farms and ranches of the United States.[1] That the greater part of it is produced by cattle is shown by the data given in Table 10. The value of this manure in terms of the increased yield of crops which would result if it were completely recovered and carefully used is enormous. For example, a 3-ton application of manure per acre made once in 3 years to the rotation corn, oats, and wheat with legumes plowed under at the Illinois Station

[1] Ohio Bulletin 605, 1939, p. 3.

TABLE 10

ANNUAL PRODUCTION OF MANURE BY DIFFERENT CLASSES OF FARM ANIMALS*

Class of Animals	Solid Excrement (1000 tons)	Liquid Excrement (1000 tons)	Combined Excrement (1000 tons)	Percentage of Total Production
Horses and mules	85,787	19,504	105,291	12
Cattle	519,258	193,698	712,956	79
Sheep	15,890	9,856	25,746	3
Hogs	31,163	17,893	49,056	6
Chickens	4,768	—	4,768	0.5
Total	656,866	240,951	897,817	100.5

*Ohio Bulletin 605, 1939, p. 4.

resulted in increased yields of crops worth $13.82 per acre annually on the basis of grain and hay prices prevailing during 1946–1949. Since the manure was applied at the rate of 1 ton per acre per year, a return of $13.82 was obtained for each ton of manure used.   (See Table 11.)   While this return is somewhat higher per ton than would

TABLE 11

VALUE OF MANURE IN INCREASING CROP YIELDS*
(Average for 1946–1949)

	Average Annual Acre Yield			Annual Gross Acre Income	Less Treatment Costs		Less Growing Costs	
	Corn (bushels)	Oats (bushels)	Wheat (bushels)		Net	Index	Net	Equivalent Acreage[a]
R, L, M	86	57	27	$73.52	$71.27	122	$62.16	80
R, L, SP	70	54	26	65.33	62.92	108	54.19	91
R, L, K	68	50	22	61.21	57.21	98	48.67	102
R, L, 2–12–6	73	51	24	64.13	61.74	106	53.04	94
R, L	66	49	23	59.70	58.20	100	49.69	100
Increase due to:								
M	20	8	4	13.82	13.07	22	12.47	20
SP	4	5	3	5.63	4.72	8	4.50	9
K	2	1	−1	1.51	−0.99	−2	−1.02	−2
2–12–6	7	2	1	4.43	3.54	6	3.35	6

*Illinois Mimeo. Report, Soil Exp. Field Studies, Agronomy Dept., 1951.
[a] Acres required to produce same investment income.
R = Crop residues (stover, legumes); L = Limestone, 890 lb. per acre annually.
M = Manure, 3 tons per acre ahead of corn.
SP = Superphosphate, 200 lb. per acre for wheat; 100 lb. per acre for corn.
2–12–6 = Complete fertilizer, 200 lb. per acre for wheat; 100 lb. per acre for corn.
K = Muriate of potash, 100 lb. per acre for wheat; 100 lb. per acre for corn.
(Superphosphate and complete fertilizer applied first 8 years only; none since 1942.)

be expected from the less frequent but heavier applications usually made, it shows the great value of manure for increasing crop yields. Farmers who feed all their grain, hay, and the protein concentrate required to make well-balanced rations have need to buy but little commercial fertilizers to maintain the fertility of their soils.

Fertilizing Constituents Excreted. The principal plant food elements, from the standpoint of depleted soils, are nitrogen, phosphorus, and potassium. Plants differ as to the percentages of their total composition represented by these elements, but in general legumes contain a larger amount of nitrogen and phosphorus than do other forage plants and cereals. Animals require a certain amount of these elements for growth of new tissues, especially muscle and bone, and for the supply

TABLE 12

RECOVERY AND DISTRIBUTION OF FERTILIZING ELEMENTS
CONTAINED IN THE FEED*

| | Percentage Recovery | | | | | |
| | Nitrogen | | Phosphoric Acid | | Potash | |
	In Feces	In Urine	In Feces	In Urine	In Feces	In Urine
Dairy cows: Ohio	40	28	63	1	17	61
Total excrement	68		64		78	
Steers, Ohio	61		87		82	
Steers, Pennsylvania	69		75		81	
Steers, England	96		93		99	
Heifers, England	78		78		86	
Average	75		80		85	

* Ohio Bulletin 605, 1939, pp.8–9.

of salts in the blood and other body fluids. Old animals that have reached their maturity retain very little of these elements, while young animals use a considerable amount in the process of growth. Consequently, the percentage of the nitrogen, phosphorus, and potassium consumed that is voided in the excrement depends upon the character of the feed and the age of the animals. Non-pregnant cows that are wintered on clover or alfalfa hay will return well over 90 per cent of all three constituents, while young calves fed a poorly balanced ration of corn and timothy hay will probably return not more than 20 to 25 per cent of the first two elements, and not more than 50 per cent of the potassium in the feeds eaten. The approximate percentages of the fertilizing elements, contained in the feed, that are excreted in the manure are shown in the following list.

Average

Percentage of consumed nitrogen excreted, 50 @ 90........ 75 per cent
Percentage of consumed phosphorus excreted, 70 @ 90.... 85 per cent
Percentage of consumed potassium excreted, assumed...... 90 per cent
Percentage of consumed organic matter excreted, 20 @ 50 30 per cent

Although these percentages are somewhat higher than those we should expect to get with yearlings or calves, they emphasize the great saving in soil fertility that cattle feeding makes possible.

Maintenance of Fertility by Cattle Feeding. One sometimes hears the argument advanced that livestock farming is really less efficient than grain farming in maintaining the fertility of the land, since livestock raising involves the feeding of the legumes grown, while grain farming provides for their plowing under, thereby returning 100 per cent instead of only 75 to 90 per cent of the nitrogen and phosphorus in these important soil-building crops. This argument can be successfully refuted by replying that the man who plows under clover nearly always sells his grain, while the man who feeds his clover feeds his grain as well. The accompanying figures, obtained from an Illinois

TABLE 13

PLANT FOOD ELEMENTS EXCRETED BY TWO-YEAR-OLD STEERS EXPRESSED IN PER CENT OF AMOUNTS PRESENT IN CLOVER HAY FED*

	Organic Matter Excreted	Nitrogen Excreted	Phosphorus Excreted
	%	%	%
Maintenance lot.......	91.5	334.8	650.5
One-third-feed lot.....	105.8	336.7	655.7
Two-thirds-feed lot....	114.2	324.3	602.2
Full-feed lot..........	121.2	308.6	589.3
Average..........	108.18	326.12	620.7

* Illinois Bulletin 209.

digestion experiment, emphasize the advantages possessed by the cattle feeder over the most progressive grain farmer in the matter of maintaining soil fertility. The cattle in the experiment were fed corn and clover hay during the first 22 weeks, and corn, linseed meal, and clover hay during the last 15 weeks. One part of linseed meal was fed to 4 parts of corn.

Saving the Manure. In the experiment cited above, all the elements of fertility excreted by the cattle were saved. It must be admitted that under ordinary conditions, such as prevail on the average farm, a large percentage of the manure produced by the animals never reaches the fields where it is so badly needed. Instead, it is trampled into the mud of the feed lot or is washed by the rains into a near-by stream. Under such conditions it is not to be expected that cattle feeding will do much towards maintaining the fertility of the soil. It is safe to say that under ordinary conditions fully one-half the manure produced is lost. A large part of this loss may be easily prevented by keeping the cattle on pasture and fields as much of the time as possible, in order that the manure may be deposited where it will benefit future crops. One of the advantages of feeding cattle on legume pasture instead of in dry lot is the greater amounts of the plant food elements present in the feed which are returned to the soil, where they will be available to the cultivated crops grown in the rotation. Breeding cattle, which must be kept near the farmstead during the winter months because of their need for shelter during inclement weather, should be turned onto pastures, meadows, and corn-stalk fields whenever the ground is dry or frozen hard enough to prevent serious trampling of the soil, in order that their droppings may be deposited where they will benefit future crops. To require them to stand day after day in small dirt lots not only deprives them of needed exercise but results in the loss of much valuable manure.

Losses of plant food elements in the manure of cattle that are kept in barns and sheds may be greatly reduced by using liberal amounts of bedding, by feeding the cattle in small paved lots, and by adopting proper methods of storing and handling the manure itself.

Inasmuch as approximately half of the nitrogen and fully three-fourths of the potassium excreted are in the urine, it is extremely important that the liquid manure be saved by the use of suitable bedding materials. The ability of the different bedding materials to absorb and hold moisture is shown by Table 14.

Amount of Bedding. The amount of bedding material required by cattle will depend upon the way the cattle are handled and the frequency with which the manure is removed. Purebred cattle are often kept tied in single stalls or loose in box stalls and the manure removed every day. Under such conditions the cattle are usually out of the barn for about 9 hours a day during the winter season, and are on pasture practically all the time during the summer months. Stock cattle and steers on feed, however, are generally kept in droves, varying in size from 10 to 100 or more head. They are given an open shed and are free to go in and out as they please. Rarely are such cattle removed from the lot during the entire winter or fattening period. Al-

Fig. 8. Keeping plant food materials where they are needed. By feeding cattle on rotation pastures all the fertilizer elements of the feeds are deposited where they will be available for cultivated crops.

35

though the manure accumulating in the shed may be removed every week or 10 days, the more common practice is to allow it to remain for a month or two or for the entire period, adding enough dry bedding from day to day to insure the cattle's having a dry bed.

TABLE 14
CHARACTERISTICS OF VARIOUS BEDDING MATERIALS*

Material	Litter Required to Absorb 100 pounds of Liquid (pounds)	Fixing Capacity for Ammonia-Nitrogen Held per ton of Litter (pounds)	Content of Fertilizing Elements per Ton of Air-Dry Material		
			N (pounds)	P (pounds)	K (pounds)
Wheat straw	45	4.5	11	4	20
Oat straw	35	7.1	12	4	26
Rye straw	45	3.4	12	6	17
Chopped straw	20–30	. . .	. . .	. . .	. . .
Corn stalks (shredded)	25–35	5.3	15	8	18
Sawdust	25	.0	4	2	4
Wood shavings, softwood	25	0	4	2	4
Wood shavings, hardwood	45	. . .	. . .	. . .	. . .
Spent tanbark	25	. . .	10–20	. . .	. . .
Leaf litter	25–60	26.6 [a]	16	6	6
Peat moss	10	40	16	2	3

* Ohio Bulletin 605, 1939, p. 11.
[a] Oak leaf litter.

Whisenand working at the Illinois Experiment Station found that about 8 to 10 pounds of bedding material were required daily per mature animal where the cattle were kept in well-bedded, single stalls with cement floors that were cleaned daily; only half this amount was required for 1000-pound steers fed in open sheds that were cleaned but once a month. Approximately 10 per cent more wheat straw than oat straw was required to keep cattle equally well bedded, and it was necessary to use 80 per cent more shavings than oat straw to bed cows properly in single stalls.[2]   Although there seem to be no experimental data on the value of shredded corn stover for bedding, the experience of the author leads him to believe that it should be ranked high among bedding materials.   The pith of the corn stalks is capable of absorbing a great amount of water.   Cattle fed shredded stover seldom eat more than 60 to 70 per cent of the quantity put before them. No better use can be made of the refuse than to use it for bedding.

[2] Journal of Agricultural Research, Vol. 14, pp. 187–189.

Loss of Nitrogen and Organic Matter. Animal manures are extremely good media for the development of nitrifying bacteria. Unless the action of these organisms is checked, much of the organic matter of the manure is broken down and a large percentage of the nitrogen is liberated into the air. Manure that is loosely piled in the open decomposes very rapidly with great losses of organic matter and nitrogen. The following extracts from important treatises on farm manure are given to show how serious such losses may sometimes be:

1. Two tons of manure containing 1938 lb. of organic matter and 48 lb. of nitrogen were left exposed during 4 summer months. At the end of this period the organic matter had been reduced to 655 lb. and the nitrogen to 27.7 lb. (Hopkins, *Soil Fertility*, 1910, p. 200, Ginn & Co.)
2. Manure stored in heaps in the open from November to May lost 30.6 per cent of its dry matter, 33.5 per cent of the nitrogen, and 8.3 per cent of the phosphorus. (Ind. Circ. 49, 1915, p. 8.)
3. Manure allowed to accumulate in the open barnyard for a period of from 3 to 6 months is from one-half to one-third as valuable as that hauled directly from the stall to the field or properly stored in a manure shed (where it is worked over and trampled by the cattle and hogs). (Ohio Bull. 246, 1912, p. 732.)

Fortunately, these nitrifying bacteria are aerobic; that is, they require the presence of air for their development. Consequently, their action can be partially checked by so thoroughly packing the manure that the air is largely excluded. This can be done best by allowing the manure to accumulate in the shed where it will be trampled by the cattle. The addition each day of a small amount of dry bedding will result in the formation of a compact mass into which but little air will penetrate. Such manure can be left in the shed until the following summer or fall with but little loss from decomposition. If possible, however, all manure should be applied to the land before warm weather, as decomposition is much more rapid during the summer months.

TABLE 15

Tramped vs. Loosely Piled Manure*

Method of Storage	Percentages of Plant Food in Feed Recovered in Manure		
	N	P	K
On cement floor, tramped	85	81	91.5
On earth floor, piled under cover	54	69	71.0

* Pennsylvania Bulletin 63, 1903.

Cement Floors and Paved Lots. Losses from leaching are largely, if not entirely, eliminated by the use of cement floors and paved lots. Paved lots are really more important than the cement floors, since the losses on dirt floors can be largely overcome by the generous use of bedding. Beef cattle, however, spend a considerable amount of time outside their barns and sheds. If this time is spent in a dirt lot, often knee-deep with mud, all the manure dropped in the lot is a total loss and cannot be recovered. During the winter months cows fed in single stalls spend at least one-third of the 24 hours outside the barn,

Fig. 9. Much fertility is lost when cattle are fed in a large dirt lot.

while steers and cows fed in bunks and racks, in lots adjoining open sheds, spend nearly half their time outside their shelter. As a result, from one-third to one-half the manure produced is irrecoverable, unless paved lots are provided. Some bedding or litter should be scattered over the pavement to absorb the urine, unless there is a cistern or pit into which the lot drains. If such drainage is provided, some provision should be made for shunting off the rain water that falls after the lot has been washed off. Otherwise the pit or cistern will be flooded in case of a heavy rain.

At the Ohio Experiment Station, two lots of steers were fed, one on earth floors and the other on cement floors. They were kept in the barn at all times except for two or three hours each day when they were turned out for water. No attempt was made to recover the manure deposited outside the barn. The amount of manure recovered from each lot and its composition are shown in Table 16.

Preservatives. Experiments have shown that the application of certain minerals, notably gypsum and raw rock or acid phosphate, to

TABLE 16

Cement Floors as a Means of Conserving Manure*

	Manure Recovered per Day per 100 Pounds Live Weight	Percentage of Plant Food in Feed Recoveréd		
		N	P	K
Cement floor in barn	47.5 lb.	75	78	88
Earth floor in barn	41.3 lb.	62	78	78
Difference in favor of cement floor	6.2	13	00	10

* Ohio Bulletin 246, 1912.

manure as it is formed will decrease the losses due to bacterial action and leaching. Inasmuch as most Corn Belt land is deficient in phosphorus, and also since manure is in need of more phosphorus to make it a "balanced" fertilizer, the mixing of rock or acid phosphate with the fresh manure is to be strongly recommended. If the manure is allowed to accumulate in the shed, one of these "reinforcing" materials may be scattered over the floor every two or three days at the rate of one pound per mature animal per day. If the manure is removed daily and stored, the reinforcement should be scattered over the pile. If hogs are allowed access to the pile, a thorough mixing of the materials will result.

TABLE 17

Losses from Treated and Untreated Manure*

	Percentage Lost—January to April			
	Organic Matter	N	P	K
Untreated	35.47	35.63	22.46	51.02
40 lb. rock phosphate per ton	26.71	33.61	4.47	32.96
40 lb. acid phosphate per ton	38.13	31.56	17.00	38.02
40 lb. kainit per ton	36.47	30.51	16.67	43.85
40 lb. gypsum per ton	33.11	29.65	9.73	54.37

* Ohio Bulletin 246, 1912.

Manure Produced. The amount of manure produced by a 1000-pound steer or cow depends so much upon the character and amount of feed eaten that it is impossible to give an accurate figure for the daily or yearly production. Van Slyke[3] states that a mature cow will produce, per 1000 pounds live weight, 74 pounds of manure per day, or something over 13 tons per year. Of this amount, 52 pounds are represented by the feces and 22 pounds by the urine. These figures have been quoted widely by many writers and are found in most agricultural

[3] Van Slyke: Crops and Fertilizers, Orange Judd Co., New York, 1915.

textbooks that mention the subject of farm manures. Apparently they are based upon results obtained from dairy cows that were fed large quantities of coarse roughage, and, hence, produced a great amount of feces. Digestion trials at the Illinois Experiment Station, while by no means extensive, indicate that these figures are considerably too high for beef cattle, especially where heavy grain rations are fed.

In these experiments the total length of time the steers were on feed was thirty-seven weeks. This time was divided into five periods of approximately equal length. The ratio of grain to roughage was changed at the beginning of each period, being gradually increased as the experiment progressed. The amount of feces produced varied directly with the amount of roughage fed. The production of urine, however, seemed to be independent of the character of the ration.

In studying the Tables 18 and 19 it should be kept in mind that only in the full-fed lot have we conditions likely to be encountered in practical cattle feeding. No farmer would think of maintaining a drove of

TABLE 18

MANURE PRODUCED BY TWO–YEAR–OLD STEERS WEIGHING 800 to 1000 POUNDS*

	Average Feces per Day	Average Urine per Day	Total Excrement per Day
	lbs.	lbs.	lbs.
Maintenance lot......................	11.1	7.6	18.7
One-third-feed lot......................	19.8	9.2	29.0
Two-thirds-feed lot......................	27.5	11.7	39.2
Full-feed lot......................	36.8	11.9	48.7

* Illinois Bulletin 209, 1918.

stockers or dry cows on a ration composed of even 50 per cent grain by weight, not to mention the higher ratios used in the experiment. The figures in the table, however, are very valuable for showing that the weight of manure produced depends quite as much on the character of the ration as on the amount of feed fed. It seems safe to assume that cattle on a maintenance ration of roughage alone would produce a greater weight of manure than steers getting a heavy feed of concentrates. However, the manure of the animals receiving the concentrated feed would contain a much higher percentage of valuable plant-food materials.

Under farm conditions, the term "manure" refers to both the excrement and the bedding. The farmer is interested primarily in the amounts of such mixture that he will have available to apply to the land. At the Illinois Experiment Station, Whisenand[4] found that

TABLE 19

EFFECT OF CHARACTER OF RATION ON AMOUNT OF MANURE PRODUCED*

Ratio of Hay to Corn to Linseed Meal	Average Feces per Day			Average Urine per Day			Total Excrement per Day		
	Maintenance	Full Fed	Average	Maintenance	Full Fed	Average	Maintenance	Full Fed	Average
	lbs.	lbs.	lbs.	lbs.	lbs.	lbs.	lbs.	lbs.	lbs.
1 : 1 : 0	19.2	57.1	38.4	9.0	12.0	9.7	28.2	69.1	48.1
1 : 3 : 0	11.0	44.2	27.3	10.8	13.1	11.7	21.8	57.3	39.0
1 : 5 : 0	8.5	26.7	18.0	5.6	8.0	9.0	14.1	34.7	27.0
1 : 4 : 1	7.7	22.3	15.8	6.6	14.3	10.2	14.3	36.6	26.0

* Illinois Bulletin 209, 1918.

TABLE 20

MANURE OBTAINED FROM CATTLE FED IN
SMALL PAVED LOTS ADJOINING AN OPEN SHED*

	Number of Lots Averaged	Average Days Fed	Average Manure per Head	
			Total Period (tons)	Per Month (tons)
Calves				
Full fed with silage	29	229	1.82	0.23
Full fed with dry roughage	10	235	2.18	0.30
Full fed with ear corn silage	8	231	2.16	0.28
Wintered without grain	5	132	1.59	0.36
Yearlings				
Fed over 140 days	4	150	2.24	0.45
Fed under 101 days	11	91	1.52	0.51
Dry beef cows	4	134	2.91	0.66

* Illinois Station, A. H. Mimeo. Report, 1940.

purebred beef cows, kept overnight in single stalls that were cleaned daily, produced about 44 pounds of manure per day. Approximately 36 pounds represented the actual excreta, and the other 8 pounds the straw used as litter. Assuming that the cows were kept in the barn

[4] Journal of Agricultural Research, Vol. 14, 1918, pp. 187–189.

for six months, the total amount of manure saved per cow during the wintering period was about 4 tons.   Approximately the same amount is obtained from yearling steers kept in open, well-bedded sheds during a 6- or 7-months' feeding period.

More manure, of course, is saved where the cattle are on pavement when they are outside their shelter. Tests conducted at the Ohio Experiment Station, already referred to, show that the use of concrete floors under the shed alone results in an increase of 15 per cent in the amount of manure saved.   Inasmuch as cattle spend from one-third to one-half the time outside their shelter, it seems reasonable to suppose that from one-third to one-half their excrement is deposited in the lot. While the losses from manure dropped outside may be considerable, owing to excessive leaching from heavy rains, it is not unreasonable to expect from one-half to two-thirds of a ton of manure per month from yearling steers that are fed in well-bedded sheds and paved lots cleaned at frequent intervals.   (See Table 20.)

PART · 2

The Breeding Herd

4 ————— Advantages and Disadvantages of a Breeding Herd[1]

Government livestock estimates indicate that there were approximately twice as many beef cows in Illinois in 1951 as there were in 1938. What happened to make beef cows so popular? Whereas money put into a cow herd 15 or 20 years ago was regarded as a speculative risk, money so spent today is considered to be as wisely invested as it would be if left on time deposit in a bank or spent for government bonds. Many Illinois farmers who in the past have shown little interest in raising beef calves are now seriously considering the advisability of establishing a breeding herd and are attempting to weigh the advantages and disadvantages of such a venture. I hope that what I shall say on this topic will assist them in making a wise decision.

Disadvantages of a Herd of Beef Cows. Let us first note some of the disadvantages of a herd of beef cows. The breeding and raising of calves is not all roses, else there would be many more breeding herds than there are at the present time. Probably the chief disadvantage of a herd of beef cows on a Corn Belt farm is that it is a long-time proposition; hence, it is not easily adapted to tenant farming. Both landlords and tenants who operate under short-term leases are reluctant to undertake the time and expense of establishing a breeding herd, which may have to be sold at public auction after 2 to 5 years in order to dissolve the partnership.

Another disadvantage of a breeding herd is that it does not offer the flexibility of management possible with purchased feeder cattle. Feeder cattle, both in respect to the time of purchase and number bought, may vary from one year to another with the feed supply, whereas the breeding herd is present and must be fed the year round. Moreover, the size of the herd cannot be adjusted easily to the feed supply, since a reduction in numbers made at a time of threatened feed shortage will probably result in good feed going to waste a few months in the future, when growing conditions are more favorable. In other

[1] Paper given by author during Farm and Home Week, University of Illinois, February, 1951.

45

words, a breeding herd cannot be expanded or contracted quickly to meet an unusual feed situation.

A third disadvantage of a breeding herd from the point of view of Corn Belt farmers is the labor required in its care and management. Although the feeding of cows is much simpler than the feeding of steers, there are several management practices connected with a breeding herd that require both time and skill for their successful performance. Among them are dehorning, castration of bull calves, vaccination for black leg in black-leg-infected areas, and the periodic testing of the breeding herd for TB and contagious abortion. None of these operations requires much time, but when they coincide with important field work they are annoying and may undermine the enthusiasm which was felt for a breeding herd while it was being established.

Advantages of a Breeding Herd. Since beef cows have increased so rapidly in Illinois and adjoining states in recent years, they must have some important advantages. Undoubtedly the most important advantage possessed by beef cows over other kinds of cattle is their ability to utilize pasture and roughage. Farmers without pasture and roughage have no business keeping beef cows, but farmers with large amounts of these feeds cannot operate their farms efficiently without them. Beef cows are the only kind of cattle that perform their job the year round and one year after another without eating any grain. Pasture in the summer and hay, corn stalks, and straw in the winter are the usual feeds for the beef cow, and if these feeds are of reasonably good quality she will need nothing more. As farmers seed down more of their rolling fields to pasture they need more beef cows to utilize the grass. With the adoption of better rotations more cows will be required to consume the legume pasture and hay. Soil improvement programs for most Corn Belt farms depend upon beef cattle, especially beef cows, for their ultimate success, for without cattle to utilize the resulting pastures and hay these crops will not be grown. The recent marked increase in the number of beef cows on Illinois farms is evidence that they are needed in the soil conservation program.

Another advantage possessed by beef cows is that the breeding and rearing of calves is a comparatively simple and direct program. Each summer the cows are bred. Each spring the calves are born. Each fall the calves are weaned and put into the feed lot or sold to a neighbor to fatten. Raising a crop of beef calves is much like growing a crop of corn or beans. Farmers who have a herd of beef cows should regard their crop of calves as much a product of their fields as are wheat, corn, oats, and soybeans. The principal difference is that the

Fig. 10.   Approximately one-fourth of the total acreage of the Corn Belt states is too rolling to be planted to cultivated crops. Beef cattle utilize the pasture and hay which should cover such areas. Note erosion in corn field in background.

calf crop requires less labor and equipment and is much more valuable relative to the plant food removed from the soil.

A farmer who has a breeding herd does not spend days and nights wondering if he should or should not feed cattle during the coming year. The calves are already on the farm; it is obvious that they must be fed. He does not worry whether he should feed steers or heifers. Having some of each, he naturally makes plans for feeding both sexes. He does not debate where, when, or how he should buy his feeders, for he already has title to them by virtue of having owned them from birth. Relieved as he is from the cares and worries connected with the purchase and shipment of a drove of feeder cattle, he can concentrate his entire attention on their feeding and management. Having raised them on the farm, he can start them on feed when the feeds are ready and not delay feeding operations for one or two months, while feeder cattle of the desired age and weight are being found.

A third advantage possessed by beef cows is that they entail little speculative risk. When one buys a drove of feeder steers he buys them in the hope of selling them at an advance in price. But when one buys cows or heifers for a breeding herd, he has no intention of selling them soon but expects to keep them until they are worn out or are outdated by heifers of better type, much like a tractor which is traded in for an improved model while it is still serviceable. The profit on cows is made, not by selling them for more than they cost, although this has happened frequently in the past, but by selling their calves for much more than the cost of production. When beef cattle prices are high, a nice profit is obtained from the breeding herd. When prices are low, the herd still contributes something to the net income, since without the cows nothing at all would have been received for the pasture, hay, straw, and stover.

The last advantage to be mentioned for a breeding herd is that it is a long-time project and hence lends itself to continual improvement. Each drove of feeder steers is a project in itself. When they are sold, one must start from the beginning with another drove. Not so with a herd of cows. By the use of good bulls, constant culling of the less desirable cows, and the careful selection of replacement heifers, a marked improvement is observed in the quality, weaning weight, and feeding abilities of the calves. By following such a program of breeding and selection Corn Belt farmers can within 10 years restore native-bred steers to the favorable market position which they enjoyed sixty to seventy years ago, before the fine breeding herds of the Middle West were dispersed as a result of the severe competition encountered from the Western Range.

5 ———————————— When to Start a Breeding Herd[1]

You ask me when you should start a breeding herd? I ask you first to tell me when you should buy a car, a hay baler, or a tractor? You probably would reply that you would buy these items of equipment whenever you thought you needed them to operate your farm more efficiently. In like manner I answered the question which you have put to me: you should start a breeding herd whenever you need such a herd to operate your farm most advantageously. A herd of beef cows should be regarded as a piece of equipment like a mowing machine, a hay baler, or a manure spreader—as a matter of fact, it is all of these and a great deal more, for beef cows may also be called corn pickers, sweet-clover harvesters, and hay and straw converters without over-playing the imagination.

The decision to establish a breeding herd is not one to be made lightly. When you decide to do so, you take it for keeps, for better or for worse, as you take a wife or adopt a baby, or accept a hound pup. Of course, you can get rid of a breeding herd later if you find you cannot manage it, much as you can divorce a wife, but you should have no mental reservations to that effect when you cast the die.

No Best Time to Buy. Too often breeding cattle are bought like securities on the stock market or grain futures on the board of trade. In other words, one tries to wait and buy in at the low spot of the market just before prices start on a steep climb upward. When prices hit the peak you sell out completely or reduce your herd to a few old cows and sit around and wait for another low spot to arrive. When it comes you start building up your herd again in order to have lots of cattle to sell when peak prices return. Of course, the "catch" to this method of operating is the difficulty of knowing just when the low and high prices will occur. But those who recommend this method have at hand a little device called "the beef-cattle price cycle" which is supposed to give them this information in a nutshell. It is a wavy line drawn on cross-section paper. The peaks of the lines show in what years cattle prices have been highest, and the troughs of the

[1] Paper given by the author during Farm and Home Week, University of Illinois, February, 1950.

line show when prices have been lowest for the period covered. Always the period immediately ahead is shown by a dotted line or is left completely blank because no one can say for certain what the future has in store. Still, economists have much faith in the cattle cycle, for they believe it indicates for how long a period prices will decline before they start back up and, when once they start up, how long they will continue to rise before they start back down again.

Such a system may be all right for buying something you expect to sell again, like stocks and bonds or corn and wheat futures or even stocker cattle which are to be kept for a year or two before they are marketed, but it has little value for the farmer who is pondering the advisability of establishing a breeding herd. For a breeding herd is operative equipment, not a speculative commodity. A farmer either needs a breeding herd or he does not, just as he either needs or does not need a tractor, a hay baler, or a combine. If a man really needs one of these items of equipment he seldom postpones purchasing one for two or three years in the hope that prices will come down, for the fact that he thinks he needs one implies that he believes the savings the machine will effect over the years it will be used are substantially greater than its cost.

Likewise with a breeding herd. If a herd is really needed it means that pasture, hay, and other roughages now poorly utilized or perhaps going to waste would be converted into choice home-bred calves for the feed lot if a breeding herd were established to make use of them. If all available feed supplies are now being utilized reasonably well by other livestock a need for a breeding herd does not exist, and none should be established. Hence, it is the available feed supplies rather than the level of the cattle market that should be given major consideration in deciding if or when a breeding herd should be established.

Waiting for Lower Prices. But are not cattle prices too high to justify starting a herd now? Should not I wait until prices are lower?

Well, if you wait until you can buy cattle lower it is almost certain that the market will be still lower when you have cattle to sell. If you get in when prices are high they may still be high when you sell your first crop of calves and not too low when you sell your second and third crops.

"Wait for lower prices" was the advice given by the economists to prospective cattle breeders during the period 1937–1940. Cattle numbers were much larger than they had been in the previous decade, and a surplus of beef and lower prices of cattle were predicted with certainty by those studying the beef-cattle cycle. Well, those who followed the advice and waited were still waiting when cattle prices became fully twice as high as they were 10 years before. However, those who bought enjoyed a decade of cattle prices higher than any previous generation of cattlemen had ever dared dream of.

Moreover, the original cost of a breeding herd is not a serious handicap, even with high prices, if you start with heifer calves. Most of

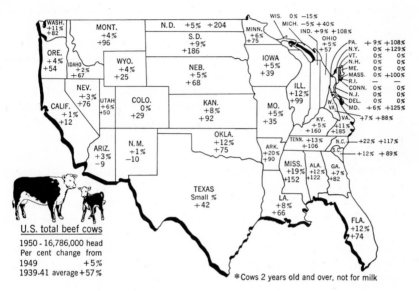

FIG. 11. Distribution of beef cows, Jan. 1, 1950. States are sized to give each cow equal space. Upper figures show change from 1949; lower figures change from 1939–1941 average. It is evident that many Corn Belt farmers believed that 1940–1950 was a good time to start a breeding herd. (*Courtesy U.S.D.A.*)

the cost price of a 400-pound heifer calf at 25 cents a pound, namely, $100, is likely to be recovered when you sell her as a mature cow weighing 1100 pounds at 8 or 9 cents. And cattle prices will have to decline far below their present levels before cows will be selling for 8 or 9 cents a pound. If you have feed that is going to waste you cannot afford to wait for lower prices, because each year you wait means the loss of a drove of 400-pound calves which may still be worth from $80 to $120 apiece 2 or 3 years hence.

So my answer to the question "when to buy a breeding herd" is, *this year* to the man who will have available feed supplies beginning this summer and fall; *next year* to the man whose pastures and meadows will not be ready until then; *now* to the man who has hay and straw in his barns, and pastures already established; and *never* to the man who would have no feed for a breeding herd without changing a livestock program which has been satisfactory.

6 —————————— The Selection
of Breeding Stock

The choosing of the animals that are to form the foundation stock for the breeding herd is a matter of prime importance. Far too often, insufficient attention is given to their selection. Particularly is the young breeder, in his eagerness to start operations, likely to take too little time to consider properly just what animals will best suit his needs. He grows impatient at what seems to him to be a loss of time, and to get started he purchases the animals that are immediately available, even though he knows full well that they fall far short of the kind he really wants. Such a procedure is to be avoided, for usually a herd that is established hastily in this way is found to be so unsatisfactory that it is soon replaced either by cattle of much higher merit or by some project which is entirely different from a beef breeding herd.

Aims of the Breeder. Breeders of livestock are of three kinds, depending on the aims which they seek to accomplish. First and in greatest numbers are those breeders who carry on their breeding operations for the purpose of producing animals to supply the needs of the market. This is a thoroughly commendable phase of the breeding business to follow. To produce cattle capable of making the highest quality of beef with the most economical use of feed is an ambition worthy of any man.

The cows used in such breeding operations are, as a rule, either grades or unregistered purebreds. Consequently, the amount of capital necessary to secure even a very high type of foundation stock is not large. The offspring of such cows, being disposed of for beef, command, of course, the prevailing market price and are usually sold by the pound. They have the advantage, however, of always being readily salable at a price somewhere near their actual value. Moreover, the breeding cows themselves will depreciate but little in value and can often be sold for only a little less or even more than their initial cost. Although this form of breeding does not offer spectacular profits, neither does it involve any great risks. It is always a good, safe undertaking, if conducted in a conservative manner and carried on as one of the major enterprises in a system of general farming. However, it reaches its highest development and is practiced most extensively in those sections of the country that have cheap grazing lands.

The second class of breeders consists of those who supply the first group with purebred bulls, and to some extent with purebred cows as well. Necessarily, the cattle that they keep are purebred and are registered in the books of the breed associations. Although most of these men are always hoping to produce an animal of outstanding merit, which will rank along with the best of the breed, their principal aim and business is to furnish a high grade of breeding stock, especially bulls, to the farmers who are producing cattle for the open market. Bulls and cows of a distinctly high order of merit are extremely scarce. Should they, when produced, pass directly into the hands of commercial cattlemen who breed solely for the market, their ability to improve the cattle stock of the country would be largely curtailed. Indeed, this very thing occasionally happens—a good breeding bull being recognized only after he has served his period of usefulness with a lot of mediocre purebred or common grade cows. It is the business of this second group of breeders to conserve the qualities of such an individual by mating him with cows of distinct merit, and thus make these qualities available, in but slightly diluted form, to a large number of breeders through his offspring and their descendants. In this way the blood of a great bull or cow may aid in improving the cattle of many herds widely dispersed throughout the country.

Since only registered animals are used by this second class of breeders, more capital is necessary to engage in this phase of the cattle business than in raising stock for the market. Likewise, more risk is incurred from the possible death of the animals and from adverse fluctuations of prices. However, these disadvantages are overcome, in the opinion of the purebred stockman, by the opportunities offered for greater profits, and by the chance of some day producing a phenomenal animal which will bring both fame and fortune to the breeder. Also, there is no doubt that a considerable amount of pleasure and satisfaction is derived from the handling of purebred stock, entirely apart from the profit that they may return. To breed superior animals is a mark of distinction, social as well as commercial, since it is a business engaged in by only the more progressive farmers who are the natural leaders in their communities.

In the third class of breeders are those few men who seem to possess the rare ability to reckon correctly the true breeding worth of an animal. They seem to have unusually good judgment in deciding what animals should be mated together to produce the best results. Thus, they are able not only to increase the number of good animals in the breed but to produce a few animals that are distinctly superior to anything that they or other breeders previously possessed. Especially are they able, by judicious mating, to correct points in which the breed as a whole is deficient, thereby making possible its improvement in those respects. It is successive generations of men of this sort who, starting with nothing better than the long-horned, coarse-boned, late-maturing cattle of old England, have produced, by long years of rigorous selection and careful mating, the refined, easily fattened, early-maturing beef cattle of to-day. To these "master breeders" too much praise cannot be given. To them belongs the credit for effecting improvement that has been of great economic importance. They have refused to be swerved from their plans by the momentary popularity of a particular type of cattle, or by the importance attached by others to temporarily fashionable pedigrees. Rather, they have continued in their purpose to breed good cattle, regardless of the opinions of others, knowing full well that in the end it is merit and merit alone that will stand the test of time. The number of such breeders has never been large. It is not large now. Working quietly and patiently at their task, they sometimes are not recognized until after they are dead and buried. But whether recognized in life or not, their work goes on so long as descendants of their herds remain.

Before making his initial purchases the prospective breeder should decide what his ultimate objective as a breeder is likely to be. Even though he has had considerable experience with livestock it obviously would be unwise to proceed on the assumption that he will soon become a master breeder. However, even a young man may hope to attain such a position some day, being quite content to spend a number of years getting the necessary experience and training, first from handling ordinary commercial cattle and later from breeding purebred stock of a good, useful sort.

Choosing the Breed. In some ways it is unfortunate that we have several breeds of beef cattle of the same general type, since many men waste considerable time and effort in attempting to decide which breed is best for their particular conditions. The choice of a breed is, in general, unimportant for the Corn Belt farmer, since all of the modern breeds of beef cattle are well adapted to the climate and feed conditions of this region. So much more variation exists between the individuals of any one breed that between the best, or even the average representatives, of any two of them that it is almost useless to argue over their respective merits. One thing is certain: If a man has a distinct preference or liking for a particular breed, that breed in all

probability is the one for him to use. It is not likely that he will ever
be entirely satisfied with any other, for he will find it hard to be en-

TABLE 21

A Comparison of Calving and Weaning Records of Commercial
Cow Herds of the Major Breeds of Beef Cattle*
(10-year average)

	Angus	Hereford	Shorthorn	Totals and Averages of All Breeds
Number of herds	165	171	38	374
Number of cows	5,011	4,910	934	10,855
Number of calves	4,779	4,679	904	10,362
Calf crop, per cent	95.4	95.3	96.8	95.5
Average weaning age, days	208	207	202	207
Average weaning weight, pounds	448	446	426	445
Average daily gain	1.76	1.77	1.71	1.76

* Charles R. Kyd, Missouri Extension Service. Information to the author.

thusiastic about a breed other than that of his choice.   In the absence
of such a preference, however, he should choose the breed that is most
popular in the community in which he lives.   The very fact that it is
prominent is a good indication that it is well suited to the conditions
of that locality.   Moreover, such a choice will enable him to avail
himself of the services of the outstanding bulls of the community and
to use the selling agencies that have been perfected by the older
breeders.   But perhaps the most important advantages that come from
such a choice are the opportunity to observe the methods employed by
other breeders, to compare their cattle with his own, and to make
purchases from herds about which he has definite knowledge.

TABLE 22

Registrations, Transfers and New Members
Reported by Major Beef Breeds in 1949–1950*

	Aberdeen Angus		Hereford		Shorthorn	
	1949	1950	1949	1950	1949	1950
Number of animals registered	87,512	110,442	370,015	426,961	40,615	48,661
Per cent increase		26.2		15.4		19.8
Number of transfers made	74,826	98,591	239,403	326,507	24,204	31,058
Per cent increase		31.8		36.4		28.3
New members	1,802	2,431	Not reported	Not reported	Not reported	Not reported
Per cent increase		34.9				

* Information obtained from annual reports of breed secretaries.

Crossbreeding. The crossing of breeds is much less widely practiced with beef cattle than with either hogs or sheep. Indeed it has been done so infrequently and on such a limited scale that insufficient data are available to permit making a sound appraisal of its value. Apparently the increased productivity, termed hybrid vigor or "heterosis," commonly observed in crossbred chickens and hogs, has not been sufficiently large in crossbred beef cattle to justify the trouble and expense of maintaining two or more separate breeds. In most tests the crossbred offspring have been only intermediate in size, rate of gain, and other characteristics in respect to which the parent breeds differ noticeably. For example, crossbred calves resulting from crossing Shorthorn bulls on Hereford cows at the United States Department of Agriculture Experiment Station at Miles City, Montana, were heavier at weaning time and gained more rapidly during the fattening period than purebred Hereford calves with which they were compared.[1] Since no comparison was made between these crossbred calves and purebred Shorthorns, it is possible that the increase in weight and rate of gain noted was due principally to the use of a sire of a larger breed and not to hybrid vigor or heterosis.

Some evidence that heterosis may result from the crossbreeding of beef cattle is found in the results obtained by Knapp, Baker, and Clark of the United States Department of Agriculture, who mated the crossbred Shorthorn × Hereford heifers referred to above with Aberdeen Angus bulls, and the heifers from this cross with Hereford bulls.[2] Thus, the first or F_1 generation were ½ Shorthorn and ½ Hereford; the second or F_2 generation ½ Angus, ¼ Shorthorn, and ¼ Hereford; and the third or F_3 generation ⅝ Hereford, ¼ Angus, and ⅛ Shorthorn. Practically every crossbred offspring was somewhat heavier at weaning and after a period of full feeding than purebred Hereford calves with which they were compared. It should be noted, however, that most of the crossbred groups were much smaller than the purebred groups. Consequently, they may not have been truly representative of a larger number gotten by less carefully selected sires. (See Table 23.)

One of the most carefully conducted crossbreeding tests with beef cattle reported to date was performed at the Ohio Station with Angus and Hereford cattle. The results of this test, which extended over 8 years and involved both purebred Angus and Hereford offspring as well as reciprocal crossbred calves, are summarized in Table 24. Since both kinds of purebred and both kinds of crossbred calves were produced each year in the Ohio experiment and the same bulls were used

[1] U. S. D. A. Circular 810, 1949.
[2] U. S. D. A. Circular 810, 1949.

for siring purebred and crossbred offspring, environmental factors were reduced to a minimum. Yet it is difficult to find in the results any significant effect of hybrid vigor. A more logical explanation of the

TABLE 23

THE VALUE OF CROSSBREEDING IN INCREASING THE
GROWTH RATE OF BEEF CATTLE*

	Steer Calves				Heifer Calves			
	1st Trial		2nd Trial		1st Trial		2nd Trial	
	Pure-breds	Cross-breds	Pure-breds	Cross-breds	Pure-breds	Cross-breds	Pure-breds	Cross-breds
F₁, Shorthorn bulls × Hereford cows								
Number of bulls used	4	2	5	2	2	2	3	2
Number of calves	29	23	38	34	21	23	34	30
Average weaning weight, lb.	403	429	403	417	389	391	385	396
Final feed-lot weight	875	928	884	968	738^a	766^a	718^a	785^a
Daily gain on feed	1.68	1.77	1.81	2.08	...	...	...	...
Gain per 100 lb. T. D. N.	17.7	17.8	18.3	18.5	...	...	...	...
F₂, Angus bulls × F₁ cows								
Number of bulls used	6	1	6	2	8	1	8	2
Number of calves	45	6	46	18	55	13	68	24
Average weaning weight, lb.	395	439	386	441	379	416	377	419
Final feed-lot weight	923	1008	851	941	709^a	792^a	701^a	767^a
Daily gain on feed	1.94	2.08	1.79	1.93	...	...	...	...
Gain per 100 lb. T. D. N.	18.4	17.6	18.2	17.2	...	...	...	...
F₃, Hereford bulls × F₂ cows								
Number of bulls used	8	1	15	4	10	1	16	4
Number of calves	63	4	98	16	96	3	156	11
Average weaning weight, lb.	373	432	402	503	352	405	375	465
Final feed-lot weight	865	1002	959	1064	683^a	805^a	708^a	729^a
Daily gain on feed	1.92	2.23	2.28	2.41	...	...	...	...
Gain per 100 lb. T. D. N.	19.3	19.3	18.8	17.5	...	...	...	...

* U.S.D.A. Circular 810, 1949.
^{a} Weight at 18 months of age. The heifers were not fattened but grown out principally on pasture and roughage.

differences noted is to be found in the normal differences in size and weight of the two breeds and in the difference in milking ability of Angus and Hereford cows. Until more definite information is available on the advantages of crossbreeding, it would seem that it should be employed principally for the purpose of quickly obtaining valuable characteristics that have already been achieved in another breed and not in the expectation that the crossbred calves will possess any characteristic in higher degree than it is found in one or the other of the breeds used.

TABLE 24

A COMPARISON OF PUREBRED AND CROSSBRED CALVES*
Eight-Year Summary

	Pure-bred Hereford	Hereford Bull × Angus Cows	Angus Bull × Hereford Cows	Pure-bred Angus
Male calves, number weaned, 8 years	46	50	46	49
Average birth weight lb.	69	66	67	62
Average weaning age, days	219	227	224	235
Average weaning weight lb.	394	473	432	486
Average gain on full feed	338	352	346	331
Average days on full feed	197	203	197	202
Average daily gain:				
a. Birth to weaning, lb.	1.48	1.79	1.63	1.80
b. On full feed	1.72	1.73	1.75	1.64
Corn eaten per cwt. gain	526	586	594	641
Female calves, number weaned, 8 years	51	42	48	42
Average birth weight lb.	68	63	63	56
Average weaning age, days	219	226	218	229
Average weaning weight, lb.	386	447	394	420
Average gain on full feed	306	302	310	295
Average days on full feed	190	185	192	186
Average daily gain:				
a. Birth to weaning, lb.	1.45	1.70	1.52	1.59
b. On full feed	1.61	1.63	1.62	1.59
Corn and cob meal eaten per cwt. gain	562	597	606	620

* Ohio Research Bulletin 703, 1951.

Obviously, crossbreeding is of interest only to the breeder who is producing calves for the feed lot. Even breeders of this group use it only now and then to increase the size of their cattle or to increase the fleshing or milking ability of heifers that they plan to add to the breeding herd. The tendency of many feeder buyers to discard all off-colored cattle, such as brockle-faced, red-necked, and spotted, renders crossbreeding of doubtful value for breeders who sell their steers and heifers as stockers and feeders.

Selection of Individuals within the Breed. In selecting animals for the breeding herd, due consideration should be given to each of the following items: (1) individuality, (2) breeding and production records, (3) pedigree, (4) age, (5) freedom from disease, (6) guarantee made by the owner as to health and breeding ability, (7) cost delivered. Any animal failing to measure up to the expectations of the purchaser in any of these factors should be promptly eliminated from further consideration. Exceptions may occur, but they are so rare as to merit no lengthy discussion.

1. Individuality. The individuality of an animal includes all those characteristics that belong to it as an individual and that may be noted from a visual inspection. Form, quality, breed type, sex character, size, temperament, and so forth, all come under this heading. Needless to say, individuality is an item of great importance in selecting animals for the breeding herd. Fortunately, however, it is usually uppermost in the mind of the breeder and is not likely to be overlooked. In many instances, it is practically the only basis on which the selections are made.

In making the initial purchases for a breeding herd, the logical way to proceed is first to buy the major portion of the cow herd and then to buy a bull that will mate well with them. To start the herd by purchasing the bull will usually result in one of two things: either much time, travel, and expense in getting together a herd of excellent cows that will go well with the chosen sire; or, what is more likely, a heterogeneous lot of cows, some of mediocre merit, bought with the hope that their several faults and lack of uniformity will be corrected by the bull.

Choosing the Cows. The first decision to make regarding the females that are to go into the breeding herd is to determine the type of animal one regards as the best or ideal. It goes without saying, of course, that the animals must all be of approved beef type, wide and blocky in conformation with thickness and smoothness of flesh. But the breeder must decide as to the amount of size his cows should possess; whether he is willing to sacrifice a little quality in favor of ruggedness and constitution; and whether a good flow of milk will compensate to any extent for a slight tendency towards upstandingness and rangy conformation. Few animals will be found for sale that are above criticism. Let the breeder decide at the beginning which defects he will allow and which ones he will stand firmly against. For constructive breeding, a herd of cows must possess uniformity above all else. Since it is a foregone conclusion that there will be defects at the beginning, let the herd be uniform in its deficiencies as well as in its points of merit. Then, by using bulls that are especially strong where the cows are weak, these faults may be eliminated from the herd in the shortest possible time.

However, the beginning breeder should understand that there are certain defects that normally render a cow undesirable for the herd no matter how good she may be in other respects. Chief among these are distinct undersize; lack of sex character, as shown by an overdevelop-

Fig. 12.   These yearling heifers show remarkable uniformity of type.   Uniform females are of paramount importance in constructive breeding.

ment of neck and front quarters; lack of sufficient depth of middle, making impossible any large feeding capacity; a marked lowness of back or loin; and a high, narrow rump. Although it occasionally happens that cows with these defects produce normal offspring, the chance of their doing so is so small that the beginning breeder cannot afford to purchase them even at a low price. Moreover, the presence of animals with such glaring faults in the herd detracts greatly from its appearance.

Selecting the Type. Cattle breeders differ in respect to the type of cow which they believe to be most profitable under average farm or ranch conditions. Some men argue for cows with plenty of size, even though they are somewhat upstanding, on the grounds that such cows are more rugged than those which are smaller and more compact, are better milkers, and will wean larger, heavier calves. Other men, especially purebred breeders, stoutly champion the smaller, more compact type, claiming that such cattle require less feed for maintenance, fatten more readily, mature earlier, and produce better carcasses than larger animals with less quality. Several experiments have been set up in past years to compare cattle of small and large types, but little information of value has resulted from them. Apparently many of our so-called "small-type" and "big-type" animals are smaller or larger as the case may be than the breed average because of environment rather than heredity. Consequently, their offspring when raised under the same environmental conditions show much less variation than their parents. This condition is well illustrated by a comparison of large- and compact-type Hereford cows made at the New Mexico Station, the results of which are given in Table 25. Although the large-type cows used in this test were 12 per cent heavier than the compact-type and 8 per cent heavier than the cows in the unselected herd, their calves were only 6 per cent heavier than the calves from the compact cows and 4 per cent *lighter* than the calves from unselected cows.

TABLE 25

INFLUENCE OF TYPE OF COW UPON SIZE AND GAINING ABILITY OF CALVES*

	Herd No. 1	Herd No. 2	Herd No. 3
Type of cow	Large	Compact	Unselected
Type of bull	Large	Compact	Unselected
Average weight of cows, lb.	1085	895	1004
Average age of calves at weaning, days	207	196	202
Average weaning weight of calves	431	392	441
Weaning weight adjusted to same age	429	403	445
Average grade of calf (score)	105	109	106

* New Mexico Experiment Station, 58th Annual Report, 1947, pp. 40–41.

One of the best-planned comparisons between small- and large-type beef cattle has been made by the Montana Experiment Station over a period of 10 years and with 9 crops of calves. The cows, which were grade Herefords, were divided into two equal groups on the basis of size, and the large cows were bred to large-type bulls and the small cows to small-type bulls. From then on the two herds were maintained as separate units, which were fed and managed alike both winter and summer. In this test the calves from the large-type herd were heavier at birth and weaning than those from the small-type herd and maintained this weight advantage throughout their period in the feed lot or in the breeding herd. The large-type steer calves averaged heavier into the feed lot and made slightly larger gains during the fattening period. However, no significant difference in cost of gain or in selling price per hundred was observed between the two types. In half the feeding trials the small-type calves returned a little higher profit, while in the other half the large-type steers were slightly more profitable. Consequently the large-type herd was more profitable than the small type only if their calves at weaning were sufficiently heavier to pay for the larger feed bill of their mothers. Unfortunately the winter feed and summer pasturage requirements of the two herds are not reported, so that a comparison of maintenance costs is not possible. It seems likely, however, that the excess weight of the large-type calves would ordinarily have a higher value than the extra feed required to maintain the large-type cows. (See Table 26.)

Choosing the Bull. The females having been chosen with due regard to their uniformity of type, it ought not to be a hard matter to decide on the kind of bull to buy. It is, however, often extremely difficult to locate such an animal that is for sale. Time used in finding a bull that exactly suits and money spent to obtain him are both well invested and will never be regretted. If, on the other hand, a breeder buys the first bull he sees because the bull is cheap and "within easy trucking distance of home," his career as a breeder will in all likelihood be endangered at the very start. A really good bull is cheap at almost any price, while a common bull is expensive even at beef values. Certain it is that the bull must possess merit distinctly superior to that of the cows, if real improvement is to be effected.

In regard to the detailed characteristics of a herd bull, little need be said. Suffice it to say that he should have no marked defect of conformation or quality. In particular, he should be strong in those points in which the cow herd is somewhat deficient. The matter of size is often overstressed in selecting a bull. As a rule, bulls of medium size are more satisfactory than animals that are unusually large. A bull should be distinctly masculine in appearance, have a certain burliness about his head and neck, and show evidence of being active and energetic. While all males have a tendency to be somewhat heavier in fore-than in hind-quarters, lightness of hind-quarters is by no means to be condoned. Any bull that shows a tendency to be shallow in body, cut up in the flank, narrow in the rump, or light in thighs and twist is almost certain to do much damage if used to head a herd of good cows.

2. Breeding and Production Records. The past performance of an animal is the best proof of its future usefulness. A bull 4 or 5 years of age that has sired two or three crops of calves of the right type is a much safer animal to purchase than a yearling or 2-year-old that has yet to demonstrate his breeding ability. Likewise, mature cows that have produced good calves practically every year since they became of breeding age are much to be preferred to untried heifers, or to cows that have a mediocre breeding record, either as to the number or the individ-

TABLE 26

A Comparison of Small– and Large–Type Hereford Cattle
(Montana Bulletin 401, 1942)

	Full Fed Roughage First Three Winters				Roughage Limited First Three Winters			
	Small Type		Large Type		Small Type		Large Type	
	A.D.G. for Period	Final Weight	A.D.G. for Period	Final Weight	A.D.G. for Period	Final Weight	A.D.G. for Period	Final Weight
Heifers selected for test:								
1st winter (calves)	0.95	...	1.04	...	0.17		0.18	
1st summer (yearlings)	0.89	717	0.94	797	1.23	671	1.31	679
2nd winter (yearlings)	0.94	...	1.04	...	0.04	...	0.01	...
2nd summer (2-year-olds)	0.71	998	0.67	1099	1.18	945	1.20	951
3d winter (2-year-olds)	0.97		1.18		0.07		0.07	
3d summer (3-year-olds)	−0.30	1037	−0.36	1117	−0.01	963	0.07	972
4th summer (4-year-olds)		1088		1142		1049		1032
5th summer (5-year-olds)		1120		1194		1086		1057
Calves born during test:								
Average birth weight, lb.	...	70	...	78	...	69	...	74
Average weaning weight	1.56	372[a]	1.75	400[a]	1.57	381[a]	1.71	407[a]

	Steer Calves During Fattening (Average 4 Years, 208 Days)	
	Steer Calves from Small-Type Cows	Steer Calves from Large-Type Cows
Average initial weight, lb.	408	441
Average final weight	798	868
Average daily gain	1.90	2.09
Feed eaten per cwt. gain		
Grain, lb.	535	514
Hay, lb.	209	203
Average selling price per cwt.	$10.17	$10.23
Average dressing percentage	59.2	59.5

[a] Average weaning weight of heifer calves only.

uality of their offspring. Animals with unsatisfactory breeding records should not be tolerated in the herd, no matter how good their individuality nor how fashionable their pedigrees. But those that have demonstrated their ability to produce offspring of a high order of merit should be kept as long as they continue to breed, although they themselves may be sadly lacking from the standpoint of showyard excellence. As a rule, such defects as they possess can be laid to advanced age and to the fact that they have calved at such short intervals that they have had no opportunity to rest between pregnancies and lactations and lay on fat.

Fɪɢ. 13. An excellent Shorthorn bull and some of his calves. A sire of proved breeding ability is much to be preferred to one that has not yet produced offspring.

Considerable variation exists among breeders in respect to the disposition that is made of cows that have not weaned a calf during the current year. Many owners of grade herds, especially in the range states, follow the practice of selling all dry cows at weaning time. Such cows usually are fat and heavy at this season of the year and will bring a good price on the market. Other breeders hold them over until spring in the hope that they are in calf. Undoubtedly, the best plan is to have all dry cows examined for pregnancy[3] at the time of the fall roundup in order that only those that are open will be sold.

Usually a purebred cow that has not conceived or has lost her calf during the past year is shown more tolerance than a grade, especially if the probable value of her next calf is several times the cost of her yearly keep. Consequently, dry purebred cows with better than average offspring are usually retained in the herd for awhile in the hope that they will produce at least one more outstanding calf apiece. However, even purebred cows of proven potential breeding ability should not be kept for more than a reasonable period. If they are found to be open upon examination and do not settle after three or four services,

[3] *Cf.* p. 108.

they should be shipped to market to make room for their replacements, for while an outstanding calf may be worth two or three calves of average merit, one of average merit is certainly of more value than no calf at all.

Production Record. If an animal is being considered as a possible addition or replacement to the breeding herd, attention should be given not only to its breeding record but to its production record as well. Unfortunately, few beef cattle breeders obtain and record their young cattle's birth weights, weaning weights, and weights at one year of age or keep a record of the feed consumption per head to permit the calculation of feed eaten per pound of gain. Yet data of this kind are exceedingly valuable in selecting breeding animals, since many of these characteristics are inherited to a noticeable degree. Breeders who will take the trouble to collect such data, especially on the calves of bulls and cows from which they expect to obtain their replacement heifers and future herd sires, will make much faster progress than those who make their selections almost entirely on general appearance and personal opinion.

TABLE 27

VALUE OF WEANING WEIGHT OF FIRST CALF FOR PREDICTING AVERAGE
WEIGHT OF CALVES PRODUCED SUBSEQUENTLY BY SAME COW*

Cow Groups	Average Weaning Weight of First Calf from 3-Year-Old Cows	Average Weaning Weight of Calves from Same Cows for Next 4 Years
1	321	404
2	349	417
3	383	430
4	409	443
5	441	456

* New Mexico Experiment Station, Journal of Animal Science, Vol. 6, 1947, pp. 461–466.

That information on the weaning weights of calves is of much value in culling out unprofitable cows is shown by the data in Table 27, which shows a close relationship between the weaning weight of the first calf of a cow and the average weight of those she produces during the following four years. On the basis of these New Mexico data one may expect to increase the weaning weight of his entire calf crop by about 20 pounds a head by the simple plan of selling all 3-year-old cows that have produced calves weighing less than 400 pounds at weaning time.

Production Testing. Of all the characteristics possessed by beef cattle, those are of most importance which contribute to the young animals' ability to convert farm feeds into high-quality beef. That cattle differ widely in this ability no one will deny. Yet little definite information is available on this point besides the generally accepted belief that deep-bodied, low-set, compact animals require less feed per pound of gain and produce heavier and better carcasses than cattle that are shallow, upstanding, and rangy. Granting that this is true, at least in respect to animals that differ widely in these character-

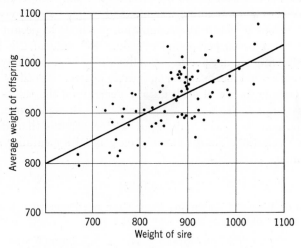

Fɪɢ. 14.   Relationship between weight of sire and weight of offspring at 15 months.
(*Journal of Animal Science*, 1950, *Vol.* 9, *p.* 586.)

istics, there are still wide differences in economy of gain, dressing percentage, and carcass merit to account for among cattle that are essentially the same type. Since rate of gain and carcass grade are inherited to a high degree (see Table 28), definite knowledge of the extent to which these characteristics are present in prospective breeding animals is needed if noticeable improvement in these characteristics is to be achieved. Especially is it needed in selecting a herd sire, which may easily beget two or three hundred calves during the period he is used in the herd. A saving of 10 per cent in the feed costs of growing and fattening this number of offspring to an average weight of 1000 pounds may easily amount to $3000 or $4000 when feed is scarce and high in price.

Geneticists employ two methods to determine the approximate ability of a parent to transmit a given characteristic or trait to its descendents: (1) analyzing the variance or difference in respect to that characteristic which exists between the offspring, especially half brothers and sisters, and comparing these variations with those observed among unrelated animals under like conditions, and (2) analyzing the degree of development of the characteristic in both the parent and the off-spring. The first method enables us to estimate the ability of a bull to transmit a characteristic or trait entirely from data obtained from his offspring, while the second method may be used only if data has been obtained on both the bull and his calves when both were fed under essentially the same conditions. The first method is called "half-sib correlation obtained by analysis of variance," while the second is referred to as "sire-progeny regression obtained from co-variance analysis."[4] That the actual employment of either of these methods taken independently agrees rather closely should give the breeder confidence in their accuracy and practical value. The heritability of some of the more common characteristics of beef cattle, as determined by these methods, is given in Table 28.

TABLE 28

ESTIMATED HERITABILITY OF ECONOMIC CHARACTERISTICS OF BEEF CATTLE*

Characteristics	Number of Progeny Group	Estimated Heritability (per cent)	Lower Limits of Heritability (per cent)
1. Birth weight	110	53	26
2. Weaning weight (corrected for age)	110	28	7
3. Final feed-lot weight, 15 months	110	86	54
4. Gain in feed lot	110	65	37
5. Weaning score	86	28	4
6. Slaughter steer grade	104	45	19
7. Carcass grade	104	33	10
8. Area of rib-eye muscle	64	68	31

* Knapp and Clark, U.S.D.A., Journal of Animal Science, November, 1950, p. 582.

Obviously it would be impractical for purebred breeders to test all their prospective breeding cattle for rate and economy of gain because of the high labor cost of feeding them individually in separate stalls and pens. However, the importance of knowing whether or not a prospective herd sire is above or below the average in these important characteristics should induce the more progressive and constructive breeders to pay a sufficiently high premium for young high-scoring, production-tested bulls to cover the extra labor involved. Moreover, it has been found that a long period of individual feeding is not neces-

[4] Journal of Animal Science, 1946, Vol. 5, pp. 62–69.

sary to distinguish the superior from the mediocre and inferior animals. In studies made by the United States Department of Agriculture at its beef cattle breeding station at Miles City, Montana, individual feeding for 196 days immediately following weaning or during the last 84 days of a 252-day feeding period was found to give as reliable information on the rate and economy of gain of young beef cattle as individual feeding throughout the entire period.[5] Thus it appears that individual feeding, at least of young bulls that are prospective herd sires, does not entail more labor and expense than the value of the results justify.

Progeny Testing. Since heredity appears to be largely responsible for the variations observed in the rate and economy of gains of growing, fattening calves, especially during the last third of a 7- to 9-month feeding period, the progeny testing of bulls and cows by using their calves in feeding tests would seem to offer an excellent opportunity to select breeding animals that are outstanding in their ability to produce calves which gain rapidly and make good use of their feed. However, since eight or more offspring are required for a test that will yield reliable results, progeny testing is of practical value only in testing mature bulls that have sired a sufficient number of calves the previous year to permit the selection of a uniform group for a reliable test. That data on available bulls in respect to the weaning weight, rate of gain, economy of gain, dressing percentage, and carcass grade of a representative group of their calves are of great value in deciding which one to purchase for a herd sire is shown in Table 29.

That progeny tests are reliable when based on six or more offspring is indicated by the data given in Table 30. The fact that all five of the bulls listed in this table had the same rating when mated with unrelated cows as they had when mated with their half sisters and first cousins indicates that the differences observed in the rate of gains of their calves were due principally to hereditary factors.

Obviously, progeny testing is limited to mature bulls which will have sired their second and third crops of calves by the time production data are available on the calves they sired as yearlings. Consequently, it is of no value in preventing the use for at least two years of young bulls which have satisfactory individuality but are sub-standard in respect to rate and economy of gain. Fortunately, performance testing is available for spotting either sub-standard bulls or heifers before they are added to the breeding herd. Indeed, if performance records are obtained on all prospective breeding animals and rigid selections made on the results obtained there will be little need for progeny tests except

[5] Journal of Animal Science, 1947, Vol. 6, pp. 174–181.

to determine the slaughter and carcass merit of a bull's offspring. Obviously, information in respect to such characteristics can be obtained in no other way.

TABLE 29

EVALUATION OF BEEF BULLS ON THE BASIS OF THE PERFORMANCE OF THEIR PROGENY IN THE FEED LOT*

November 24, 1948–April 1, 1949 (128 Days)

Bulls	Number of Progeny Included in Test	Initial Weight	Final Weight	Total Gain, 128 Days	Average Daily Gain	Score[a] Initial	Score[a] Final
Publican Domino 128	6	591	912	321	2.50	18.1	16.7
Domestic Mischief	7	419	730	311	2.43	22.5	18.2
Mossberger	6	486	795	309	2.41	23.3	20.6
N. M. Real Domino	6	433	739	306	2.39	22.3	18.6
Prince Burwell 10th	6	344	648	304	2.38	23.4	24.0
Spade	6	535	835	300	2.34	23.1	20.5
J. P. Domino 70th	6	531	814	283	2.21	13.9	15.1
King	6	500	781	281	2.20	22.7	21.7
Reel Silver Domino 327th	9	391	664	273	2.13	17.5	17.9
Star Dust 60th	8	356	622	266	2.08	18.6	17.6

* Texas Agricultural Experiment Station, Balmorhea, Texas, Mimeograph Report, April 9, 1949
[a] Meaning of numerical scores: 10–12, Choice; 14–18, Good; 20 and above, Medium.

TABLE 30

THE ABILITY OF BULLS TO REPEAT THEIR PROGENY TESTS WITH RELATED AND UNRELATED COWS*

Bull Number	Average daily gain of 6 to 8 steer offspring (pounds) Relation of Cows to Bull None	Average daily gain of 6 to 8 steer offspring (pounds) Relation of Cows to Bull Half Sisters and First Cousins
17	1.75	1.68
15	1.79	1.69
16	1.80	1.78
22	2.07	1.94
28	2.09	2.02

* Knapp and Norskog, U.S.D.A., Journal of Animal Science, 1946, Vol. 5, p. 68.

Both production and progeny testing must be done under carefully controlled conditions if the results obtained are to be useful for analysis and interpretation. Weaning weights of calves must be corrected for age and sex differences before they are compared. The

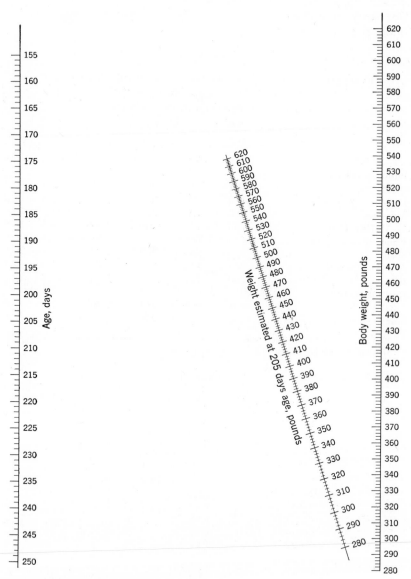

Fig. 15. A chart for estimating the weights of calves at a constant age of 205 days. Using a ruler or straight-edge, connect the age in days on the left-hand scale with the observed weight on the right-hand scale. The estimated weight at 205 days is read on the center line, where it is intersected by the ruler.

(*Journal of Animal Science*, 1945, *Vol. 4, p.* 287.)

nomograph shown as Fig. 15 may be used for making age corrections, while the weights of heifer calves may be converted to a steer-calf basis by adding 32 pounds after correcting the weights for differences in weaning age.[6]

In comparing the weaning weights of the progeny of different bulls consideration probably should also be given to differences in the ages of dams. Reference to Table 31 will disclose that the average weaning weight of calves from 3-year-old cows is only 86 per cent of the average weight of calves from 6-, 7-, and 8-year-old cows, while the average weight of calves from 4-year-old cows is but 90 per cent as much. Also calves from 9- and 10-year-old cows are 3 and 6 per cent lighter, respectively, at weaning than calves from cows in their prime. Although the data cited are from range cows and calves, which had poorer grazing than is likely to be available in the Corn Belt states, they may be used for making corrections for age of dams, pending the availability of similar data obtained under Corn Belt conditions.

TABLE 31

EFFECT OF AGE UPON THE WEIGHT OF BEEF COWS AND UPON
THE WEANING WEIGHT OF THEIR CALVES*

Age of Cows (years)	Average Weight of Cows (pounds)	Average Weight of Calves (pounds)	Age of Cows (years)	Average Weight of Cows (pounds)	Average Weight of Calves (pounds)
3	908	387	7	1024	454
4	952	405	8	1017	450
5	983	429	9	993	436
6	1013	447	10	981	422

* New Mexico Press Bull. 1004.

3. Pedigree. Broadly speaking, the pedigree of an animal comprises all its blood relatives except its own offspring. In practice, however, the term is limited to include only the ancestors which appear in the direct line of ascent. Often when we speak of a pedigree we have in mind a printed record, usually in tabular form, of the animal's ancestors to three or more generations.

From the printed pedigree of the animal, the breeder is able to discover two things: first, the names of the immediate, and sometimes the distant, ancestors of the animal; and second, the names of the men in whose herds these ancestors were used. Although it often happens that a perusal of a pedigree brings to light few or perhaps no animals

[6] Koger, M., and Knox, J. H., Journal of Animal Science, 1945, Vol. 4, No. 1, pp. 15–19.

about which definite knowledge is had, still the very fact that these animals were owned and used by reliable, constructive breeders makes it almost certain that they possessed real merit. Of particular value is a pedigree that shows that successive generations of animals have been retained in a prominent herd, since such a fact is good evidence that all such ancestors were pretty much the same type. Such a pedigree is one of the best possible guarantees that the animal possessing it will produce offspring like itself, or, as we say, that it will be "prepotent."

Although the pedigree is of considerable value in selecting breeding animals, it frequently happens that too much importance is attached to it. In particular, too much emphasis is often placed upon "fashionable families" and "popular lines of breeding," which are based largely on the individuality or breeding record of some cow or bull far back in the line of ancestry, rather than on any special merit of the immediate ancestors of the animal concerned. From the standpoint of constructive breeding it is unfortunate that the stamp of approval is withheld from some excellent cattle because of their so-called "plain pedigrees," but there seems to be small chance of a change of attitude in this respect on the part of leading breeders in the near future. Consequently, the man who is looking forward to a career in the purebred cattle business must give some consideration to the present-day notions of families and popular blood lines in selecting his breeding stock. Otherwise he will be limited, in the disposal of surplus animals, to breeders who sell bulls to commercial cattlemen and steers on the open market.

To place pedigree above individuality is to gamble with fate. If the ancestry represented by the pedigree has failed to produce the merit desired in the present generation, there is even less likelihood of its producing it in the next, since it will be still further diluted. Of course, there is always a chance that characters that are "latent" in animals of the present generation will show forth in the next, but it is a chance that few breeders can afford to take.

Cows with similar breeding will prove much more satisfactory than those that are wholly unrelated. They will in all probability be much more uniform in their appearance and will also produce a more uniform lot of calves. No better advice can be given a young breeder than to recommend that he go to some reliable, long-established breeder and purchase as his foundation stock only daughters and granddaughters of a bull of recognized merit. Or, a herd may be started by buying an old cow together with two or more of her heifers. By retaining the female descendants of such a "family," a herd of cattle is soon built up that will be noted for its uniformity of type, resulting from the regularity with which it transmits its characteristics to its offspring. Young breeders occasionally get the notion that their herds are not up to date unless they contain at least one representative of each of the popular "families," and daughters or grand-daughters of most of the leading sires of the day. Accordingly, they travel far and wide, buying a heifer here and a heifer there. When females with such different blood lines are mated with the same bull, it is not surprising that the resulting calves are often lacking in uniformity.

The most valuable way to study the pedigree of an animal is not from a catalog prepared for an auction sale but from a critical inspection of the sire and dam, full or half brothers and sisters, and other close relatives on the farm of the breeder. If these animals measure up to the standards of the buyer, the printed pedigree should require only enough inspection to insure that the blood lines represented are reasonably popular and are not so widely different from those of the present herd as to constitute an outcross that would be undesirable.

Inbreeding. In carefully selected herds where much attention has been given to constitutional vigor and regularity of breeding, as well as to the more commonly recognized items, better results will usually be obtained if the bull and females represent the same general line of descent. The mating of animals of totally different blood lines sometimes introduces conflicting tendencies which interfere with the inheritance of highly desirable characters, whereas the mating of related animals tends to favor their appearance in the next generation. Close breeding was regarded with much disfavor only a few years ago, but it is now recognized as a useful tool to rid a herd of undesirable characters which might persist for years in latent form without inbreeding to facilitate selection. Inbreeding tends to produce some offspring that are homozygous or pure for the desirable character, some that are homozygous for the bad character, and some that are heterozygous or mixed like the parents. Thus, by keeping the animals that are homozygous for the good character and selling those that are homozygous for the bad, a breeder will eventually obtain a herd from which the bad character or trait has been eliminated entirely.

From a practical standpoint, however, the inbreeding of beef cattle has some serious objections. In the first place, most of the undesirable characters to be eliminated are carried by recessive genes, like horns in the Polled Hereford and Shorthorn breeds and red color in Angus cattle. Consequently, their elimination is a slow process, since these characters exist in latent form in the heterozygous individuals. Secondly, the time that must elapse between successive generations of females, allowing for bull calves, is from 4 to 5 years, so that few breeders can hope to achieve in their lifetime a herd that is 100 per cent homozygous for more than one or two characters. Thirdly, the fact that the average beef cow produces only 5 or 6 calves, half of which are bulls, greatly limits the degree of freedom that may be exercised in selecting her replacement. It is probable that most breeders must retain from 30 to 50 per cent of their heifer calves to maintain the size of their herds, thus leaving little opportunity for rigid selection for more than one homozygous character.

Because of these disadvantages, intensive inbreeding is much less common in improving beef cattle than in breeding hogs and sheep, which attain breeding age more quickly and are more prolific. However, a mild form of inbreeding termed "linebreeding" is widely practiced by breeders of purebred beef cattle. An animal is said to be "linebred" if its parents are less closely related than half brother and half sister.

The Coefficient of Inbreeding. It is frequently desirable to compute the degree of inbreeding that will result when animals which have one or more common ancestors are mated. For this purpose the following formula, which has been developed by Sewall Wright, formerly of the United States Department of Agriculture, is used:

$$F_x = \sum [(\tfrac{1}{2})^{n+n'+1}(1 + F_a)]$$

where F_x stands for the coefficient of inbreeding to be calculated; Σ (sigma) indicates that, if there is more than one common ancestor, the coefficient of each is to be determined separately, and then all added together; n and n' are the number of generations between the sire and dam, respectively, and the common ancestor; and F_a is the coefficient of inbreeding of the common ancestor if that animal is itself inbred.

The coefficient of inbreeding expresses the extent to which homozygosis has been increased by the mating of related animals. In a herd in which no inbreeding has been practiced and in which, therefore, 50 per cent of the paired genes may be assumed to be homozygous (alike) and 50 per cent heterozygous (unlike) in every individual, if a bull were to be mated to his half-sisters the coefficient of inbreeding of the offspring would be $\tfrac{1}{8}$ or 12.5 per cent. This means that 56.25 per cent (50 + 12.5 per cent of 50) of the paired genes of the offspring would be homozygous and 43.75 per cent heterozygous.

The practical use of the coefficient of inbreeding results from its value in (1) appraising the probable prepotency of an animal in respect to characters dependent upon homozygous genes; (2) predicting the probability of the occurrence of defects or faults that are

FIELD COMMANDER

Bred by John Doe, Westville, Ia. Calved March 23, 1949. Tattoo R-42

		Band Major	Drum Major
	Proud Major		Rosalind
Sire		Princess 14th	Drum Major
Major General			Princess 10th
		General	Colonel
	Kitty Lee 3rd		Eudora
		Kitty Lee	Defender
			Kitty
		Proud Major	Band Major
	Proud Major 2nd		Princess 14th
Dam		Prudence	Lancier
Penelope			Patience
		Deck Officer	General
	Priscilla 8th		Fanny May
		Priscilla 4th	North Star
			Priscilla 3rd

FIG. 16. The pedigree of an inbred bull which shows 8.6 per cent inbreeding.

due to recessive conditions; and (3) reducing the occurrence of such defects by planned matings that will represent the lowest possible coefficient of inbreeding.

4. Age. Seldom is it advisable in founding a purebred herd to buy only heifers. Heifers require more care and assistance during calving than older cows, and, as a rule, the percentage of calves saved is not as high. Also, the danger of securing non-breeders is greater with untried heifers than with older cows with well-established breeding records. Consideration should also be given to the fact that heifers safely in calf usually sell for a higher price than cows of equally good individuality and breeding, but showing somewhat less "bloom" and condition because of age. If possible, the herd should be about equally divided between mature cows, varying in age from 3 to 8 years, and heifers bred for their first calves. In general, calves and yearling heifers are not a wise investment for the beginning purebred breeder. If purchased they must be carried along for at least two years before they reach a productive age. Most young breeders will find it to their advantage to confine their attention to their cows and calves for the first two years, instead of trying to take care of too many animals. Moreover, breeders should early adopt the policy of breeding their own females to replace the cows that are, because of age or poor breeding qualities, to be sold from the herd.

Probably the best way to start a commercial breeding herd is to purchase a drove of heifer calves or unbred yearling heifers. High-grade or unregistered purebred heifers are available in large numbers in the fall in the western states, and a carefully sorted drove will cost little more than their market value for feeding purposes. Purchase at the ranch or farm is to be preferred to purchase on a large livestock market,

TABLE 32

EFFECT OF AGE OF RANGE BEEF COWS UPON THEIR PRODUCTIVITY*

Age at Calving Time (years)	Number of Cows	Production			
		Cows		Calves	
		Percentage Dry	Percentage Pregnant	Percentage Born Alive	Percentage Born Dead[a]
3	412	15.0	85.0	95.4	4.6
4	397	19.4	80.6	96.2	3.8
5	341	14.1	85.9	96.9	3.1
6	288	15.6	84.4	96.7	3.3
7	219	18.7	81.3	97.2	2.8
8	176	14.8	85.2	98.0	2.0
9	128	13.3	86.7	98.2	1.8
10	76	15.8	84.2	92.2	7.8
11	37	18.9	81.1	100.0	0.0

* Baker and Quesenberry, U.S.D.A., Journal of Animal Sci., **3**, p. 81, 1944.
[a] Abortions, stillbirths, and losses due to inclement weather.

as one is able at the ranch to ascertain the merits of the sires and dams, not of each individual heifer, of course, but of the group as a whole. Even though the utmost care is taken to select only heifers of the desired quality and type, some will fail to develop properly as they grow older. This is particularly true of heifer calves, the appearance of which at weaning time does not always foretell the merit they will have at maturity. Consequently, it is advisable to purchase a considerably larger number of heifers than will be needed for the breeding herd, in order to permit further culling and selection before they are bred. Those that fail to meet the standard set for the breeding herd should be put into the feed lot and sold for beef when they have attained a satisfactory finish for their age and weight.

Many breeders prefer to buy a yearling or 2-year-old bull because they believe he has a longer period of usefulness before him, and because he can usually be bought for less money than an older bull. Such a position is not always justified. As a rule, breeders who own only one bull do not find it advisable to retain him for more than 3 years, as by that time his daughters are of breeding age. Consequently, a bull 7 or 8 years old when purchased will still be serviceable for the length of time that he can be used. Moreover, a bull that is mature will require much less grain and care than a yearling or 2-year-old. And, most important of all, the older bull can be bought on the breeding record he has already made, whereas the breeding qualities of a young bull are largely a matter of speculation.

Fig. 17. A Hereford bull still sound and vigorous at 12 years of age. The practice of selling bulls for slaughter when around 6 years old and replacing them with young, untried animals has resulted in the loss of many valuable sires. (*Courtesy University of Illinois.*)

However, few bulls are offered for sale after they have proven their ability to sire calves of superior type and quality. Since really good bulls are relatively scarce, other breeders secure options on them as soon as their superior merit is clearly established. On the other hand, breeders are constantly discarding bulls after 2 or 3 years of unsatisfactory or mediocre service in their herds. Consequently, the breeding records of a bull that is offered for sale after 2 or 3 years of service should be carefully investigated to determine the merit of his calves before he is purchased to head a herd of better than average cows.

Culling for Age. Breeders differ in their opinion as to when cows should be sold from the herd because of advanced age. Seldom are grade cows sufficiently well marked or branded to make it possible to determine their ages accurately. Usually in the fall when the calves

TABLE 33

ATTRITION SUFFERED BY 412 BEEF COWS DURING THEIR STAY IN THE BREEDING HERD*

(Data from U.S.D.A. Range Experiment Station, Miles City, Montana)

Age at Calving (years)	Total Cows	Cause of Disposal								Total Disposals		
		Dry 2 Years		Abortion or Reactors		Died During Year		Other Sales[a]		Number	Percentage[b]	Cumulative Percentage[b]
		Number	Percentage[b]	Number	Percentage[b]	Number	Percentage[b]	Number	Percentage[b]			
3	412	...	...	1	0.2	9	2.2	5	1.2	15	3.6	3.6
4	397	31	7.5	16	3.9	3	0.7	6	1.5	56	13.6	17.2
5	341	6	1.5	8	1.9	17	4.1	22	5.3	53	12.9	30.1
6	288	8	1.9	17	4.1	6	1.5	38	9.2	69	16.7	46.8
7	219	5	1.2	10	2.4	6	1.5	22	5.3	43	10.4	57.2
8	176	4	1.0	2	0.5	3	0.7	39	9.5	48	11.7	68.9
9	128	2	0.5	6	1.5	1	0.8	43	10.4	52	12.6	81.5
10	76	1	0.2	3	0.7	1	0.2	34	8.3	39	9.5	91.0
11	37	0	0.0	0	0.0	1	0.2	36	8.7	37	9.0	100.0
Total	412	57	13.8	63	15.3	47	11.4	245	59.5	412	100.0	

* Baker and Quesenberry, U.S.D.A., Journal of Animal Science, 1944, Vol. 3, p. 82.

[a] Including sales for undesirable type, unsatisfactory calves, old age, cancer eye, etc.

[b] Percentage of the original number of cows.

are weaned the cows which "look" to be too old to be kept over for another calf are separated from the herd, and those that are found to have too few good incisor teeth to graze short grass are shipped to market.

Records of weaning weight kept at the New Mexico Station over several years indicate that both the weight of a cow and the weaning weight of her calf decline noticeably after she is 8 years old. Consequently, it appears advisable to sell all range cows at that age, even though doing so increases the number of heifer calves that must be retained for replacements. (See Table 31.) It is probable that grade cows might well be retained until 9 or 10 years of age in the Corn Belt because of the better feed conditions prevailing there.

Purebred breeders, of course, have an accurate record of the ages of their cows, but in few purebred herds is "across-the-board" culling practiced on the basis of age, as is often the case with grade cows. Instead, the cows are culled on the basis of the merit shown by their calves. Thus, it frequently happens that a purebred cow 15 or more years of age is kept for another calf, even though she must be fed a special ration because of her inability to eat ordinary feeds. On the other hand, far more rigid culling is practiced by purebred than by grade breeders among their 4- and 5-year-old cows. Purebred cows of this age which have not produced calves of at least average merit are either shipped to market or sold into purebred herds where the average merit is noticeably below that of the animals added.

5. Freedom from Disease. Unfortunately, cattle are susceptible to contagious abortion, a very serious infectious disease that is widely prevalent throughout the country. In buying animals for the breeding herd every precaution should be taken to guard against the introduction of this plague. In so far as possible, selection should be made only from herds that are known to be clean and healthy. Herds that are being dispersed for no plainly evident reason should be regarded with suspicion, as some unscrupulous breeders have in times past used this method of ridding themselves of cows that were practically worthless as breeders because of contagious abortion.

Both cows and bulls may be tested for contagious abortion. In fact, all states now require the testing of all breeding cattle that are brought into the state, while some require the testing of all breeding cattle that are moved from one farm to another within the state. Some states make an exception for intrastate movement of cattle which have received "calfhood" vaccination[6] against the disease. For such animals a certificate of vaccination is accepted in lieu of an agglutination test. Contagious abortion is a disease so prevalent that breeding cattle should be purchased only from breeders who either test their herds annually and dispose of all reactors or vaccinate their calves with a protective bacterin. In either case cattle should be purchased subject to a test made by a state or federal veterinarian not more than 30 days before the delivery of the animals to the buyer.

Formerly, many herds of beef cattle harbored animals that were infected with tuberculosis, but a nationwide campaign of testing all herds periodically and removing the reactors has almost eradicated this disease. Whereas during the early years of the testing program nearly 10 per cent of the animals tested in the United States were reactors, only 0.19 per cent of the nearly 9 million cattle tested in 1948 were so classified.

Cattle should be bought only on the condition that they successfully pass tests for both contagious abortion and tuberculosis administered by a state or federal veterinarian. The expense of such tests should be borne by the seller and the tests made before the cattle are delivered.

[6] *Cf.* p. 603.

Even though the tests are passed successfully, the cattle should not be added to the herd immediately, but should be isolated for a period of 60 to 90 days, at the end of which time they should be retested before they are released from quarantine. Nearly all states have in force sanitary regulations compelling the isolation and retest of all breeding animals that are purchased outside the state. Breeders should adopt the same policy for all animals regardless of their origin, unless the animal in question is from an "accredited" herd.[7]

Inasmuch as, in a number of states, all stocker and feeder cattle purchased at public stockyards or on the range must be held in quarantine until tested, heifers that are purchased for breeding should be tested preferably before they leave the stockyards or concentration point. If the test discloses any reactors the entire drove should be sold immediately to prevent contamination of the farm. The charge made for the combined tuberculosis and blood test is approximately $2 a head when made by state veterinarians at public stockyards.

Cattlemen should inform themselves of the laws and regulations pertaining to the control of contagious diseases. Otherwise they may find that they have bought or sold animals on which they cannot get clearance for shipment. The transportation across state lines of cattle that do not have the required "health certificates" is a federal offense and is punishable by a heavy fine.

6. Guarantee. Custom has decreed that every animal of breeding age at the time of sale be guaranteed a breeder. Cows in calf or with calves by their sides are regarded as proved breeders and no further guarantee is given. Bred heifers that prove not to be pregnant and open heifers that the buyer is not able to settle must be reported to the seller promptly, usually within 6 months of the date of sale. The seller then has the right to have the heifer returned at his expense for further trial. If he succeeds in getting her pregnant, he returns her to the buyer at the buyer's expense; if not, a substitute animal is furnished or the purchase price is refunded, as the buyer prefers. Bulls are commonly guaranteed to be breeders if they are not used until they are 14 months old and are not permitted to run with the breeding herd until they are 20 months of age. The same provisions for returning non-breeding bulls as pertain to heifers should be stipulated in the guarantee.

While the practice of guaranteeing animals to be breeders is almost universal among the larger breeders, some of the smaller breeders are not acquainted with it. Hence, to have a definite agreement on the matter at the time of purchase will often avoid a serious misunder-

[7] *Cf.* p. 603.

standing later on. The seller should also agree to refund the purchase price or to substitute another animal of equal value if the 60-day retest for tuberculosis is not passed successfully. Any breeder who will not willingly make these guarantees is an unsafe man from whom to buy purebred cattle. Obviously, a guarantee can hardly be expected for grade cows and heifers, since their breeding value is but little more than their value for beef.

7. Cost Delivered. It is probable that purebred beef cattle show a greater price range at any given time than almost any other agricultural commodity. In the same issue of a breed journal are often found reports of public sales with averages that range all the way from $500 to $3000. Even in the same sale one animal may sell for ten or even twenty times as much as another of approximately the same age, general type, and breeding. One animal is so nearly perfect that prominent breeders desire to own it to strengthen their show herds. The other animal's plain head, high tailhead, or slight deviation from the standard color pattern may confine the bidding largely to the owners of small purebred herds, who attend the sales of outstanding breeders in the hope of getting a few animals of superior breeding at bargain prices.

To decide what a particular young bull or heifer is worth is a very difficult problem. Occasionally breeders refuse a high price for an animal and a few weeks later see it sell in an auction sale for possibly only half the original offer. On the other hand, buyers have refused to pay the prices asked for animals at private treaty only to pay several hundred dollars more for them at a public auction.

Studies made of the prices of purebred breeding cattle over a period of years indicate that their average price at public auction sales has been about three times the market value per head of choice 1000-pound steers.[8] This is a good price basis on which to buy or sell purebred cows and heifers. A satisfactory rule to use in buying a bull is much more difficult to devise, since so much depends upon the quality and breeding of the cow herd and the reputation and salesmanship of the buyer. Usually a sufficiently good bull can be bought at a price not more than the value of the three best cows in the herd in which he is to be used. Obviously, if one that is satisfactory can be bought for less, so much the better, but this amount should not be considered excessive if it must be paid to obtain a bull with the individual merit and breeding needed to achieve further improvement.

Far too often the price of an animal is the all-important factor in deciding on its purchase. As a matter of fact, it should be the last,

[8] *Cf.* pp. 566–567.

within certain reasonable limits. If an animal suits and gives every promise of fulfilling the breeder's needs he should buy it if the price is in reason. If it doesn't suit he should not take it even as a gift, unless he knows where he can resell it immediately at a profit. To refuse to pay an extra $50 or $100 for an animal costing $500 to $1000 is to attempt to shade values more finely than is humanly possible. In founding a herd, if one has not the money to buy what he really wants, he had better delay making his purchases until he gets it. With a herd already established, every purchase made should represent a distinct advance over what is already owned, even though several of the plainer animals of the present herd must be sold to provide funds to pay for those to be added.

A young animal husbandry student who had spent a considerable amount of time studying the history of a leading breed of beef cattle wrote in a term paper that "it is beyond question that the failure to own a really good herd sire has put more men out of the purebred business than ever did the purchase of sires at prices that were too high." This statement contains much food for thought. There is little chance for constructive breeding if more attention is given to the saving of a few dollars than to the obtaining of outstanding merit in the animals from which further merit is sought.

Reproduction and Mating

Cattle, like all other higher forms of animal life, reproduce by means of special reproductive organs which produce the sex cells necessary for the formation of a new individual and which afford protection and nourishment to the young until it is sufficiently well developed to exist alone. As the part played by the female in the generative process is of much practical concern to the cattleman, her part in the process will be treated in some detail.

The Generative Organs of the Cow. The generative system of the cow consists of the genital tract, which may be described as a tube extending from the posterior end of the body forward into the body cavity. This tube varies considerably in size and shape throughout its length, and inasmuch as each part performs a special function in the process of reproduction, each part is spoken of as an *organ* of the reproductive system. In accordance with such a definition, the following generative organs exist in the cow:

1. *The Vulva.* The vulva is the exterior opening of the female genital tract. It consists of two labiæ, or lips, which close the opening of the tract, and of an internal chamber just within the labiæ, called the vulvar cavity. Into this cavity opens the urethra, the duct from the bladder.

2. *The Vagina.* That portion of the tract just forward of the vulvar cavity is called the vagina. It is about 10 inches in length and lies immediately below the colon. Its principal function is to afford a passage from the uterus to the exterior.

3. *The Os Uteri.* This is a constriction in the genital canal that marks the division between the vagina and the uterus. It is often called the *cervix*, or neck, of the uterus, and is really a cone-shaped part of that organ which projects back into the anterior end of the vagina. During œstrum and at the time of parturition, the os uteri is much dilated, but normally it is contracted so as to close the uterus. When it is closed so tightly as to make the passage of the spermatozoa into the non-pregnant uterus impossible, sterility, of course, results. During pregnancy the os uteri is tightly closed and is sealed against the entrance of bacteria by a plug of mucus secreted by the mucous membrane of this region.

4. *The Uterus.* The uterus is that portion of the genital tract which is designed to retain and nourish the embryo between the time of fertilization and parturition. In form the uterus consists of a main portion, or *body,* lying just beyond the os, and two branches, or *horns*

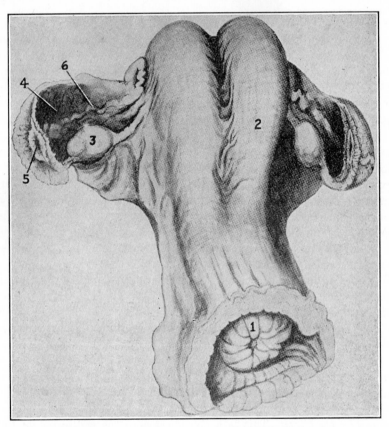

FIG. 18. The reproductive system of the cow. 1, os uteri; 2, right horn of the uterus; 3, ovary; 4, broad ligament; 5, the pavilion of the oviduct; and 6, the oviduct. (*After Williams in "The Diseases of the Genital Organs of Animals."*)

(cornua), into which the uterus branches at its forward end. In the cow, the body of the uterus is relatively small, whereas the horns are long and large. For a short way they extend forward nearly parallel to each other, then curve downwards, outward, and backwards and then upwards, terminating near the lower wall of the vagina. The horns of the uterus are held in place by a tough, elastic membrane called *the broad ligament,* which forms a connection between the uterus and the abdominal walls.

5. *The Oviducts.* At the terminal of each horn of the uterus is a thread-like tubule called the oviduct, which leads to the ovary. As there are two horns, so there are two ovaries and two oviducts. Although the ovaries are but a short distance from the termination of the uterus, the oviducts are so tortuous that the total length of each is some 5 or 6 inches. At its anterior extremity the oviduct broadens out to form a funnel-shaped opening called the *pavilion,* into which the ripened egg falls when liberated from the ovary. The walls of the oviduct are covered with cilia, which facilitate the passage of the egg down into the uterus.

6. *The Ovaries.* The ovaries are groups of specialized cells which produce, at fairly regular periods, the *eggs,* or *ova,* as the female sex cells are called. In the cow the ovaries lie loosely in the body cavity alongside the forward part of the vagina. They are oblong in form, having a greater diameter of about 1 inch. They may be felt with comparative ease by inserting the hand through the rectum. During pregnancy, of course, the ovaries are greatly displaced by the enlargement and falling forward of the uterus. Each ovary really consists of a cluster of small egg sacs, probably several thousand in number. Each little sac is called a Graafian follicle. Every female is born with, or obtains very soon after birth, a definite number of Graafian follicles, each containing an egg, which is capable of being impregnated and growing into a new individual. The follicles remain in an unchanged state until the advent of puberty, when, one at a time, they begin to enlarge through an increase in the amount of follicular liquid within, until eventually the wall is ruptured and the ovum liberated. Theoretically, the reproductive ability of a female persists until all the ova have perished through ovulation or because of disease or old age. As a matter of fact, probably less than a hundred ova are liberated through ovulation during the normal life of a cow. The thousands not liberated are injured, or even destroyed, by diseases that affect the genital organs, or, escaping this fate, the ova tend to become atrophied and degenerate with the advent of old age. In either case, of course, the animal is rendered barren.

The rupture of the ovisac produces a lesion or scar, which usually behaves differently according to whether the discharged ovum becomes fertilized and undergoes development into a fœtus or, failing of fecundation, perishes. The crater resulting from the rupture of the sac becomes filled with lymph, blood, or other products of the disturbances of the tissues. Should the ovum perish, the lesion tends to heal rapidly, the blood and lymph in the crater are resorbed, and from its walls there forms a characteristic tissue, known as the corpus luteum of œstrum. It is identical in form, consistence, and volume with the corpus luteum of pregnancy, but its color differs. In the non-pregnant cow it is chocolate-colored. Prior to the next œstrum, it atrophies.

Should the ovum become fecundated and undergo normal development, the corpus luteum forming in the crater is almost always markedly yellow, lemon, or orange. It projects beyond the ovarian surface. It persists regularly up to the time of parturition or abortion and for a varying length of time thereafter. It is known as the true corpus luteum. In the cow it is frequently larger than the remainder of the ovary—approximately ⅝ to ¾ inch.[1]

From physiological studies that have been made it is now known that reproduction is a very complex process, which is carefully controlled by substances called "hormones" or regulators. The process is initiated by the very tiny pituitary gland situated at the base of the brain, which secretes a hormone called "gonadotropin," which upon being taken up by the blood stream stimulates the growth of a Graafian follicle in one of the ovaries. Now this enlarging Graafian follicle itself produces a hormone called "estrogen," which upon entering the blood stream stimulates the secretion of mucus in the vagina and acts upon the central nervous system to cause the cow to show signs of "heat." Upon the rupture of the Graafian follicle the production of estrogen is stopped and a corpus luteum is formed in the crater of the follicle. The corpus luteum secretes a third hormone called "progesterone," which (1) inhibits the production of gonadotropin by the pituitary, thereby preventing the development of another Graafian follicle, and (2) prepares the mucous lining of the uterus to receive and nourish the fertilized egg. However, if the cow was not bred or, being bred, has not conceived, the corpus luteum begins to degenerate in about 15 days, and the secretion of progesterone is stopped, whereupon the pituitary gland again begins the production of gonadotropin to start the process all over again. But, should the cow be bred during œstrum and the ova be fertilized, the corpus luteum remains in the ovary throughout pregnancy and continues to produce progesterone, which prevents the development of Graafian follicles and hence, the occurrence of œstrum. Occasionally, a corpus luteum fails to atrophy at the normal time, inducing temporary sterility. Such a "retained" corpus luteum is commonly termed a "cyst." If the cyst is expelled from the ovary by a veterinarian working through the rectum, the cow will usually come in heat and can be bred 3 or 4 days later.

Œstrum and Conception. From the standpoint of the practical cattleman, the process of reproduction begins with the appearance of œstrum, or the "period of heat" in the female. Ordinarily, this condition is first observed in heifers soon after they reach 1 year of age.

[1] W. L. Williams, Veterinary Obstetrics, 1917, pp. 16–17.

Liberal feeding appears to hasten the advent of puberty, and scanty feeding tends to retard it. A few hours after the end of œstrum an egg is liberated by the rupture of a Graafian follicle, thereby presenting the conditions for conception and pregnancy. The interval between the end of œstrum and ovulation varies from 6 to 20 hours (see Table 34), whereas the time required for the male sperm to travel from the vagina to the oviducts, where fertilization normally occurs, is only 4 to 9 hours. Consequently, it is advisable to delay breeding until near the close of the heat period to favor the presence of strong, vigorous sperm in the oviduct at the time the egg is liberated. Since the duration of œstrum in cattle is very short, seldom exceeding 18 hours, to delay breeding too long may result in the cow's being out of heat when mating is attempted. In studies made at the Michigan Station with beef cows, 4 P.M. was the earliest and 10:30 P.M. the average time of day at which œstrum ended. Hence, it would seem that cows that are to receive only a single service should be bred in mid-afternoon. If two services are possible, one should be made soon after the cow is observed to be in heat and another attempted in the evening. Artificial breeding is most likely to be successful if insemination is made on the morning of the day after œstrum.

TABLE 34

THE TIME INTERVAL BETWEEN ŒSTRUM AND OVULATION IN BEEF COWS*

End of Œstrum		Time of Ovulation		Interval Between End of Œstrum and Ovulation	
Hour of Day	Number of Cows	Hour of Day	Number of Cows	Interval in Hours	Number of Cows
4– 5 P.M.	2	10–11 P.M.	1	1– 2 hours	0
6– 7 P.M.	7	12– 1 A.M.	0	3– 4 hours	0
8– 9 P.M.	7	2– 3 A.M.	0	5– 6 hours	2
10–11 P.M.	7	4– 5 A.M.	0	7– 8 hours	1
12– 1 A.M.	10	6– 7 A.M.	1	9–10 hours	0
2– 3 A.M.	4	8– 9 A.M.	7	11–12 hours	8
4– 5 A.M.	2	10–11 A.M.	5	13–14 hours	8
6– 7 A.M.	0	12– 1 P.M.	5	15–16 hours	11
8– 9 A.M.	0	2– 3 P.M.	11	17–18 hours	6
10–11 A.M.	1	4– 5 P.M.	5	19–20 hours	1
Total observations	40	6– 7 P.M.	1	21–22 hours	2
		8– 9 P.M.	2	26 hours	1
Mean ending of œstrum, 10:30 P.M.		Total observations	38	Total observations	40
		Mean hour of ovulation, 1:00 P.M.		Mean interval observed, 14.6 hours	

* Adapted from Journal of Animal Science, 1942, Vol. 1, p. 192.

Signs of Œstrum. Cows vary greatly in their behavior during œstrum. However, the condition can usually be detected by marked nervousness on the part of the animal, and by her attempts to mount other members of the herd, which in turn often mount her. A close examination usually discloses a noticeable swelling of the labiæ of the vulva, which often appears slightly inflamed in light-skinned animals.

As a rule, œstrum is accompanied by a slight mucous discharge. Rarely is there any loss of blood until a day or two after œstrum, when a slight bloody discharge or "menstruation" sometimes occurs. Many herdsmen believe that the appearance of blood on the genitals, hips, or tail following breeding is an indication that conception has not taken place, but this theory is refuted by Trimberger of the University of Nebraska, who found no definite relation between menstruation and conception in dairy cows and heifers. (See Table 35.)

In dry cows and heifers there may be a slight swelling or enlargement of the udder during œstrum. In lactating cows a decrease in milk production sometimes occurs.

Duration and Recurrence of Œstrum. As has already been mentioned, the heat period of a cow is very short. While the entire time that she is in an abnormal physical condition may be as great as 24 or even 36 hours, the interval during which she may be bred is generally much shorter, usually not over 12 hours. Seldom does œstrum continue overnight or from early morning until late afternoon.

Unless fertilization takes place, heat periods normally recur at intervals of approximately three weeks. There is some variation in the length of the œstral cycle even in the same individual. As a rule, however, it is seldom shorter than 18 or longer than 21 days. Cows that are to be bred should be closely observed at least twice a day during the third week following their last heat period.

Œstrum, of course, does not normally appear during the period of pregnancy. Its occurrence at this time is often followed by abortion, though there are numerous instances on record where pregnant cows have been served in apparently normal heat periods with no ill effects whatever on the embryo. Normally, about 6 weeks after parturition œstrum again appears. However, few farmers breed their cows so soon after calving, the common practice being to wait about two or three months, so that the calves will be born at the desired time of year.

Conception, of course, does not always follow mating, owing to the failure of the spermatozoa to come in contact with the ovum, or to the failure of the fertilized ovum to become attached to the walls of the uterus. In either case, œstrum reappears at the end of three weeks exactly as if mating had not occurred.

TABLE 35

OCCURRENCE OF MENSTRUATION FOLLOWING ŒSTRUM AND ITS RELATION TO CONCEPTION*

Group	Number of Females	Number Menstruating Within 5 Days	Number Conceiving	Conceiving and Menstruating		Number Not Conceiving	Not Conceiving but Menstruating	
				Number	Percentage		Number	Percentage
Heifers (open)	100	100	..	..	..	..	..	..
Cows (open)	100	61	..	..	..	..	..	..
Heifers (bred)	100	81	61	52	85.3	39	29	74.4
Cows (bred)	100	61	72	50	69.4	28	11	39.3

* Journal of Dairy Science, 1941, Vol. 24, No. 9, p. 821.

Age at which to Breed Heifers. Inasmuch as the process of reproduction imposes a heavy tax upon the mother, heifers should not be bred until they are reasonably mature. Nature apparently provides that the growth of the fœtus and care of the young shall take precedence over everything else, even over the requirements of the body of the mother for maintenance and growth. Young pregnant heifers tend to lay on fat which will insure a good flow of milk during lactation, even though the growth of their own bodies is noticeably retarded during gestation.[2] Whether or not growth so arrested is resumed later depends upon the treatment accorded the heifer after parturition and lactation. If she is rebred soon after parturition, she will have no chance to resume growth and will be permanently stunted. If, however, she is given a rest of a few months before rebreeding, she will be likely to recover her lost growth to some extent, the amount depending upon her age at the time of parturition.

There is much evidence that gestation has a less stunting effect upon immature heifers than has lactation. This statement seems reasonable in view of the fact that the new-born calf contains only about 15 pounds of protein and 3 pounds of fat, whereas about 65 pounds of protein, 70 pounds of fat, and 90 pounds of carbohydrates are in the milk produced by the young mother during the first 4 months of lactation.[3]

Consequently, it appears that the average daily demands on the mother during lactation are several times greater than those during gestation. This fact has considerable importance in the accidental pregnancy of an immature heifer. If the calf is removed immediately after parturition and the heifer dried up, the loss of size may not be serious, but, if the calf is allowed to nurse until it is 5 to 7 months of age, the heifer almost surely will receive a setback from which she will never completely recover. Frequently nature comes to the aid of heifers that have calved considerably short of maturity by decreeing that they be free from the burdens of motherhood until they have made good their own growth requirements. Frequently heifers that calve as 2-year-olds do not conceive while they are suckled; consequently they do not calve the following year. In some of the western states, where feed supplies are often inadequate for the proper maintenance of the breeding herd, a high percentage of the heifers calving at 2 years of age are temporarily barren. (See Fig. 19.)

Since a majority of farmers and ranchers desire their calves to be born over a 2- to 3-month period in the spring, replacement heifers

2 *Cf.* p. 244.
3 California Extension Circular 131, 1946, pp. 100–101.

must be bred to drop their first calves very close to either their second or third birthdays.   Much difference of opinion exists as to which is the better practice.   Several experiments and surveys have been made,

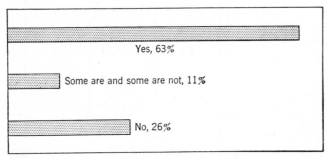

Fɪɢ. 19. Replies of 135 Nevada ranchers to the question, "Are heifers bred as yearlings and calving at 2 years of age temporarily barren?" (*Courtesy University of Nevada.*)

particularly in the range states, to obtain information on this important question.   Although the results do not agree in all respects, they tend to justify the following statements, which appear in Circular 131 of the California Extension Service:

1. If heifers are to be bred as yearlings the following conditions and practices should be observed:
   a. Heifer calves kept for breeding should weigh 450 pounds or more when weaned, should be fed to gain at least 1 pound a day during their first winter, and should weigh 650 to 700 pounds when bred.
   b. Pregnant heifers should be fed liberally during the second winter so that they will grow and fatten enough to be in "good" grade slaughter condition by calving time.
   c. The heifers should be watched closely during their calving period, as timely assistance with difficult parturitions will prevent excessive loss of heifers and calves.
   d. The calves should be sold for veal at 8 to 10 weeks of age to stop the drain of lactation, stimulate rebreeding, and permit normal development of the heifers.
   e. Yearling heifers should be bred to a small-type, fine-boned bull to produce small calves that will be delivered with as little trouble as possible.   Crossing Hereford or Shorthorn yearling heifers to Angus bulls is advisable if small-type bulls of these breeds are not available.
2. Unless early breeding is managed as recommended above, the following disadvantages will more than offset the value of the extra calves obtained:
   a. Heavy death losses of heifers and calves at calving time.

TABLE 36

THE EFFECT OF EARLY BREEDING UPON RANGE COWS*

Lot	1	2	3	4
Number of cows in each lot at beginning of test, Nov. 1, 1915	20	20	20	20
Number at present time (1920)	20	18	18	20
Present age of cows (Spring, 1920)...................	5 yrs.	5 yrs.	5 yrs.	5 yrs.
Winter feed until all lots were of producing age (1915–16–17)..............	Roughage and Grain	Roughage and Grain	Roughage	Roughage
Winter feed following winters (1918–19).............	Roughage only	Roughage only	Roughage only	Roughage only
Summer feed during entire time of test..............	Range grass	Range grass	Range grass	Range grass
Average winter feed cost per cow per day until three years of age (1915–16–17)	$.156	$.156	$.083	$.083
Average weight of these cows as weanlings Nov. 1, 1915, when test began.........	446 lbs.		445 lbs.	
Average weight of these cows after their calves were weaned in fall of 1919......	1167 lbs.	1094 lbs.	1103 lbs.	1055 lbs.
Average growth of each cow.	721 lbs.	648 lbs.	658 lbs.	610 lbs.
Cow's age when first calf was dropped.............	3 yrs.	2 yrs.	3 yrs.	2 yrs.
Average weight at weaning time of calves produced in 1917...................	.....	366 lbs.	.....	353 lbs.
Average weight at weaning time of calves produced in 1918..................	420 lbs.	367 lbs.	422 lbs.	353 lbs.
Average weight at weaning time of calves produced in 1919...................	375 lbs.	350 lbs.	389 lbs.	338 lbs.
Average weight of calves produced to date.........	397.5 lbs.	361.0 lbs.	405.5 lbs.	348.0 lbs.

* Kansas Agr. Expt. Station, Ft. Hays Branch; Report for the year, 1919-20.

b. Posterior paralysis and permanent injury to the genital tract at calving.

c. Stunting of heifers during the nursing period, which will interfere with intelligent selection and culling.

d. Inferior, light-weight calves due to insufficient milk for normal growth.

e. Failure to rebreed, resulting in a large percentage of dry 3-year-olds.

Since some of these misfortunes are likely to be encountered, even with the best care and management, the breeding of grade yearling heifers can not be recommended as a general practice. Even if a good

TABLE 37

Breeding Heifers as Yearlings: The Effect upon Their Development and upon the Weaning Weights of Their Calves*

Age When First Bred	Number of Calvings[a]	Total Calves Born	Average Birth Weight of Calves (pounds)	Number of Calves Weaned	Average Weaning Weight (pounds)	Total Weaning Weight (pounds)	Fall Weight of Cows When 6–8 Years of Age (pounds)
Yearlings	5 to 7	210	68	183	367	67,070	1,144
2-year-olds	4 to 6	196	69	176	403	70,930	1,112

* University of Illinois, Dixon Springs Experiment Station Mimeo. Report, 1951.

[a] Approximately 15 heifer calves assigned to each group for 3 successive years (1942–1944). Heifers born in 1942 which were bred as yearlings had produced 7 crops of calves, whereas those born in 1944 and bred as 2-year-olds had produced only 4.

percentage of the calves were saved, the high cost of the winter feed required by pregnant yearling heifers would largely offset the value of their calves.

Fortunately, purebred breeders do not have the temptation to breed their heifers as young as do the owners of grade herds, for it is not so important that purebred calves be born at a particular season of the year. Indeed, it usually is advisable to have two or three calving periods with about an equal number of cows calving during each. By spreading the calving over the greater part of the year, labor requirements are more easily met, fewer bulls are required, less shelter and equipment are needed, and a better age assortment of young bulls and heifers is obtained to meet the preferences of prospective buyers and the requirements of the show ring.

Purebred breeders usually breed their heifers at the first breeding season after they are 18 months old. Purebred heifers are almost always better fed and cared for than grades and, therefore, are larger and better developed for their age. Consequently, they usually are sufficiently large and mature to calve safely when 28 to 30 months old. Occasionally, heifers with more size than is desired by present-day breeders are bred as early as 15 or 16 months in order to retard their growth. However, Hereford breeders should keep in mind that calves produced by Hereford cows under 24 months of age cannot be registered.

The Breeding Season. The time of breeding season will, of course, depend upon the wishes of the farmer as to when he would most like his calves to be born. The average gestation period being 283 days, mating should begin approximately 9 months and 5 days before the earliest date on which calves are wanted. Although it is highly desirable to have all calves born as close together as possible, it will be found that, because of irregular œstral periods of some cows and failure of others to conceive from the first service, the period of calving, even in the better managed herds, usually extends over 2 or 3 months. Any greater irregularity than this, however, in the time of calving is to be regarded as highly unsatisfactory, especially from the standpoint of a commercial herd. Usually cows that are not settled within 4 months of the opening of the breeding season should either be held over until the next season or disposed of for beef. This statement, of course, does not apply to valuable purebred cows that have demonstrated their ability to produce calves of outstanding merit. Such cows should be bred whenever they are in heat, regardless of the time of year, so that as many offspring as possible may be obtained from them. The practice, however, of keeping "shy breeders" year after year, just because they happen to have a "fancy" pedigree, usually proves to be a waste of both time and money.

Spring and Fall Calves. In so far as possible, the commercial cattleman tries to have his calves born at a time when the weather conditions are most favorable. This means that they should be born either in the spring, after the cold weather of winter but before the heat and flies of summer, or in the fall, before winter has arrived. The exact calendar dates will depend somewhat upon the latitude, and, in the western states, upon the altitude as well. By far the greater number of the calves of the country are born in the spring. However, some farmers, especially in the central states, find it more to their advantage to have the calves dropped in the fall. Below are listed the principal advantages claimed for spring- and fall-born calves, respectively:

A. *Advantages of Spring Calves.*
  1. Dry cows can be wintered more cheaply.
  2. Calves are of good age by winter and can stand cold weather better.
  3. Cows milk better while on grass than they do on dry feed.
  4. Saves labor—cows and calves run together on pasture.
  5. Calves may be sold at weaning time with no wintering, or as yearlings with but one wintering.
  6. Cows are bred while on pasture, when they are most likely to conceive.

B. *Advantages of Fall Calves.*
  1. Cows are in better physical condition for calving in the fall than in the spring; calves are likely to be stronger.
  2. Young calves escape the severe heat and the flies of midsummer.
  3. Upon being weaned, the calves may be turned on grass instead of being put in a dry lot; grass takes the place of milk to a considerable extent.
  4. Cows that freshen in the fall milk longer than those that freshen in the spring. Grass stimulates milk flow, while changing to dry feed in the fall tends to diminish it.
  5. Cows give heavy flow of milk during the winter months when butter and cream sell well, and when labor is available to care for any surplus milk.
  6. The greatest number of cattle are on hand during the winter season when labor for their care is available.
  7. Cows are bred in the winter when hand mating is convenient.

It will be seen that the advantages of spring calves have the most weight under extensive rather than intensive methods of cattle production. Fall-born calves, on the other hand, are particularly well suited to small farms where beef cattle are but one of the several items that contribute to the profits of the general farmer, and where the herds are handled according to dual-purpose methods.

TABLE 38

THE EFFECT OF MONTH OF BIRTH ON THE SURVIVAL, GROWTH, AND WEANING WEIGHT OF BEEF CALVES*

Month	Number of Cows	Number of Calves	Percentage of Calf Crop	Average Age Weaned	Average Weaning Weight	Average Daily Gain	Percentage of Total
January	130	128	98.5	275	558	1.72	1.24
February	714	676	94.7	250	503	1.69	6.52
March	3,625	3,474	95.8	221	466	1.75	33.53
April	4,366	4,183	95.8	198	433	1.79	40.37
May	1,548	1,447	93.5	180	402	1.79	13.96
June	335	326	97.3	163	374	1.81	3.15
July	20	20	100.0	130	355	2.10	0.20
September	11	10	91	336	596	1.53	0.10
October	16	15	93.7	284	517	1.61	0.13
December	90	83	92.2	304	557	1.57	0.80

* Charles R. Kyd, Missouri Extension Service. Information to the author.

Junior and Senior Calves. Breeders of purebred cattle who make a practice of exhibiting their young stock at state fairs and other livestock shows usually breed their cows at such a time as will insure calves that have as much age when exhibited as is allowed by the showyard classification. Practically all large cattle shows offer classes for junior, senior, and summer calves, and for junior and senior yearlings. For the purpose of classifying beef cattle at shows and fairs the year is divided into three periods of approximately equal length, the critical dates being January 1, May 1, and September 1. Calves born during the months of January to April inclusive of the current year are known as *junior* calves; those born during September to December inclusive of the previous year are called *senior* calves; while those born from May 1 to August 31 of the previous year are classed as *summer* calves or yearlings. Junior yearlings, of course, are 1 year older than junior calves, while the senior yearling class usually includes all animals that were eligible to show in the summer and senior calf classes the year before. It stands to reason that, in any particular class, calves born soon after the determining initial date have a big advantage in size and all-round development over animals born

2 or 3 months later. Yet, according to the showyard classification, such animals must compete against one another in the show ring.

In order that their animals may show to the best possible advantage, prospective exhibitors breed their best cows to calve as soon after January 1, May 1, and September 1, as possible. As calves born a few days, or even one day, before these dates are practically worthless as show animals, care is taken that mating is begun sufficiently late to guard against the possibility of a cow's calving just a day or two earlier than is desired. April 1, August 1, and December 1 may be regarded as entirely safe dates on which to begin breeding for junior, summer, and senior calves, respectively, as the probability of a cow's calving short of 275 days is rather remote.

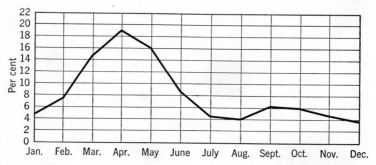

Fig. 20.   Births of calves by months.   Nearly 50 per cent of all calves are born during March, April, and May.   (*Courtesy U.S.D.A.*)

As a rule, purebred breeders prefer to have their calves distributed fairly uniformly throughout the year. In this way they are able to give the young calves more attention and care than would be possible if all were born at approximately the same time. Also, a goodly number of calves of the various ages is desired in order that suitable material may be had for making up the show herd.

Methods of Mating. Three methods of mating are followed: hand mating, pasture mating, and artificial insemination. In hand breeding the bull is kept separate from the cow herd. Whenever a cow is observed to be in heat during the breeding season, she is turned in with the bull, where she remains until she is bred; or, as is often done in purebred herds, she is led into a level lot or into the breeding crate by an attendant, and held while she is being served. The bull may or may not be managed by another attendant. As a rule, but a single service is permitted in hand mating, the cow being removed immediately after copulation.

Usually, a bull is somewhat excited after he has bred a cow and will, if allowed to remain out in his lot, wear himself out by walking back and forth along the fence, seeking a way to come again with the cow. Consequently, it is advisable to return him to his stall in the barn for an hour or two until he quiets down. A cow while in heat should be kept away from the herd whether she is served or not. Otherwise the entire herd is likely to be disturbed by her riding and being ridden by the other cattle. When such riding is done by cows well along in calf, abortion sometimes results.

In pasture mating, the bull is allowed to run with the breeding herd throughout the breeding season. This method saves the labor involved in the daily inspection of the herd for cows that are in heat and in driving them to the breeding pen for service. Moreover, it precludes

TABLE 39

THE CALCULATED ŒSTRAL PERIOD AT WHICH COWS CONCEIVED
DURING A BREEDING SEASON WITH PASTURE MATINGS*

(Data from U.S.D.A. Experiment Station, Jeanerete, Louisiana)

Œstral Period (20-day Basis)	Number of Cows Conceiving	Percentage of Herd			
		100% Fertility		73% Fertility	
		For Period	Cumulative	For Period	Cumulative
1st	295	52	52	38	38
2nd	155	28	80	20	58
3rd	61	11	91	8	66
4th	30	5	96	4	70
5th	19	3	99	2	72
6th	3	1	100	1	73
Total: 120 days (4 months)	563	100		73	

* Journal of Animal Science, Vol. 3, p. 156.

the possibility of a cow's "going by" unbred, due to the failure of the herdsman to detect her œstrum. The objections to this method are the following:

1. All cows that run in the same pasture will be bred by the same bull, or by any one of several bulls, if there is more than one bull present. This objection greatly limits the use of pasture mating in purebred herds where two or more bulls are kept.

2. Bulls wear themselves out by repeatedly serving the cow while she remains in heat. Sometimes as many as six or more services are performed. Because of this tax on the energy of the bull, fewer cows can be cared for by him. Instances are not uncom-

mon where immature bulls are rendered permanently sterile through excessive copulation.

3. If two or more cows are in heat at the same time, the bull may give all his attention to one of them, allowing the others to go unbred.

There is little doubt that in a herd of commercial cattle the disadvantages of pasture mating are more than balanced by the saving of labor involved and the greater certainty of getting all cows in calf. With purebred cattle, however, pasture mating is less widely used. Here, certain knowledge as to whether a cow has been served, the particular bull performing the service, and the date on which it occurred is so important, especially in the case of a sale, that many purebred breeders resort to pasture breeding only as a check on their cows after they have been handbred. Pasture mating is also used to some extent in large breeding establishments where the number of bulls and pastures is such as to permit the division of the herd into lots of 15 to 25 cows, each with a bull at the head.

Artificial Insemination. Artificial breeding has not been practiced as widely by beef cattle breeders as it has by dairymen. No doubt the absence of an objective method of measuring merit in beef cattle, comparable to the milk production records of dairy cows, has been largely responsible for the limited use made of this method of breeding. Until some standard more definite than showyard winnings is devised for measuring the breeding value of beef bulls, a majority of breeders will be reluctant to pay high service fees for the semen of a bull which, after all, may be no better than their own. Also a number of the more prominent breeders have developed blood lines and families which they wish neither to dilute with outside blood nor to lose the prestige they now enjoy by being the principal source of cattle of this particular type and breeding. Consequently, they are neither interested in inseminating their cows with the semen of outside bulls nor willing to permit the use of their own bulls on cows owned by other breeders.

A third and more important reason for the limited use made of artificial insemination by the practical cattleman is the difficulty of determining when beef cows are in heat. Beef cows that run together day after day are much less inclined to ride one another than dairy cows, which are stabled at night and turned together after being milked in the morning. The fact that the breeding season for beef cows comes at the time of year when they are on pasture, often on a remote part of the farm, makes it very difficult not only to determine each day which cows should be bred but to separate these cows from the herd and drive them to the barn or corral where they are to be inseminated. The daily sorting out of cows suspected of being in heat, driving them to the corral, confining them in the squeeze gate, and returning them to pasture result in a great deal of disturbance to both cows and young calves, which is harmful to the herd. Added to all these disadvantages is the fact that often a relatively low percentage of cows conceive at the first insemination. Usually after 2 or 3 months of artificial breeding a bull is turned with the herd to settle the cows that are still open. As a result, the next year's calves show much variation in age and weight, thereby complicating their feeding and management.

No doubt artificial insemination will be found satisfactory by the small breeder who owns but 4 or 5 carefully selected purebred cows or 8 to 10 high grades—too few to justify purchasing and keeping a really good bull. It also is of great value in large purebred herds to permit the mating of a noted sire to many more cows than he could handle by either hand or pasture breeding. Lastly, it can be employed to advantage in prolonging the usefulness of valuable sires which because of accidents or advanced age can no longer perform natural service.

Use of Breeding Stocks. The term "breeding stocks" is somewhat of a misnomer, and the same may be said of "breeding crate," inasmuch as the apparatus resembles neither of the articles suggested by the names. The term, "breeding stall," would probably describe the nature of the apparatus better than any other, but, unfortunately, it is not found in the vocabulary of the practical cattleman. The so-called breeding crate resembles a narrow, single stall, merely wide enough to admit a mature cow easily. The sides of the stall are surmounted by 2- by 10-inch planks at such a height as to permit the bull to support himself during service on his front legs, which rest on these planks. This, of course, relieves the cow from supporting the weight of the bull. Breeding stocks are of considerable value when 2-year-old heifers are mated with an old, heavy bull. They are also used in breeding cows that exhibit outward signs of œstrum, yet refuse to stand to be served. This use, however, is not very common. It should be stated that some bulls absolutely refuse to work in a breeding crate, whereas others that have been long accustomed to the crate almost refuse to serve cows outside it. Occasionally a bull is encountered, that, because of some peculiar conformation of abdomen or sheath, has difficulty in performing service unless the hind-quarters of the cow are lowered. This can easily be done by digging a hole at the rear of the crate and standing the hind feet of the cow in this hole.

Directions for constructing a breeding crate, together with an illustration of same, may be found in Chapter 33.

Number of Cows per Bull. The number of cows that can be successfully bred by a single bull will depend upon, first, the age of the bull, and second, the manner in which the cows and bull are handled. Yearling bulls may be allowed an occasional service, in no case to exceed 12 or 15 cows during a breeding season of 2 or 3 months. Two-year-old bulls are capable of caring for 25 to 30 cows, and a bull 3 years old or over can be counted on for 40 to 50 if hand mating is practiced. If pasture mating is followed these figures should be reduced approximately 30 per cent. In no case should a bull under 20 months of age be allowed to run with his cows. Instead, hand mating should be used, and but a single service allowed.

As the size of the herd is increased, the ratio of bulls to cows grows larger, since there is always a tendency for a large herd to break up into small groups of from 10 to 50 animals each. The number of bulls in the herd should be sufficient to make sure that the chance of any such group of cows remaining long without a bull is very small.

The accompanying table compiled from published records of the Kansas Beef Production Contest indicates that more than about 25 cows per bull is likely to result in a calving period that extends over 4 to 6 months or even longer if the bulls are left with the herd until all the cows are settled. If they are removed earlier some of the cows will not have been bred and will produce no calves the following year.

TABLE 40

EFFECT OF BULL-COW RATIO UPON LENGTH OF CALVING PERIOD*

Cows per Bull	Number of Herds	Number of Cows	Average Calf Crop (per cent)	Length of Calving Period				
				Average (days)	Minimum Period		Maximum Period	
					Number of Cows in Herd	Days	Number of Cows in Herd	Days
20 or less	5	756	95.4	77	51	53	455	99
21–30	36	3682	94.5	102	101	41	110	219
31–40	12	1223	93.1	118	34	46	80	212
Over 40	12	2027	93.6	132	82	73	110	243

* Compiled from Mimeographed Reports of Kansas Beef Production Contest, 1946–1950 inclusive, Kansas Extension Service.

8 ———————————————— Pregnancy

Inasmuch as œstrum normally precedes ovulation by several hours, the spermatozoa of the male usually have sufficient time to reach the oviducts, where they await the liberation of the ripened egg. Normally, fertilization occurs in the pavilion of the tube, though there may be times when it does not take place until the egg reaches the uterus. The length of time required for the ovum to traverse the Fallopian tube is not definitely known, but probably is approximately 10 days. During this time the fertilized egg, now known as a zygote, is undergoing division or segmentation. While increasing little, if any, in size, the egg by successive steps of cleavage divides first into 2, then 4, 8, 16, 32, and so forth, segments, finally reaching a condition known as the morula, or mulberry, stage. Soon after reaching the uterus, the ovum becomes greatly enlarged by the absorption of fluids, and segmentation proceeds at a very rapid rate. Also, the cells begin to exhibit marked differences in size and shape, first assuming the appearance of well-defined layers; later, the differentiation of cells and tissues to form the different systems of organs of the embryo takes place.

For the first 5 or 6 days, the segmented ovum lies free within the uterine cavity, but shortly thereafter it becomes attached to the walls of the uterus. This attachment not only serves to protect the embryo from sudden and violent displacements during pregnancy, but also affords a method for the transfer of nutritive material from the mother to the young, and the contrary transfer of waste products, thereby making possible growth and development. As soon as this exchange of materials begin to take place, the embryo is called a fœtus.

The Fœtal Membranes. The fœtal membranes consist of three separate structures or parts, the chorion, the amnion, and the allantois. The chorion is the outer membrane surrounding the fœtus and lies close to the mucous membrane of the uterus. The surface of the chorion is much greater than that of the impregnated horn. Consequently, it may extend into the non-pregnant horn, as well as into the body of the uterus. It has very many blood vessels which lead into the placentæ. The amnion is a membrane that begins at the navel and surrounds the fœtus like a sac, enclosing it entirely. It contains a liquid which serves

102

to protect the fœtus from external injury. In the cow, there are about 6 or 7 quarts of this liquid, which is called the amniotic fluid. During parturition, the amniotic fluid serves to lubricate the vagina, thus aiding in the expulsion of the fœtus. The allantois is a large membranous sac, between the chorion and the amnion, containing the fœtal urine. The urine enters the allantois through a tube from the fœtal bladder, called the urachus. All of these membranes, taken together, constitute the fœtal membranes, or "afterbirth."

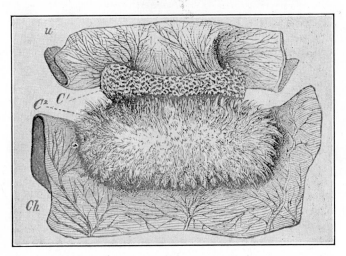

FIG. 21. Cotyledon of cow, showing relation of the maternal and fœtal circulations. *u,* uterus; *Ch,* chorion; C^1, maternal and C^2, fœtal portion of cotyledon. (*After drawing by Colin.*)

The Placenta. The term placenta refers to those portions of the fœtal membranes and their annexes that serve to unite the mother and the fœtus. While there is no direct vascular connection, the blood vessels of each lie very close together so that an interchange of materials can be effected through their extremely thin, extensive walls. The capillaries of the fœtal membranes, especially those of the allantois, which penetrate the chorion, become imbedded in the mucous walls of the uterus, where they come in contact with the capillaries of the uterus. Through their walls "there is a free interchange of nutritive and waste products, but not of cellular elements. The separation of the fœtal from the maternal circulation is so complete that most micro-organisms of disease do not ordinarily pass through."[1]

This penetration of the capillaries of the fœtal membranes into the

[1] Williams, W. L., Veterinary Obstetrics, 1917, p. 128.

walls of the uterus is by no means general over the entire surface of the impregnated horn. Rather, such contact is made only at certain specialized areas, known as cotyledons or maternal placentæ. These areas are merely small prominences resembling scars or warts in the non-pregnant cow, somewhat oblong in shape, with their long axis at right angles to the long axis of the Fallopian tube. Since there are

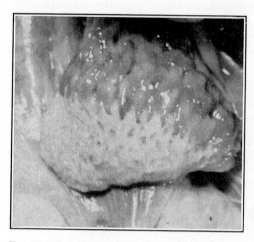

FIG. 22. Cotyledon of cow, showing the crypts of the maternal portion (bottom) and the tufts of the fœtal portion (top) in considerable detail.

from 40 to 60 cotyledons in each horn, the cow is said to have a multiple placenta.

During pregnancy these cotyledons greatly enlarge,[2] and numerous follicles or depressions form on their surfaces. Into these follicles the villi of the chorion and the other fœtal membranes are inserted, thus making an extensive and extremely close attachment between the fœtus and the mother. These groups of villi of the fœtal membranes are termed the fœtal placentæ. Since each fœtal placenta surrounds and "dovetails" into a maternal placenta, it follows that the fœtal and maternal placentæ are present in equal numbers. Between the placentæ the chorion is free from the walls of the uterus.

The Umbilical Cord. The bond of union between the fœtus and the placenta is termed the umbilical cord. Practical stockmen usually refer to it as the navel string. Its sheath is composed of amniotic membrane, within which are found two umbilical arteries, two umbilical veins, and the urachus, the tube that leads from the urinary bladder into the allantois. Interspersed between these vessels is a gelatinous mass called the Whartonian gelatin. The umbilical arteries carry the blood from the fœtus to the capillaries of the fœtal placenta, while the veins carry it back. These blood vessels have very strong muscular walls, which contract strongly when ruptured to prevent excessive bleeding. As the umbilical arteries are attached to the umbilical ring only by loose connective tissue, their severed ends retract within the

[2] "In highly pregnant animals they vary from the size of a mulberry to 10 cm. long and 5–6 cm. wide." De Bruin: Bovine Obstetrics, 1897, p. 16.

abdominal cavity of the calf upon being ruptured at birth. This retraction prevents the entrance of disease-producing bacteria through the severed vessels. It also serves to check the flow of blood. The umbilical veins, however, are attached firmly to the umbilical ring and do not retract when severed. Instead they remain open for a time and are occasionally the avenue for pus-forming bacteria.

Position of the Fœtus in the Uterus. In the early stages of its development the embryo floats freely in the amniotic liquid, occupying no distinct position. With the growth of the fœtus, however, it becomes fixed in position, usually with the anterior end, or head, toward the os uteri, and its dorsal surface, or back, forming a convex arc whose cord forms an angle of approximately thirty degrees with the longitudinal axis of the mother. As the end of gestation is approached, the weight of the fœtus is such that it rests upon its side upon the abdominal floor of the mother, rather than upon its ventral surface with its concave border downward. As the available space in the abdominal cavity of the cow is limited, the fœtus tends to occupy that part of the abdomen not taken up by other organs. As the rumen, or paunch, occupies the entire left side, the fœtus must arrange itself on the right. The crowded condition of the abdomen also results in the doubling up of the fœtus in such a way as to occupy as little space as possible. The head and neck are bent down and back until the chin approaches the forward end of the sternum; the front legs are flexed at the elbows and knees, so that the knees lie alongside the head with the front feet just forward of the brisket; the hind legs are bent forward under the body in much the same position as they assume in sternal recumbency of the adult animal.

Multiple Pregnancy. The cow, as a rule, is uniparous, more than one fœtus seldom being formed in the uterus. However, twin calves occur occasionally, and triplets and quadruplets are not unknown. When only one calf is present it usually occupies one horn of the uterus; with twins, each horn usually contains a calf. Should the fœtal membranes of twin calves of opposite sexes become fused in such a way as to establish a more or less common circulatory system, the development of the reproductive organs of the female fœtus is arrested. This condition is presumably brought about by a certain substance which inhibits the development of the reproductive system of the female. This substance is called a "hormone" by the scientists and is thought to be secreted by the male sex cells. Apparently the hormones of the male are dominant over those of the female; or, as seems more likely, the male sex cells are the first to appear in the development of the two fœtuses. Inasmuch as the fœtal membranes of calves are very large and extensive, filling, even in a single birth, nearly the entire uterus, those of twins are almost certain to be in close contact and to become fused together. Thus, heifer calves born twin with bulls are very likely to be sterile, because of the imperfect development of their reproductive organs. Such heifers are called *free-martins*.

Signs of Pregnancy.[3] The gestation period of the cow is approximately 283 days. Long before this time, however, certain changes are observed in the pregnant female that indicate the existence of the developing fœtus. As a diagnosis of pregnancy is often of the greatest importance, every cattleman should understand clearly the means whereby pregnancy may be determined. Unfortunately, none of the signs of pregnancy which can be observed by the layman is infallible during the first half of the gestation period. However, there are certain changes commonly observed in pregnant cows which at least form a good reason for suspecting pregnancy in any bred female that exhibits them. As the gestation period progresses, more direct signs of pregnancy appear, though even these are sometimes misleading, owing to the presence of certain diseases which produce changes in the affected animal similar to those caused by a developing fœtus. Only direct examination made after the third month of the gestation period will disclose without the possibility of doubt the presence or absence of pregnancy. In the discussion that follows, the signs of pregnancy are grouped under three heads: (1) physiological or subjective signs; (2) physical or objective signs; and (3) signs observed in the course of direct examination.

1. Physiological or Subjective Signs of Pregnancy. The first noticeable effect of conception is a cessation of œstrum or periods of heat. Normally, non-pregnant cows show signs of œstrum approximately every three weeks. If no such signs appear after the cow is bred, it is assumed that she has been safely settled and is with calf. However, the absence of heat periods is by no means absolute proof of pregnancy, since most cows occasionally "pass over" without being observed. Also, it sometimes happens that a cow well along in her gestation, as later results show, will exhibit definite signs of œstrum and will even submit to the service of a bull.

Pregnancy is usually accompanied by a more tranquil disposition on the part of the cow. She is slower and more deliberate in her move-

---

[3] For much of the subject matter that follows the author is indebted to the late Dr. W. L. Williams, Professor of Obstetrics in the New York State Veterinary College, Cornell University, who very kindly granted permission to make free use of his exceedingly valuable book, entitled Veterinary Obstetrics, published by W. L. Williams, Ithaca, New York, 1917.

ments, often exhibiting a laziness wholly lacking before conception. Particularly do pregnant cows show little inclination to engage in unnecessary fights with other members of the herd. Rather, they tend to withdraw from the herd where they will be molested as little as possible.

A sudden tendency of a cow to improve in appearance and lay on fat is usually regarded as a sign of pregnancy. This probably results from the strong, keen appetite which usually follows conception and from the quiet, lazy type of life led during the gestation period. Thus, more energy is available for the formation of body fat. Slaughter tests of bred and open heifers fed equal amounts of feed have given significant evidence that pregnancy accelerates improvement in condition and the attainment of a satisfactory market finish.[4] The factor that brings about these changes is called the "hormone of pregnancy."

2. Physical or Objective Signs of Pregnancy. The physiological signs of pregnancy appear very soon after conception has taken place. The physical or objective signs, on the other hand, are not evident until the period of gestation is well advanced. However, they are somewhat more reliable than those already discussed, becoming almost unmistakable proof a few weeks before parturition occurs.

Five or six months after being bred, pregnant cows begin to exhibit an unusual fullness of the abdominal region. Indeed, the increase in volume of abdomen is generally much greater than can be accounted for by the size of the developing fœtus, which at this stage is but little larger than a cat. In all probability the increase in abdomen is due mainly to the deposit of fat, to the large amount of feed consumed, and to the increase in the amount of the fœtal fluids. As the time of parturition draws near, a still further enlargement of the lower abdomen takes place, especially on the right side, while a falling away or sinking of the upper flank regions is often apparent. This last-mentioned condition no doubt results from the tendency of the abdominal organs to rest on the abdominal floor, which has been much displaced by the great weight of the fœtus. The upper portion of the abdominal cavity, being left rather empty, offers little resistance to the body walls, which tend to collapse at the rear flanks.

The approach of parturition is also heralded by an enlargement of the udder, which may even be accompanied by the secretion of milk a considerable time before delivery actually occurs. In very few cases, however, will it be found necessary to relieve the distention of the udder by milking.

The approximate time of parturition can be determined by a noticeable sinking of the hips and widening of the pin bones, resulting from a

[4] *Cf.* p. 244.

softening of the ligaments that unite the two branches, or halves, of the pelvic girdle. As a rule, this softening and falling away at the hips is first noticeable about 8 or 9 days before calving. It is accompanied by a marked œdema of the lips of the vulva, which are slightly inflamed, because of the unusually large flow of blood necessary for the physiological changes going on in the pelvic region. Not only is there a softening of the internal ligaments of the pelvic region, but there is a marked relaxation of the external muscles of the hips and rump. The muscles of the whole pelvic region become soft and flabby and offer no resistance to the enlargement of the pelvic girdle during parturition.

3. Direct Examination for Pregnancy. The only certain proof of the existence of pregnancy is based upon direct observation of the presence of the fœtus in the uterus. Unfortunately, such observations can be made with a high degree of certainty only by a veterinarian. They are highly useful and are frequently employed in determining whether cows offered for sale are safely settled before being catalogued. Their use also prevents the possible sale for slaughter of a valuable female that is suspected of being barren when, in reality, she is well along in calf.

In general, there are four means of determining the presence of the fœtus in the uterus. Listed in the order of their value for indicating pregnancy as soon after mating as possible, they are:

1. Internal examination of the uterus.
2. Abdominal ballottement.
3. Auscultation of fœtal heart beat.
4. Fœtal movements.

1. *Internal Examination of the Uterus.* To establish pregnancy beyond a doubt, an internal examination should be made of the uterus. Occasionally it happens that a fœtus as young as 2 months old can be discovered by this method, although drawing a conclusion based upon negative results is warranted only when the examination is made after the third month. An internal examination of the uterus is made through the rectum.

The success of rectal examination depends on the fact that the non-pregnant uterus and ovaries lie just beneath the colon and can easily be felt through the wall of the large gut. If the fœtus be present, it can, of course, be felt and distinguished beneath the floor of the rectum. When gently pressed by the hand, it slips away as though it were floating in a liquid, but returns immediately to its original position. Under the weight of the fœtus, the uterus and ovaries are pulled down within the abdominal cavity as the period of gestation advances. In this state it generally happens that neither the uterus nor fœtus can be felt by the operator. However, careful exploration will disclose "the vagina drawn far forward over the brim of the pelvis and the posterior end of the uterus constituting a large, thick, firmly stretched band passing downward and forward into the abdominal cavity beyond the examiner's reach."[5]

2. *Abdominal Ballottement.* By palpation, or ballottement, is meant the discovery of the fœtus by external examination of the abdominal region against which the fœtus normally rests. It is performed in the following manner: The operator stands on the right side of the cow and places the palm of his hand, or preferably his closed fist, against the abdomen in the lower right flank region. By executing a short, vigorous, inward-upward thrust in this area and retaining his hand in place, he should encounter a hard body (the fœtus), which recedes from his hand to fall back immediately to its original position. This displacement and return to position is due to the suspension of the fœtus in the amniotic liquid. Under the sudden pressure it floats away, but is returned to position by the tension of the fœtal membranes. Ballottement yields best results from the fifth to the seventh month of pregnancy, at which time the fœtus is sufficiently large to be easily felt, while its membranes are still weak enough to allow its displacement.

3. *Auscultation of Fœtal Heart Beats.* The determination of pregnancy by means of the heart beats of the fœtus is more uncertain in the cow than in some of our other domestic animals. However, it is not unusual to detect the sound of the fœtal heart after the sixth month of pregnancy. If possible, a stethoscope should be used in this examination, although good results are sometimes had by placing the ear against the right lower abdominal region and listening intently for sounds from within. No difficulty should be had in distinguishing the beat of the fœtal heart from that of the mother, as the sound of the fœtal heart is lighter, of higher pitch, and approximately twice as frequent. While auscultation, if successful, is positive proof of a living fœtus, a negative result does not constitute dependable evidence of a non-pregnant condition, because of the uncertainty of this method.

4. *Fœtal Movements.* Observance through the abdominal wall of movements of the fœtus constitutes the most reliable proof of pregnancy that one could desire. Not only does it establish the presence of the fœtus, but it shows clearly the existence of life as well. Like all other direct evidences, it is useful only during the latter half of the gestation period, as the movements that occur previously are too weak

[5] Williams, W. L., Veterinary Obstetrics, 1917, p. 154.

to be felt through the abdominal wall. As there are no means available for inducing the fœtus to move, the observer must wait patiently
until voluntary movement is sufficiently great to be observed. The
inhumane practice of giving cold water to a very warm and thirsty cow
to cause the fœtus to move by its proximity to the cold water in the
stomach cannot be too strongly condemned. Shocks of this kind are
to be avoided in so far as possible.

A few weeks before parturition, the movements of the fœtus may be
so violent as to be easily observed at some distance. However, the
chance of such movements occurring during the particular hour or half
hour that the observer is present is indeed small. Consequently, the
following method of examination will usually save considerable time.
Moreover, its employment will sometimes result in the detection of
movement as early as the fifth or sixth month of pregnancy:

> For this purpose one occupies the right side of the cow, turning the face
> toward the hind quarters, places the right hand upon the back of the animal,
> the palm and surface of the left hand being placed against the abdomen in
> front of the stifle. For this examination much patience is required, as quite
> some time may pass before fœtal movements are appreciated. Ordinarily
> they cannot be hastened by pushing against the abdominal wall. In the sixth
> and seventh months the movements are more wave-like and weaker than later,
> when they are shorter but stronger and of a kicking nature. Mistaking it for
> peristalsis is hardly possible after some practice. Toward the end of gestation,
> palpation in lean cows often reveals which part of the calf is presented.[6]

Duration of Pregnancy. The length of the gestation period of cows
is approximately 9 months and 1 week. Most authorities agree that
the average length is 283 days. Considerable variation may exist between different members of the herd, though few cows calve less than
270 or more than 290 days after service. Greater variation than this
is likely to be the result of a diseased condition of the mother or some
abnormality of the offspring. Many breeders believe that heifers are
likely to carry their first calves a few days less than mature cows and
that heifer calves usually are carried a few days less than bull calves.
However, these differences, if true, are too small to be of any value in
predicting the date of calving or the sex of the offspring of an individual heifer or cow.

Care of Pregnant Cows. If possible, pregnant cows should be kept
separate from the rest of the herd. A good plan to follow, where adequate lots and pastures are available, is to remove all bred cows from
the herd about the middle of the gestation period. To leave them with
the herd is to invite injury and possible abortion from riding, butting,

[6] De Bruin, Bovine Obstetrics, 1897, p. 37.

and fighting. As stated above, pregnancy results in less activity on the part of the cows. They move about but little and appear to save themselves as much exertion as possible. Consequently, they should be kept by themselves where they will not be disturbed. Especially should they not be harassed by horse and mules, which often seem to take special delight in dashing in among the cattle, scattering them in all directions. Neither should they remain in a field occupied by hogs, since the hogs would be almost certain to consume any prematurely born calf. Indeed, instances have occurred where the cow, herself, has been attacked by hogs while she was laboring through parturition.

It must not be supposed that the pregnant cow needs no exercise. Indeed, the opposite is the case. Except during cold, stormy weather, there is no better place for her than out of doors where she can move about freely. In the winter months she should, of course, be stabled at night the same as any other animal. However, a windbreak and a dry place in which to lie are all the shelter that she requires until she approaches her date for calving, when a box stall in a closed barn should be provided if the weather is cold or stormy.

No special attention need be paid to the feed of the pregnant cow beyond that provided the rest of the herd. She should, of course, receive a sufficiently nutritious and well-balanced ration to supply adequately the needs of herself and the developing fœtus. This implies that she will gain considerably in weight during the gestation period— at least enough to account for the weight of the fœtus and to put herself in good flesh by calving time. Care should be taken to see that only feed that is free from dust, rust, and molds is supplied. While such damaged feeds are no more likely to cause sickness in pregnant cows than in non-pregnant animals, it should, of course, be understood that sickness of pregnant animals is usually much more serious, sometimes resulting in abortion.

Pregnant cows should be carefully protected against sudden shock. For this reason all non-urgent operations, such as dehorning and branding, should be postponed until after parturition. For the same reason, very cold water should be withheld from a pregnant cow that is warm and very thirsty.

"Normal parturition is the birth or expulsion of the living, healthy fœtus at the natural time, promptly, without artificial assistance, and in a state of development which enables it to live."[1]   The immediate or direct causes of parturition are not definitely known.   Numerous theories have been advanced by different investigators respecting the initiation of the act of birth, but there are few reliable data to support any of them.   Among the more common explanations are the following:

(*a*) The nutrition of the fœtus is arrested by a progressive fatty degeneration of the external layer of the maternal placenta; consequently, it must be born.

(*b*) Birth occurs whenever the fœtus attains a size sufficient to cause, through pressure, a relaxation of the uterine sphincter muscle, in much the same way that accumulations of urine and feces cause periodic relaxation of the sphincter muscles of the bladder and rectum.

(*c*) Birth is due to the disappearance of the corpus luteum, or yellow body, of the ovary furnishing the impregnated egg.   So long as this is present, reflex irritation of the nerves of the uterus is inhibited; but, upon its disappearance, œstrum, menstruation, and accompanying uterine contractions recur.   This theory would explain the tendency of a cow to abort at about the time her œstrum would occur if she were not pregnant.   However, it cannot be applied to a cow that calves normally, since the corpus luteum regularly persists for 30 to 60 days after parturition, or until she is again in heat.

(*d*) Birth is due to the toxic effect of the fœtal excretions, which in time cause sufficient irritation of the nervous system of the mother to cause the contraction of the uterus.

Signs of Parturition.   During the last few days of the gestation period, certain changes occur in the pregnant animal that signify to the experienced observer that parturition is not far off.   The more important signs that are commonly observed are the following:

[1] Williams, W. L., Veterinary Obstetrics, 1917, p. 260.

1. A relaxation of the pelvic ligaments (sacro-sciatic ligaments), which permits the muscles of the rump to drop inward, causing a noticeable falling away or sinking about the tail head and pin bones, and a general softening or loosening of the flesh in this region.
2. An enlargement and thickening of the lips of the vulva, which appear swollen and somewhat inflamed.
3. A noticeable enlargement of the udder, and a somewhat sudden change in the contents of the udder from a watery secretion to the thick, milky colostrum.

These changes are usually discernible some 3 or 4 weeks before birth occurs, but become more and more pronounced as the time of parturition draws near. As a rule, they appear sooner in heifers than in old cows, the latter sometimes calving with little or no "notice."

Labor Pains. The act of birth is accomplished through much exertion on the part of the mother and is accompanied by intense pain. This pain is a perfectly natural phenomenon, and in this respect is quite unlike all other pains and sufferings, which are due entirely to unnatural causes. The term "labor pains" is used to refer not only to the actual pain experienced by the mother, but also to the periodic muscular contractions which it provokes.

The first labor pains are usually of a colicky sort and give rise to the contraction of the uterine muscles only. Their advent usually occurs several hours before parturition and is indicated by a noticeable uneasiness on the part of the animal. Often the animal turns her head to the side, glancing nervously to the rear. Frequently she lies down and gets up at short intervals, thereby showing that she is in distress.

These preliminary contractions of the uterus are extremely important, inasmuch as they result in shifting the fœtus from a lateral, recumbent position on the floor of the abdomen to a longitudinal, upright attitude immediately in front of the pelvic girdle, from which position it can be easily expelled. These contractions also bring about a dilation or enlargement of the os uteri. In fact, this restriction, which normally separates the vagina and the uterus, is practically obliterated, so that these two organs form one continuous passage to the exterior. This enlargement of the os uteri is brought about largely through pressure exerted by the walls of the uterus upon the fœtal fluids. These fluids, within their elastic membranes, are forced into the rear portion of the uterus by the pressure exerted upon them; and by transmitting this pressure equally in all directions, serve as an elastic dilator, first of the cervix and later of the parts beyond. Assisting

the uterine muscles in this and the subsequent steps of parturition are
the large muscles of the abdominal walls, as well as the diaphragm.
These muscles, contracting in unison with those of the uterus at intervals of from 1 to 2 minutes, exert a tremendous force upon the fœtus.
Normally they will bring about its expulsion, unassisted, within 30 or
40 minutes after they first arise.

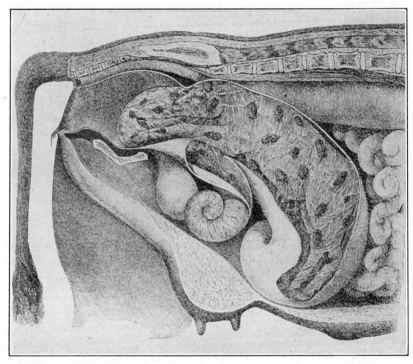

Fig. 23.   The normal position of the fœtus at the time of birth.   (*After Skelett.*)

The effect of this great pressure upon the fœtus is to cause it and its
enveloping membranes to be displaced backward through the dilated
os into the vagina.   The chorion, or outer membrane, being firmly
attached to the walls of the uterus except near the fundus, does not
permit of much displacement and is soon ruptured by the increasing
pressure.   This step in the process of birth is highly essential to the
well-being of the young, since the continuation of close contact between
the chorion and uterus makes possible proper nourishment of the fœtus
throughout the time of parturition.   With the rupture of the chorion,
the allantois with its contained liquid escapes into the vagina to appear

at the vulva as a "bright glistening tumor of more or less bluish tinge, separating the vulvular lips."[2]   Gradually the contained straw-colored liquor escapes beyond the vulva to form a bladder varying in size from a pint to a quart vessel.   This bladder is called the first "water bag." Usually it increases in size until it ruptures from the weight of the contained liquid.

It is very important that this water bag be allowed to break of its own accord.   Upon the escape of the allantoic fluid, the pressure exerted by the uterus and the abdominal muscles is applied directly to the foetus suspended only in the amniotic fluid.   Should this pressure be applied before the foetus attains its proper position or before the genital passages are sufficiently enlarged, the difficulty of birth will be greatly increased.   Hence, the longer the water bag remains intact the better.

Normally the rupture of the water bag is closely followed by the appearance of the amniotic bladder (the second water bag), with the contained foetus.   This membrane is glistening white in color and contains a rather viscid, slimy, opalescent liquid.   Within this membrane can be plainly seen the presenting portion of the foetus, usually the anterior limbs.   With each labor pain more and more of the liquid is forced out to form a bladder which, upon bursting, materially lubricates the genital passage.   The rupture of the amniotic membrane is followed by violent throes and strainings on the part of the cow, which soon force the head and then the shoulders of the foetus through the pelvic canal.   At this stage the cow often proceeds to get on her feet, during which act the rest of the calf emerges under the influence of gravity.

Rendering Assistance.   Assistance should not be given except where actually necessary.   Some herdsmen are prone to rush in and "take" the calf by force at the first appearance of the water bag through the vulva.   Such a practice is to be strongly condemned, as injury is likely to be sustained by both cow and calf in the form of torn membranes and strained ligaments.   If no progress has been made toward delivery within approximately 2 hours after the beginning of labor pains, a careful examination should be made, by a veterinarian if possible, to ascertain whether or not an abnormal presentation is the cause of the delay.   If this is found to be true, a veterinarian or an experienced herdsman should be sent for with all possible haste.

While unnecessary aid is to be strongly discouraged, one should not make the opposite mistake of permitting the cow to labor until she is completely exhausted before aid is furnished.   Occasionally a calf is encountered with an abnormally large head or with unusually heavy

[2] De Bruin. Bovine Obstetrics, 1897, p. 67.

shoulders, which greatly delay or totally obstruct the passage through the pelvic cavity. Also, in the case of a posterior presentation, the hips of the calf very frequently cause trouble, due largely to the small size of the allantoic bladder in the region of the hind-quarters, which results in the making of an insufficient opening in the cervix. In either case, assistance should be given by fastening small ropes well above the pasterns to avoid injuring the soft hoofs, and pulling backward and downward each time the cow labors. No more force should be exerted than is necessary to overcome the obstruction. Under no condition should traction be applied except when the cow labors, unless she is exhausted to the point where she refuses to labor. If this is the case, the calf must be removed wholly by the traction exerted by such helpers as are available.

So long as no tension is exerted upon the umbilical cord, there is no cause for hastening the act of birth. However, when the head has advanced as far as the eyes the cord becomes pressed against the floor of the pelvis in such a way that the placenta circulation is jeopardized. Hence, at this point it is highly advisable to rupture the amnion, if still intact, to permit respiration and to prevent the calf from drowning in the contained fluid. Since respiration is not likely to be effective so long as the chest is in the vice-like grasp of the genital passage, birth should be hastened by traction in such cases. In a posterior presentation there is always considerable danger of the calf's suffocating through rupture or strangulation of the umbilical cord. Hence, assistance in hastening parturition is much more likely to be necessary in posterior than in anterior births.

Care of the New-Born Calf. After the calf is born, it is a good plan to clear all membranes from its nostrils to facilitate breathing. In case parturition has occupied a long interval and intra-uterine respiration has occurred, haste should be made to clear all amniotic liquid from the nasal passages and throat. This can usually be accomplished by holding the calf head-down for an instant to permit the material to drain out, after which artificial respiration should be begun at once and continued until breathing is started. Many calves apparently dead can be revived by this method.

Because of the shortness of the umbilical cord (12 to 15 inches), it is always ruptured during the act of birth—usually about the time the fore-quarters pass through the vulva. If proper sanitary precautions have been taken in preparing clean quarters for the parturient cow, there is little likelihood of any trouble from navel infection. However, some cattlemen make a practice of applying either tincture of iodine or formalin to the navel stump to destroy any pus germs that may possibly be present. Others dust the stump with antiseptic powder to hasten its drying up and sloughing off.

As soon as possible after birth, the cow and calf should be left alone. The cow apparently derives great satisfaction from drying her calf by licking it. Apparently this "labial massaging" is Mother Nature's form of artificial respiration. Also, it greatly stimulates the functioning of the circulatory system.

Usually the calf will stand and nurse of its own accord. The taking of nourishment a few minutes after birth is neither necessary nor advisable. If at the end of 5 or 6 hours the calf has not nursed, it should be given assistance in finding the udder. Seldom is more than one lesson necessary. Most authorities agree that the colostrum, or first milk, acts as a mild purgative on the digestive tract of the young calf, causing a more rapid discharge of the accumulated excretion in the intestines, known as meconium, than would otherwise occur. It is highly desirable that the cow and calf be left together for at least a week or 10 days. Frequent nursings during this time will tend to relieve any udder inflammation and will ensure the calf's getting a good start. Thereafter the cow may be turned out with the herd during the day, but should, if possible, be kept with the calf at night for a week or two longer. After the calf is 1 month old, it need be turned with the cow only to nurse.

Cows calving in midwinter should be accorded the best shelter that the farm affords. Otherwise the newly born calves may suffer from frostbitten ears and tails in zero weather. In summer very young calves should be kept in cool, darkened stalls to minimize the discomforts caused by stable flies and oppressive heat. At other seasons they are quite as well off out of doors as inside, except during stormy weather.

It is highly important that young animals receive plenty of sunshine and exercise. Both are necessary for health and rapid growth. Calves born on pasture naturally get sufficient exercise in following their mothers back and forth over the field. Fall- and winter-born calves, not having this advantage, should be provided with a good-sized, well-drained lot in which they may scamper and run on nice days when the ground is dry or frozen. In addition to this, a small paved pen on the south side of the barn is highly desirable as a "sun parlor" on days when the larger lot is wet and muddy.

Expulsion of the Afterbirth. After the young is born, the outer fœtal membranes are still attached to the walls of the uterus by means of the cotyledons. With parturition, however, the exchange of nutritive elements between the maternal and fœtal placentæ immediately ceases. With the stoppage of this circulation there is a shrinkage of the villi of the cotyledons, which results in loosening the attachments between the chorion and the uterus. This loosening is greatly hastened and facilitated by the contractions of the uterus, through which the uterus returns to its normal size. One by one, the fœtal placentæ separate from the cotyledons of the uterus and the freed portion of the membranes is gradually forced out through the vulva by the contractions of the uterus. With the severance of the union at the last cotyledon the whole mass of freed membranes drops to the ground. The expelled placenta should be removed promptly from the stall or lot as soon as observed and destroyed by burning or burying. The practice of allowing it to decompose on the manure pile cannot be too strongly condemned.

Retention of the Afterbirth. Normally, the fœtal membranes are expelled from 2 to 6 hours after parturition. If they remain longer than 10 or 12 hours, it is exceedingly likely that an abnormal condition exists and that manual assistance will be required in their removal. Cattle are more susceptible to this malady than are any other species of domestic animals, and it is by no means uncommon to encounter herds in which nearly 20 per cent of the cows are troubled with this affliction during some calving seasons.

The exact cause of the retention of the placenta is not definitely known. Some authorities regard it as a disease of the fœtal membranes which causes them to adhere with abnormal tenacity to the maternal placentæ. In all probability, the majority of cases are due to the presence of infection which causes inflammation and enlargement of the maternal cotyledons. With their enlargement, the finger-like villi of the fœtal membranes are gripped fast in the recesses of the uterine cotyledons, thereby preventing normal separation of the membranes. Such infection may have been present before parturition, as in the case of contagious abortion, or it may have occurred while assistance was being rendered in an abnormal presentation. Also, retention is very likely to accompany a failure of the uterine walls to contract promptly, as a result of a general weakness on the part of the animal or its exhaustion from an especially long and painful parturition. Cows that are thin and half-starved, as well as cows that are in high show condition, are likely to be troubled with retained placentæ after calving. In either situation there is an unhealthy condition of the genital tract which tends to weaken the walls of the uterus, delaying its contraction beyond the normal period.

A retained placenta is an ideal medium for the development of putrefying bacteria. Almost invariably, a string-like portion of the unexpelled membranes hangs from the vulva, where it comes in contact with the tail and hind-quarters of the cow. It, of course, becomes heavily laden with all sorts of bacteria, which quickly spread into the interior. Decomposition and putrefaction begin in a remarkably short time. Except in cold weather an obnoxious odor, warning the owner that attention is urgent, appears within 48 hours after parturition. This odor becomes more and more pronounced, until at the end of a week or 10 days the stench is fairly nauseating.

The effect on the cow of acting as host to countless millions of putrefying bacteria soon becomes apparent. The absorption of the toxic products of decomposition causes her to take on an unthrifty appearance. She shows a marked decrease of appetite and a gradual loss of body weight; her milk flow is scanty or fails entirely; her skin loses its pliableness, and her hair becomes harsh and dry; her eyes, instead of being bright and alert, become dull and listless. Altogether the cow gradually acquires a haggard, unthrifty, run-down appearance which may continue for months, until she finally dies or recovers. Recovery is generally slow and is usually accompanied by sterility.

Removing Retained Placenta. If the fœtal membranes have not come away within 24 hours after calving, immediate steps should be taken to retard their decomposition, pending their ultimate removal. For this purpose bismuth subnitrate, iodoform, and other feebly soluble disinfectants suspended in mineral, olive, or raw linseed oil may be introduced, preferably by means of gelatin capsules.[3]

Considerable difference of opinion exists among practicing veterinarians as to the proper time to remove a retained placenta. Some recommend its removal as soon as 24 hours after calving. Others advocate waiting another day in order that the attachments may be partly loosened by the process of decomposition. Still other authorities advise postponement until the fourth or fifth day after calving, to permit the uterus to contract sufficiently to enable the operator to reach readily all parts of the affected horn. However, seldom in a case of retained placenta does the uterus show any tendency to contract. Delay not only increases the likelihood of permanent injury to the uterus but also results in a more disagreeable and dangerous task from the standpoint of the operator, because of more advanced decomposition of the membranes. Even though some delay may be advisable for one of the reasons stated above, an early examination is highly desirable, since it is very important that the afterbirth be taken away as soon as it can be removed without injury to the uterus.

[3] Williams, W. L., Diseases of the Genital Organs of Animals, third ed., 1943, p. 568.

If possible, the services of a trained veterinarian should be obtained for removing a retained placenta. The inexperienced operator who attempts to carry out printed instructions is very likely to damage seriously the walls of the uterus, especially the cotyledons. Moreover, the danger of the layman's introducing harmful bacteria into the uterus, as well as infecting himself through a cut or skin abrasion on the arm, is very great. Few laymen realize the importance of observing proper sanitary precautions throughout the operation. Others will go to the opposite extreme and use strong antiseptic solutions that sear and deaden the tender membranes of the genital tract. Under no condition should the layman attempt to remove a retained placenta until he has seen several removed by trained practitioners and has learned from actual experience and observation the exact method of procedure. Instead he should send for a veterinarian or an experienced herdsman who he knows is qualified to perform the operation. To do otherwise will almost certainly result in the sterility of the animal.

It would hardly seem necessary in this day and age to condemn the old practice of tying a brick or small bag of sand to that part of the placenta hanging from the vulva to bring about the shedding of the membranes through the action of gravity. Nevertheless, such primitive methods are still employed in some sections of the country. While a small weight of itself might serve a good purpose in exerting gentle traction on the placenta, the dangling of such an object about the legs of the cow usually results in the breaking of the membranes within the genital tract. When this occurs the removal of the remaining part is rendered much more difficult.

Irrigation of the Uterus. In cases of retained placentæ, as well as other diseased or injured conditions of the genital tract, it is usually advisable to inject a mild antiseptic solution into the uterus. Care should be taken that the solution used is not too strong. It should be kept in mind that the membranes lining the genital organs are very delicate and are easily injured by strong medicines. A solution that is irritating will cause the cow to strain, and such straining may result in the prolapse or eversion of the uterus. Probably the best antiseptic for the cow is a ½ per cent solution of carbolic acid.[4] Creolin or lysol in 1 per cent solution or potassium permanganate in a dilution of 1 to 2000 is also satisfactory. Corrosive sublimate (mercury bichloride) should not be used because of its caustic properties. Care should be taken, in preparing any of these solutions, to guard against excessive strength. Probably the safest and most satisfactory irrigant for the layman to use in all cases of diseased reproductive organs is a

[4] Approximately 1 tablespoonful per gallon of water.

normal salt solution, made by dissolving 1¼ ounces (approximately 2 tablespoonfuls) of common salt in a gallon of boiled water.

As a rule, the solution injected should be at body temperature. Exception is made where pronounced contraction of the uterus is desired, in which case the solution may be made with moderately cold water. The injection can best be made through a ⅜-inch rubber tube, to the outer end of which is fitted a funnel. Most veterinarians use a special aseptic enema pump by means of which the solution is forced into the uterine cavity under moderate pressure. The use of an ordinary bucket spray pump cannot be recommended, as the pressure exerted is too great.

Usually, sufficient solution is injected to fill the genital tract completely. When this condition is reached the liquid escapes from the vulva as fast as it is poured in through the funnel. After the removal of the tube, the cow should be watched carefully to see whether or not the solution is expelled by the forceful contraction of the uterus. In case the animal does not throw out the injected liquid, it must be siphoned out as completely as possible. To leave the uterus full of liquid would impose upon its muscular walls an undue strain which might permanently lessen their contractile power. Especially is this likely to occur where irrigation is carried on daily over an extended period.

Occurrence of Œstrum after Parturition. As a rule, cows do not show signs of œstrum until some 6 or 8 weeks after parturition. Some cows go even longer before coming in heat. If for any cause there is an urgent reason for rebreeding a cow as soon as possible after parturition, she should be tried on the tenth day after calving. While some cows will accept the service of the bull on this day, seldom will they show any visible signs of being in heat. Also, the likelihood of pregnancy resulting from breeding at this time is rather small. Ordinarily it is much better to wait until the cow has recovered from the effect of parturition, and breed her at the first reappearance of œstrum.

Size of the Calf Crop. The term "calf crop" refers to the percentage of cows in the breeding herd that produce calves of weaning age. This percentage often varies widely between different herds and in the same herd in different years. The more important factors that determine the size of the calf crop are the following:

1. Small percentage of pregnancies, due to:
   a. Failure to detect cows in heat.
   b. Unthrifty or diseased condition of cows.
   c. Impaired breeding qualities of bull.
   d. Too large a number of cows per bull.

2. Abortion: Where more than 2 or 3 per cent of the cows abort, the abortion is probably a contagious form.[5]
3. Loss of calves during or soon after birth. Abnormal presentations, exposure, scours, and congenital weakness frequently account for the loss of a small percentage of calves before they are a month old.
4. Loss of calves over 1 month old but under weaning age. The percentage of loss here is small. Pneumonia, bloat, and various accidents that result in broken legs, etc., claim an occasional calf during this period of life.

TABLE 41

PRODUCTION RECORD OF BREEDING HERD OF U.S.D.A. RANGE EXPERIMENT
STATION, MILES CITY, MONTANA*

| | | Percentage of all cows in Herd | | | | |
| | Number of | Cows | | Normal | Calves | Loss to |
Year	Cows	Open	Pregnant	Birth	Weaned	Weaning†
1925	106	14.2	85.8	84.0	81.1	5.5
1926	104	26.9	72.1	72.1	69.2	4.0
1927	126	9.5	90.5	77.0	71.4	21.1
1928	161	14.9	85.1	80.7	78.3	6.8
1929	168	22.0	78.0	75.0	74.4	4.6
1930	186	8.6	91.4	86.6	85.5	6.5
1931	234	11.5	88.5	87.2	85.9	2.9
1932	291	16.2	83.8	81.8	79.7	4.9
1933	331	11.8	88.2	86.7	84.3	4.1
1934	353	14.7	85.3	83.6	81.6	4.3
1935	366	23.0	77.0	71.9	70.8	8.2
1936	314	14.6	85.4	81.8	79.9	6.3
1937	233	31.8	68.2	66.1	64.4	5.7
1938	290	9.7	90.3	88.3	86.2	4.6
1939	305	6.6	93.4	92.5	90.5	3.2
1940	351	8.5	91.5	89.2	86.9	5.0
1941	388	12.1	87.9	87.1	84.5	3.8
1942	446	12.8	87.2	85.9	83.4	4.4
Total	4,753	Ave. 14.4	85.6	83.1	81.0	5.4

* Baker and Quesenberry, U.S.D.A., Journal of Animal Science, 1944, Vol. 3, p. 80.
† Based upon number of pregnant cows.

With so many possible adverse factors, it is not surprising that seldom does a herd of 10 or more cows entirely escape all of them. In other words, seldom is a perfect calf crop (100 per cent) realized. Instead, the crop is likely to lie somewhere between 70 and 95 per cent. As a rule, the size of the calf crop varies inversely with the size of the

[5] Cf. pp. 601, 625, 626.

herd, owing to the smaller amount of individual attention that the animals of larger herds receive. However, studies carried on by the United States Department of Agriculture, both in the Corn Belt and Range areas, indicate that good care and management on the part of the owner are much more important factors in determining the percentage of calves raised than the size of the breeding herd or even the ratio of bulls to cows. In many instances great variation was found to exist in the size of the calf crop on practically adjoining ranches "with no perceptible difference in range, feed, water facilities, quality of animals, or animal losses." Undoubtedly such differences are due largely to the care with which the breeding herd is culled for non-breeding cows, the amount of attention given to the conditioning of bulls previous to the breeding season, the amount of time spent in systematic inspection of the herd for in-heat cows, and the attention given the cows during the calving period. Nevertheless, even with the same system of management, considerable variation in the percentage of calves raised was found to occur on the same farm or ranch from one year to another. Weather conditions, particularly as they affect the feed supply of the cow herd and the exposure to which the young calves are subjected during the 2 or 3 weeks following birth are largely responsible for these yearly variations. These can be overcome to a large extent by providing sufficient feed supplies and adequate shelter facilities to meet such emergencies.

The influence of the size of the calf crop upon the net cost of raising calves to weaning age is well shown by Table 42. Attention is called to the fact that 68 per cent of these Texas ranches realized a calf crop under 80 per cent. In sharp contrast with these figures are the records made by over 100 small breeders in the North Central states, many of whom weaned calves from 90 per cent or more of their cows. (See Table 43.) In view of the fact that the size of the calf crop decreased gradually from east to west, it seems probable that feed conditions and available shelter were the chief causes for the variations noted. The data in both of these tables were obtained several years ago when many breeders, especially large ranchers, gave less attention to their herds than they do now. The effect of good care and management upon the calf crop is well illustrated by the results obtained by the winning contestants in the beef production contest sponsored by the Kansas Extension Service and the Kansas City Chamber of Commerce. (See Table 44.) Ordinarily the calf crop varies inversely with the size of the herd, since more care is usually given to each cow and calf if the herd is small. The little relation to be found between size of herd and calf crop in these Kansas records indicates that

TABLE 42

THE INFLUENCE OF SIZE OF CALF CROP UPON THE NET COST PER CALF*

(North central Texas ranches, 1920 to 1924.)

Per Cent Calf Crop (by Groups)	Number of Ranches in Each Group	Number of Calves	Net Cost per Calf (4 yr. aver.)	Per Cent of Total Calves
30–40	1	590	$43.92	1.4
40–50	2	585	49.21	1.3
50–60	14	11,880	36.15	27.4
60–70	18	8,020	38.88	18.5
70–80	22	10,848	28.03	25.6
80–90	22	9,749	25.46	22.5
90–100	5	1,695	22.15	3.9
Totals & Averages	84	43,367	$31.95	100.0

* California Bulletin 458, 1928.

TABLE 43

PERCENTAGE OF CALVES RAISED IN CORN BELT HERDS*

State	Number of Farms	Aver. Number of Cows per Farm	Aver. Per Cent Calf Crop
Indiana	6	16.5	96.2
Illinois	13	21.0	89.3
Missouri	33	22.1	90.2
Iowa	76	31.1	86.5
Minnesota	12	21.7	85.0
South Dakota	6	30.2	86.4
Kansas	46	50.4	81.5
Nebraska	38	27.0	78.9
Total	230	31.5	84.9

* U.S.D.A. Report 111, 1916.

number of cows is of less importance than care and management in obtaining a calf from almost every cow.

Feeds for Suckling Calves. As a rule, young calves will begin to eat when about 3 or 4 weeks of age. Whether pains should be taken to provide feeds and facilities for eating during the suckling period depends upon the disposition that is to be made of the calves after they are weaned. The feeding of grain cannot be begun too soon with calves

TABLE 44

Calf Crop Obtained by Some Breeders Enrolled in the Feeder Calf
Section of the Kansas Beef Production Contest*

Name of Breeder	1946			1947			1948		
	Cows Bred (number)	Bulls Used (number)	Calf Crop (per cent)	Cows Bred (number)	Bulls Used (number)	Calf Crop (per cent)	Cows Bred (number)	Bulls Used (number)	Calf Crop (per cent)
Briggs and Bailey	214	5	96.7	210	5	95.2	219	5	91.3
Ralph Deewall	48	2	96.0	45	2	95.5	46	2	95.6
C. C. Piester	123	6	90.0	117	5	86.0	107	5	88.0
Joe W. Pruitt	45	2	93.3	41	2	100.0	39	2	100.0
Wear and Pruitt	122	4	94.3	111	4	93.7	104	4	98.0
H. P. Parkin	178	5	98.3	...	..	...	188	6	85.1
Wayne Walker	101	4	93.6	51	3	94.0	...	...	...

* Kansas Beef Production Contests, Kansas Extension Service, Mimeograph reports.

that are to be marketed as fat calves or baby beeves. However, whole milk and grass or some good form of roughage are quite sufficient for calves that are to be fattened in a leisurely way over a rather long feeding period or carried as stockers for awhile before going into the feed lot.

The breeder of purebred cattle, of course, is anxious to secure as much growth and development as possible in his young bulls and heifers. Hence, he follows the practice of teaching his calves to eat grain when they are about a month or 6 weeks of age. The advantage of feeding a good grain ration to calves during the suckling period is well demonstrated by a series of tests conducted at Sni-a-Bar Farms, Grain Valley, Missouri, under the supervision of the Missouri Agricultural Experiment Station and the United States Department of Agriculture. In these experiments, which were carried on for 3 years, spring-born calves that were fed grain during their first summer gained nearly 50 per cent faster and were fully 100 pounds heavier at weaning time than similar calves running with their mothers on pasture but receiving no grain. (See Table 49.)

In the Sni-a-Bar Farm experiments young calves learned to eat more quickly when their grain was cracked or ground. However, after the calves were accustomed to eating, whole grain was found to be fully as satisfactory as ground grain.

Many experienced herdsmen have a high regard for wheat bran as a feed for suckling calves. Calves learn to eat bran quickly, since it adheres to their noses during their inquisitive exploration of the feed boxes, and is swallowed without any chewing. A mixture of equal parts by measure of wheat bran, ground shelled corn, and ground oats is widely used for young calves during the period in which they are learning to eat.

The hay supplied calves having no access to pasture should be clean and bright. A little care on the part of the feeder to select a forkful of hay that is especially fine in texture and that has an abundance of leaves will be well worth while. The manger should be cleaned out daily and fresh hay provided, even though some of that given the previous day still remains uneaten. The material removed, probably consisting largely of stems, should be given to the older animals, as they are better able to utilize it.

As a rule, there is little choice between alfalfa and clover hay for calves. Occasionally, alfalfa hay will cause very young calves to scour, while in some it has a tendency to produce mild bloating. If either of these conditions is experienced, clover hay should be supplied if possible. If no clover is available, the alfalfa should be fed in restricted amounts, along with a little oat straw.

10 —— The Summer Management of the Breeding Herd

In theory the feeding and management of the breeding herd during the summer are relatively simple, as the herd is then running on pasture and requires little attention. In practice, however, some of the cowman's most difficult problems arise during this season of the year. First in importance is the difficulty of estimating the forage supply, which will be determined largely by weather conditions, and these can be neither predicted nor controlled. Should the weather be unfavorable for the growth of grass, a critical shortage of feed may be encountered long before the usual end of the grazing season. Second, the breeding season for most beef herds comes during the summer, at which time the cows should be inspected daily to determine whether or not they are coming in heat regularly and are being successfully bred. Farmers are invariably busy with field work at this time of year and are prone to limit inspections to once or twice a week, especially if the herd is on a pasture at some distance from the farmstead. Lastly, early summer is the proper time to castrate bull calves that were born on pasture or were too young to castrate while the herd was still in the dry lot. If this job is put off until the urgent field work is finished, the calves are big and hard to handle when it is finally done.

Despite these difficulties, breeders invariably welcome the arrival of spring, for they know they will soon be relieved from many of the morning and evening chores which they have been performing all winter. The cattle welcome it, too, for they sense that fresh, green grass will soon replace the coarse, dry roughage for which they have less and less appetite as the weather becomes warmer.

Pasture. Pasture is relied upon almost entirely for feed for the breeding herd during the summer months. On most farms no feed other than pasture is given. As has been stated in a previous chapter,[1] pasture is considered so essential for the breeding herd that few beef cows are kept by farmers who do not have sufficient grass to carry them through the summer. This attitude on the part of the stockmen is based upon long experience as well as upon scientific facts. In the first place, cattle on pasture are living under the most natural conditions

[1] *Cf.* p. 3.

Fig. 24. An ideal pasture area for a beef breeding herd. However, the stand of grass has become very thin and has been partly replaced by weeds. Heavy discing, fertilizing, and reseeding will probably double the carrying capacity of this field over the next 10 years.

that can be provided, and with no class of cattle is an approach to natural conditions so desirable as with the breeding herd. Cows with young calves instinctively seek seclusion, and nowhere else on the farm can they find it so well as in the pasture. Young calves need a large amount of milk, and there is nothing better than grass to stimulate the milk flow during the lactation period. The first food other than milk that a young calf receives should be soft, palatable, and easily digested. Green grass fulfills all these requirements. Moreover, it furnishes an abundance of protein, vitamins, and minerals, three factors that are highly essential to the normal growth of young animals.

Both cows and calves need plenty of exercise, fresh air, sunshine, and warm rain baths to keep them healthy and free from disease. Seldom are cattle troubled with lice, ringworm, pneumonia, or foul feet while they are on pasture. When kept in barns and small lots, on the other hand, these afflictions are frequently encountered. It is even claimed by some men that cattle living out of doors are not so likely to contract tuberculosis as those kept in barns. Thus, from practically every standpoint it is very desirable that the breeding herd be kept on pasture for as long a period as possible. Over most of the Corn Belt, pasture of some kind or another can be counted on to carry the breeding herd for 7 to 8 months, leaving only 4 to 5 months for dry-lot feeding.

Kinds of Pasture: *Permanent and Temporary.* As a rule, pasture areas are occupied by perennial plants, i.e., plants that do not die after ripening their seed but continue to grow year after year. Kentucky bluegrass, redtop, brome grass, Bermuda grass, and nearly all the native grasses of the Western Plains region are perennials, and they together occupy by far the greater percentage of the total pasture area of the country. However, during recent years there has been a marked increase in acreage of temporary pasture crops, especially in the Corn Belt where new seedings made in small-grain crops are allowed to stand for a year or two as part of the general crop rotation. These seedings may be harvested for hay or grass silage the first year and pastured for a year or two thereafter before they are plowed under for corn. Or they may be left standing for only one year, in which case the first crop is sometimes cut for hay or grass silage and the second crop pastured. Or they may be grazed by beef cattle or other stock from early spring until late fall. Obviously, the method of utilizing a particular field will be determined largely by the need for additional pasture at the time it is ready to be used for that purpose.

The plant species most widely used in seeding temporary pastures consist largely of legumes, since the principal reason for including a year of pasture in the crop rotation is to improve the fertility of the soil. Consequently, alfalfa and red, alsike, and sweet clovers, either seeded alone or mixed with grasses, are commonly used. A mixture of red clover, sweet clover, and timothy is a very satisfactory seeding for a pasture that is to be used for only 1 year, but alfalfa usually should be included in seedings that are to be allowed to stand 2 years or longer.

On farms on which less than half the total area is tillable, permanent pastures will furnish grazing for the breeding herd during most of the summer. But on level farms that are not subject to serious erosion temporary pastures are more profitable and, consequently, should comprise most of the pasture area.

Advantages of Temporary Pastures:
1. More feed is furnished per acre, which makes possible a larger herd for a given pasture area.
2. A large percentage, if not all, of the forage is legumes.
3. Temporary pasture crops, as a rule, withstand the heat and drought of summer better than bluegrass.
4. The temporary pasture crop can be included in the regular farm rotation, thus making possible the utilization of the legumes grown primarily for soil improvement. At the same time, those benefits accruing to the soil through pasturing and feeding on pasture are shared by different parts of the farm.
5. Any surplus forage can be utilized for hay or silage.

Of these advantages, the last two are of most importance. The others, important in some years, are open to question when a long period of time, involving all kinds of seasons and weather, is considered. It is undoubtedly true that with a good stand and ordinary weather conditions most temporary pasture crops will produce more forage than bluegrass on similar land will furnish, and that these crops, being legumes, will be more nutritious and withstand the heat of summer better than the ordinary, perennial pasture plants. However, experience has shown that, under ordinary farming conditions, in not more than 4 years out of 5 is a perfect stand of legumes secured, while in about 1 year out of 7 or 8 the crop is almost a total failure. At such times the common practice is to sow oats, rye, Sudan grass, or other non-legume crops for pasture.

Since the advantages of temporary pastures have been mentioned, it might, perhaps, be worth while to list the principal objections raised against them.

Disadvantages of Temporary Pastures:
1. They require an annual outlay for seed, preparation of seed bed, etc.
2. Stand of crop is often uncertain and sometimes a total failure.
3. Plants do not form a good turf; hence, the fields are often trampled badly in wet weather.
4. Adequate shade and water are provided with difficulty.
5. Temporary pasture crops are likely to cause bloat.
6. Tight fences are required around every field.
7. Some of the temporary pasture plants tend to ripen and dry up in later summer and early fall.

The last disadvantage mentioned can be dismissed with the statement that most of the common, temporary pasture crops are biennial legumes which ripen and dry up only in the fall of the second year. By this time the seedling pastures started in the spring of that year are large enough to graze, and the stock can be shifted to them. Likewise, the sixth objection can be met with the statement that all fields of the farm should be well fenced, whether in pasture or not, to permit the utilization of stalk fields, oat and hay stubble, etc., by cattle.

TABLE 45

A COMPARISON OF DIFFERENT PASTURES FOR BEEF COWS AND CALVES*

Kind of Pasture	No. of Cows	No. of Calves	Days on Pasture	Average Weaning Weight[a]	Average Total Gain of Calves	Average Daily Gain of Calves
Bluegrass only	1878	1799	176	378	262	1.49
Bluegrass and lespedeza mixture	2235	2120	176	414	294	1.67
Bluegrass in spring and lespedeza in summer (alone or after harvest of small grain)	5847	5610	176	470	343	1.95

* Charles R. Kyd, Missouri Extension Service, information to the author.
[a] All lots weaned at an average age of 200 days.

That temporary forage crops have a real place in cattle raising cannot be denied. However, it would appear that their greatest use is to supplement rather than displace permanent pastures. The danger of not securing a stand, and thus being without any forage, is too great to warrant the farmer to rely exclusively on them for maintaining a breeding herd.

The best plan is to depend on neither permanent nor temporary pasture alone for maintaining the breeding herd but to provide enough of each to insure a continuous supply of nutritious, palatable forage throughout the summer. Especially is some permanent pasture advisable for use in early spring and late fall, at which seasons temporary pastures often cannot be used without damage to the stand because of wet weather. Permanent pastures, like bluegrass and brome grass, which form a thick, dense sod, are damaged much less seriously not only during extremely wet weather but also during occasional periods of severe drought, when all pastures become little more than exercise lots.

Permanent pastures usually are ready for grazing earlier in the spring than temporary pastures, not only because they have a denser sod but because they are lower in moisture and hence are less laxative. They are most productive during cool, moist weather and may be grazed heavily from the last of April to the middle of June. They are relatively dormant during July and August but make considerable growth in the fall upon the return of cool weather.

Most temporary pastures, 1 year old or older, are at their best in June, July, and August. Often they are so productive during the early summer that only a portion of the area is needed for grazing, making possible the cutting of the remainder of the field for hay. The second crop comes on quickly, and this fresh growth combines with the more mature forage of the grazed area to make an ideal pasture for beef cattle.

If temporary pastures are spring sown, like Sudan grass, which is seeded alone, or sweet clover, Korean lespedeza, or alfalfa, which are seeded in small grain, they are usually ready to be grazed by the last of July or the middle of August and furnish excellent grazing until the first killing frost.

Cattle should be removed from all legume pastures immediately after a killing frost, as frozen legume forage may cause serious bloat and scouring. However, it may be grazed with safety 2 or 3 weeks later after the stem and leaves have become dead and brown. Obviously, it is much less palatable and nutritious after being frozen than it was while still green. Fortunately, at this season of the year permanent pastures usually are in excellent condition and constitute an ideal supplement to the cured legume forage remaining in the fields.

Length of the Grazing Season. The length of the grazing season will, of course, vary with the latitude and with the species of plants used for pasture. It also depends to a considerable extent upon the weather conditions that prevail during the growing season. In gen-

FIG. 25. A breeding herd on a rotation pasture. Temporary pastures that are included in the regular crop rotation usually have a high carrying capacity because they are grown on fertile soil and consist largely of legumes. (*Courtesy American Shorthorn Association.*)

eral, however, it may be stated that on the average about 5, 7, and 9 months' grazing are obtained in the northern, central, and southern latitudes of the United States, respectively. Probably the average for the Corn Belt is not far from 6 months. As stated above, unusual climatic conditions will affect the growth of grass very much, and this in turn will materially increase or decrease the length of the grazing season, as the weather is favorable or unfavorable. For example, during the 10 year period 1913–1922, at Urbana, Illinois, the length of time the pastures were used varied from 147 days in 1916 to 228 in

TABLE 46

RECOMMENDED GRAZING SCHEDULE FOR A HERD OF 30 BREEDING COWS AND
CALVES MAINTAINED ON HIGHLY PRODUCTIVE PASTURES

Period	Days	10 Acres Permanent Pasture (cow-days)	20 Acres Temporary Grass-Legume[a] (cow-days)	30 Acres Spring Seeding in Grain Stubble (cow-days)
April 25–May 10	15	450		
May 10–June 10	31		930	
June 10–July 1	21	630		
July 1–August 30	60		1800	
August 30–September 30	31			930
September 30–October 30	30		900	
October 30–November 20[b]	21	630		
April 25–November 20	209	1710	3630	930
Total days grazed		57	121	31
Total cow-days per acre		171	181.5	31

[a] It is assumed that 10 acres of the grass-legume mixture will be cut for hay, leaving 20 acres to be grazed.

[b] If the permanent pasture is used in connection with stalk fields during this period, its use may be extended to December 20 or even later.

1921. In 1916 the spring was unusually late and the summer very hot and dry. Moreover, no rain fell sufficiently early to produce any fall pasturage. In 1921, on the other hand, the summer was moist and rather cool. Cold weather did not arrive until after Thanksgiving, and the grass remained green until the middle of December. Ordinarily, however, in this latitude, the pasture season extends from May 1 to November 1. The average time spent by the breeding herd on grass during the 10-year period mentioned was 168.5 days. Under farm conditions, the grazing season is usually extended another month or 6 weeks by the use of stubble and aftermath pastures, which are available in the fall after small grain and hay crops, respectively.

Area per Cow. Because of the poor management of most permanent pastures and the resulting thin stand of grass, it is customary to allow from 2 to 3 acres of bluegrass for each cow and calf. However, this area can be greatly reduced even on rough land, by discing in fertilizers and reseeding with improved grasses and legumes that are well adapted to local soil and climatic conditions. The ambition of every farmer who lives in the Corn Belt should be to have pastures that will carry a cow and calf throughout the grazing season for each acre of pasture, exclusive of the spring seedings of grasses and legumes in grain stubble, which are usually available for light grazing in the late summer and early fall. If 30 to 40 per cent of the total pasture area is permanent bluegrass or brome grass and 60 to 70 per cent is temporary pasture consisting of mixed grasses and legumes grown as a part of the regular farm rotation, adequate grazing should be available from late April to late November. (See Table 46.)

TABLE 47

GAINS MADE BY BEEF COWS WITH YOUNG CALVES DURING THE SUMMER
(Illinois Experiment Station)

	1916	1917	1918	1919	4-Year Average
Second-year Sweet Clover........					
Area per cow, acres...........	.625	1.0	.80	1.0[a]	.85
Days pastured without extra feed	70	91	76	60	74
Gain during this period, lbs....	58	−50	6.0	−15	0.0
Total days pastured during season[b].....................	147	105	168	145	141
Total gain for season[b].........	4	−41	−36	55	−4.5
Bluegrass					
Area per cow, acres...........	1.0	1.0	1.0	1.25	1.1
Days pastured without extra feed	70	84	95	35[c]	71[c]
Gain during this period, lbs.....	164	103	Not weighed	103	123
Total days pastured per season[b].....................	98	161	161	180	150
Total gain for season[b].........	163	65	59	187	119

[a] Spring-sown sweet clover.
[b] In some years an additional area was allowed during the latter half of the summer.
[c] Bluegrass pasture badly damaged by army worms in June, 1919.

Gains Made by Cows on Pasture. The gains made by cows on pasture during the summer will depend upon a number of factors, among which are the abundance and nutritive value of the forage, the condition of the cows when turned onto pasture, the age of the suckling calves, and whether or not the calves are creep fed. In most sections of the Corn Belt the cows have calved before they are turned onto pasture and have lost considerable weight from parturition and subsequent suckling. This loss not infrequently amounts to 150 to 200 pounds a cow. Half or more of this loss usually is regained during the first two months on pasture while the grass is fresh and abundant, and the remainder is regained during the fall and winter after the calves are weaned. Frequently the cows will lose in weight during the middle of the summer when the pastures are scorched and dry, and the calves, now grown to good size, sap the strength of their mothers by their frequent nursing. One advantage of creep-feeding calves that run with their mothers on pasture is to relieve the cows of part of the burden that their offspring impose upon them during the latter half of the summer. In the Sni-a-Bar experiments previously referred to, the mothers of the creep-fed calves gained, as an average of the three summers, 36 pounds a head more than the mothers of the calves that were not creep fed.

Inasmuch as cows usually suffer a considerable loss in weight during the winter period, including that due to parturition, it is highly essential that they show a gain for the summer and fall periods which is at least as large as the winter loss. It is recommended that all cows be weighed individually when they are turned onto pasture in the spring and when they are taken off in the fall. A comparison of these weights will be of much value in planning the winter feeding program and in determining the approximate pasture area which should be provided for the summer period.

Calving in Pasture. As has already been stated, there is no better place for a cow to deliver her calf than in an open pasture. As a rule, the danger from infection will be much less than in the ordinary cattle barn. However, if she requires assistance during parturition it cannot be given so readily, especially if the pasture is some distance from the farmstead. Consequently, it is desirable to have a small grass paddock near the barn in which cows well advanced in pregnancy may be kept. Under no circumstance should pregnant cows be allowed to remain in a pasture where there are hogs.

It often happens that a cow, calving in pasture, will hide her calf in a clump of bushes or a patch of tall weeds, and, although she visits it frequently to allow it to nurse, she will not attempt to get it to leave its place of seclusion. In doing this, she, of course, is simply following the practice of her wild ancestors, which had to hide their young from many beasts of prey. Sometimes the hiding is done so cleverly that several hours of searching will not disclose the calf.

Separating Cows and Calves. Whether the calves should be allowed to run with their dams on pasture depends upon the abundance of grass and shade and whether it is planned to give the calves additional feed. That young calves should not be kept during the heat of summer in a field that affords no shade from the scorching sun needs no argument. Neither should they be expected to find their sustenance in a field the herbage of which is burnt brown by intense heat or prolonged drought. Mature animals may be able to thrive on this naturally cured grass, but young calves cannot; the calves should be removed to a fresh pasture, such as a field of second-growth clover, where there is plenty of shade. If no pasture with shade is to be had, the calves should be kept in a well-ventilated barn during the day and turned on the pasture at night. The cows should be turned to the calves both morning and evening to allow them to nurse. Not only the calves, but the cows as well, will benefit by such separation. With the calves out of the way, the cows are better able to stand the heat, since the frequent, energetic, even violent nursing of a big, lusty calf causes the cow considerable worry during hot weather.

If the calves are to be fed grain during the summer, it may be inadvisable to let them go out to grass with their mothers at all. Most men who handle purebred cattle prefer to keep at least their best calves near the barn where special attention in the way of feed and protection from sun and flies can be provided. The calves are kept in a cool stable during the day and allowed the run of a good grass paddock at night. Although such a practice involves considerable labor, it is to be recommended where the value of the animals is sufficiently high to justify the extra expense. It is only by employing such painstaking care as this that strictly first-class cattle are produced.

One of the advantages resulting from the separation of cows and calves is the opportunity afforded to observe the cows themselves during their semi-daily visit to the farmstead. Cows and calves running together in a distant pasture often get too little care and attention. Especially are the cows likely to pass through their heat periods unobserved. Also, injuries, caked udders, and sickness are likely to go unnoticed until too late to be treated effectively. However, when the cows are brought to the farmstead twice a day and kept there half an hour or so while the calves nurse, the herdsman has ample opportunity to detect any animal that is in any way abnormal.

Supplementary Feed for Cows. Unless the pasture area used by the cattle is sufficiently large to insure the accumulation of a reserve supply of grass, it will be necessary during periods of drought to give the cows some feed in addition to that furnished by the pasture, if their milk flow and flesh are to be maintained. In the absence of such an area some cattlemen follow the practice of guarding their supply of grass against possible exhaustion by supplementing the pasture with other feeds from the very beginning, or soon after the beginning, of the grazing season. Such a practice is to be recommended on farms where the pasture acreage is small, since it makes possible the carrying of a greater number of cattle on a given area without exhausting the grass supply long before the normal end of the grazing season. Experience has shown that about 1½ to 2 acres of ordinary, permanent bluegrass are required to carry a cow and calf from about May 1 to November 1. However, this area can be materially reduced if additional feed is supplied. Table 48 shows how the pasture area was reduced 33 and 66 per cent respectively at the Illinois Station by the use of different amounts of supplementary feed.

TABLE 48

Effect of Supplementary Feed upon the Pasture Area Required per Cow and Calf*

Pasture Acreage per Cow and Calf (Bluegrass)	No. of Days Pastured	No. of Days Supplement Was Fed	Average Daily Supplement per Cow for Period Fed		Average Daily Supplement per Cow for Entire Period	
			Cottonseed Meal	Corn Silage	Cottonseed Meal	Corn Silage
			Lbs.	Lbs.	Lbs.	Lbs.
1.50	161	12	.52	18.6	.04	1.35
1.00	145	93	.35	14.0	.22	9.06
.50	161	153	.73	29.2	.70	27.85

* Illinois Experiment Station; Average of three years' work.

One of the most satisfactory feeds with which to supplement pastures is corn or grass silage. It is palatable, succulent, and usually reasonably cheap. Seldom will cattle refuse to eat 15 to 20 pounds of silage per day, even though the supply of grass be abundant. On the other hand, dry hay or straw will remain in the racks almost untouched, so long as the supply of grass holds out.

Probably no feed is used more extensively during periods of drought and grass shortage than green corn. The entire corn plant is cut off a few inches above the ground and hauled out and scattered on the pastures. If the corn is reasonably ripe when it is fed, such a practice is to be commended. However, it frequently happens that supplementary feed is needed when the corn is barely past the roasting-ear stage, or at least long before it is mature. To cut it at this time entails considerable waste, since growing corn continues to gain in total food nutrients until it is ready to be shocked. Moreover, very green corn tends to scour the cattle and occasionally causes bloat. If a supply of silage is available for summer feeding the use of immature, green corn will be unnecessary.

Farmers often make the mistake of delaying summer feeding too long. If it is to be a supplement to the grass and is to prolong the grazing period, it must be begun long before the grass is exhausted. The excuse so often heard—that the farmer hoped for a rain which would make feeding unnecessary—is not valid, since a closely cropped pasture seldom recovers as quickly after a rain as one that has had better treatment. It is much easier to discontinue feeding when it proves to be unnecessary than it is to repair damage to grass and cattle resulting from delaying feeding too long.

If no silage is available, it may be necessary to feed some grain to the cows during the summer. If so, only a limited amount of corn should be given, since it is too fattening and tends to produce too much heat. Bran and oats are preferable from the standpoint of the cattle, although the cost of these may prohibit their use. A mixture of 2 parts oats, 1 part bran, and 2 parts ground-ear corn is offered as a suggestion for a summer grain ration. Six to 8 pounds of grain a day will usually be sufficient.

Supplementary Pasture Crops. In view of the fact that pastures frequently become brown and bare toward the end of the grazing season, the far-sighted breeder will take steps to provide forage crops with which he may supplement his regular pastures should a shortage of feed develop. Clovers seeded in early spring in small grain are excellent for this purpose. Red, sweet, and alsike clovers, seeded alone or in simple mixtures, will, except in unusually dry weather, be ready for light pasturing soon after the grain in which they have grown has been harvested. Usually good grazing is furnished by such "stubble pastures" from about the middle of August until the latter part of September. Close grazing of spring-sown clover is inadvisable, as close grazing tends to weaken the young plants, making them very susceptible to winter-killing. As a rule clover pastures should be grazed with extreme caution after the first heavy frost, as frosted clover tends to cause both bloat and excessive scouring in cattle.

Sudan grass, seeded alone or with soybeans, is an excellent pasture crop for late summer and early fall. Sudan grass should be sown, preferably in ploughed and carefully prepared ground, about the middle of

June.   If sown at this date in fertile soil it will be fully knee high and ready to pasture by August 1, which is the approximate date that second-year sweet clover pastures begin to fail.   Thus, Sudan grass is an excellent crop to grow where sweet clover is the principal spring and mid-summer pasture forage.   Should the spring-sown sweet clover prove adequate for the needs of the cattle during the late summer and fall, the Sudan grass may be cut for hay or made into silage.[2]   Sudan grass should not be pastured after it has been severely frosted, as freezing may result in the development of prussic acid in this plant.

Shade and Water.   Ordinarily, too little attention is paid to providing adequate shade and sufficient fresh water for cattle during hot weather.   Many Corn Belt pastures are entirely without shade of any kind, and the cattle are exposed to the heat and glare of the sun throughout the long days of summer.   In the author's opinion, there has been entirely too much clearing of natural wooded areas, with the result that many pastures, formerly covered with fine, native timber, now have scarcely any shade at all.   Fields without sufficient trees, if they are to remain in permanent pastures, should be replanted without delay.   As it is perhaps inadvisable to have trees along the borders of fields that are pastured but once every 4 or 5 years, it will be necessary to erect sun shades in rotated pastures, using posts set firmly in the ground to support an overhead board covering.   Fifteen to 20 square feet of such shade should be allowed for each cow and calf.

Water tanks should be kept filled with good, pure water.   They should be emptied and scrubbed thoroughly at least once a month during warm weather, to prevent the growth of algæ or green "scum."   If the tanks are made of wood, rather than iron or steel, the water will remain much cooler.   With any type, about two-thirds of the tank should be covered, to prevent the sun from striking the surface of the water.

Protection from Flies.   That flies annually cause millions of dollars of loss to cattlemen will hardly be denied.   The horn fly is the principal species that annoy cattle grazing on pasture, and the stable fly is the more troublesome to animals confined in barns and feed lots during the summer months.   Both species are bloodsuckers, and the loss of blood suffered by animals of all ages during a long period of heavy fly infestation constitutes a serious tax upon the herd.   But to this must be added the severe physical torture that the flies inflict, the large amount of energy expended by the cattle in trying to shake off their relentless enemies, and the small amount of grazing done by the harassed cattle in the daytime.   Any one of these alone would pre-

[2] *Cf.* p. 418.

clude normal growth and fattening. When all occur together, stoppage of growth and loss of flesh must result.

Fortunately, cattle may be protected from both horn and stable flies by dipping or spraying the animals with an effective insecticide, such as a solution of chlordane or DDT.[3] The first application should be made in the spring at the same time or soon after the cattle are turned onto pasture, and additional sprayings should be made during the summer at intervals of 4 to 6 weeks. Sheds, barns, and feeding equipment used by the cattle during the summer should also be sprayed with an effective fly-killing agent to destroy house and stable flies which breed in moist straw and manure around the farmstead.

If for any reason spraying is impractical, fairly good protection from flies is afforded by a well-darkened barn, in which the cattle are stabled during the day. At night they are turned out to graze and exercise when the flies cause no annoyance.

Salt. Cattle on grass usually consume a somewhat larger quantity of salt than they do in the dry lot. Apparently, salt is highly necessary in the digestion of green food material. Ordinary "Sunday morning" salting is not sufficient, unless enough salt is given to last the entire week. The practice of keeping block salt constantly before the cattle is strongly recommended. A mature cow requires about 0.1 pound of block salt per day, or 18 pounds during a 6 months' grazing season. About 20 pounds a head should be supplied, as a small amount is dissolved by the rain.[4]

Breeding on Pasture. Cows that are to calve in the springtime must be bred during the early summer months. At this time they are, of course, on pasture, where their heat periods are likely to pass by unobserved. Also, this is the time of year when farmers are very busy with field work, so that the temptation to let a cow "go over" unbred is often strong. For these reasons, it is usually advisable to let the bull run in the pasture with the cows during the breeding season. It is, of course, to be understood that a bull so handled should be sound and mature. Also, the herd should be divided, so that there will not be more than 25 or 30 cows with each bull.

Many breeders of purebred cattle seldom resort to pasture breeding. The importance of knowing the breeding dates and of being absolutely certain which bull has made the service is sufficiently great to make hand mating preferable. There is always considerable risk that a bull running in a pasture may jump a fence and get with cows that are being kept for mating with another bull, or get with heifers that are

[3] *Cf.* p. 621.
[4] *Cf.* p. 460.

too young to be bred.   The man with valuable purebred cattle cannot afford to take such risks.

Creep-Feeding Calves on Pasture.   Whether or not nursing calves should be fed during the summer depends, for grade calves, upon how soon after weaning they are to be sold.   If they are to be sold at weaning time as feeder calves, creep-feeding usually is a highly profitable practice, as the calves are much heavier and also command a

TABLE 49

ADVANTAGE OF FEEDING NURSING SPRING–BORN CALVES*
(Sni-a-Bar Farms — Average of 3 trials)

Lot	1	2	3	4
Method of Feeding	None	Creep-Fed in Pasture	Separated from Mother Fed in Shed	Creep-Fed in Pasture Last Few Weeks only (Aver. 39 days)
Av. Initial Age of Calf	73 days	69 days	71 days	68 days
Av. Initial Weight of Calf	221 lbs.	218 lbs.	217 lbs.	212 lbs.
Av. Final Weight of Calf	490	593	588	522
Av. Daily Gain (161 days)	1.66	2.31	2.29	1.91
Av. Daily Ration:				
Corn	....	2.86	2.88	2.83†
Oats	....	1.25	1.26	1.13†
Linseed meal	....	.37	.36	.56†
Total	....	4.48	4.50	4.52†
Av. Appraised Value per Cwt. when Weaned	$ 9.30	$11.30	$10.90	$9.75
Av. Value per Head when Weaned	$45.14	$68.17	$65.75	$51.14

* U.S.D.A. Technical Bulletin 208, 1930.
† Only for actual time fed.

higher price because of their nice appearance.   However, if the breeder plans to feed the calves himself after weaning and sell them in slaughter condition, creep-feeding usually is not advisable, except for January and February calves which will be sufficiently fat and heavy to be sold in November, December, or January, when prices for slaughter cattle normally are still high.   Calves born after April 1, even though creep fed, will seldom attain satisfactory market weight and condition before March or April of the following year, at which time fat cattle prices are usually much lower than they were in November and December. Obviously, such calves, being far from mature, would continue to make fairly good gains if they were kept on feed 4 or 5 months longer, pending the return of better prices for fat cattle. However, the fact that they were creep fed and were half-fat or better when weaned results in their making slow and expensive gains, if they are fed beyond 14 months of age. A better plan for the farmer who breeds late March and April calves for his own feed lots is not to creep-feed during the nursing period but to full feed in dry lot for 8 or 9 months following weaning, or to winter on a good growing ration and full feed on pasture for 4 months, followed by 2 months in dry lot. With either plan the calves will be in good market condition during the late summer or fall, when prices for fat cattle are usually higher than at any other season of the year.

Purebred calves should always be creep fed if they are running with their mothers on pasture, or they should be fed grain in the barn if they are separated from the cows except at morning and evening, when they are allowed to be with them long enough to nurse. More growth and development is secured from grain fed during the nursing period than can be obtained from it after the calves are weaned. Moreover, creep-feeding insures that the calves will get a good start and will be sufficiently well developed to be sold to other breeders at from 12 to 15 months of age.

When to Begin Creep-Feeding. If full advantage is to be taken of the ability of young calves to make economical gains, creep-feeding should be begun as soon as the calves are old enough to eat, which usually is at about 4 or 5 weeks of age. At any rate, it is highly important that at least the older calves be accustomed to enter a creep to eat while the herd is still in the dry lot. Otherwise, the calves will not enter the pasture creeps readily, and the summer may be half over before they are eating enough grain to make creep-feeding worth while. An excellent example of how not to creep feed calves that are to be fattened for the market is shown in Table 51. These calves weighed 248 pounds on June 28 when creep-feeding was begun; consequently, they must have been approximately 3 months old. Their total grain consumption during the 106 days they were creep fed was only 154 pounds a head, or slightly less than 1.5 pounds per day. This indicates that the calves were very slow in learning to eat, since calves of this age and weight would ordinarily average 5 or 6 pounds of grain per head daily during the entire summer if they were accustomed to eating grain from a creep before they were turned onto pasture. With this larger consumption of grain their gains would have been well over 2 pounds a day instead of only 1.60 pounds, and they would have weighed from 100 to 125 pounds more than the calves that were not creep fed

TABLE 50

EFFECT OF CREEP-FEEDING CALVES*

I. Upon Weaning Weight and Rate of Gain

	Number of Herds	Number of Calves	Days Creep Fed	Corn (bushels)	Protein Concentrate (pounds)	Hay (pounds)	Average Weaning Weight	Average Daily Gain
					Feed per Head			
Creep fed	99	1,780	176	21.6	49	117	619	2.10
Not fed	374	10,362	None	...	...	...	445	1.49[a]

[a] Average daily gain of 1799 calves during the 176 days the creep-fed calves were fed.

II. Upon Rate and Economy of Gains on Full Feed after Weaning

	South Dakota Bulletin 371 (Average of 4 Years)		Oklahoma Bulletin 235 (Average of 4 Years)	
	Creep Fed	Not Fed	Creep Fed	Not Fed
a. Nursing period				
Days fed	158	None	95[a]	None
Total gain, pounds	320.7	248.1	38 more[b]	No report
Weaning weight	496.9	424.4	419.6	384.7
Average daily gain	2.03	1.57	No report	No report
Grain fed per calf	763.4	...	302	...
b. Fattening period				
Days fed	205	218.5	163	163
Total gain, pounds	401.8	463.1	334.4	355.0
Final weight	898.7	895.0	754.0	739.7
Average daily gain	1.96	2.12	2.05	2.18
Feed per cwt. gain				
Concentrate	720	656	596	539
Hay	268	240	148	144
Selling price	$10.35	$10.11	$9.25	$9.15
Dressing percentage	...	..	59.9	58.1
Return over calf cost and feed cost				
1. Nursing period only	$6.06	$3.09	..	...
2. Both periods	$16.95	$20 00	$15.49	$20.19

* Charles R. Kyd, Missouri Extension Service. Information to the author
[a] Average of last 2 years.
[b] Thirty-eight pounds more than the lots not fed.

instead of only 35 pounds more.   (See Table 49.)   It is very doubtful that the labor and expense of creep-feeding is justified if an additional gain of only 35 to 50 pounds per calf is to result from it, unless the calves are to be sold at or soon after weaning.

Equipment for Creep-Feeding. Creep-feeding is likely to be most satisfactory in pastures where there is only one available water supply or only one small group of trees for shade.   If the creep is located near one of these areas where the herd gathers two or three times a day to drink or rest the calves will have ample opportunity to enter the creep and eat. Creep-feeding is seldom successful in large wooded pastures having several springs and streams where the cattle may drink.

TABLE 51

GRAIN CONSUMPTION AND GAINS OF CALVES WHICH WERE NOT CREEP FED UNTIL MID-SUMMER*

Period fed: June 28–October 12, 1935 (106 days)

	No Creep	Creep Fed
Calves per lot	11	11
Initial weight June 28, pounds	263	248
Weaning weight October 12, pounds	398	418
Total gain in 106 days, pounds	135	170
Average daily gain, pounds	1.27	1.60
Oats fed per calf in creep, pounds		154
Average grain per calf daily, pounds		1.4

* Oklahoma Experiment Station, mimeographed report, no date.

If possible, the creep should be built adjacent to or across the route the herd is accustomed to follow in going to its favorite watering place or shade. Since all of the calves will seldom enter the creep at the same time it need not be large enough to accommodate them all, but it should afford facilities for at least half of them to eat together without crowding. If eating is to be permitted from only one side of the feeder the pen should be 10 feet wide, and the feeder should be placed against the other dimension of the inclosure. This will afford sufficient room for calves entering the pen to pass to the rear of those that are already eating. If the calves are to eat at both sides of the feeder the pen should be 16 feet wide, with the feeder located in the center. Openings through which the calves may enter and leave the creep should be made in at least two different places to afford an entrance when one of the openings is blocked by a calf's standing half-way in the pen after he has finished eating. Inclosures around two-sided feeders should be sufficiently long to allow the calves to pass around both ends easily. Three feet on either end is the minimum space necessary, and 4 or 6 feet are to be preferred.

The feeder itself should be a small self-feeder with sufficient bin capacity to hold at least 3 day's feed supply. Feeders either 6, 8, or 10 feet in length are recommended, depending on the number of calves to be fed. A one-sided feeder 6 feet long will accommodate 8 to 10 small calves, while a two-sided feeder 10 feet long will take care of

20 to 30.   A type of calf feeder which has been found satisfactory is shown in Fig. 67.

Feeds for Nursing Calves.   A mixture of ground shelled corn, ground oats, and wheat bran is recommended for calves that are only learning to eat.   However, whole grain is to be preferred, as soon as they are eating nicely, as it feeds down in the feeder better and is not so seriously damaged by damp weather.   Only a little moisture entering the feeder during a heavy rain will cause ground feed to mold and become unpalatable.

A good grain mixture for creep-fed calves is 7 or 8 parts of shelled corn and 1 part of a protein supplement such as linseed or soybean meal.   This ration produced somewhat larger gains than either shelled corn alone or a mixture of 2 parts of shelled corn and 1 part of oats in three tests carried out at the Sni-a-Bar Farm by the United States Department of Agriculture and the Missouri Experiment Station.[5]   However, the gains secured from the three rations were so nearly the same in some of the trials as to make questionable the need for a protein concentrate in the grain ration of nursing calves that are to be fed for 4 or 5 months after they are weaned.   (See Table 52.)   The fact that the calves fed the protein concentrate were valued considerably higher per hundred at weaning time than the other lots emphasizes the desirability of supplying a protein concentrate to nursing purebred calves and to commercial calves that are to be sold at or soon after they are weaned.   Pea-size meal or small pellets are better than a finely ground protein concentrate both because they mix better with shelled corn and whole oats and because they are not so seriously damaged by dampness.

Dry Cows and Two-Year-Old Heifers.   Dry cows and heifers that will not calve during the grazing season require comparatively little attention during the summer.   Ordinarily, the cows with calves are given the best pasture, while the dry cows are required to get along on somewhat less abundant forage.   Also, it is a common practice to take the dry cows to that pasture farthest removed from the farmstead, inasmuch as they do not require the daily attention needed by the unbred cows and those with calves.   Only in case of very dry weather or pronounced overstocking will feed other than grass be necessary.

Summer Management Without Pasture.   That pasture is not absolutely necessary for the well-being of cattle in summer has been proved rather conclusively by Rusk of the Illinois Station, who kept 10 heifers in a small paved lot from the time they were weaned until they were 4½ years old.   This period covered 4 summers, during the last 2 of which the cows were suckling spring-born calves.   During

[5] U. S. D. A. Technical Bulletin 397, 1933.

TABLE 52

COMPARISON OF GRAIN RATIONS FOR NURSING BEEF CALVES

Rations Compared	1st Series Av. of 3 Years*			2nd Series Av. of 2 Years†		
	Shelled Corn	Sh. Corn 8 parts C.S.C. 1 part	Sh. Corn 2 parts Oats 1 part	Sh. Corn 8 parts C.S.C. 1 part	Gr. Corn 8 parts C.S.C. 1 part	Gr. Corn 8 parts C.S.C. 1 part Gr. Alfalfa-Molasses‡
Initial Age.........	79 days	81 days	81 days	77 days	81 days	85 days
Initial Weight......	222 lbs.	221 lbs.	220 lbs.	216 lbs.	217 lbs.	217 lbs.
Final Weight.......	501	522	496	536	529	524
Total Gain.........	280	301	277	320	312	307
Daily Gain.........	2.0	2.15	1.98	2.29	2.23	2.19
Grain Eaten per Cwt Gain............	177	199	251	187	241	233
Final Value per Cwt.	$11.65	$12.10	$11.60	$6.80	$6.80	$6.70
Feed Consumed Daily 1st 28 days.......	.5	.9	1.0	.7	1.4	1.4
2nd 28 days......	1.8	2.8	3.0	1.9	3.7	2.8
3d 28 days.......	4.0	4.7	5.4	4.3	5.7	5.1
4th 28 days..	5.1	5.9	6.9	6.5	6.9	7.1
5th 28 days......	6.3	7.0	8.4	8.0	9.1	9.0
Total, 140 days.....	3.5	4.3	5.0	4.3	5.4	5.1

* U.S.D.A. Technical Bulletin 397, 1933.
† U.S.D.A. Technical Bulletin 564, 1937.

the entire 4 years the cows received nothing except corn silage, supplemented with cottonseed meal at the rate of 2½ pounds of cottonseed meal to 100 pounds of silage. The daily feed of silage for the mature cows was 40 pounds. These cows, kept constantly in the dry lot, maintained their weight nearly as well as other cows that were on pasture each summer, and they produced calves that were in every way normal. The only trouble experienced during the summer was a few cases of foot rot among the calves, caused, no doubt, by the presence of manure on the pavement. These experiments, together with the knowledge we have regarding the wide use made of soiling crops in Europe, prove conclusively that pastures are not indispensable in raising beef cattle. However, the great amount of labor involved in caring for cattle under such conditions precludes any wide use of such methods in this country at the present time.

TABLE 53

YEAR-ROUND FEED SCHEDULE OF BEEF COWS

(Illinois Experiment Station)

An attempt to keep 10 beef cows on the unsalable roughage produced on 40 acres of level land, on which was practiced a rotation of corn, corn, oats seeded with sweet clover, and sweet clover. Feed not furnished by the area shown in bold type. Average of 5 years, 1922 to 1926.

Period	Feed Fed	Total Days	Percentage of Year
May 9–Aug. 15 ..	Second-year sweet clover pasture	98	26.7
Aug. 15–18......	**Bluegrass pasture** (used for 17 days in 1924)	3	.8
Aug. 18–Sept. 23..	Spring-sown sweet clover pasture in oat stubble...........................	36	9.8
Sept. 23–Nov. 18.	**Whole corn silage**	55	**15.0**
Nov. 18–20......	Corn stover silage (used for 10 days in 1926)	2	.5
Nov. 20–Dec. 5..	Corn stalks pasture	15	4.1
Dec. 5–Apr. 25...	Corn stover silage Oat straw 1 lb. prot. conc.	141	38.4
Apr. 25–May 12..	**Whole corn silage and hay**	17	**4.7**

Percentage of total time fed from area 79.5

Typical Feeding Program of Experimental Breeding Cows — 20 cows until Sept. 9; 19 thereafter.

1932–33	Feed Supply per Head	Gain per Head, lbs.
Summer April 20–Sept. 9.. (142 days)	1 acre bluegrass pasture 570 lbs. corn silage	112
Fall Sept. 9–Oct. 13 .. (34 days)	14 lbs. prot. conc. 1 acre meadow aftermath (17 calves weaned Oct. 13	−14
Winter Oct. 13*–Feb. 1.. (111 days)	Av. wt., 365.3 lbs.) 5 acres corn stalk pasture (6 fields pastured consecutively)	66
Feb. 1–April 29 .. (88 days)	Clover hay, 1,226 lbs. Oat straw 760 lbs. Ear corn† 177 lbs. (17 calves born. Av. wt. April 29, 142 lbs.)	−45

Total gain for year... 119

* Corn from first field pastured had been husked early for hogs.
† Ear corn fed April 1–29 after most of calves were born.

The Winter Management of the Breeding Herd

11

Winter is the busy season for the cow man. So long as the weather is warm his worries are few, but with the coming of winter they multiply rapidly. Now his four-footed charges are dependent solely on him for their feed and shelter, and, if he has not made adequate provision for supplying them with both, he will have worries aplenty. Fortunate, indeed, is that cattleman who has literally "made hay while the summer sun shone," and who has repaired sheds, lots, and feed racks during the pleasant days of autumn. For such a man, the sudden coming of a cold, driving rain just before dusk on a late November day has no fears. With a feeling of genuine satisfaction, he opens the barnyard gate before which the wet cattle have gathered and, after a few minutes' work with the pitchfork, goes to his supper, leaving the cows and calves contentedly chewing hay in the dry, well-bedded sheds. Meanwhile, his less provident neighbor has made a fairly good start on a 2 hours' job of fence fixing, after which he must bring in from the pastures some feed bunks that are now badly needed in the sheds. With good luck the cattle may be inside by seven or eight o'clock. Let us hope that they do not have to stand knee-deep in manure left there from the previous winter, as they crowd around the feed racks.

Economy is and should be the principal idea in planning for the winter management of the breeding herd. Economy does not imply a niggardly, stingy attitude on the part of the owner in supplying feed, nor the use of a ramshackle, tumble-down barn for shelter. What it does mean is that the expense of wintering should be no greater than the minimum necessary to insure the cattle a reasonable degree of comfort and to keep them vigorous and healthy. The production of beef calves is often conducted on a narrow margin of profit. At no point of the enterprise is a possible profit so likely to disappear and be replaced by a loss as during the wintering operations. Consequently, it behooves the cattleman to spend some time in thoughtful planning as to the best method of carrying the breeding herd through the winter months.

It is obvious that the management of the breeding herd during any period of the year will depend to a great extent on whether the cows are suckling calves or are dry. In a herd of purebred cattle both spring and fall calves usually are produced, so that there are both milking and dry cows on hand at all times. The breeder of commercial cattle, on the other hand, usually has all his cows freshen at about the same time. Often he will prefer to carry a cow dry an extra 7 months rather than have her calve out of season.

If the herd is of average size, it is better to keep the dry cows separate from those that are suckling calves. Since they require less feed and shelter, they can be handled more economically than the rest of the herd. If facilities are not available to keep them alone, they may be allowed to run with the 2-year-old heifers. In a very small herd, numbering perhaps less than 20 head, it will seldom prove practicable to separate the females of breeding age during the winter. Any advantage that might be gained by such a practice would in all likelihood be overcome by the extra labor involved.

Buildings and Equipment. One of the advantages claimed for the beef cow by her ardent supporters is that she requires a small outlay for shelter and equipment. Expensive barns are by no means necessary. In fact, in some instances they may be a positive disadvantage. Certain it is that from a financial standpoint an investment of much over $100 per cow in buildings and equipment will impose an unnecessary financial burden upon a herd of beef cows that are kept solely to raise calves for the open market. The situation is, of course, quite different with high-priced, registered cattle. But even here the elaborate barns and paddocks so often seen in connection with large purebred establishments are by no means indispensable. In more than one instance large barns have been erected at great cost, only to be discarded later for inexpensive, open sheds in which the cattle seem to do better.

In fact, dry cows prefer to live entirely in the open, if the ground is sufficiently well drained to afford them a reasonably dry area on which to lie and is protected from high winds by hills and trees. Such a place is provided by rolling pastures in which are some sheltered valleys protected by surrounding hills on which are thick stands of timber. Here the cows will spend the entire winter in apparent comfort, even in near-zero weather. However, on few farms are such sheltered areas sufficiently near the feed supply to permit feeding the cattle without considerable labor. Moreover, the manure produced by the cattle thus wintered is largely lost. Consequently, the breeding herd usually is wintered at or near the farmstead, where it may be fed with a minimum of labor and where much of the manure may be saved and returned to the cultivated fields.

A deep shed opening to the south offers ideal sheltering conditions for dry cows. Here the cows may run together in groups of 10 to 50 head each, or, if need be, even larger. When so handled they can be fed with a minimum of labor, as only half as much bedding is required as is necessary where the animals are kept in single stalls. Cows that are approaching parturition and those with very young calves should be kept in box stalls or in sheds occupied by only a few animals. However, after the calves are 10 days old, their mothers may be re-

Fig. 26. "Come and get it!" Feeding hay or corn stover on open fields when the ground is dry or frozen gives the cows needed exercise and deposits the manure where it will benefit next year's pastures and field crops.

turned to the main cow lot, into which the calves are turned twice a day to nurse. In a small herd the calves may be allowed to remain with the cows if a "creep" is erected at one end of the shed, in which a deep, dry bed is provided for the calves. It is also recommended that the open side of this creep be boarded up, so that the calves will be protected from any rain or snow that might come from that direction.

The lots occupied by the cattle need not be large. If possible, it is best to have two lots—a small paved lot adjoining the shed, affording about 50 or 60 square feet of space per cow, and a much larger lot or paddock into which the cattle may be turned for exercise when the ground is dry or frozen. If pasture land or stalk fields are available the larger lot is unnecessary. The small paved lot, however, is almost indispensable during the spring when the ground is soft and muddy. Pavement is much more desirable in the lot just outside the shed than under the shed itself. Not only will it keep the cattle more comfortable and lessen the labor of feeding, but it will repay its cost many times over in the extra amount of manure saved.

The reader is referred to the special chapter on equipment for suggestions regarding feed bunks, hay racks, water tanks, etc. In this connection the author wishes to state that it has been his observation that too little attention is often given to an adequate supply of pure water. Tanks should be kept clean, well filled and free from ice in the winter time. Because of the large amount of dry roughage eaten by cows on maintenance rations, the consumption of water is considerable, even during cold weather. Sometimes it may exceed that drunk during the summer when the cattle are on grass.

Winter Rations for the Breeding Herd. The winter ration of beef cows should consist largely of the common farm roughages. Indeed, it usually will be possible to maintain dry cows satisfactorily during the winter on roughages alone. As such materials should be, and usually are, regarded as by-products of grain production, their value per pound or per ton is low, thus making for economy of maintenance. Even those roughages that meet with a reasonably ready cash sale, such as clover and alfalfa hay, are grown by farmers principally to maintain the nitrogen supply of the soil. Consequently, it is hardly fair to charge such feeds against the cattle at their actual market value. Theoretically, the amount charged against the cattle for a ton of clover hay should be the market value of the hay diminished by the value of the elements of fertility recovered in the manure. While such a method of evaluation may be impractical from the feeder's standpoint, most cattle men will agree that legume hays should be fed on the farm where they are grown, even though their immediate return is somewhat less than the price for which they can be sold.

Corn Silage. In the Corn Belt, where corn can be so successfully grown, corn silage is an excellent winter feed for the breeding herd. Because it is moist and succulent, it tends to stimulate a good flow of milk and to keep the digestive system well regulated, resembling fresh grass in these respects. When made from corn of the type usually grown in the Corn Belt, it combines grain and roughage content in nearly the right proportion for breeding cows. Its high yield per acre enables the farmer with a limited area to winter a considerable number of cattle. Its physical nature makes for ease and cheapness of storage.

However, corn silage is not a well-balanced ration. It is low in protein in comparison with its content of carbohydrates or starchy and fatty compounds. This condition can be remedied easily by using a protein feed along with silage. Cottonseed meal, linseed meal, clover hay, and alfalfa are all rich in protein, and any of them can be used for supplying the nitrogenous material or protein that the animals require. At the Illinois Experiment Station, 10 heifers were carried on silage and cottonseed meal alone from the time they were weaned until they had grown to maturity and produced two crops of calves. Altogether, these cattle received only these two feeds for approximately 4 years. No ill effects of any kind were observed, and the calves produced by the cows appeared strong and vigorous. It is believed, however, that the ration would have been better from the standpoint of the cattle, as well as less expensive, if some dry roughage had replaced part of the silage.

Corn silage because of its corn content is usually considered a higher-cost feed than straw, stover, and other dry roughages which have little cash sale value. Consequently, it usually is fed to grade cows in limited amounts, along with some cheap, dry roughage which is fed according to appetite. Sometimes no corn silage is fed until the cows start to calve, when feeding is begun at the rate of 20 to 30 pounds per head daily. Purebred cows, which are kept in fairly good flesh to enhance the sale value of their offspring, will stay in about the desired condition on 5 to 8 pounds of legume hay and a full feed of corn silage, which for an average size cow is about 40 pounds.

Hay Crop Silage. Silage made from mixed grasses and legumes is even better than corn silage as a winter feed for dry cows. Because of its high protein, vitamin A, and mineral content, it is an ideal source of nutrients for cows during both gestation and lactation. It is sufficiently low in total digestible nutrients to be fed according to appetite, but better results usually will be secured if a small amount of dry roughage is fed to supply variety to the ration. West Virginia Station tests of corn silage and legume grass silage disclosed no significant difference between these feeds for pregnant and lactating beef cows when they were fed in such quantities as would furnish the same amount of dry matter. (See Table 54.) The making of silage from grasses and legumes not needed for pasture during the summer is an excellent way to extend the pasture season, since good-quality hay-crop silage is very similar in physical nature and digestible nutrients to fresh pasture forage. Because of its high protein content, no protein concentrate or legume hay is required; consequently, additional roughage, if fed, may well be straw or corn stover.

Corn Fodder and Corn Stover. On farms that have no silos corn fodder and shock corn are used extensively for wintering cattle, including breeding cows. Sometimes the entire plant (corn fodder) is fed; in others, the ears are husked out by hand, and only the stalks and leaves (corn stover) are fed to the cow herd. These feeds are considerably inferior to silage because they are higher in fiber and lower in protein and vitamin A. Also, approximately 30 per cent of the weight of corn stover is so coarse and unpalatable that it is refused by cows, whereas corn silage is eaten with no appreciable waste.

TABLE 54

COMPARISON OF CORN SILAGE AND LEGUME-GRASS SILAGE FOR
WINTERING BEEF COWS*

	Corn Silage	Legume-Grass Silage
Average initial weight, Dec. 1, 1944, pounds (bred yearling heifers)	807	789
Average final weight, Dec. 1, 1949	1164	1143
Average gain per head	357	354
Average winter ration:		
First winter (yearling heifers)		
Silage, pounds	20	20
Alfalfa hay	6	6
Cracked corn	1	3
Soybean oil meal	.75	...
Average next 4 winters (2- to 5-year-old cows)		
Silage	31.4[a]	27.7[a]
Legume-grass hay	6.5	6.5
Average winter gain (cows plus newborn calves), pounds	94.2	79.8
Average birth weight of calves	66.2	67.3
Average weaning weight of calves (corrected to 180 days of age)	368.5	377.8

* West Virginia Station, Mimeo. Report, 1951.

[a] Silages were fed in such amounts as would furnish equal amounts of dry matter to both groups of cows.

The Illinois Experiment Station once carried three lots of cows through the winter on clover hay and oat straw, plus silage, shock corn, and corn stover, respectively. The results obtained from this test are given in Table 55.

The following comments about the experiment are from Illinois bulletin 111:

As the experiment progressed, even a casual observer could see that the cows in Lots I and II were much more thrifty and in much better spirits than those in Lot III. The staring coats of the cows in Lot III indicated that they were out of condition, while the hair of the cows in Lots I and II was as sleek and glossy as could be desired. . . . The droppings from the corn stover cows were very irregular, especially before the clover was added, it often being the case that from one cow they would be very dry and offensive, while from another cow they might be of such a thin consistency that they could almost be properly designated as scours. This showed that the feed which Lot III was receiving was not ideal for keeping the digestive tract in order.

Although shock corn containing a normal amount of corn is too expensive and corn stover is too low in protein and vitamins to constitute more than approximately half the ration, either may be fed to this extent in combination with other roughages such as oat straw, legume hay, and corn silage. Even though fodder or stover is not a regular item of the ration, an occasional feed is desirable to add variety to the ration. Furthermore the cattle are induced to take exercise if the fod-

TABLE 55

CORN SILAGE, SHOCK CORN, AND CORN STOVER FOR WINTERING BEEF COWS*

140 Days	Lot I Fed Silage	Lot II Fed Shock Corn	Lot III Fed Corn Stover
Average Daily Gain	1.07 lb.	.758 lb.	.41 lb.
Average Daily Ration			
Corn Plant Component	16.65	8.70	13.70
Clover Hay	3.50	3.50	1.56†
Oats Straw (appetite)	9.56	10.83	8.19
Acreage Consumed per Cow during Winter Period:			
Corn Plant Component	.144 acre	.141 acre	.505‡ acre
Clover Hay	.14	.14	.062
Oats Straw	.669‡	.758‡	.573‡
Totals	.953	1.089	1.140

* Illinois Bulletin 111, 1906.
† Average for entire period, although clover hay was added to Lot III 35 days after the beginning of the experiment.
‡ The grain produced in addition to the stover is not here considered.

der or stover is scattered over the frozen ground of a distant pasture. Exercise is especially important for pregnant cows. Cattle that are fed only silage in bunks or hay in racks are disposed to take altogether too little exercise.

Where a considerable amount of corn stover is fed, the common practice is to shred it, rather than to feed it whole. It is generally believed that shredding increases the consumption of this material, since the coarser parts of the stalk are broken up into small pieces. It has also been stated that shredded stover is more digestible than whole stover. Investigations indicate that neither of these opinions is correct. A somewhat extensive study of bulletins reporting the results of feeding trials in which stover was used discloses the fact that shredding has but little effect upon the consumption of stover. Experiments at the

Missouri Experiment Station with yearling stockers indicate that shredding may be detrimental both from the standpoint of the amount consumed and the ability of the cattle to digest it.[1]

Undoubtedly the principal benefit to be derived from shredding is the destruction of corn borers and the greater ease in handling. The practice of feeding whole stover in lots or on pastures can no longer be approved, because of the difficulty of destroying the corn borer larvæ likely to be present in the stalks that are not consumed. It is often difficult to store whole stover in large quantities, with the result that it must be hauled in almost daily from the field. Moreover, whole stover is hard to feed in racks, and the refuse is much less satisfactory for bedding than is the refuse from shredded stover.

Corn Stover Silage. If roughage is so scarce and expensive that it is necessary to utilize the coarser parts of corn stover to satisfy the appetites of cows during the winter, the siloing of stover is preferable to shredding or grinding it. It should be understood, however, that siloing does not make the stover more digestible; it merely renders it more palatable by making the hard, woody stalks soft and succulent. As a result practically all the stover is eaten, whereas approximately 30 per cent of the weight of dry stover is refused. Consequently, a given quantity of corn stover will feed a herd of cows a considerably longer time in the form of stover silage than it would in the form of dry stover. Another advantage of stover silage over dry stover is that its very high moisture content reduces the danger of impaction and other digestive disorders which are sometimes encountered among cows which are fed large quantities of dry corn stover.

Corn that is to be made into stover silage should be cut a little greener than for ordinary shock corn and left in the shock until the ears are dry enough to crib. It should then be hauled to the silo, the ears husked out by hand, and the stover run through a silage cutter and blown into the silo. If a quantity of stover silage is to be made every year the purchase of a combination husker and silo filler will prove a good investment.

An amount of water equal approximately to the weight of air-dry stover siloed must be added if a good quantity of silage is to be obtained. This weight of water is far too great to be blown up the cutter stack along with the dry stover. Instead it must be pumped to the top of the silo and added through the distribution pipe. Care must be taken to distribute the water evenly over the silo. Thorough tramping of the silage is necessary to pack it tightly and exclude all air, which if present will cause the silage to spoil.

[1] Missouri Bulletin 75, 1919.

A special kind of stover silage is "green stover" silage, which is made from the green stalks left in the field after the immature ears have been gathered for "ear corn" silage.[2] This silage is greatly superior to dry stover silage, since it is much lower in fiber and, consequently, is more digestible. Moreover, it can be cut with a binder or field cutter and hauled directly to the silo, thus saving the labor of shocking and rehandling involved in making dry stover silage. Cows will keep in good thrifty condition on 40 to 50 pounds of green stover silage and 4 to 6 pounds of legume hay, or on a full feed of green stover silage, one pound of a protein concentrate, and free access to oat straw.

TABLE 56

GAINS MADE BY DRY BEEF COWS ON CORN-STALK
PASTURES WITHOUT ADDITIONAL FEED

(Unpublished Data, Illinois Station)

Year	Area per Cow	Period Grazed	Days Grazed	Days Grazed per Acre	Change in Weight
1923	1.0	Nov. 24 to Dec. 18	24	24	−59
1924	1.0	Nov. 26 to Dec. 16	20	20	−19
1925	1.0	Nov. 24 to Dec. 15	21	21	−36.5
1926	1.0	Nov. 23 to Dec. 4	11	11	−36
1931	1.6	Oct. 19 to Nov. 14	26	16	37
1935	2.1	Nov. 9 to Dec. 28	49	23	13

Stalk Fields. It is estimated that approximately 80 per cent of the corn in the Corn Belt is harvested for grain and the stalks left standing in the fields. These stalks furnish a considerable amount of pasture for cattle during the late fall and early winter months. Particularly good use can be made of them by breeding cows, since the digestive systems of cows are capable of handling large amounts of coarse roughage. Ordinarily, they may be relied upon to furnish the major part of the sustenance of the breeding herd during the months of November and December. Stalks, however, are very low in protein and are very dry and non-succulent. Consequently they, like corn stover, should be supplemented with some more nutritious, more laxative feed. For this purpose there is nothing better than a good bluegrass or clover pasture, to which the cattle have free access. In the absence of pasture, 4 or 5 pounds of clover or alfalfa hay should be fed daily after most of the ears left by the husker have been eaten and only the dry stover remains.

As a rule, stalk fields have been pretty well picked over by Christmas, so that they are of little value for feed after that time. How-

[2] *Cf.* p. 284.

ever, they still retain considerable value as a means of providing exercise for the cattle. Opportunity should be taken, on days when the ground is frozen and the weather not too blustery, to turn the cows out in the stalks for a few hours. If possible one should reserve a field of stalks close to the barns for this very purpose. However, even in a field of rather cleanly picked stalks, cattle will wander around to a

Fig. 27. Hereford cows gleaning what the corn picker has left. Stalk fields afford a valuable means of inducing cows to exercise on bright winter days. Manure dropped on the fields will benefit cultivated crops.
(*Courtesy Illinois Experiment Station.*)

considerable extent, searching for a stray "nubbin" or a mouthful of undamaged husks.

Straw. Next to corn stover, the straw of small grain crops is the most abundant Corn Belt roughage material. The value of straw for feeding purposes is determined largely by the stage at which the grain is cut and the amount of damage done by rains before and after threshing. Good bright oat straw cut with a binder when a little short of fully ripe and cured in well-constructed shocks has considerable feeding value, ranking only a little below timothy hay in the amount of total digestible nutrients. However, oat straw obtained after a combine is much less valuable than threshed straw because it is cut when it is much riper and consequently is much higher in fiber. Moreover, most of the leaves and chaff, which are the best parts of the straw, are lost during combining and subsequent raking. Straw from barley is of somewhat less value as a feed than oat straw, whereas that from wheat has still less merit. Straw from bearded wheat or barley is, of course, less satisfactory to feed than that made from the smooth varieties. The beards often produce sore mouths in cattle eating such straw. The beards are very sharp and may become imbedded in the gums, where they cause small ulcers.

Although dry breeding cows will practically maintain their weight when given free access to bright oat or headed wheat straw, an exclusive straw ration is not to be recommended. Straw, like stover, is very low in protein and does not supply enough of this nutrient to care properly for the needs of the developing fœtus. Moreover, it is non-laxative and tends to provoke disorders of the digestive tract. When combined with other feeds, such as corn silage, linseed meal, and legume hay, straw is a highly desirable component of a maintenance ration. From the standpoint of cheapness it is practically unexcelled, both because it is to a great extent unmarketable and because little or no labor is expended in preparing it for cattle. For this reason it is usually desirable to feed the breeding herd the maximum amount of straw consistent with the health of the cows and the proper development of the fœtuses. Straw may safely be relied upon to furnish one-half to two-thirds of the total dry matter of the winter ration of dry cows.

Miscellaneous Roughages. Silage and fodder made from the improved forage varieties of *grain sorghums* are fed extensively to beef cows in the western and southern states. Frequently they are grown in the Corn Belt for beef cows and young stocker cattle that are to be carried through the winter. Usually the silage or fodder from a given area of grain sorghum will supply feed for more cattle than that from an equal area of corn because of the greater yield per acre, although it may not produce as much gain because of the lower grain content. However, gain per acre is often of less importance than cow-days-per-acre in evaluating a feed for dry beef cows.

Corn cobs have been used successfully as a source of energy for cows during the winter season. Because of their low palatability and almost complete absence of protein, minerals, and vitamins, they must be fortified with various supplements that will furnish these essential nutrients. Also, the cobs must be finely ground to make them more easily eaten and to facilitate thorough mixing with other feed materials.[3] One part of ground ear corn, 2 parts of ground corn cobs, and 1 part of ground alfalfa hay fed free-choice through a self-feeder should maintain beef cows in satisfactory condition during the winter. If they increase noticeably in weight on this mixture, the amount of ground cobs should be increased. If they eat less than 2 pounds of the mixture per hundred pounds liveweight, about 1 pound of 50 per cent molasses feed per head should be added to the mixture daily.

[3] *Cf.* p. 201.

Legume Hays. No better feed than clover or alfalfa hay could be recommended for breeding cows. However, an exclusive ration of legume hay would be unduly expensive, and for animals in average condition would supply more food nutrients than are actually needed. If enough legume hay is fed to furnish from 20 to 30 per cent of the total dry matter requirement, the remainder being supplied by carbonaceous roughages, the ration will be sufficiently well balanced for dry cows in ordinary condition. Soybean and cowpea hay have practically the same feeding value as alfalfa and red clover. Soybean straw (obtained from threshed beans) is high in crude fiber, as many of the leaves are lost during the process of cutting and threshing. However, it is an excellent feed for breeding cattle, but it must be fed more liberally than soybean hay. It is approximately half as valuable pound for pound.

Lespedeza hay is an excellent feed for cows if it is cut at the proper stage of maturity. If allowed to become too ripe, the stems are very hard and the hay is much less palatable and digestible. The lespedeza straw obtained when the crop is cut and threshed for seed is practically worthless for feeding livestock. Dry cows that were given a full feed of lespedeza straw at the Illinois Station showed a pronounced dislike for it and lost 70 pounds in 60 days, whereas similar cows fed 8 pounds of low-grade alfalfa hay and a full feed of oat straw gained 42 pounds apiece.

Winter Pasture. So far, the discussion of the winter feeding of the breeding herd has dealt almost entirely with the use of harvested feeds. Nevertheless, a majority of the beef cows of the country live almost the year round on grass that they harvest themselves. Also, considerable use is made of grass for winter maintenance in certain areas in the Corn Belt.

Pastures that are intended for winter use should be grazed lightly, or better, not at all, during the summer. This will insure a thick, heavy covering of long grass, capable of furnishing feed for a large number of cattle, at the beginning of winter. Moreover, the heavy growth of grass, now fallen down and thickly matted together, acts as an insulator to the ground, keeping it from thawing and becoming soft at every rise of temperature above the freezing point. Such ground freezes slowly in the fall and stays frozen until late winter or spring. Consequently, it can be used almost daily without serious damage from trampling.

Winter pastures, like stalk fields, are valuable as a means of inducing cattle to take sufficient exercise to keep them vigorous and healthy. No matter how generous the morning and evening rations at the barns, cattle enjoy roaming over a thick growth of cured bluegrass on cold, bright, winter days. If the growth of grass is particularly heavy, dry cows and mature heifers may require no extra feed. However, on most Corn Belt farms the amount of such pasture will be limited, if, indeed, any is present at all. It is recommended that on all livestock farms at least 10 acres of pasture be set aside each summer for winter use. Even this small area will furnish a considerable number of cattle an opportunity to take exercise and will lend variety to their ration on one or two days each week.

Use of Concentrates. Whether the cows of the breeding herd will require any concentrates during the winter months will depend upon three things:

1. The amount and type of roughage given.
2. The condition of the cattle.
3. Whether or not they are suckling calves.

Dry cows in ordinary flesh will need grain during the winter only if the supply of roughage is such that it must be fed in limited quantities, or if the roughage used is of poor quality and low feeding value. The use of only carbonaceous roughages, such as straw and silage, will, of course, require the addition of a nitrogenous concentrate to supply the necessary protein. Ordinarily, the feeding of ½ to 1½ pounds of cottonseed or linseed meal per head daily will take care of the protein requirement. When 4 or more pounds of legume hay are fed, nitrogenous concentrates are not usually needed.

Carbonaceous concentrates are recommended only when it is evident that the cattle will not maintain their weight and condition on the roughage that is available. In this connection it should be kept in mind that it requires much less feed to keep cattle from losing flesh than it does to restore them to the proper condition after they have become thin. Hence, it is good economy to introduce a little grain into the ration as soon as the cattle begin to show signs of malnutrition. Corn, oats, and barley are of approximately equal value for this purpose, since the somewhat higher fiber content of oats and barley is largely offset by their higher percentage of protein. However, the addition of any of the common cereal grains does not lessen materially the need for a nitrogenous concentrate if all the roughage is non-leguminous.

Not all cows suckling calves will need to be fed grain. However, a majority of cows of beef breeding will give comparatively little milk on dry roughage alone, especially if the roughage is of low quality. Whether a larger milk flow is of enough value to justify the feeding of grain will usually depend upon the disposition that is to be made of the calves. If the calves are to be fattened for baby beeves, the cows probably should be fed a little grain if they calve more than a month before they will be turned onto pasture. Cows that calve in the fall usually should be fed 4 to 6 pounds of grain daily during the winter to stimulate a good flow of milk for their calves. The feeding of grain to nursing cows is seldom necessary if corn or grass silage is fed, since silage-fed cows usually give plenty of milk.

Purebred breeders will usually find it to their advantage to feed some grain to their cows during the winter months. Such men should realize that the condition and general appearance of their breeding animals are of great weight in favorably impressing prospective purchasers. Animals in thin condition or showing signs of unthriftiness should be put on a good grain ration and given the best of care until they are restored to good flesh and health. A certain percentage of the feed consumed by a herd of purebred cattle, above that needed to maintain good health and vigor, should be charged rightly to advertising costs. Certain it is that no more effective means of advertising can be found than thick-fleshed, well-conditioned animals, regardless of the season of the year.

An additional reason for feeding some grain to purebred cows is that it causes them to maintain a heavy flow of milk for as long a period as possible. With purebred calves an abundance of milk is almost indispensable, if the maximum amount of growth and development is to be realized. And any purebred breeder who is content with anything short of the maximum should get out of the purebred business and confine his efforts to raising grade animals for the feed lot.

Computing Winter Rations for Beef Cows. Every animal should be fed a ration which provides the kinds and amounts of nutrients it needs and which also is sufficiently bulky to satisfy its appetite reasonably well. Otherwise, the animal will be on its feet most of the time, anxiously awaiting the next feeding. In group feeding at least one item of the ration should be fed according to appetite, in order that those animals that eat slowly may get all they want to eat. With beef cows this item usually is corn stover, oat straw, or some other low-grade roughage which is fed more as a "filler" than as a source of important feed nutrients. Although cattle vary somewhat in their digestive capacity and will, of course, eat larger amounts of highly palatable feeds than of coarse, low-grade feeding stuffs, a fairly accurate rule to use in estimating the total air-dry feed requirements of beef cows is that the total air-dry weight of the ration should be from 1¾ to 2¼ per cent of their live weight, depending upon their condition of flesh. However, this rule takes no account of any protein concentrate that may be fed, since the addition of 1 or 2 pounds of such feed per head will not diminish the consumption of other items of the ration. The amount of air-dry feed required daily by dry beef cows may be estimated as approximately 2 per cent of the live weight of cows in average flesh, $2\frac{1}{4}$ per cent of the weight of thin cows, and $1\frac{3}{4}$ per cent of the live weight of cows that are in good condition and consequently are unusually heavy in relation to their digestive capacity.

Farm grains and dry roughages as ordinarily fed are assumed to be in an air-dry condition, and their actual weights are used without correction. The weight of silage, however, must be reduced to an air-dry basis by multiplying the moist weight by 35, 40, or 45 per cent, depending upon whether the silage is high, medium, or low in moisture. In the absence of information to the contrary, the moisture content of silage is assumed to be average, and its weight is multiplied by 0.40 to convert it to an air-dry basis.

Although the bulk of a ration is important, it is secondary to the kinds and amounts of nutrients supplied. The two factors to which most attention should be given are protein and energy. Since beef cows are usually dry during most of the winter and the needs of the developing fœtuses are relatively low,[4] they require only a little more protein and energy than are needed for maintenance. The protein requirement of dry cows will usually be met by feeding at least 4 pounds of good-quality legume hay or 1 pound of protein concentrate per head daily. Except for unusually thin cows, the energy requirements will be satisfied by supplying as much net energy as would be furnished by a weight of legume hay equal to 1.5, 1.75, or 2.0 per cent of their live weight, depending upon whether they are in good, average, or thin condition. Since it is seldom advisable to feed such a large amount of legume hay to beef cows, the legume hay-energy equivalents (LHEE) of other common feeds have been calculated on the basis of their net energy content. The legume hay-energy equivalents of the feeds commonly fed to dry beef cows, stated in terms of 5 pounds of legume hay in order to avoid the use of fractions, are given in Table 57. An example of how they are used in calculating the feed requirements of a herd of beef cows is given in Table 58.

Unless the cows are in better-than-average condition at the time of parturition their ration should be increased noticeably after calving, especially if they will not be turned onto pasture for 4 to 6 weeks. Cows suckling calves should receive a minimum of 6 pounds of legume hay or 1.5 pounds of protein concentrate per head and approximately 0.25 pound more legume hay-energy equivalent per 100 pounds live

[4] *Cf.* p. 90.

TABLE 57

LEGUME HAY-ENERGY EQUIVALENT OF FEEDS USUALLY USED IN
WINTERING BEEF COWS

Feeds	Approximate Net Energy per 100 Pounds (Therms)[a]	Weight of Feed Having Approximately the Same Net Energy as 5 Pounds of Legume Hay (LHEE)
1. Legume hay: alfalfa, clover, lespedeza	42	5
2. Non-legume hay: timothy, brome, prairie	37	6
3. Corn stover (portion eaten)[b]	35	6
4. Oat straw	23	9
5. Wheat straw	10	20
6. Corn silage	20	10
7. Grain sorghum silage	15	13
8. Legume and grass silage	14	15
9. Ear corn, corn and cob meal	70	3
10. Oats	72	3
11. Shelled corn, barley, grain sorghum	80	2.5
12. Protein concentrates, cottonseed meal, linseed meal, soybean meal	78	2.5

[a] Morrison, F. B., Feeds and Feeding, 21st ed., 1948.
[b] Approximately 70 per cent of corn stover fed to beef cows and stocker cattle is eaten.

TABLE 58

USE OF LHEE IN CALCULATING RATION FOR BEEF COWS

1. Before calving
   20 cows × 1100 pounds = 22,000 pounds
   (average condition)

	ADF:	LHEE:	Minimum Protein:
Required:	2% of Live Weight (440 pounds)	1.75% of Live Weight (385 pounds)	4 pounds of Legume Hay per Day (80 pounds)
Supplied:			
100 pounds clover hay	100	100	100
500 pounds corn stover (70% edible)	340	283	. . .
Total	440	383	100

2. After calving
   20 cows × 1000 pounds = 20,000 pounds
   (thin condition)

	ADF:	LHEE:	Minimum Protein:
Required:	2.25% of Live Weight (450 pounds)	2.25% of Live Weight* (450 pounds)	6 pounds of Legume Hay per Day (120 pounds)
Supplied:			
150 pounds clover hay	150	150	150
500 pounds corn silage	200	250	. . .
100 pounds oat straw	100	55	. . .
Total	450	455	150

* Requirements for thin dry cows plus 0.25 per cent of live weight because they are suckling calves.

TABLE 59

METHOD OF CALCULATING WINTER RATIONS FOR BEEF COWS BY USING "LEGUME HAY ENERGY EQUIVALENTS"

Initial Weight of Cows (pounds)	Condition of Flesh	Recommended Air-Dry Feed per 100 Pounds Live Weight (pounds)	Calculated Air-Dry Feed Required (pounds)	Recommended LHEE per 100 Pounds Live Weight (pounds)	Calculated LHEE Required (pounds)	Recommended Ration	Air-Dry Feed Furnished	LHEE Supplied
950	Average	2.0	19	1.75	16.6	5 lb. alfalfa hay 15 lb. corn silage 8 lb. oat straw	5.0 6.0 8.0 19.0	5.0 7.5 4.4 16.9
1200	Good	1.75	21	1.50	18	14 lb. clover hay 7 lb. oat straw	14.0 7.0 21.0	14.0 4.0 18.0
900	Thin	2.25	20.2	2.00	18	8 lb. alfalfa hay 9 lb. oat straw 3 lb. ear corn	8.0 9.0 3.0 20.0	8.0 5.0 5.0 18.0
1100	Average	2.0	22	1.75	19.3	8 lb. clover hay 20 lb. corn stover	8.0 14.0 22.0	8.0 11.7 19.7

TABLE 60

An Analysis of Some Winter Rations of Beef Cows to Determine Their Merits and Shortcomings

Station	Initial Weight of Cows (pounds)	Average Daily Ration	Average Dry Feed Supplied per 100 Pounds Live Weight (pounds)	LHEE Supplied per 100 Pounds Live Weight	Protein Concentrate Equivalent per Head (pounds)	Gains or Loss in Weight During Winter (pounds)	Remarks
Illinois (unpublished)	1072	5 lb. alfalfa hay; 15.8 lb. oat straw	1.9	1.3	1.2	−136[a]	Bulk and protein satisfactory, but insufficient energy supplied.
Illinois (unpublished)	1042	1 lb. CSM; 40 lb. corn silage	1.5	2.1	1.0	+1.0[a]	Insufficient bulk. Cows constantly hungry and restless. Unduly expensive.
Kansas (Ft. Hays Report, 1917)	962	11.3 alfalfa hay; 9.0 oat straw; 15 sorgo silage	2.6	2.3	2.8	+121	More feed than cows needed. Some probably wasted. Gains too large unless cows were thin.
Kansas (Ft. Hays Report, 1920)	1021	2 lb. CSM; 11.6 lb. straw; 30.0 cane silage	2.3	2.1	2.0	+64	Very satisfactory. A little more CSM was fed than needed.
Montana (Bulletin 187)	1021	29.7 lb. corn silage; 8.2 lb. straw	1.9	1.9	None	+30	Bulk and energy satisfactory. Too little protein supplied.

[a] Final weights taken after calving.

weight daily than would be required by dry cows of the same weight and condition of flesh. Table 58 shows how the requirements of a herd of 20 cows would be met before and after calving.

Emergency Winter Rations for Beef Cows. Many of the combinations that have been fed to breeding cows in feeding experiments are of more value to the practical cattleman as emergency rations than as regular rations for the reason that beef cows can stand a great deal of punishment from underfeeding or improperly balanced rations for a winter or two without serious damage either to themselves or the calves which they carry *in utero*. The fact that beef cows spend one-half to two-thirds of the year on green pastures which provide an abundance of protein, vitamins, and minerals makes it possible for them to store enough of these materials in their bodies during the summer to last them during a winter when a ration far short of their needs is supplied. Apparently the deficiencies that arise from improper winter rations are soon corrected when the cows are given access to green pastures in the spring. However, the fact that a herd of cows was able to live through a single winter and produce healthy calves on a sub-maintenance ration is not proof that such a ration will be either adequate or profitable for a herd year after year. At best such a ration can be recommended only in an emergency when feeds adequate for the needs of the herd are not available. Some examples of emergency rations are given in Table 61.

Winter Gains of Beef Cows. The amount of gain a cow should make during the winter depends upon her condition at the beginning of the winter period. Cows in ordinary flesh should gain at least as much as will be represented by the increased weight of the foetus, membranes, and fluids with the advance of gestation. This may be estimated to be approximately 60 pounds from the fifth to the ninth month of pregnancy. Consequently, cows should gain at the rate of approximately one-half pound a day if they are to carry the same amount of flesh at the time of calving as they did at the beginning of winter. Cows that are very thin should be fed sufficiently well to gain from 100 to 150 pounds during the winter or enough to offset the loss they will sustain during calving. On the other hand, fleshy cows may have their ration restricted to the point where they will show no gain at all or even a small loss in weight up to the date of calving. Experiments at the Montana Station emphasize that cows should be in sufficiently good flesh and thrift at the time of calving to permit them to nourish their calves properly. However, for cows in fair condition at the beginning of winter a total gain of about 75 pounds a head appears to be

TABLE 61

WINTER RATIONS FOR BEEF COWS

Average Daily Ration	Adequate Rations*(Recommended)			Inadequate Rations†(Recommended only in an emergency)		
	Ration 1	Ration 2	Ration 3	Ration 1	Ration 2	Ration 3
Days Fed................	120	114	168	120	118	116
Initial Weight, lbs.......	956	972	1222	1023	1041	1209
Final Weight, lbs........	1047	1084	1284[b]	1020	1061	1234
Total Gain, lbs...........	91	112	62[b]	3	20	25
Estimated Gain of Foetus and Fluids[c]...........	70	70	70	70	70	70
Net Gain in Body Weight.	21	42	−8[b]	−67	−50	−45
Source of Data..........	Kansas Circular, Ft. Hays, 1917	Montana Bull. No. 187	Ohio Bi-monthly Bull. No. 83 and 84	Kansas Circular, Ft. Hays, 1921	Montana Bulletin No. 275	Illinois Exp. Sta. Unpub. Data

* Ration 1 —
　Alfalfa hay, 11 lbs.
　Wheat straw, 9 lbs.
　Cane silage, 15 lbs.

Ration 2 —
　Corn silage, 22 lbs.
　Alfalfa hay, 4.6 lbs.
　Oat straw, 9 lbs.

Ration 3 —
　Dry stover full feed, 11 lbs.[a]
　Oat straw, full feed, 3.5 lbs.
　Ground corn, 3.6 lbs.
　Cottonseed meal, 1.0 lb.

† Ration 1 —
　Headed wheat straw, 25.5 lbs.

Ration 2 —
　Corn fodder, 13 lbs.
　Oat straw, 9 lbs.

Ration 3 —
　Stover silage, 53 lbs.
　Oat straw, 5 lbs.
　Soybean meal, 1 lb.

[a] Probably the amount actually consumed.
[b] Applying daily gains made by 4 calving cows up to date of calving to the whole period.
[c] Assuming that fœtus and fluids weigh 30 lbs. at beginning of winter and 100 lbs. at end of winter.

as satisfactory as twice this amount, from the standpoint of both the cow herself and her calf at either birth or weaning time.

The approximate daily change in weight of a dry, pregnant cow may be estimated rather closely by, first, calculating the increase in weight of flesh due to the amount of legume hay-energy equivalent she consumes in excess of her maintenance requirements and, second, estimating the daily increase in weight of the developing fœtus, membranes, and fluids. Since 1 pound of flesh (principally fat) made by mature cows represents approximately 2 Therms of net energy and 1 pound of legume hay has a net energy value of 0.4 Therm, 0.2 pound of gain in body weight may be assumed for each pound of legume hay or its energy equivalent eaten over and above that required to maintain her

TABLE 62

EFFECT OF WINTER GAINS OF COWS UPON WEIGHTS OF CALVES*

I. High-protein Rations vs. Low-protein Rations

Rations	Number of Cows	Av. Winter Gain (lbs.)	Calves at Weaning	
			Av. Weight (lbs.)	Av. Age (days)
Low-protein Rations: (Combination of corn fodder, corn silage, and straw, or fed alone)	106	54.2	378.3	163
High-protein Rations: (Addition of cottonseed cake and/or alfalfa to above rations)	97	92.7	377.1	162

II. High, Medium, and Low Winter Gains

	Number of Cows	Av. Winter Gain (lbs.)	Calves at Weaning	
			Av. Weight (lbs.)	Av. Age (days)
8 high winter gaining lots.	62	110.4	348.4	161.0
8 medium winter gaining lots.	50	66.9	370.2	162.3
8 low winter gaining lots.	61	21.2	362.4	160.1

III. Winter Gains vs. Winter Losses of Cows

	Cows			Calves		
	Av. Winter Gain (lbs.)	Av. Wt. at end of Winter (lbs.)	Av. Wt. after Calving (lbs.)	Av. Birth Weight (lbs.)	Av. Weaning Weight (lbs.)	Av. Age at Weaning (days)
11 highest winter gaining cows.	42.6	1,064.4	844.2	65.6	379.1	170.7
11 lowest winter gaining cows.	−62.7	981.3	781.3	64.6	326.9	177.1

* Montana Special Circular 7 (An. Husb.) 1930.

weight and provide for the needs of the fœtus. The approximate weight of the uterus and its contents may be estimated for any month of gestation by the formula $M(M + 1) = W$, where M is time in months which has elapsed since conception and W is the total weight of the uterus and contents. For example, the increase in weight due to the growth of the fœtus between the fourth and eighth month of pregnancy will be $8(8 + 1) - 4(4 + 1) = 72 - 20 = 52$ pounds, or approximately 0.4 pound per day.

Fig. 28. Solid comfort! A pile of straw on the south side of the barn affords an ideal "sun parlor" for young calves.

Winter Care of Nursing Calves. As a rule, small calves should not be permitted to run with their dams during the winter months. Separation of cow and calf, except at nursing time, results in economy of equipment, feed, and bedding, and prevents numerous cases of chapped and cracked teats during cold, freezing weather. Cows that are kept away from their calves require much less shed room than would be needed if all ran together. Also, they are able to get along in a much less expensive shed than would be necessary to furnish adequate protection for the calves. Most important of all, the best morsels of feed and the driest forkfuls of bedding can be supplied the calves only if they are kept separated from their dams.

If it is impractical to separate the calves from the cow herd, they should at least be provided with a well-bedded creep in one corner of the shed where they can lie in comfort without being disturbed and where they may learn to eat grain, if they are to be creep-fed during the summer while running with their mothers on pasture.

Frequent nursing on the part of the calf in cold weather is likely to cause the udder of the cow to become chapped and sore. It sometimes happens that a quarter will become so sore that the cow will refuse to allow her calf to suck it. Unless this is noticed and promptly attended to, the quarter will become dry and the calf will get less milk.

TABLE 63

ADVANTAGE OF FEEDING GRAIN TO SUCKLING FALL CALVES*
(Sni-a-Bar Farms, Grain Valley, Missouri — Average of 3 trials)

Lot	1	2	3
Method of Feeding	With Mothers, No Feed	With Mothers, Creep-Fed	Separated from Mothers; Fed in Shed
Av. Initial weight	186 lbs.	186 lbs.	184 lbs.
Av. Final weight	453	562	582
Total gain	267	376	398
Av. Daily Gain	1.44	2.04	2.17
Av. daily ration:			
Shelled corn	....	2.96	3.44
Oats	....	1.38	1.60
Linseed meal	....	.23	.29
Alfalfa hay	....	.51	.65
Av. Feed cost per head	....	$14.47	$17.05
Value per cwt. about June 1	$11.35	12.90	12.85
Value per head about June 1	49.41	70.53	72.52
Value per head above feed eaten	49.41	56.05	55.47

* U.S.D.A. and Missouri Experiment Station Mimeo. Reports.

Young calves should have as much sunlight as possible during the winter months. It is highly desirable that their "boxes" be on the south side of the barn and be well supplied with windows to admit the light. Except on bad, stormy days, the calves should be turned out in a dry lot, well protected from the north and west winds, where they may sun themselves and get much-needed exercise.

As has been stated in a previous chapter, calves will begin to eat grain at about 3 or 4 weeks of age. Purebred calves and those intended for baby beef production should be taught to eat as soon as possible. The grain feeding of young calves is much more important during the winter than during the summer period, inasmuch as the roughages fed during the winter are usually coarse and unpalatable compared with the fresh, green grass of summer. Even fall and early winter calves that are to be carried on pasture without grain after weaning should be fed at least a light grain ration.

Winter Management of Bulls. The winter months are the proper time to condition bulls for the breeding season of the following year. Bulls that have been running out on pasture with the breeding herd are likely to be thin and should have sufficient grain to put them in proper flesh before the arrival of spring. Young bulls should be fed more liberally than old, mature animals, as their growth requirements must be met before any improvement in condition can take place. A grain mixture composed largely of feeding stuffs that are growth-producing rather than fattening will be found best for bulls. Equal parts by measure of crushed oats and bran make a good basal ration, to which corn may be added only if a marked improvement in flesh is desired. Animals that are in a run-down condition or that show signs of lack of thrift should have from 2 to 4 pounds of linseed meal or other protein concentrate per day, depending on age and weight. Mature bulls, already carrying sufficient flesh, may be wintered largely on choice roughages such as legume hay and silage.

Bulls can be kept strong and vigorous during the winter only if they be given sufficient exercise as well as plenty of feed. To accomplish this they should have the run of good-sized lots, or better yet, be turned with a few pregnant cows into a bluegrass pasture or stalk field whenever the weather will permit. Where two or more bulls are kept, it is highly desirable to run them together, as they will take more exercise when together than when alone. Although the turning together of old bulls that are strangers to each other is attended with some risk, a young bull may be put with an older one with comparative safety.

The importance of having bulls in the pink of condition at the opening of the breeding season can scarcely be overemphasized. Valuable time is often lost by the use of a bull with impaired breeding powers. A small calf crop, with many of the calves coming late, is the disheartening experience that is sure to follow. Western ranchers realize, perhaps better than Corn Belt cattlemen, the importance of conditioning their bulls previous to the breeding season. That they are well repaid for their pains is shown by the data gathered on 15 ranches in northern Texas by Parr and Kelmmedson over a 3-year period. "On 10 of the 15 ranches the bulls were taken out of the cow herds in the fall for conditioning and were returned to the cow herds around June 1 of the following year. On the other 5 ranches the bulls were kept with the cows during the entire year. The ranches on which the bulls were removed from the cow herds had a 77 per cent average calf crop for the three years, and on the ranches where the bulls were not removed the average calf crop was 64 per cent for the same time."[5]

While the better feed conditions prevalent in the central states make conditioning of bulls less urgent than on the range, more attention to this point on the part of Corn Belt breeders will result in a material decrease in the number of cows that fail to raise calves through no fault of their own.

[5] Parr and Kelmmedson, An Economic Study of the Costs and Methods of Range Cattle Production, U. S. D. A. Mimeograph Report, April 1, 1924.

12 — Weaning, Dehorning, Castration, and Marking of Calves

Beef calves ordinarily are weaned at 6 to 8 months of age. Usually the date is determined largely by necessary changes in the management of the herd. Spring-born calves are generally weaned about the first of November, when the herd is removed from grass; while fall calves are weaned in the spring when the cow herd is taken to some outlying pasture. Fall-born calves are often allowed to nurse until mid-summer, since green pasture will cause cows to increase greatly their production of milk if they are still being suckled when they are changed from dry lot to pasture.

Calves that have been running with their dams should be removed from them once and for all. If they can be placed beyond even the sound of the cows, so much the better. The practice of turning them back on the second or third day to suck out the cows cannot be recommended, as it will tend to prolong the period during which they pine for their mothers and may give rise to digestive disorders caused by the stale milk. After weaning, the udders of the cows should be examined every few days to make sure that those showing signs of inflammation are given prompt attention. Cows that are to be dried up should not be milked dry, but only enough milk should be withdrawn to relieve any undue congestion.

DEHORNING

Although a nicely shaped pair of horns undoubtedly adds to the appearance of an animal of the horned breeds in the show ring or pure-bred herd, the presence of horns on commercial cattle is considered very objectionable. Horns are the cause of so much loss to the large slaughtering establishments in damaged hides and bruised carcasses that polled or dehorned cattle normally sell from $1 to $2 per hundred-weight higher than horned cattle of equal merit in other respects. This is particularly true when the animals have been shipped some distance and have been in crowded cars for several hours. Horns are also

objectionable on the farm and in the feed lot. Cattle with horns require more shed room per animal, as well as more space at the feed
trough and hay rack. Among horned cattle there is always a tendency
for some to be "bossy" and to keep the timid ones away from their
share of shelter and feed. Dehorning tends to curb the aggressiveness
of such animals, thus lessening feed-lot disturbances of this sort.

Although, ordinarily, few beef cattle exhibit a vicious disposition
toward men, an occasional animal of this nature is encountered. Bulls,
of course, are more likely to be unruly than cows, although cows may
prove dangerous, particularly when strangers approach their young
calves. Any horned animal of either sex that shows any inclination
to attack a man should be dehorned immediately. Not only will the

Fig. 29. Polled bulls are effective dehorners. Many purebred polled bulls will
produce polled calves even when mated with horned cows.

removal of the horns lessen the actual harm done in an attack, but also
the act of dehorning itself tends to lessen the likelihood of an attack's
being made. Animals that were really vicious before dehorning have
often proved to be quiet and docile afterwards.

The presence of horns on even the most gentle cow is sometimes the
cause of a serious injury. A horned cow fighting flies may injure other
cattle, or her owner, by an accidental toss of her head. The haltering
and tying of horned cows, especially in small stalls, is always accompanied by a certain element of danger.

Methods of Dehorning: Breeding. The use of a polled bull will
result in a majority of hornless calves. If such a bull is a "pure"
polled, carrying in his germ plasm no factor for producing horns, all
his calves will be polled, even though all their dams have horns.
If, however, the bull is an impure polled, the product, let us say, of
mating a pure polled bull with a horned cow, only half his calves from

horned cows will in the long run be polled, and the rest will have horns. Thus, we see why it is that Aberdeen-Angus bulls (which are almost invariably "pure" polled) seldom sire any but polled calves, whereas some polled bulls of the other two important beef breeds often beget a number of horned offspring.

Although the removal of horns through the use of polled bulls is accomplished without labor to the owner or pain to the calves, the general employment of this method is wholly impracticable, because the supply of good polled bulls is very limited. In many sections of the country they are quite unavailable. Consequently, if many farmers should attempt to employ this method of eliminating horns, a considerable number would be compelled to replace good horned bulls with relatively inferior polled individuals. Other men, who have developed a purebred herd of a particular line of breeding, hesitate about introducing a polled bull of totally unrelated blood. However, these disadvantages will tend to disappear whenever polled animals of all beef breeds become sufficiently numerous to offer farmers in every state a wide range of selection. But until this time arrives a majority of the cattlemen of the country will have to employ other means for the removal of the horns.

Use of Chemicals. A very satisfactory way to prevent the growth of horns in new-born calves is to burn the embryo horn with a strong chemical. This is best done when the calf is from 3 to 10 days old. The agent most commonly used is caustic potash (potassium hydroxide), although caustic soda (sodium hydroxide) is equally effective. Either of these chemicals may be purchased in the form of pastes, liquids, or slim sticks which are about the size and appearance of blackboard crayons. Care should be exercised in using caustics, as they will cause serious burns if they come in contact with the hands of the operator. While in use, the stick should be wrapped with a piece of heavy paper held in place with a rubber band. The paper will afford protection to the hands as well as prevent the absorption of moisture from the air. When not actually in use, stick caustic should be kept in a tightly closed bottle, as a few hours' contact with moist air will cause it to melt and dissolve.

In removing horns with caustic one should proceed somewhat as follows: With a pair of hand clippers or ordinary scissors, clip away the hair as closely as possible immediately over the budding horn, so as to expose clearly its outline. While not absolutely necessary, it is a good plan, after the clipping has been done, to wash each clipped area with soap and water to remove any dirt that may cover the skin. Next, *slightly* moisten one end of a stick of caustic by dipping just the exposed tip in a cup of water (not touching to the lips or tongue), and rub it lightly with a rotary motion on each horn button. If the paste or liquid is used a thin coating of caustic should be applied with the dauber or applicator to each horn area. Care should be taken not to apply too much, as it may spread to the skin surrounding the horn, causing serious burns. Inexperienced operators should guard against such an accident by applying a thin coating of vaseline or lard to the surrounding skin, leaving only the horn button exposed.

The effect of the caustic is to deaden the matrix or root of the horn. In a few days, a scab appears over each horn button; this soon drops off, leaving a smooth spot of skin devoid of hair, no larger than a quarter. Even these spots are soon hidden by the growth of the adjacent hair, so that no trace of the operation is apparent.

Since the use of caustic, to be successful, should be made before the calf is 2 weeks old, this method of dehorning is attended with much labor where the calves are born on pasture. Consequently, we find it employed mainly on small farms where the calves are not numerous and can be caught and treated with but little trouble and labor.

The Electrical Dehorner. An electric dehorning iron is sometimes used instead of a chemical for dehorning young calves on farms where electricity is available. After the iron has been heated to the proper temperature, it is fitted over the horn button and held firmly against the head until the matrix has been destroyed. Considerable care must be exercised to make the burn deep enough to destroy the horn tissue but not so deep as to produce a bad sore. The operation is much more painful and requires more time than chemicals. However, it may be used to dehorn calves up to 2 months of age.

Dehorning Older Cattle. In large herds of commercial cattle, especially in the Range area where the cows and calves are dispersed over a wide area, dehorning is usually postponed until the calving season is practically over, in order that all calves may be dehorned, castrated, and branded with but one working of the herd. At this time the horn buttons of most of the calves are well developed but are still so soft and loosely attached to the skin as to be easily removed with a knife-like dehorning tool which separates the horn button from the adjoining skin with but little or no loss of blood. Such tools are called "gougers," "spoons" and "tubes," depending upon their shape and the way in which they are used. (See Fig. 30, *a* and *b*.)

Calves that are not dehorned under 3 months of age usually are allowed to retain their horns until late in the fall after they are weaned or until the following spring when they are approaching 1 year of age. The younger the animal when dehorned the better, since the horns are softer and can be removed with less shock than is suffered by older animals. Moreover, the labor required to restrain young animals is

less, and their horns are severed much more easily and quickly.   Either
a dehorning saw or some type of dehorning clippers is used in dehorning cattle more than 4 months of age.   (See Fig. 30, c and d.)

Equipment for Dehorning.   For dehorning calves, not much equipment is necessary.   Often they are simply snubbed to a fence post and
held firmly against the fence by an attendant while the operator cuts
off the exposed horn.   After the removal of one horn, the calf is reversed with the other side against the fence, and the other horn re-

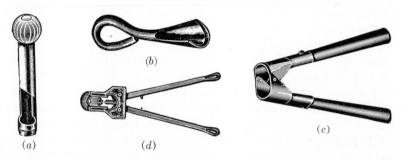

Fig. 30.   Dehorning tools, in the order of age of calves for which they are best
suited.   (a) dehorning tube, 1 to 3 months; (b) dehorning spoon, 3 to 5 months;
(c) Barnes dehorners, 5 to 12 months; (d) Leavitt clippers, 12 to 20 months;
(e) dehorning saw (not shown), over 20 months. (*Courtesy O. M. Franklin
Serum Company, Denver, Colorado.*)

moved.   However, if calves are to be dehorned year after year, it is
highly advisable to construct a regular dehorning chute such as is
recommended for older cattle in the following paragraph.

For yearlings and older cattle, some special means of restraint are
necessary, especially if the number of animals to be dehorned is large.
Various types of dehorning chutes, pinch gates, squeeze pens, and cattle
stocks have been devised, all of which are designed to secure the animal
while an operation is being performed.   Some of them are more suited
for dehorning than are others, because of the rapidity with which cattle
may be driven in and let out—a highly desirable feature when a large
number of animals are to be treated.   (See Fig. 98.)

Sawing vs. Clipping.   In former years the saw was almost universally used in dehorning cattle.   Lately, however, it has been largely
superseded by various forms of shears or clippers.   The principal
advantages of the saw are as follows:

1. There is no danger of crushing the horn as is sometimes done
   with clippers.

2. The action of the saw blade produces a lacerating of the blood vessels rather than a clean-cut cross section. The danger of excessive bleeding is thus minimized.

3. There is more likelihood of the cut's being made at just the right place.

The use of the saw, however, has the following disadvantages:

1. The animals must be secured much more firmly.

2. The operation is relatively much slower.

3. The wound made by the saw is more irregular, and, consequently, heals more slowly.

4. The saw is more painful to the animal than are clippers.

Ordinarily the clippers will prove more satisfactory except in the case of mature animals with hard, brittle horns.

The principal point about dehorning with clippers or saw is to take off enough of the horn to stop effectually further growth and also to give the skin tissue a chance to cover the wound. The proper method is to cut the horn entirely off at its base, practically even with the skull. This requires amputation slightly under the level of the skin and taking off with the horn fully a quarter of an inch or perhaps half an inch of the ring of skin which appears at the horn base and extends upward from the head. It is more dangerous to cut the horn one or two inches distant from the head than at the skull, because the blood vessels which circulate through the horn are separated at its base in very small capillaries, while a little further out these small vessels unite into larger veins which would bleed much more dangerously than the capillaries.[1]

The Barnes dehorner shown in Fig. 30 literally lifts the horn out by the roots and crushes the blood vessels so that only a mere trickle of blood is normally produced. However, it is suitable only for dehorning calves and short yearlings.

As a rule, no special precautions are necessary to prevent excessive bleeding. Although the flow of blood may be considerable immediately after the horn is removed, it usually diminishes rapidly, owing to the formation of a heavy clot and the contraction of the capillaries. If a heavy flow of blood persists to the point where the animal becomes weak and faint, the severed artery should be ligated with a piece of cotton or silk thread or its severed end should be seized with an artery forceps and the artery broken off deep in the skull by traction.

Effects of Dehorning. The shock sustained by animals from dehorning is often given undue importance by agricultural writers. Ordinarily the pain experienced is momentary, and the loss of blood

[1] Georgia Circular 63, 1907.

sustained by the cattle is not sufficiently great to be given serious consideration. Excessive bleeding may occur if the cattle have been on sweet clover pasture or have been recently fed a considerable quantity of sweet clover hay.[2] Moreover, if the general vitality of the cattle should be suddenly lowered by exposure to a cold, driving rain immediately after dehorning, the effect of the operation is quite a serious matter. Under such conditions large losses may occur. Also, if cattle are dehorned during fly time some of the horn cores are almost certain to become infested with maggots. This condition, also, is very grave, and treatment is administered with difficulty. For these reasons dehorning should be done in either the early spring or late fall when neither flies nor cold weather are likely to cause complications.

THE TRAINING OF HORNS

Purebred Shorthorn and Hereford calves that are to be retained or sold for breeding purposes are seldom dehorned. Horns are a breed characteristic of considerable importance, and their removal detracts considerably from the general appearance of purebred cattle, causing them to resemble grades. Each breed of cattle has its own peculiar shape and size of horn, to which the horns of all animals of that breed should conform. Unfortunately, however, wide departures from the ideal shape are of frequent occurrence.

The ideal horn of both Shorthorn and Hereford cattle describes almost a semi-circle, with the tip a little below the level of the eyes. Many variations from this form occur, the most objectionable being that in which the horns take an upward direction. When this condition is noted, metal weights should be attached to the ends of the horns to pull them down. The size of the weights should be in proportion to the size and length of the horns. Short, stubby horns require heavier weights than do those of average length. The best results are secured with animals about fourteen months of age. The horns of older animals are, as a rule, too hard and heavy to be satisfactorily trained. Rasping the horn on the outer border of the desired curve is of some help in making it take the proper direction.

Various kinds of horn trainers have been devised, some of which have been patented and are manufactured and sold by firms that handle stockmen's supplies. The principal factors to keep in mind in making or purchasing horn trainers are: (1) the security with which they are fastened to the horn, so as to prevent their becoming lost; and (2) the likelihood of their getting caught in a fence in such a way as to result in

[2] Cf. p. 620.

a broken horn as the animal struggles to get loose. The latter objection is particularly applicable to those types of trainers designed to make a pair of spreading horns curve inward.

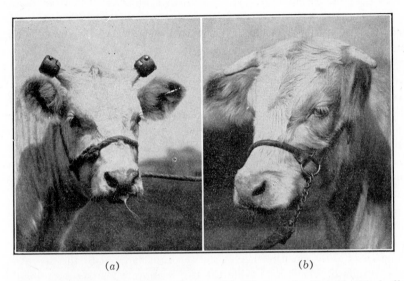

(a)   (b)

Fig. 31. The effect of weighting horns. (a) Nine-month-old calf with badly upturned horns; (b) same animal a few months later, showing horns properly shaped by the use of 1½-pound weights. (*Courtesy University of Illinois.*)

CASTRATION

The castration of bull calves is performed for purely economic reasons. It results in a more symmetrical development of body—in particular, a better balance between front and hind-quarters—and improves the texture, tenderness, and flavor of the beef. Moreover, steers are much quieter in the feed lot than bulls. This fact alone would justify castration.

Age and Season. Castration is best done when calves are from 4 to 10 weeks old. Many writers on the subject recommend that the operation be performed when the calf is only a few days old, claiming that less pain and loss of blood will result than if done later. While such claims are undoubtedly true, the testicles of very young calves are so small and soft that it is often difficult to distinguish them from the surrounding tissues. Also, it occasionally happens that the testicles do not descend into the scrotum until several days after birth. The castration of older animals is, of course, attended with more risk, but seldom do any serious complications develop. As a matter of fact, during the early part of the twentieth century scores of range bulls were successfully castrated every fall at the big central markets after their sale to Corn Belt cattle feeders. These animals were mainly yearlings and 2-year-olds. If not too thick and heavy in front quarters, they often sold on a par with ordinary steers when finished and returned to market. Bulls over 2 years of age are seldom castrated, but are fattened and sold entire.

Like dehorning, castration should be performed when weather conditions are the most favorable. The spring and fall months are considered the best, although winter castration is not objectionable if it is done on a mild, bright day and if adequate protection is furnished the following night. As a rule, calves born during the winter and early spring are castrated just before being turned to pasture, whereas those born during the summer and fall are allowed to go until they are brought in from the pasture in the fall. On the range, castration is performed at the summer and fall round-ups.

Method. Young calves are usually thrown to be castrated, but animals over 4 months of age may be operated on better while standing. In throwing, the calf is placed on its left side and the feet held or "hog tied." This position leaves the scrotum exposed to the operator, who stands or kneels alongside the calf's rump. The scrotum should first be scrubbed with a sponge, or piece of absorbent cotton, saturated with a mild antiseptic, to remove any dirt that might otherwise get into the wound. The hands of the operator and the knife should also be washed in an antiseptic solution. The scrotum is grasped close to the belly with the left hand, and the left testicle is pulled down until its outline is easily discerned through the skin. Then with a sharp, sterile knife (a special castrating knife used for no other purpose is recommended), an incision is made along the left side of the scrotum from a point well above the middle of the testicle to its apex. The incision should be deep enough to cut through the skin, the subcutaneous connective tissue, and the thin membrane surrounding the testicle (tunica vaginalis), but should not penetrate to any extent the testicle itself. If the body of the testicle is deeply cut, it is likely to lose its characteristic form, thereby becoming difficult to recover if a sudden movement of the animal causes it to escape from the hand of the operator and be drawn up into the scrotum. This accident is most likely to happen in castrating very young calves with soft, immature testicles.

If the incision has been properly made, the pressure exerted by the left hand will expose the testicle sufficiently to permit it to be grasped and held by the right hand, while the left is used to separate the gland from the supporting tendons of the cremaster muscle attached to the back and lower part of the testicle. The knife should be laid in the antiseptic solution during this operation. With the left hand now holding the testicle and with one of its fingers inserted between the testicle and the tendons, the knife is again taken in the right hand and the cremaster tendons severed close to their lower attachments. With the knife laid aside as before, the testicle is again taken in the right hand and drawn several inches clear of the scrotum, while the spermatic cord is stripped of all surrounding membranes with the left hand. With the left hand exerting a strong tension on the cord, the testicle is allowed to drop and the cord is scraped with the knife until it is severed. As much of the cord should be removed with the testicle as possible. The right testicle is now removed in a similar manner, the incision being made along the right side of the scrotum.

In castrating an animal while it is standing, the operator stands close against the left thigh, facing to the rear, and with the left hand draws the scrotum back between the hind legs. In all other respects the operation is the same as that described above. In using the standing position, care should be taken to exert a strong pull on the scrotum at all times; otherwise a serious injury from kicking may result. Even this precaution is not always successful, though kicking by animals under a year old is extremely rare. Experienced operators who employ this method usually make both incisions at once and remove both testicles with the right hand, keeping a firm grasp on the scrotum with the left throughout the operation.

After Treatment. After the testicles are removed the scrotum should be examined to make sure that the incisions are sufficiently large and low to afford proper drainage. The calves should be put in a clean box stall for a few hours until all danger of excessive bleeding is past, after which they may be turned into a clean pasture or lot if the weather permits. Care should be taken that they have a clean place to lie. For this reason they should not be permitted access to lots covered with mud or manure, or to sheds that have not recently been cleaned and rebedded. Daily examinations should be made for a week or ten days to make sure that any swelling due to faulty drainage is promptly relieved by reopening the incision and irrigating the scrotum with an antiseptic solution.

Castration Pincers. Several years ago there was introduced into this country from Italy a unique kind of castration pincers called the "Burdizzo." These pincers and others of similar type manufactured in this country have blunt jaws which close with enormous force when sufficient pressure is exerted on the handles to lock them into the closed position. In using the pincers the object is to crush or sever the spermatic cord and the blood vessels that supply the testicle so that the testicle will degenerate for want of circulation.

The advantages of the Burdizzo over the knife are that there is no loss of blood and that the skin is not broken to permit flies to deposit the eggs from which the dreaded screw worms develop. Nevertheless, the jaws of the pincers cut deeply into the skin, and there is some danger that the scrotum itself may slough off for want of blood supply. This, however, may be prevented by severing each cord separately, one a little higher than the other, so that some of the blood vessels leading to the lower part of the scrotum will escape injury. When such care is exercised an unusually attractive, well-shaped cod is acquired in the feed lot by animals that have been castrated with Burdizzo pincers.

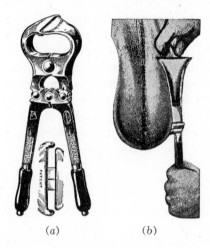

(a)   (b)

Fig. 32. (a) Burdizzo castration pincers; (b) correct method of using to insure crushing of spermatic cord. (*Courtesy O. M. Franklin Serum Company, Denver, Colorado.*)

At first very favorable results were reported from the use of the Burdizzo, and it appeared that this method of castration would eventually supersede the knife, especially in Texas and adjoining states where the presence of blow flies and screw worms makes castration with a knife unsafe after March 1. However it soon became evident that the use of the pincers under practical conditions did not always sever the cord and blood vessels sufficiently well to arrest the development of the testicle. The result was a calf called a "slip," which would begin to show signs of stagginess when about a year old. When used under unfavorable conditions or by inexperienced operators the percentage of "slips" would sometimes amount to 10 or 15 per cent. "Slips" are almost eliminated by an improved type Burdizzo that holds the cord in place when the jaws are closed. (See Fig. 32, a.)

More recently a new type of castration instrument called the **elastator** has been used with good success in castrating grade calves. It is a pincer-like instrument, which is used to slip a strong elastic rubber band around the scrotum close to its attachment to the groin. The pressure exerted by the rubber band shuts off the blood supply to the scrotum and testicles, causing them to slough off, leaving no more loose skin between the hind legs than is usually seen in a heifer. Some cattle feeders object to steers that have been thus castrated, because with no cods they appear light and shallow in the twist.

MARKING

It is highly desirable that all animals in the herd bear some mark or tag whereby each can be positively identified. On the Western Range, marking or branding is necessary to establish ownership. In the small herd it is essential to establish ancestry or pedigree. Altogether too many farmers trust to their memory of certain individual differences of form and color to identify their animals. In such cases a long absence of the owner from home, due to sickness or business, may result in considerable confusion, particularly concerning the identity of younger animals that have grown up in the meantime. Instances may be cited where herds of high-class, purebred cattle have been reduced to the value of ordinary market stock by the sudden death of their owners, who left no written records setting forth the methods of identification.

The means employed for marking will depend upon the object for which it is done. When the object in view is to establish ownership, as it is on the range and in poorly fenced pastures, ease of recognition is of paramount importance. Under such conditions, branding with a hot iron is probably the best method. Although much has been said against branding because of the pain inflicted and the damage done to the hide, no good substitute for the iron has yet been devised. However, a brand should be no larger than is necessary to permit easy identification at a distance of 30 or 40 feet, and no deeper than is needed to destroy the hair follicles.

Other forms of ownership marks sometimes employed are ear "notching," "slitting," and "grubbing." The principal objection to such marks is that they detract greatly from the appearance of the animals. Another mark of this sort is the slitting of the dewlap in such a way as to cause one or two "wattles" of skin to hang down from the throat. This is a rather common way of marking cattle in certain grazing sections in the West.

To establish the identity of each individual animal in the herd, numbered neck straps and chains, ear notches, ear labels, horn brands and tattooes are all employed. The principal objection to neck chains is that they are frequently lost. If they are adjusted properly when the cattle are turned on pasture in the spring, they become either too tight or too loose later on in the summer as the cattle gain or lose flesh. It is particularly difficult to keep the neck chains of growing calves and yearlings properly adjusted.

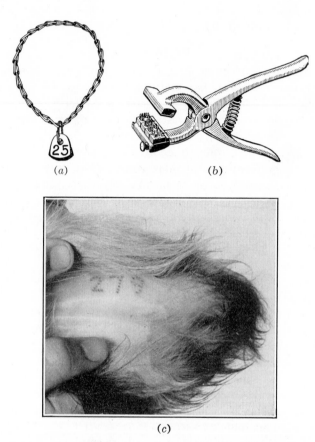

(a)   (b)

(c)

Fig. 33. Devices for marking cattle: (a) adjustable neck chain; (b) tattoo pincers; (c) a correctly tattooed ear. (*Courtesy O. M. Franklin Serum Company, Denver, Colorado.*)

While it is possible to adopt a system of ear notching that will permit each animal to have its own "ear number," such a practice is seldom followed because ears so mutilated are very unattractive. Moreover, the notches are difficult to see even at short distances because they often are obscured by the hair.

Many forms of ear labels are on the market and may be purchased by the stockman for a small sum. As a rule, they are easy to attach, but usually are also easily lost and remain in but a short time. Probably the round aluminum "ear button" is the best label of this sort, as it is least likely to be torn out.

Horn branding is an excellent means of numbering mature horned cattle, but is, of course, useless with calves and yearlings. Obviously, the polled breeds cannot be horn branded. This is the common method of numbering cattle at purebred Shorthorn and Hereford sales, where the horn brand of each animal is made to correspond with the catalog number. One-half inch copper brands are the proper size to use for this purpose.

The best mark of identity that has yet been devised for the cattle of a breeding herd is tattooing the ear with indelible ink. The advantages of this method are that the mark is permanent and in no way disfigures the animal. Its only serious objection is that the animal must be caught and the ear closely examined before the mark can be seen. Tattoo ear-marking outfits, including an initial letter and a set of 20 figures, may be purchased from any stockmen's supply house for about $6. All purebred record associations now require that calves be properly tattooed before they are accepted for registration.

VACCINATION

Calves born on farms in blackleg-infested areas should be vaccinated against this disease before they are 8 months of age.[3] Vaccination at a much younger age is advisable if an outbreak has occurred in the vicinity of the farm within the past 2 years.

Heifer and bull calves that are to be kept or sold for breeding should be vaccinated for contagious abortion at 4 to 8 months of age, unless the herd is "accredited"[4] as a result of annual clean tests. Although the value of calfhood vaccination is questioned by some breeders and veterinarians, cattle that have been so vaccinated and that later have passed the blood test are regarded by most breeders to be much less likely to contract the disease than unvaccinated animals. While calfhood vaccination is more urgently needed in purebred than in grade herds because of the greater risk of exposure, the vaccination of grade heifers that are to be added to the breeding herd is recommended, as they too may be exposed to the disease through contacts with cattle on adjoining farms. Vaccination for abortion must be done by a state veterinarian, who must tattoo a "V" and the date of injection in the right ear.

[3] *Cf.* p. 598.
[4] *Cf.* p. 603.

13 — Feeding and Care of Young Cattle

The problems of developing young cattle are of three kinds: (1) fattening for market; (2) growing out young animals through the winter or summer with a view to finishing them at some later time; (3) developing young bulls and heifers for the breeding herd. Each of these problems is distinct from the others and demands somewhat different treatment. No attempt will be made in this chapter to deal with the questions of fattening, as these matters will be treated in detail in special chapters devoted to that phase of the subject. Rather we will confine our attention to calves and yearlings that are not to be fattened immediately, but are to be allowed to grow for awhile before being consigned to the feed lot. It is customary to refer to such animals as "stockers," and to speak of their being on a maintenance rather than a fattening ration.

Object in Maintaining Stockers. In planning the management of stocker cattle it should be kept in mind that such animals are kept for one or both of two reasons: (1) to insure a supply of the right kind of cattle for the feed lot at the proper time; or (2) to utilize farm roughages, otherwise unmarketable. No matter which of these objects is uppermost in the mind of the owner, economy in feeding and management is of the utmost importance.

Ordinarily, thin steers can be bought in the fall for $2 to $5 less per hundredweight than cattle of similar quality and flesh can be purchased in the spring. This is due to the fact that western ranchers habitually dispose of all surplus stock at the end of the grazing season in order to avoid the trouble and expense of wintering. As a result, the supply of thin cattle received at the big markets in the fall is somewhat above the trade's requirements, whereas that in the spring is usually less. Thus, a farmer who wishes to buy steers to graze the following summer will not only have a wider choice of cattle in the fall, but will also be able to buy them more cheaply. Indeed, the difference in price will usually be enough to enable him to put them on pasture the following spring with much less total expense than he would have incurred had he waited until spring to buy. An entirely different situation is likely to result, however, if proper attention is not paid to economy in every detail of the wintering operation.

Most Corn Belt farms produce more coarse roughage than can be profitably utilized by the livestock normally kept. Particularly is this likely to be true where considerable grain is sold from the farm, or where the bulk of the corn crop is fed to hogs. Under such conditions the wintering of stocker steers offers one of the most effective ways to utilize the surplus roughage. At the end of the winter period the cattle may either be grazed on clover or bluegrass pasture—thus utilizing still more roughage—or sold to some neighbor for grazing and feeding purposes. Although the gains made by young cattle fed only roughages or pasture are not large, they are usually made at less cost per pound than the market price of the cattle. Thus, a small profit is made on the gain, as well as on the original weight by selling it for 2 to 5¢ a pound more than it cost the previous fall.

Winter Gains of Stocker Cattle. Stocker cattle should be maintained with the minimum outlay for feed consistent with health and vigor. Increase in weight beyond that represented by normal growth

TABLE 64

YEARLY GAINS MADE BY CATTLE ON DIFFERENT PLANES OF NUTRITION*

Period (Age of Cattle)		Group I (Maximum Growth Without Fattening)	Group II (Growth Distinctly Retarded)
30 to 360 days.........	Weight gained	409.7 lbs.	241.6 lbs.
	Daily gain	1.24	.73
360 to 720 days........	Weight gained	320.8	235.6
	Daily gain	.89	.65
720 to 1080 days.......	Weight gained	126.9	121.2
	Daily gain	.35	.34

* Missouri Research Bulletin 43, 1921.

is not to be expected. In fact, a noticeable increase in condition is usually undesirable, if the steers are to make the most efficient use of grass the following spring and summer. With cattle in ordinary flesh at the beginning of winter, daily gains of 1 to 1½ pounds should be considered satisfactory. The amount of gain necessary to account for normal growth will depend, of course, upon the age of the animal. Growth is most rapid in young animals and gradually decreases as the animals approach maturity. Hence, calves will make larger gains than yearlings, and yearlings more than 2-year-olds when all are on the plane of nutrition which will permit normal growth but little or no improvement in condition. In fact, 2-year-old steers grow so slowly that it is seldom advisable to carry them on non-fattening rations except for relatively short periods. Since they require a large amount of feed for maintenance, gains that represent only growth are very expensive.

Fig. 34. Stocker calves in winter quarters. (*Courtesy Illinois Experiment Station.*)

The amount of gain desired during the winter will depend largely upon the way the cattle are to be handled the following summer. If they are to be fed on pasture they should be wintered better than if they are to be only grazed. Also, if they are to be grazed until only midsummer and then full fed for the late fall market, they should be wintered at a higher level than would be advisable if they were to be grazed the entire summer and fall. This is especially true of yearling cattle, which are difficult to fatten during a short feeding period unless they are in fairly good flesh when they are started on feed.

As far as possible, the winter ration should prepare the cattle for making the maximum use of the summer ration, viz., grass. It is a well-established fact that half-fat cattle or cattle carrying a noticeable amount of condition do not do well when turned on grass in the spring. Indeed, it sometimes happens that such cattle actually lose weight during the first 3 or 4 weeks of the grazing season. This situation is particularly likely to occur when cattle that have received a liberal grain ration during the winter are turned on grass and the grain feeding discontinued. The amount of gain made in summer varies inversely with the amount of gain made during the winter. Consequently, if cattle are being wintered for the purpose of converting grass into beef the following summer, the winter gains should not be so large that the cattle's ability to utilize grass will be impaired.

TABLE 65

EFFECT OF WINTER GAINS UPON GAINS MADE ON GRASS DURING THE FOLLOWING SUMMER*

	Winter Gains (Pounds)	Gains Following Summer and Fall (Pounds)	Total for Year (Pounds)
Average of four lots, making less than 50 lbs. winter gains....................	20	257	277
Average of seven lots making from 50 to 99 lbs. winter gains....................	77	235	312
Average of six lots making from 100 to 149 lbs. winter gains....................	121	227	353
Average of four lots making from 150 to 199 lbs. winter gains....................	167	212	379
Average of five lots making 200 or more lbs. winter gains....................	222	165	387

* Oregon Bulletin 182, 1921.

Theoretically, it would appear that cattle making no gain, or even losing slightly in weight during the winter, would make the best use of grass. This is true for the summer period only, and such cattle, if not so thin as to be unthrifty, are often a profitable purchase at the beginning of the grazing season. However, the man who winters his own steers is interested in total gains for the entire period rather than those of the summer alone. Probably from three-fifths to three-fourths of the total yearly gain should be made from grass, if the maximum profit is to be realized.

Winter Rations for Stockers. As has already been stated, the wintering of stock cattle is not likely to prove profitable unless the ration consists largely of farm-grown roughages of little or no market value. The presence of much grain in wintering rations is not justified. As a matter of fact, the use of any grain at all is seldom necessary for yearling cattle. Calves usually will require 3 to 5 pounds of grain daily to insure satisfactory gains unless they are fed practically a full feed of silage. But with plenty of good silage and legume hay, grain may be omitted even with calves. In the absence of some kind of legume roughage, it is highly advisable to feed sufficient linseed meal, cottonseed meal, or soybean oil meal to supply the protein require-

TABLE 66

RELATION BETWEEN WINTER AND SUMMER GAINS OF STOCKER CATTLE

Lots	Missouri Livestock Day Progress Report 8, 1949		Missouri Livestock Day Progress Report 11, 1950	
	Winter Gains (pounds)	Summer Gains (pounds)	Winter Gains (pounds)	Summer Gains (pounds)
1	136	236	69	142
2	175	215	146	97
3	163	224	93	119
4	137	255	140	99
5	191	231	. . .	. . .

Lots Compared	Difference Between Winter Gains (pounds)	Difference Between Summer Gains (pounds)	Ratio of Differences	Difference Between Winter Gains (pounds)	Difference Between Summer Gains (pounds)	Ratio of Differences
1 and 2	39	21	1.9:1	77	45	1.7:1
1 and 3	27	12	2.3:1	24	23	1:1
1 and 4	1	−19	. . . .	71	43	1.7:1
1 and 5	55	5	11:1	. .	. .	. . . .
2 and 3	12	9	1.3:1	53	22	2.4:1
2 and 4	38	40	1:1	6	2	3:1
2 and 5	16	16	1:1	. .	. .	. . . .
3 and 4	26	31	0.8:1	47	20	2.3:1
3 and 5	28	−7	. . . .	. .	. .	. . . .
4 and 5	54	24	2.3:1	. .	. .	. . . .
Total	296	132	2.2:1	278	155	1.8:1

ments of the growing animals. Usually, 1 pound of such feeds per head daily will be sufficient. If 4 or more pounds of good legume hay are fed, protein concentrates may be dispensed with entirely.

Although it is true that the less the gain made by young cattle during the winter the more they will gain on pasture the following summer, the winter and summer gains are not inversely proportional,

TABLE 67

RECOMMENDED WINTER GAINS FOR STOCKER CATTLE

Method of Feeding and Management the Following Summer	Calves		Yearlings		2-Year-Olds	
	Total (pounds)	ADG (pounds)	Total (pounds)	ADG (pounds)	Total (pounds)	ADG (pounds)
1. Grazed entire summer; sold as feeders or started on feed in late fall (November)	115	0.75	100	0.66	50	0.33
2. Pasture only until about June 1; then full fed on pasture and marketed late fall (November)	150	1.00	115	0.75	75	0.50
3. Grazed until Aug. 1; full fed until late fall or early winter (November or December)	185	1.25	150	1.00	115	0.75
4. Full fed during summer in dry lot; marketed in early fall (September)	225	1.50	185	1.25	150	1.00
5. Full fed during entire summer on pasture; marketed in fall (October)	225	1.50	185	1.25	150	1.00

as is often believed. For example, if one lot of steers gains twice as much during the winter as a second lot, its summer gains will not be limited to half that of the second lot, but will probably be 70 to 90 per cent as much. Consequently, it usually happens that the cattle which make the largest winter gains also make the largest total gain for both periods. Although the effect of the winter gain on the summer gain varies widely from year to year and between different droves of cattle, a good rule for the practical cattle man to follow is that for every additional pound that stocker calves gain during the winter, they will gain ½ pound less during the following summer. (See Table 66.) Calves that gain less than 250 pounds during the winter, or less than 1.5 pounds per day, usually will not gain enough during the summer to weigh in the fall what they would have weighed had they been wintered on a higher level of nutrition.

Gains that may be regarded as ideal for cattle of different ages which are to be handled in the more common methods of feeding are given in Table 67.

TABLE 68

IMPORTANCE OF ADEQUATE PROTEIN IN THE RATION OF STOCKER CATTLE
Nebraska Bulletin 357, 1944

Concentrate Fed	None	0.5 lb. Cotton- seed Cake	0.75 lb. Cotton- seed Cake	1.0 lb. Cotton- seed Cake	1.5 lb. Cotton- seed Cake
Number of trials averaged	5	2	3	3	2
Average initial weight, pounds	408	418	433	385	363
Average final weight	433	543	596	564	548
Average total gain	25	125	163	179	185
Average daily gain	0.15	0.73	0.92	1.10	1.16
Average prairie eaten daily	10.6	12.7	13.7	13.2	11.6
Average summer gain	259	231	222	212	190
Average total gain	284	356	385	391	375

Illinois Mimeographed Reports

	Calves 1942–1943		Calves 1942–1943		Yearling Steers 1946–1947	
Concentrate Feed	First Period	Second Period	First Period	Second Period	First Period	Second Period
Average initial weight, pounds	471	567	464	564	682	729
Days in period	140	20	140	20	70	105
Average daily ration:						
Shelled corn	....	....	2.4	4.8	....	....
Protein concentrate	....	1.0	....	1.0	....	....
Legume hay	3.7	3.8	3.9	3.8	3.0	5.0
Timothy hay	....	....	7.2	6.6	....	....
Corn silage	18.1	21.9	....	....	30.0	30.0
Average daily gain	0.68	1.75	0.71	1.73	0.68	1.16

The importance of supplying plenty of protein in the ration of stocker cattle is clearly shown by the results of the feeding experiments summarized in Table 68. In the Oklahoma experiments the addition of ½ pound of cottonseed cake to a full feed of prairie hay increased the daily gain 0.58 pound, while the addition of another ½ pound of cake increased the gain 0.37 pound still further. In the Illinois trial with calves the addition of 1 pound of protein supplement increased the daily gains by a full pound, whereas in the trial with yearlings, feeding 2 more pounds of clover hay increased the daily gains from 0.63 pound per steer daily to 1.16 pounds a day. It is doubtful that a more profitable use of feed can be cited from any feeding test than that made of the protein concentrates and the additional legume hay which were fed in these wintering experiments. These tests show that calves and yearling cattle should have from ¾ to 1 pound of high-grade protein supplement or 4 to 5 pounds of good legume hay if they are to make satisfactory gains. In fact, results secured at the Indiana Station from feeding 2 to 2.5 pounds of protein concentrate to calves wintered on corn silage, oat straw, corn cobs and soybean straw indicate that relatively high levels of nitrogenous supplements, as well as minerals and vitamins, must be fed with low-grade roughages if the

TABLE 69

VALUE OF LOW-GRADE ROUGHAGES FOR WINTERING STOCKER CATTLE
WHEN FED WITH A COMPLETE SUPPLEMENT*

	First Trial Dec. 21, 1949–Apr. 12, 1950 112 Days			Second Trial Dec. 8, 1950–May 4, 1951 147 Days		
	Oat Straw	Corn Cobs	Corn Silage	Soybean Straw	Corn Cobs	Corn Silage
Average initial wt., pounds	485	479	478	480	478	481
Average final wt.	589	671	721	595	698	806
Average total gain	104	192	243	115	220	325
Average daily gain	0.93	1.72	2.18	0.78	1.50	2.21
Average daily feed						
Roughage	12.4	12.8	31.0	13.3	13.4	37.0
Supplement A[a]	3.5	3.5	3.5	3.5	3.5	3.5
Minerals[b]	Free choice	Free choice	Free choice	0.06	0.05	0.04
Feed per hundredweight gain						
Roughage	1337	742	1423	1707	890	1671
Supplement A	377	202	160	449	233	158

* Indiana Mimeo. AH 47, 1950, and AH 59, 1951.
[a] Supplement A consisted of 2.25 lb. soybean oil meal, 1 lb. molasses feed, 0.18 lb. bone meal, 0.06 lb. salt, and 0.01 lb. vitamin A concentrate.
[b] Mineral mixture fed free-choice during both tests: 2 parts steamed bone meal, 1 part iodized salt, plus 1 oz. cobalt sulfate per 100 lb. of salt.

feed nutrients in such roughages are to be efficiently utilized. The theory underlying this practice is that these supplements are required to feed the bacteria in the paunch in order that they may break down the cellulose and other complex carbohydrates of the roughage and render them digestible.[1] (See Table 69.) Apparently a serious protein deficiency cannot be corrected by feeding a high-energy feed like shelled corn. However, 2 pounds of ground barley or ground wheat, 3 pounds of wheat bran, or 4 pounds of ground alfalfa hay have been

[1] Cf. pp. 202–204.

satisfactory substitutes for 1 pound of cottonseed meal at the Kansas Station for both stocker calves and yearlings fed a full feed of sorgo silage.[2]

The character of the roughage fed should depend somewhat upon the age of the cattle. Two-year-old steers can make considerable use of corn stover and straw. Calves, on the other hand, should be fed a limited amount of such materials. If possible, corn or grass silage and legume hay should furnish at least 70 per cent of the dry matter of the roughage ration for calves, 50 per cent for yearlings, and 30 per cent for 2-year-old steers. The remainder may well consist of corn stover or straw.

It is highly important that the cattle be given all they will eat of some component of the ration; otherwise their hunger will not be satisfied, and they will be restless and waste some of their energy in moving about. As a matter of economy, the better practice is to limit the quantities of legume hay and silage to the amounts actually required to produce the desired gains, and supply a cheaper feed like stover or straw in sufficient quantity to keep it before the cattle at all times.

Although corn stover and the straws of grain crops are excellent roughages in combination with more nutritious feeds for wintering stockers, young cattle should not be expected to thrive on such feeds alone. Not only are they quite deficient in protein, but they are so coarse and unpalatable that often the quantities eaten are but little in excess of maintenance requirements, leaving insufficient nutrients and energy to promote proper growth.

It not infrequently happens that trouble is experienced in getting even older cattle to consume the desired quantities of stover and straw. For them it is highly important that large quantities be eaten, as the bulk of their ration is made up of such feeds. Various methods of improving the palatability of these roughages have been tried, chief among which are cutting or chafing straw and shredding or grinding stover.

Shredded or Ground Stover. It is commonly believed that shredding or grinding corn stover and other coarse roughages makes them more palatable and digestible. However, feeding experiments indicate that these suppositions are not well founded. It is true that cattle fed a limited amount of shredded or ground stover will eat almost all of it, but only a slightly greater weight of ground stover than of whole stover is eaten if both kinds of stover are full fed. Indeed, in some experiments shredding has decreased the consumption of feed by forcing the cattle to eat the coarse, woody parts of the stalk along

[2] Kansas, Fort Hays Branch, Reports, 1933 and 1938.

with the leafy, palatable portions of which they will eat large quantities if allowed to choose what they want. Digestion studies with ground stover show that the butts of corn stalks have a negative nutritive value; i.e., more energy is expended by the animal in passing the material through the alimentary tract than is extracted from it. Consequently, if stover is shredded or ground it should be for other reasons than improving its feeding value, such as to permit storage under cover or to make the refused stover more satisfactory as a bedding material.

Corn and Cane Silage. Silage is the most satisfactory feed for wintering stocker cattle. Its palatability insures a sufficient consumption of feed to produce good growth and development. Its succulent nature makes it a good substitute for grass and thus keeps the digestive system in a healthy condition. It is usually sufficiently cheap to permit its being fed liberally without unduly increasing the cost of wintering. In fact, when yield per acre, ease of feeding, and the amount required to produce a given gain are considered, corn silage is usually the cheapest feed that may be fed to young stocker cattle wintered in the Corn Belt. Outside the Corn Belt proper, cane silage made from the improved varieties of grain sorghum has given highly satisfactory results. (See Table 70.)

Weanling calves should be fed as much silage as they will consume, which will average approximately 32 pounds a day if they are fed no hay. Older cattle, if fed silage according to appetite, are likely to lay on too much fat to make the most efficient use of grass the following spring. Hence, the silage should be limited to 3 or 4 pounds per hundredweight and additional roughage supplied in the form of hay and straw. Silage is low in both protein and minerals. Hence, approximately 1 pound of protein supplement and 1/10 pound of finely ground limestone should be fed daily per head unless 4 or more pounds of leafy legume hay are present in the ration.

Corn Stover Silage. Dry stover, instead of being shredded, may be ensiled along with sufficient water to bring its moisture content up to somewhere near that of normal silage. As a rule, the weight of water added should be approximately equal to the weight of the dry stover. As it is impossible to blow so great a quantity of water up through the conveyor, it must be added through the top of the distributor. It is very important that the water come in contact with every particle of stover and that the wet stover be well packed in the silo. Even a few handfuls of dry material will contain sufficient air to cause a good-sized pocket of spoiled silage.

Silage made from first-class stover has considerable merit as a feed

for cattle that are being maintained through the winter.   Shocks badly
damaged by rain or made from over-ripe corn, on the other hand, should
never be put into the silo, as the resulting silage will be of little value.

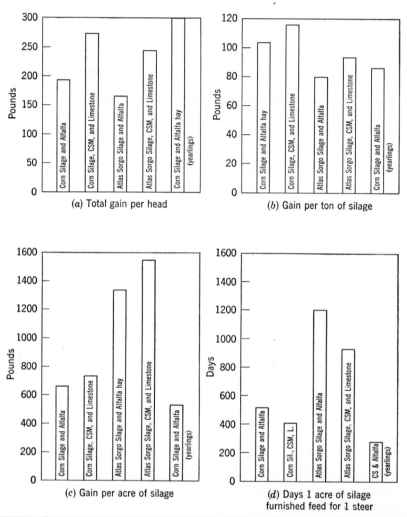

FIG. 35.   Some important factors to consider in selecting winter rations for stocker
cattle.   In addition to those shown are the gain per head and per acre made on
pasture the following summer.   (*Nebraska Mimeograph Cattle Circular* 146, 1934.)

Well-made stover silage has an appearance and aroma not unlike ordinary silage, and cattle, other than those on a fattening ration, will eat
considerable quantities of it.   However, the process of siloing adds

nothing to the feeding value, nor does the fermentation that goes on in the silo increase to any extent the digestibility of the stover. Hence, cattle receiving stover silage *ad libitum* will gain but little faster than cattle getting all the dry stover they care to eat. The advantages

TABLE 70

SILAGE VS. DRY ROUGHAGES FOR WINTERING STOCKER CATTLE

	Illinois Bulletin 73, 1902		Missouri Mimeo. Report, 1933–1934		Nebraska Mimeo. Report 134, 1932 (3 year av.)			Kansas (Ft. Hays Report), 1926		Illinois Report, 1938–1939	
	Corn Silage Mix. Hay Oats	Shock Corn Mix. Hay Oats	Shock Corn Alfalfa	Alfalfa Hay	Corn Silage Alfalfa	Shelled Corn Alfalfa	Ground Shock Corn Alfalfa	Cane Silage C.S.M.	Cane Fodder C.S.M.	Corn Silage	Alfalfa Hay
Av. initial wt., lb..........	504	492	400	402	381	381	377	794	805	424	427
Days fed.....	88	88	140	140	143	143	143	90	90	150	150
Av. daily ration Silage or fodder...	26.1	13.2	7.8	..	32.4	..	14.0	67.3	31.9	18.9	..
Hay.......	4.0	4.0	5.0	11.4	2.4	10.6	2.4	..	..	3.0	11.0
Straw (straw fed to only one lot)..	..	..	..	..	..	..	..	..	..	..	2.0
Concentrate	2.0	2.0	..	..	..	3.0	..	2.0	2.0	1.0	..
Av. daily gain	1.68	1.42	.99	.81	1.55	1.43	1.53	2.08	1.41	1.32	.95
Gain per acre of corn (or cane)....	992	588	..	..	541	..	473	606	309	1649	600*
Steer days per acre of corn (or cane)....	590	413	..	..	340	..	282	291	220	1249	634*

* Per acre of alfalfa hay, 3½ tons per acre.

possessed by the stover silage are: (1) the entire stalks are eaten, thus greatly reducing the amount of material wasted; (2) the silage is succulent, and so has a much better effect on the digestive system than dry stover.

Silage made from green stover from which the ears have been gathered for ear corn silage[3] is a much more satisfactory basal winter ration for young cattle that are to be grazed the following spring. Such silage is much more palatable than that made from ripe stover, as it is

[3] *Cf.* p. 284.

made while most of the plant tissues are still green and tender and while a considerable portion of the carbohydrates is still in the form of soluble sugars. Moreover, the presence of sufficient moisture in the harvested corn to permit storing without the addition of water simplifies greatly the process of ensiling and practically eliminates the moldy

TABLE 71

CORN STOVER SILAGE FOR WINTERING STOCKER CATTLE*

Silage Fed	Yearling Steers (110 days)		Steer Calves (133 days)	
	Green Stover Silage	Dry Stover Silage	Green Stover Silage	Normal Corn Silage
Initial weight..............	651 lbs.	642 lbs.	463 lbs.	463 lbs.
Average daily gain...........	.53	.44	.65	1.16
Average daily ration:				
N. Concentrate...........	1.0	1.0	1.0	1.0
Silage...................	47.6	43.3	24.6	22.1
Dry roughage............	....	....	2.0	2.0
Av. daily gain following summer when full fed on pasture.	....	....	2.29	2.04

*Illinois Experiment Station, unpublished data.

spots frequently encountered in feeding silage made from dry stover or shock corn. Results secured from wintering cattle on both green and dry stover silage at the Illinois Experiment Station are given in Table 71.

Grass and Legume Silage. Silage made from mixed grasses and legumes cut at the proper stage of maturity and carefully siloed is an excellent feed for stocker cattle. Such silage has a high protein content and does not need to be supplemented with a protein concentrate or legume hay. However, it is much lower in energy than corn silage, and smaller gains will result from its use, unless corn or oats is added to it at the rate of 4 or 5 bushels a ton. If both corn silage and legume-grass silage are to be fed to a drove of cattle during the winter, the legume-grass silage should be fed out first, since it usually is less palatable than corn silage. For the same reason oat straw, corn stover, or other low-grade dry roughage is preferred to choice-quality hay for cattle that are expected to consume large amounts of legume silage.

Stalk Fields. Stalk fields furnish much cheap feed for stocker cattle during the late fall and early winter. Many Corn Belt feeders follow the practice of buying their feeder cattle in October or November and running them on stubble and stalk fields until about the first of January, when they are put into the feed lot and started on corn. Two-year-old steers are better than yearlings for this method of handling, inasmuch as they are better able to make use of the coarse roughage that stalk fields furnish. Cattle, particularly yearlings, should never be maintained wholly on stalks, as stalks are very low in net energy and very deficient in protein. Unless access is had to a

TABLE 72

A COMPARISON OF DIFFERENT SILAGES FOR YEARLING STOCKER STEERS*

	Corn Silage	Legume Silage[a]	Sorgo Silage	Barley Silage
Percentage of moisture when fed	63.7	74.1	72.9	77.5
Percentage of protein	3.0	4.4	2.1	2.7
Yield per acre, tons	8.5–9.0	...	15.0	...
Preservative added, pounds	None	78	None	45
Initial weight of cattle, pounds	738.8	739.7	738.8	739.9
Average daily gain, 126 days	1.85	1.34	1.21	1.00
Average daily ration				
Silage	32.1	38.1	35.1	40.2
Alfalfa hay	6.6	6.7	6.6	6.8
Feed eaten per cwt. gain				
Silage	1734	2834	2890	4012
Alfalfa hay	357	497	547	679

* Missouri Mimeo. Report, June 1, 1942.
[a] The legume silage was made from a mixed seeding of alfalfa, sweet clover, and red clover, which was siloed the last week of May.

good bluegrass or clover pasture, cattle on stalk fields should be fed 4 to 6 pounds of legume hay or 1 to 1½ pounds of protein concentrate per head daily.

Corn Cobs for Stocker Cattle. Chemical analyses and digestion trials indicate that corn cobs have a feeding value comparable with that of timothy or prairie hay, but they are so unpalatable in their natural state that cattle refuse to eat them. However, when the common farm roughages are scarce and unusually high priced, corn cobs may be used to carry stocker cattle over the winter period, provided the cobs are finely ground,[4] are mixed with molasses to make them palatable, and are reinforced with the nutrients and vitamins in which they are deficient.

Steer calves and yearlings wintered principally on corn cobs at the Indiana Experiment Station made very satisfactory gains and at a

[4] Fineness of grinding is highly important, as cattle will refuse cob particles more than ⅜ inch in diameter.

cost considerably below those made by a check lot fed mixed hay. It should be pointed out, however, that the average amount of hay fed daily to the check lot was unusually large, being 3.3 per cent of the average live weight in the first test and 3 per cent in the second. Consequently, it is likely that an appreciable amount of the hay was wasted, either because of its poor quality or because the mangers were not large enough to hold such amounts as were fed without some being nosed out and wasted. If the amount of hay actually consumed is estimated at 2.5 per cent of the average live weight, the cost per hundred pounds gain for the hay lot will be reduced by approximately 25 per cent in the first trial and 15 per cent in the second. Even when so corrected, the gains of the lots wintered on corn cobs costing $10 a ton (including grinding) were significantly cheaper than were the gains of the lot wintered on mixed hay costing $25. (*Cf.* Table **73**.)

Before a farmer decides to feed corn cobs he should consider some of the problems connected with their handling and feeding. Undoubtedly the best cobs from a feeding standpoint are those obtained from corn shelled in the late summer after the cobs are thoroughly dry. However, the storing of such cobs in a dry location, where they may be ground without being rehandled two or three times before they are fed, would be impossible on many farms. Cobs obtained from corn shelled only a month or two after it has been cribbed are so high in moisture that they cannot be stored for more than a few days after they are ground without becoming moldy and unpalatable. Consequently, grinding 2 or 3 times a week is necessary, even during cool weather. Unless it is convenient to shell ear corn every few days, the problem of handling and storing the cobs will present some difficult problems.

Studies made of rumen digestion indicate that the energy present in corn cobs is not available to cattle until the cellulose and other complex substances have been converted by the paunch bacteria into simpler carbohydrates which can be digested. In order that these changes may be brought about, the bacteria must be supplied with certain materials needed for their growth and development but entirely lacking in cobs. The materials with which corn cobs are usually fortified and the role they play in rendering cobs digestible are as follows:

1. *Molasses.* Molasses is used to make the cobs sufficiently palatable to be eaten in quantity and to supply the carbohydrate material that the bacteria need for rapid development. However, too much molasses may defeat the purpose for which it is fed, since the bacteria

TABLE 73

THE VALUE OF CORN COBS AS A FEED FOR STOCKER CATTLE

	Indiana Mimeo. A.H. 39, 1949				Indiana Mimeo. A.H. 48, 1950			
	Clover-Timothy Hay	Shelled corn, Clover-Timothy Hay	Corn Cobs, Mix A	Corn Cobs, Mix B	Clover-Timothy Hay	Corn Cobs II	Corn Cobs V	Corn Cobs VI
Average initial weight, pounds	552	550	551	551	595	592	592	590
Total gain	121	192	170	191	143	208	215	226
Average daily gain	0.72	1.14	1.01	1.14	0.89	1.29	1.33	1.40
Average daily ration								
Clover-timothy hay	20.0	14.0	....	....	20.0	....	....	....
Ground shelled corn	....	4.0	....	....	....	....	0.2	0.7
Ground corn cobs	....	....	16.0	15.0	....	14.6	14.6	14.5
Soybean oil meal	....	....	2.5	2.5	....	2.3	2.0	1.5
Molasses	....	....	1.0	1.0	....	1.0[a]	1.0[a]	1.0[a]
Alfalfa meal	....	....	....	1.0	....	....	....	2.0
Bone meal	0.04	0.04	0.24	0.23	....	0.18	0.18	0.18
Salt[b]	0.08	0.08	0.15	0.15	....	0.06	0.06	0.06
Cod liver oil	....	....	0.5 oz.	0.5 oz.	....	0.01[c]	0.01[c]	....
Brewer's yeast, pounds	....	....	....	....	....	....	0.18	....
Cost per cwt. gain	$35.31	$24.21	$22.77	$23.11	$28.00	$16.00	$17.00	$19.00

[a] Molasses feed, containing 45 per cent molasses.

[b] All lots fed minerals free-choice in 1950 test, as well as bone meal and salt mixed with corn cobs.

[c] Vitamin A concentrate.

will not attack the cobs if they can get all the carbohydrates they need from the molasses.

2. *Protein Concentrate.* A protein concentrate is needed for both the bacteria and the cattle themselves. Usually 2 to 3 pounds are fed per animal daily, since there is almost no protein in the cobs.

3. *Minerals.* Cobs are low in minerals. Hence, the minerals which the bacteria require for growth, as well as those required by the cattle, must be supplied. Phosphorus is known to be essential for bacterial development. Therefore, bone meal is recommended. There is a possibility that cobalt also may be needed by the rumen flora.

4. *Vitamins.* Cobs contain none of the essential vitamins. Vitamin A is needed by cattle and possibly by the bacteria as well. Unfortunately, this vitamin cannot be supplied by feeding ordinary hay, since the feeding of an appreciable amount of hay would noticeably decrease the consumption of cobs. Consequently, either 1 to 2 pounds of alfalfa leaf meal or some kind of vitamin A supplement should be mixed with the ground cobs to insure an adequate amount of vitamin A.

Considering the difficulty of handling and storing ground cobs and the number of expensive materials that must be added to them to make them of value, it is not likely that they will be used extensively by the general farmer except during years when ordinary roughages are in short supply. On the other hand, they may be used to advantage in wintering stocker cattle near large elevators and seed-corn storage plants where a large supply of dry cobs is available and where the cobs may be ground, mixed by machinery with the proper supplements, and fed with little hand labor.

Concentrates for Stocker Cattle. Whether or not stocker cattle should be fed concentrates during the winter depends upon the amount and character of roughage fed and upon the plan of feeding to be followed during the coming summer. As a rule yearling cattle will require no concentrates other than a pound of protein supplement, and even this is not needed if 4 or more pounds of legume hay are fed. Calves that are not fed silage should be fed 2 to 5 pounds of grain daily, as they are unable to consume enough dry roughage to gain more than a pound a day, which is less than that representing normal growth and development. However, calves that are fed a full feed of good corn silage and 1 pound of a protein concentrate or 4 or 5 pounds of legume hay need not be fed grain during the winter unless they are to be marketed after only a short feed the following summer and fall. Then the feeding of some grain during the winter is advisable, as they will have a higher finish and sell for a better price when they are marketed.

TABLE 74

THE EFFECT OF FEEDING DURING THE WINTER A HALF RATION OF GRAIN TO CALVES
WHICH ARE TO BE GRAZED THE FOLLOWING SUMMER

	Missouri Exp. Station* Av. of 3 trials		Kansas Exp. Station* Av. of 3 trials	
	Grain and Roughage	Roughage Only	Grain and Roughage	Roughage Only
Av. initial weight, lbs...............	342	348	350	349
Av. winter ration				
Sh. corn, lbs.....................	3.8	...	4.6	...
Protein concentrate..............	.5	...	1.0	1.0
Corn or cane silage..............	11.2	14.3	18.4	24.0
Legume hay....................	4.2	4.5	2.0	2.0
Av. daily gain....................	1.70	.88	1.89	1.34
Grazed without grain..............	56 days	56 days	90 days	90 days
Total gain on pasture, lbs..........	22	57	98	123
Av. daily gain on pasture...........	.34	1.02	1.09	1.38
Full fed grain on pasture...........	112 days	112 days	100 days	100 days
Total gain, lbs....................	269	276	256	263
Av. daily gain....................	2.41	2.47	2.56	2.63
Final weight.....................	912	823	961	917
Market value per cwt..............	$14.17	$13.75	$14.92	$14.58
Shelled corn fed, bu...............	36.5	24.3	36.9	26.2

*Mimeographed Reports of Cattle-feeding Experiments.

Apparently there is little difference between the various protein concentrates for feeding stocker cattle provided they are fed in sufficient
amounts to furnish as much protein as is present in 1 pound of choice
cottonseed meal. Experiments carried on at the Kansas Station
indicate that 2 pounds of ground barley or wheat, 3 pounds of wheat
bran, or 4 pounds of alfalfa hay are as good supplements to a full feed
of silage as 1 pound of linseed, cottonseed, or soybean oil meal.[5]

Computing Winter Rations for Stocker Cattle. A study of a large
number of experiments with stocker cattle discloses that calves, yearlings, and 2-year-old cattle will obtain the energy they need for maximum growth without fattening if their daily rations supply net energy
equivalent to that contained in amounts of legume hay equal to approximately 2¾, 2½, and 2¼ per cent of their live weights, respectively.
Thus, a 500-pound calf would gain approximately 1¼ pounds a day on

[5] Kansas, Ft. Hays Branch, Report 1932, 1933, 1937, 1938.

a ration of 14 pounds of clover or alfalfa hay, if it had the capacity for this much feed. However, young cattle in stocker condition will eat only 2¼ to 2½ pounds of air-dry roughage per 100 pounds of live weight. Consequently, if calves are given a full feed of legume hay their energy intake will be somewhat below that needed for maximum growth. This situation must be met by replacing part of the hay with one or more other feeds, which are higher in net energy than hay and, hence, can be fed in such quantities as will furnish the amount of energy required. Such substitutions of feeds are made by using the table of "legume-hay-energy equivalents" (LHEE) given on p. 164.

Since yearling steers in stocker condition have the capacity for 2½ pounds of hay per 100 pounds of live weight and require approximately 2½ pounds per hundredweight for maintenance and maximum growth, they will make about the desired gain if they are given a full feed of good-quality legume hay. However, it may not be advisable to feed them such a ration because of its cost. The following example shows how a considerable saving may be made by limiting the hay to 1 per cent of the live weight and supplying the balance of the needed energy by feeding corn silage and oat straw.

Required: A ration for thirty 700-pound yearling steers, which will produce gains of approximately 1 pound a day.

(*a*) Ration 1: all legume hay at $30 a ton.

LHEE required $= 21,000$ lb. $\times 2.5\% = 525$ lb.	
LHEE consumed $= 21,000 \times 2.5\% = 525$ lb.	
Difference	None
Estimated daily gain (Table 76)	0.9 lb.
Cost per day, 525 lb. hay	$ 7.88
Cost per cwt. gain	$29.20

(*b*) Ration 2: hay, silage, and oat straw.

	Air-Dry Feed	LHEE
200 lb. legume hay	200	200
500 lb. corn silage	200	250
125 lb. oat straw	125	70
Total supplied	525	520
Total required	525	525
Difference	None	−5

Estimated daily gain (Table 76)		0.9 lb.
Cost per day:		
200 lb. hay	$3.00	
500 lb. silage @ $10 per ton	2.50	
125 lb. oat straw @ $12 per ton	0.75	$6.25
Cost per cwt. gain		23.15

TABLE 75

RELIABILITY OF LEGUME-HAY-ENERGY EQUIVALENT METHOD FOR ESTIMATING THE FEED REQUIREMENTS AND RATE OF GAIN OF STOCKER CATTLE

Experimental Data Computed from Reports

Station	Average Daily Gain	Number of Lots	Average LHEE per cwt.	LHPE (Legume Hay Pounds*)	Predicted† ADG (pounds)	Remarks
1. Calves						
Illinois Experiment Station	0.85 @ 1.01	4	2.5	7.5	1.0	
	1.13	1	2.7	10.0	1.2	
	1.32 @ 1.47	8	2.8	6.3	1.3	
Kansas Experiment Station	0.36 @ 0.45	3	1.9	4.0	0.4	
	0.70 @ 0.76	2	2.3	4.0	0.8	
	0.93 @ 1.14	8	2.5	4.0	1.0	
	1.20 @ 1.32	6	2.8	4.0	1.3	
	1.56‡	2	3.4	4.0	1.9	2–4 lb. shelled corn fed
Oklahoma Experiment Station	0.47 @ 0.53	3	2.2	4.5	0.7	It is possible that the sorgo silage fed in several of the tests was high in moisture and hence had a LHEE less than 13.
	0.61 @ 0.78	3	2.4	4.3	0.9	
	0.86 @ 0.93	2	2.5	5.2	1.0	
	1.07 @ 1.19	4	2.6	4.1	1.1	
	1.25 @ 1.35	5	3.0	5.1	1.5	
	1.43 @ 1.52‡	7	3.1	4.0	1.6	
Nebraska Bulletin 357	0.07 @ 0.23	5	2.1	None	0.6	Protein starvation
	0.65 @ 0.82	2	2.4	2.0	0.9	Insufficient protein
	0.80 @ 1.10	5	2.5	4.0	1.0	
2. Yearlings						
Illinois-Kansas	0.45 @ 0.47	3	2.2	5.0	0.6	
Oklahoma-Missouri Experiment Stations	0.61 @ 0.64	4	2.3	4.4	0.7	
	0.86 @ 1.09	8	2.5	4.5	0.9	
	1.14 @ 1.25	5	2.6	4.3	1.0	
	1.28 @ 1.37‡	7	2.7	4.3	1.1	

* One pound of protein concentrate is considered the protein equivalent of 4 pounds of legume hay.
† Predicted from Table 76.
‡ Cattle will begin to fatten at this rate of gain.

In calculating rations for stocker cattle consideration should be given to their protein requirements as well as to the energy value and bulk of the ration. Although young, fast-growing animals need more protein in relation to their weight than those that are more mature, the protein requirement per head is approximately the same for stocker cattle of all ages, which are in the same condition of flesh. The minimum protein requirement may be taken as the protein furnished by 4 pounds of good-quality legume hay or 1 pound of a high-grade protein supplement, such as linseed, cottonseed, or soybean oil meal. Usually calves and light yearlings will make faster and cheaper gains if this minimum protein requirement is slightly exceeded. Six pounds of legume hay or 2 pounds of hay plus 1 pound of protein supplement are recommended for calves that receive the rest of their ration in the form of corn silage or other carbonaceous feeds. Likewise, 5 pounds of legume hay or 3 pounds of hay and ½ pound of protein supplement are recommended for yearling cattle, which weigh under 750 pounds in stocker condition.

Table 76, compiled from the results of nearly 200 lots of stocker

TABLE 76

LEGUME-HAY-ENERGY EQUIVALENT REQUIRED PER 100 POUNDS LIVE WEIGHT
FOR DIFFERENT RATES OF GAIN MADE BY STOCKER CATTLE GETTING THE
MINIMUM PROTEIN REQUIRED FOR NORMAL GROWTH

Average Daily Gain	LHEE per 100 Pounds Live Weight		
	Calves	Yearlings	Two-Year-Olds
0	. . .	. . .	1.7
0.1	. . .	. . .	1.8
0.2	. . .	. . .	1.9
0.3	. . .	1.9	2.0
0.4	. . .	2.0	2.1
0.5	2.0	2.1	2.2
0.6	2.1	2.2	2.3
0.7	2.2	2.3	2.4
0.8	2.3	2.4	2.5
0.9	2.4	2.5	2.6
1.0	2.5	2.6	2.7
1.1	2.6	2.7	. . .
1.2	2.7	2.8	. . .
1.3	2.8	. . .	. . .
1.4	2.9	. . .	. . .
1.5	3.0	. . .	. . .

calves and yearlings fed at experiment stations of the Corn Belt states, may be used to compute a daily ration that will produce the desired rate of gain in a drove of stocker cattle. Conversely, it may be used to predict the approximate rate of gain that will be obtained from feeding a given ration. Obviously, the calculated results will not always agree exactly with the performance of a particular drove of cattle, since the rate of gain and feed consumption are affected by the age and condition of the cattle when put into the feed lot and by the quality of the feeds fed. However, the close agreement between the table and the results obtained in feeding trials would seem to warrant its use by the practical feeder in estimating the gains and feed requirements of stocker cattle. The following problem illustrates how to calculate a ration that will satisfy a given feeding situation.

How much corn silage, clover hay, oat straw, and linseed meal will be required by fifty 400-pound steer calves to make an average daily gain of 1.25 pounds from November 20 to May 1 (160 days)?

Solution:

Initial weight 20,000 lb. ⎫
Final weight 30,000 lb. ⎬ Average weight 25,000 lb.

LHEE required daily per 100 lb. live weight: 2.75 (Table 76).
Total LHEE required: 250 × 2.75 = 688.
Estimated air-dry feed required to satisfy appetite of calves: 250 × 2.50 = 625.
Protein requirements (in terms of legume hay)
  Minimum: 4 lb. × 50 = 200 lb.
  Optimum: 6 lb. × 50 = 300 lb.

	ADF	LHEE	LHPE[a]
Required:	625	688	200 @ 300
Average daily feed:			
3 bales clover hay (70 lbs.)	210	210	210
750 lb. silage	300	375	. . .
115 lb. oat straw	115	64	. . .
20 lb. linseed meal	. . .	40	80
Total required	625	689	290

[a] Legume hay protein equivalent.

Stocker calves fed at the Indiana and Missouri Stations have been fed more LHEE units per pound of gain than those fed at the Illinois, Kansas, and Oklahoma Stations. A study of the rations fed at these stations discloses that most of them furnished considerably more air-dry feed per hundred pounds live weight than did those used at Illinois, Kansas, and Oklahoma. Consequently, it is possible that not all the feeds were consumed, especially the hay, which may have been of low quality. Also, a number of the Indiana and Missouri calves were fed from 3 to 5 pounds of grain per head daily. Apparently grain fed in excess of 2 pounds per day has a lower LHEE than 2.5 for stocker calves, especially when fed with dry roughages. This may be due to the fact that the rumen bacteria obtain so much food nutrients from the grain that they do not break down the roughage as completely as they do when little or no grain is present.

TABLE 77

RECOMMENDED WINTER RATIONS FOR STOCKER CATTLE

Rations		Calves	Yearlings	Two-year-olds
		lbs.	lbs.	lbs.
I.	Alfalfa or Clover Hay............	5–6	4–5	4–5
	Corn Silage........	25	15	20
	Oat Straw.........	—	8–10	12–14
II.	Clover Hay........	8–10	6–8	4–5
	Corn or Oats......	3–4	—	—
	Straw or Stover....	2–4	12–15	16–20
III.	Linseed or Cotton-seed Meal.......	1–1.5	1.0	1.0
	Corn Silage........	20–25	20	25
	Straw or Stover....	2–3	10–12	14–16

Note.—1. All straw and stover should be fed according to appetite.
2. Only about 60 per cent of corn stover is eaten, while from 85 to 90 per cent of stover silage is consumed. However, approximately 50 per cent of the weight of stover silage is water. Hence, one-third more stover silage than dry stover must be fed to furnish the same amount of edible dry matter.

Winter Feeding of Young Bulls and Heifers. Naturally, young animals intended for the breeding herd should be fed more liberally than animals being grown for the feed lot. Since size and all-round development are of much importance in breeding animals, the level of feeding should be such as to insure maximum growth. Although some thought must be given to the cost of the ration, a niggardly allowance of feed is bound to prove costly in the long run. Especially is this likely to be true with purebred bulls and heifers. Nothing impresses prospective purchasers so favorably as well-conditioned young stock well grown out. Stunted, half-fed animals, on the other hand, are not wanted by breeders at any price. While it occasionally happens that a young bull or heifer is injured by overfeeding and fitting for exhibition or sale purposes, the loss so occasioned is insignificant compared with that resulting from the thousands of undersized, poorly developed animals that are grossly underfed. However, the author does not mean to excuse overfeeding. Not only does it entail a loss in money spent for unnecessary feed, but it results in injury to what are usually the most promising young animals of the herd.

It seldom pays to omit grain from the winter ration of high-class young breeding cattle. Grade heifers to be used for raising calves for the feed lot may be handled much as ordinary stockers, but young pure-bred stock are deserving of better treatment. Care should be taken lest the grain ration contain too much corn. Oats, barley, and bran are not so fattening and are more conducive to growth. A very good grain mixture for young breeding cattle is made of equal parts by measure of ground corn, crushed oats, bran, and chopped alfalfa or clover hay. This mixture is light and bulky and at the same time high in nutrients. Especially does it contain generous quantities of calcium, phosphorus, and nitrogen, all of which are needed bv growing animals. Other grain mixtures that have been found satisfactory by experienced cattlemen are the following:

I		II	
Shelled Corn	4 parts (by weight)	Shelled Corn	3 parts (by weight)
Oats	3 parts	Oats	2 parts
Linseed Meal	1 part	Bran	1 part

Young breeding cattle should have the best of roughage. Although legume hay and silage should form the bulk of the roughage fed, a considerable saving of these rather expensive feeds can be effected by allowing the cattle free access to corn stover or straw while they are outside during the day. If the feed racks are some distance from the shed or barn such feeds will induce the cattle to take more exercise than they otherwise would. Stalk fields and grass paddocks that were lightly grazed during the previous autumn are especially valuable for this purpose.

Summer Management of Young Cattle. The problems of management during the summer are simple in comparison with those arising during the winter. With the arrival of grass, feeding problems are largely solved, inasmuch as grass is an ideal ration for young growing animals. Not only is it nutritious, rich in growth-producing vitamins, and fairly well balanced as to those compounds needed for the building of bone and muscle, but its succulent nature makes for the health and thrift that normally accompany a well-regulated digestive tract. Pastures to be used by young breeding animals should not be heavily stocked, unless there are adequate facilities for feeding harvested feeds if the supply of grass becomes short.

Grass alone will ordinarily provide a satisfactory ration during May and June, or until the arrival of flies and heat imposes a heavy tax upon the ability of young cattle to continue their growth without loss of flesh. With stocker steers or grade yearling heifers intended for a commercial breeding herd, economy of maintenance will usually require that grass alone, if it is available, should form the ration for the entire summer, even though the cattle lose some flesh and are slowed up somewhat in rate of growth. If the grass fails because of dry weather, pastures should be supplemented by feeding silage, hay, or green corn.

Young purebred cattle, on the other hand, should receive some grain during mid-summer to fortify them against the deleterious effects of

Fig. 36. An ideal summer environment for purebred yearling heifers.

flies and heat. Grass alone furnishes hardly enough energy to supply fully the needs of growing animals under such conditions, and, if other feeds are not provided, the cattle will fall off in flesh and slacken their growth. A moderate amount of grain fed once a day will forestall such an occurrence and will bring the young animals through the summer in good condition. This grain may be fed in bunks placed in the pastures, but a much better plan is to feed it in the barn where the cattle may be comfortably stabled in darkened stalls during the heat of the day. Although this plan is perhaps impractical for all the young cattle in a large herd, it should be carried out with the best and most promising individuals, as well as with those youngsters that, for some reason or other, are thin or undersized and need special care and attention.

Summer Gains of Young Cattle on Pasture. The gains made during the summer by young cattle on pasture will, of course, vary greatly with the condition of the animals at the beginning of the grazing season and with the kind of forage provided. Also, they will vary from year

TABLE 78

DEVELOPMENT OF STOCKER CATTLE FROM WEANLING CALVES TO THREE-YEAR-OLD STEERS WHERE LOW FEED COSTS ARE EMPHASIZED RATHER THAN NORMAL GROWTH AND DEVELOPMENT

Winter Ration	West Virginia Bulletin 218, 1928			Kansas Circular 97, 1923	
	Clover Hay Corn Silage Wheat Straw	C. S. Meal Corn Silage Wheat Straw	Mixed Hay Grain Mixture*	Corn Silage C. S. Meal	Alfalfa Hay
1st winter as calves, days..........	124	124	124	134	134
Av. daily ration, lb.					
Hay........................	3.2	....	10.0	....	10.3
Silage......................	12.3	12.3	....	25.0	....
Straw.......................	1.0	3.3	....	....	....
Concentrate.................	....	.7	3.0	1.0	....
Av. daily gain.................	.47	.64	.91	.72	.45
1st summer on pasture, days.......	236	236	236	210	210
Av. daily gain.................	.54	.50	.42	1.32	1.44
2nd winter as yearlings, days.......	120	120	120	161	161
Av. daily ration, lb.					
Hay........................	5.0	....	5.0	....	20.2
Silage......................	18.0	18.0	18.0	35.8	....
Straw.......................	2.0	5.0	2.0	....	....
Concentrate.................	....	1.0	....	1.0	....
Av. daily gain.................	.73	.66	.33	.97	.47
2nd summer on pasture, days......	241	241	241	210	210
Av. daily gain.................	.98	1.08	1.18	.68	1.14
3rd winter as 2-year-olds, days.....		126		150	150
Av. daily ration, lb.					
Hay........................		....		....	24.6
Silage......................		26.0		35.9	....
Straw.......................		4.8		....	....
Concentrate.................		1.1		1.4	....
Av. daily gain.................		.28		.13	.25
3rd summer on pasture, days.......		141			
Av. daily gain.................		2.26			
Av. final weight...............		1,259			
Total days on stocker rations		988		865	865
Av. total gain.................		872		693	716
Av. daily gain.................		.88		.80	.83

* Grain mixture consisted of 3 parts of corn, 1 of bran, and 1 of linseed meal.

to year because of weather conditions, which greatly affect the amount and palatability of the forage. Occasionally a severe drought and the discomfort caused by flies and oppressive heat may result in a loss during mid-summer of a considerable amount of the gain put on during the spring. As a consequence, the gain for the entire season will be disappointingly small. However, such years are in the course of time offset by unusually favorable seasons, when the gains made are almost double those obtained during an average year.

Yearling cattle weighing around 550 to 650 pounds when turned onto pasture will gain at the rate of $1\frac{1}{4}$ to $1\frac{1}{2}$ pounds a day on good permanent pasture like bluegrass, brome grass, or on the bluestem pastures of Kansas—or 200 to 250 pounds for the season. Two-year-olds will gain 50 to 75 pounds more if the forage is sufficiently abundant and nutritious to cause a noticeable improvement in degree of flesh, but 50 to 75 pounds less if it provides for only growth requirements. Rotation pastures that consist largely of legumes and hence retain their freshness and palatability throughout the summer may usually be counted on for about 50 per cent more gain per head than is obtained from permanent pastures during the same season. The gain made by young cattle on pasture is treated in more detail in Chapter 25.

PART · 3

Fattening Cattle
for Market

14 ——————— Fattening Cattle for Market

Fattening cattle for market is one of the most important phases of the American agricultural economy. Although it is carried on most extensively in the Corn Belt, it is by no means confined to that area. Cattle feeding is becoming more and more important in the Pacific Coast states, in the Middle Atlantic states, and in the South with the passing of each year. The inherent nature of beef cattle to lay on fat whenever they have the opportunity to consume more nutrients than are needed for growth and maintenance makes the fattening of cattle well suited to any area that produces an abundance of grain, high-quality roughages, and good pastures.

TABLE 79

ESTIMATED NUMBER OF CATTLE PUT ON GRAIN FEED
ANNUALLY IN CORN BELT AND BORDER STATES*

(5-Year Average 1939–1943)

State	Number Fed[a] (1000 head)	Percentage of Total
Iowa	1258	29
Illinois	702	16
Nebraska	471	11
Missouri	408	9.5
Minnesota	385	9
Kansas	328	8
Indiana	220	5
Ohio	161	4
South Dakota	158	4
Michigan	109	2.5
Wisconsin	94	2
Total	4294	100.0

* U.S.D.A. Technical Bulletin 900, 1945.
[a] Includes only cattle fattened for market as a more or less distinct agricultural enterprise, and excludes small operations incidental to dairy and general farming.

Reasons for Feeding Cattle. Cattle are usually fed for one or more of the following reasons: (1) to obtain more than current prices for farm-grown grains; (2) to market roughages and pasture at a profit;

and (3) to maintain and improve the fertility of the soil. These
reasons may be combined by saying that cattle are fed to obtain the
highest net return for farm-grown feeds. This statement implies that
cattle are fattened principally on feeds grown on the farm where the
cattle are fed. This is largely true, although there are a few large

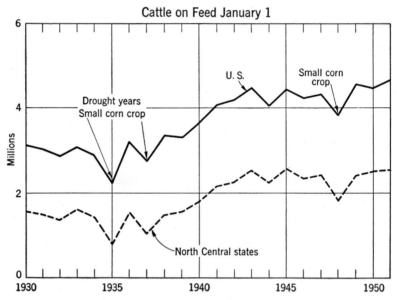

Fig. 37. Estimated number of cattle fed annually in droves sufficiently large to
constitute a major farm enterprise. (*The Iowa Farm Outlook Letters, Jan. 22,
1948, and Nov. 24, 1949, Iowa State College.*)

feeders who buy most or nearly all of their feeds and who may even
lease the ground on which their feed lots are located. Such men feed
cattle for the same reason that other men operate factories; namely,
to make a profit by combining raw materials, which are of little value
in their natural form, into a product for which there is a strong
demand and which, therefore, can be sold for a much higher price
than the cost of the raw materials.

Sources of Feeder Cattle. A considerable number of the cattle
fattened in the Corn Belt have been bred on the Western Range and
have been purchased by Corn Belt feeders either directly from the
ranchers or at public markets where they have been shipped by the
ranchers for sale. Experienced feeders usually prefer to buy direct
from the ranchers, in order to see and select the cattle under more
natural conditions and to avoid the delays and exposure to weather

and disease which cattle sold through a public stockyard sometimes encounter. Many Corn Belt feeders continue to buy their cattle from the same locality or even the same rancher year after year, because of the excellent record the cattle have made in the feed lot. However, the beginning feeder, who is inexperienced in the selection of cattle and not very well informed about prices of the different grades, usually will find it to his advantage to buy at a central market. Here he will have the help and expert advice of the feeder buyer of a commission agency in haggling over prices, sorting the cattle, making payment, and arranging for shipment. The small fee charged for these services may be but a fraction of the money saved by culling out two or three undesirable steers which the buyer might have taken if he had been making his own purchase.

TABLE 80

STOCKER AND FEEDER CATTLE RECEIVED IN EIGHT
IMPORTANT CATTLE FEEDING STATES*

(2-Year Average, 1949–1950)

	From Public Stockyards		Direct Shipment		Total		Total for 6-Month Period	
	Number	Percentage of Monthly Total	Number	Percentage of Monthly Total	Number	Percentage of Yearly Total	Number	Percentage
January...	86,700	77	26,500	23	113,200	3.5		
February..	70,500	77	21,500	23	92,000	2.9		
March....	95,300	71	38,200	29	133,500	4.1		
April......	82,400	72	31,800	28	114,200	3.6		
May......	78,800	71	31,900	23	110,700	3.5		
June......	108,500	72	41,700	28	150,200	4.7	713,800	22
July......	102,800	65	55,400	35	158,200	4.9		
August....	199,800	64	111,700	36	311,500	9.8		
September.	315,100	61	201,400	39	516,500	16.2		
October...	426,900	52	389,400	48	816,300	25.5		
November.	269,500	60	188,400	40	457,900	14.3		
December .	138,100	61	86,900	39	225,000	7.0	2,486,400	78
	1,975,400	62	1,224,800	38	3,200,200	100.0	3,200,200	100

* Ohio, Indiana, Illinois, Michigan, Wisconsin, Minnesota, Iowa, Nebraska. Compiled from monthly reports of Livestock Branch, Production and Marketing Administration, U.S.D.A.

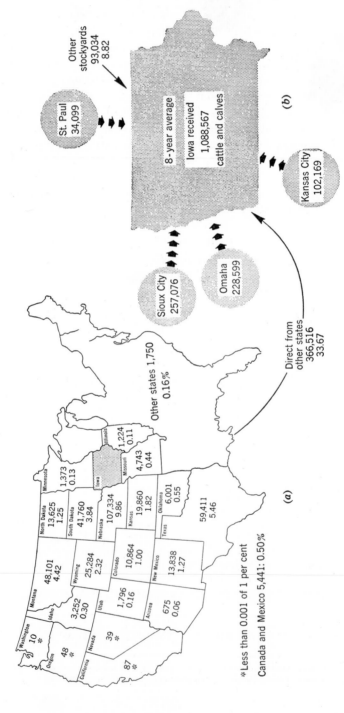

Fig. 38. Sources of feeder cattle purchased by Iowa cattle feeders (average of years from 1940 to 1947). (*a*) Direct from growers and dealers. The upper figures on the map give the numbers of cattle purchased direct from growers, and the lower figures the percentage which the direct shipments constitute of the total number of stocker and feeder cattle purchased. (*b*) Public markets (*Iowa Farm Science, Vol 4, No. 2, August, 1949, and No. 4, October, 1949, Iowa State College.*)

Although most of the cattle that are fed in droves of a carload or more are shipped-in cattle and, consequently, are listed in tabulations of direct shipments and shipments from public stockyards (see Table 80), they by no means comprise all the cattle that are fed in the Corn Belt and that are sold for slaughter from that area. The recent increase in the number of beef cow herds in the Corn Belt states has greatly added to the supply of locally bred feeder cattle. Many of these calves and yearlings are fed out by their breeders, but a number are sold to farmers in other counties and states where more corn is produced than in the areas where the cattle were bred. In several counties auction sales are held every fall to which breeders may consign their cattle and at which feeders who need cattle for their feed lots may often buy more advantageously than they can either at the market or on the range. (See Fig. 39.)

TABLE 81

SOURCES OF FEEDER CATTLE AND CALVES PURCHASED BY ILLINOIS FEEDERS*

(July 1, 1949–June 30, 1950)

Shipped from Public Stockyards			Direct from Growers and Dealers		
Point of Shipment	Number	Percentage	Place of Origin	Number	Percentage
Kansas City	136,900	30	Nebraska	67,400	19
East St. Louis	69,000	15	Montana	58,900	17
South St. Paul	59,000	13	Canada	45,200	13
Chicago	53,400	12	Texas	43,100	12
West Fargo	32,200	7	Kansas	27,800	8
Denver	25,100	5	South Dakota	23,600	7
Peoria	19,900	4	Wyoming	18,800	5
Omaha	12,100	3	North Dakota	15,000	4
Oklahoma City	10,500	2	New Mexico	13,100	4
Sioux City	9,300	2	Colorado	10,600	3
Fort Worth	7,300	2	Iowa	8,600	2
Wichita	5,200	1	Oklahoma	5,600	1.5
Other yards	18,200	4	Missouri	5,300	1.5
			Other states	11,600	3
Total	458,100	100	Total	354,600	100
Grand total		56			44

* State of Illinois, Department of Agriculture, 33rd Annual Report, 1950.

Methods of Feeding Cattle. A wide variety of methods are used in fattening cattle for market. Although there is no best method, even for a particular feeding situation, some methods are more likely to prove satisfactory than others when certain conditions prevail. Among the factors that should be given consideration in determining the method of feeding to be used are the following:

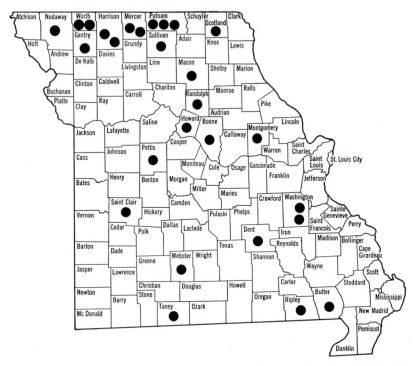

FIG. 39. Feeder calf auction sales held in Missouri, September 22 to October 20, 1951. A total of 18,000 calves and 6,000 yearlings were sold in these sales, all of which were from relatively small herds owned within a few miles of the towns where the sales were held. (*Courtesy Animal Husbandry Extension Service, University of Missouri.*)

(*a*) The period during which the cattle are to be fed.

(*b*) The amounts of grain and roughage to be marketed through the cattle.

(*c*) The availability of pasture.

On the basis of these three factors, the more common methods of feeding may be classified as follows:

(*a*) Short, medium, and long feeds. Usually anything under 120 days is termed a short feed, whereas a program that calls for the feeding of grain for more than 220 days is referred to as a long feed. Any period between these limits, of course, is regarded as a medium feed.

(*b*) Full feeding and limited feeding. Cattle that are accustomed to a heavy feed of grain within a month or 6 weeks of the start of the feeding period and that are fed thereafter as much grain as they will eat are called full-fed cattle. Those that receive much less than a full feed during half or more of the feeding period are said to be fattened on a limited grain ration. Obviously, those in the second group are fed large amounts of roughage.

(c) Methods of feeding are also classified as dry-lot feeding and pasture feeding, depending on the use made of pasture during the period in which the cattle are fed. Frequently these two methods are combined by feeding on pasture during the early part of the summer and in the dry lot during the late summer and fall.

Although relatively few cattle, other than cows, are sold for slaughter in the Corn Belt directly from pasture without their having been fed any grain, the productiveness and high nutritive value of the improved pastures now being established may make the fattening of 2-year-old steers on grass alone a common practice in some areas of this region. However, the feeding of grain for at least a few weeks before marketing will usually be highly profitable.

The Kind of Cattle to Feed. Most systems of feeding require a certain kind of cattle if they are to be most successful. Conversely, each type of cattle should be fed according to a rather well-recognized plan if they are to return the most profit. During a period when prices are rising and profits are large, a particular drove of cattle may return a profit almost regardless of the way they are fed, but when the reverse is true the kind of cattle purchased must be well suited to the plan of feeding if a profit is to be made.

Feeder cattle vary widely in those characteristics which affect their suitability for different feeding conditions and which, therefore, are important to prospective buyers. Their chief differences are as follows:

(a) Age: Calves, yearlings, and 2-year-olds.
(b) Condition: Thin, medium, and fleshy.
(c) Weight: Light, medium, and heavy. Weight, of course, is the result of both age and condition. For example, a calf 9 months old in fleshy condition may weigh as much or more than a very thin yearling.
(d) Sex: Steers, heifers, and cows. Steers may be of any age from 4 to 40 months, but feeding heifers are seldom older than 24 months. If older, they probably have produced a calf, after which time they are called "heiferettes."

(e) Quality: High, medium, low. Quality refers to the refinement and smoothness of the animal, particularly of bone and hide.

(f) Breeding: Beef, mixed, and dairy. Cattle are said to show beef breeding when they show the characteristics of the Angus, Hereford, or Shorthorn breeds. A drove of cattle of mixed breeding usually will contain at least some animals that have both beef and dairy ancestry.

(g) Grade: Choice, good, medium, and common. The grade of an animal indicates its all-round desirability for the use to which it will be put—in the case of a feeder steer its desirability for feeding. The grade of a feeder steer or heifer is determined chiefly by its form, quality, and breeding.

(h) Origin: Some cattle feeders attach some importance to the region from which the cattle have been shipped. Cattle from certain areas in Texas and New Mexico are very popular with certain Corn Belt feeders. Others maintain that such cattle lack the hardiness possessed by those bred and raised farther north. However, it seems highly doubtful if any preference should be had for a drove of cattle solely because they have come from a certain area. Every important cattle-breeding area of the country produces some excellent cattle and some that are only mediocre. Each drove should be judged on its own merit and not on that of another shipment from the same locality.

Through Billing. Many western ranchers who sell their feeder cattle at Kansas City, Omaha, Sioux City, and other markets at the western edge of the Corn Belt consign them to Chicago, but with the provision that they be unloaded at the nearer market for feed, rest, and "exposure for sale." Since cattle so billed often save the buyer several dollars in freight charges, they usually sell at a slightly higher price than they would have brought if they had been billed only to the market where they were sold. Thus, both the seller and the buyer divide the saving that results from through billing.

The buyer of through-billed cattle pays the freight for the entire distance from the loading point in the West to the unloading station in the Corn Belt. However, in paying for the cattle he is credited with the freight charge on the shipment from the loading point to the market. Since the through rate is considerably less than the sum of the two local rates, the buyer often makes a saving of $15 to $30 a car. However, in order to enjoy the advantage of a through billing, the shipment from the market must be essentially the same as that received. In other words, if any animals are culled out or added, the

TABLE 82

SEASONAL VARIATION IN NUMBER AND KIND OF CATTLE ON
FEED IN ILLINOIS, 1950*

	January 1, 1950		April 1, 1950		July 1, 1950		October 1, 1950	
	Number	Per-centage	Number	Per-centage	Number	Per-centage	Number	Per-centage
Weight classes								
Over 1300 lb...	1,000	0.1	4,000	1.0	17,000	5.0	4,500	2.0
1100–1300 lb...	32,000	6.0	25,000	6.0	36,000	11.0	20,000	8.5
900–1100 lb....	116,000	21.8	104,000	25.0	106,000	32.0	88,500	36.0
600–900 lb.....	219,000	41.3	200,000	48.0	158,000	48.0	94,000	40.5
Under 600 lb...	164,000	30.8	85,000	20.0	13,000	4.0	29,000	13.0
	532,000	100.0	418,000	100.0	330,000	100.0	236,000	100.0
Sex classes								
Steers.........	322,000	60.6	272,000	65.0	248,000	75.0	171,500	72.5
Heifers........	45,000	8.5	42,000	10.0	46,000	14.0	42,500	18.0
Calves........	156,000	29.3	100,000	24.0	33,000	10.0	18,500	8.0
Cows and others	9,000	1.6	4,000	1.0	3,000	1.0	3,500	1.5
	532,000	100.0	418,000	100.0	330,000	100.0	236,000	100.0
Time on feed								
Under 3 months	446,000	83.8	138,000	33.0	46,000	14.0	145,500	63.5
3–6 months....	75,000	14.2	263,000	63.0	132,000	40.0	41,000	16.5
Over 6 months	11,000	2.0	17,000	4.0	152,000	46.0	49,500	20.0
	532,000	100.0	418,000	100.0	330,000	100.0	236,000	100.0

* Illinois Crop Reporting Service, Quarterly Reports, 1950.

through billing becomes void. In a consignment of two or more cars, shifting of animals from one car to another is permitted; also, one or more cars may be forwarded on the billing, while the cattle in the other cars are sold on the transit market in small lots.

Thirty-Six-Hour Release. In 1873 the Congress of the United States passed a law that required railroad companies to unload livestock for feed, water, and rest before they had been confined in cars for more than 28 hours. This law was amended in 1906 to permit the transportation of animals an additional 8 hours, provided the shipper has signed a so-called 36-hour release. Since the feed is added to the freight bill, and a charge of $1 or $2 a car is made for unloading and reloading, consignors habitually sign the 36-hour release, if there is a possibility that the shipment may be en route longer than **28** hours. Moreover, each unloading stop that may be saved during a long haul means a more prompt arrival at the destination, since the law prescribes that each feed and rest period must be not less than 5 hours.

Feeding in Transit. Corn Belt cattle feeders who purchase feeder cattle at Missouri River markets or west thereof, including purchases on the range, frequently may make a substantial savings in freight charges by taking advantage of the feeding-in-transit privilege offered by railroad companies that serve this territory. This plan is offered by the railroads as an inducement to feeders to forward their cattle by rail instead of by truck when they are marketed at the end of the feeding period.

Shippers who wish to use the feed-in-transit provision will bill their cattle from point of origin to their home stations at the current tariff rate for feeder cattle, but must preserve their receipted freight bills to be presented to local agents when the cattle are rebilled to their final destination after a grazing or feeding period of **10** days to **12** months. In waybilling from the transit station the agent must note on the waybill full reference to the waybill on which the cattle were received, showing date and place of origin, the initials, number, and size of car in which the stock was received, and the amount of freight charges collected into the transit station. Also, under the title "Description of Stock" the notation *fattened in transit* will be made in large letters.

Freight charges on cattle waybilled as described above will be the sum of the three following items: (1) The through fat cattle rate from initial origin to Chicago for the weight used to determine the charge into the transit station. This usually will be the **22,000**-pound minimum established for a 36-foot car. (2) The local carload fat cattle rate from the transit station to market for all weight in excess of that used in computing incoming freight. (3) A transit charge of **$7** to **$12** a car made to cover switching and waybilling at the transit station.

Total freight charges thus calculated cannot be greater than the freight paid from point of origin to transit station plus freight charges from transit station to market for the total weight shipped at the fat cattle rate. If it is greater, the local charges into and out of the transit station apply.

Inasmuch as an extra charge per hundred pounds is made for feeding-in-transit shipments to stations not on a direct route between point of origin and final destination, the greater savings are made by feeders who live near railroads that have their own trackage into Chicago.

Contract Feeding. Occasionally a large rancher, packer, or cattle speculator will contract with one or more Corn Belt farmers to fatten

TABLE 83

EXAMPLE OF SAVING EFFECTED BY USING FEEDING-IN-TRANSIT PRIVILEGE

(Twenty-four 900-pound steers purchased at Denver; to be fed near Webster
City, Iowa, until they weigh 1200 pounds; then shipped to Chicago.)

1. Ordinary rate
   Denver to Webster City, Iowa
   22,000 pounds at 71¢ (feeder cattle rate)   = $156.20
   Webster City to Chicago
   28,000 pounds[a] at 59¢ (fat cattle rate)   =   165.20 $321.40

2. Feeding-in-transit rate
   Denver to Chicago
   22,000 pounds at $1.02 (fat cattle rate)   =   224.40
   Webster City to Chicago
   6000 pounds at 59¢ (fat cattle rate)   =   35.40
   Service charge for feeding in transit   11.92   271.72
   Saving made $ 49.68

[a] Eight hundred pounds deducted from market weight because of "fill" after unloading.

cattle without a change of ownership. Although the terms of feeding contracts vary widely, the owner of the cattle usually bills the cattle to Chicago with feed-in-transit privileges. This freight is paid by the owner, and the feeder pays the local freight rate on the added weight from the feeding station to the market. Usually the feeder agrees to feed the cattle a certain ration for a specified time for a stated charge per hundred for a minimum gain of 200 to 350 pounds a head. For all gains over this minimum he receives a considerably larger amount per hundred pounds. Death losses, if any, are usually shared by the owner to the extent of the average weight of the drove into the feed lot, which means that the feeder bears the loss of the feed eaten by the dead steers. Gains made by hogs kept in the feed lot and manure produced by the cattle usually belong to the feeder, sometimes as payment for his labor and sometimes as rental for the feed lots, buildings, and equipment used.

Contract feeding has never been popular in the Corn Belt because seldom have both parties been satisfied with the results of the arrangement. If prices are rising and the cattle return the owner a handsome profit, the feeder is unhappy that he does not own the cattle himself and thereby receive the owner's profits as well as his own. And if prices are falling and the cattle are sold for less than was expected, the owner is dissatisfied when he finds himself taking home less money than he was offered for his feeder cattle the previous fall. Since it takes two parties to make a contract and usually only one is interested in such an arrangement, very little contract feeding is normally done.

15 ——————— The Importance of Age in Growth and Fattening

On account of the increased demand by the consuming public for smaller and lighter cuts of beef, there has arisen during the past 30 years a tendency for producers to market their cattle at younger ages than was considered advisable or even possible 40 or 50 years ago. Whereas in former times the custom was to market steers at 3 and 4 years of age, fat yearlings and 2-year-olds now make up the larger percentage of market receipts. Before, the term "feeder steer" signified to both rancher and Corn Belt feeder a 2½- or 3-year-old animal weighing around 1000 pounds. At present, both of them insist on qualifying the term, and speak of "2-year-old feeders," "yearling feeders," and "feeder calves." What age of animals to feed is one of the important questions to be decided by every farmer who plans to feed cattle.

Effect of Age upon Rate of Gain. A discussion of the effect of age upon the daily gains made by cattle must necessarily be treated from two standpoints: (1) its effect upon cattle that have been sufficiently well fed from birth to permit them to grow and fatten at the same time; and (2) its effect upon cattle that are suddenly given a fattening ration after having been for some time on a ration that would produce only growth. Inasmuch as cattle make their most rapid growth during the first year and gradually slow down thereafter, it is evident that in well-fed cattle the rate of gain varies inversely with age. Young pure-bred cattle that are being developed for show purposes and are fed liberally from the time they are old enough to eat gain about 70 per cent as much the second year as they do the first, and 50 per cent as much the third as they do the second. In this connection the attention of the reader is called to Table 84.

An entirely different situation exists when thin cattle of different ages are placed in the fattening pen and are fed liberally for perhaps the first time. In this case the larger capacity of the older steers gives them a decided advantage over the younger cattle, with the results that they gain much more rapidly. Here the daily gains vary directly with the age of the animals, instead of inversely.

TABLE 84

EFFECT OF AGE UPON RATE OF GROWTH AND FATTENING

Average Weight of Steers at Chicago Fat Stock Show.   1878–1885*

Class	Number of Cattle Averaged	Average Age in Days	Average Live Weight (Lbs.)	Daily Gain from Birth (Lbs.)	Gain for Last Period	
					Total (Lbs.)	Daily (Lbs.)
Calves.............	30	297	780	2.63	780	2.63
Yearlings...........	152	612	1334	2.18	554	1.76
Two-year-olds.......	145	943	1639	1.74	305	.92
Three-year-olds......	133	1283	1938	1.51	299	.87

* Woll, F. W.   Productive Feeding of Farm Animals, p. 260, J. B. Lippincott Company, 1915.

TABLE 85

THE EFFECT OF AGE UPON THE RATE OF GAIN MADE BY FEEDER STEERS WHILE ON FULL FEED

	Calves		Yearlings		Two-Year-Olds	
	Days Fed	Av. Daily Gain	Days Fed	Av. Daily Gain	Days Fed	Av. Daily Gain
Indiana Bulletin No. 146............	270	1.93	180	2.38	180	2.57
Indiana Bulletin No. 146............	270	1.82	210	2.06	180	2.65
Indiana Bulletin No. 146............	270	1.93	210	2.24	180	2.27
Ohio Bimonthly Bulletins No. 93 and 94	175	2.19	147	2.42	119	2.81
Ohio Bimonthly Bulietins No. 105 and 106......	182	2.23	154	2.32	126	2.65
Iowa Bulletin No. 271...............	240	2.22	180	2.64	120	2.76
Iowa Bulletin No. 271...............	240	2.32	160	2.47	150	2.48
Average of 7 trials.................	235	2.09	177	2.36	151	2.60

Two, 2¼, and 2½ pounds may be regarded as average daily gains for calves, yearlings, and 2-year-old steers, respectively, for the whole feeding period.

Effect of Age upon Economy of Gains. Numerous experiments point to the fact that young animals require less feed for each pound increase in body weight than do older cattle. The principal explanation of this is found in the fact that increases in the body weight of young animals are due partly to the growth of muscles, bones, and vital organs, whereas those of older cattle consist largely of deposits of fat. Fat contains much less water and a great deal more energy than an equal weight of any other kind of animal tissue. Hence, more feed

TABLE 86

INFLUENCE OF AGE UPON ECONOMY OF GAINS*

Age............	30–360 days	360–720 days	720–1080 days	1080–1440 days
Dry Matter per lb. Gain.....	5.08 lbs.	11.26 lbs.	17.02 lbs.	23.45 lbs.

* Missouri Research Bulletin 43, 1921.

EFFECT OF AGE OF FEEDER CATTLE UPON ECONOMY OF GAINS*

	Calves	Yearlings	Two-year-clds
Av. Initial Weight, lbs................	467	715	966
Av. Time Fed, days.................	235	177	151
Feed per Cwt. Gain:			
Shelled Corn†......................	557	645	717
Protein Concentrate...............	92	97	95
Dry Roughage Equivalent†.........	232	283	307

* Average of the 7 trials which appear in Table 85.
† For experiments where corn silage was fed, 15 per cent of the weight of silage was considered its shelled corn equivalent, and 25 per cent its dry roughage equivalent.

is required for its formation. Other factors contributing to the more economical gains made by young animals are (1) a slightly larger consumption of feed in proportion to their body weight, and (2) the much greater thoroughness with which young cattle masticate their feed in eating and rumination. As a result of their relatively large feed consumption, a smaller percentage of the ration is used to satisfy maintenance requirements than is used for this purpose by older animals, thus making available a greater percentage of the total feed consumed for the production of growth and fat. That cheaper gains are made by young cattle than by old is more and more evident as the feeding period progresses. This fact is well brought out in Table 87, showing the results obtained at the Nebraska Experiment Station with steers of various ages fed for a period of 200 days. Whereas in calves the total feed required per hundred pounds gain during the last half of the period was but 18 per cent above that required during the first, in the yearling, 2-year-old, and 3-year-old steers it was 35, 44, and 69 per cent greater, respectively. These figures bear out the fact that calves may be fed profitably over a longer period

TABLE 87

INFLUENCE OF AGE UPON THE VARIATION IN ECONOMY OF GAINS THROUGHOUT
THE FEEDING PERIOD*

Feed per Hundredweight Gain

Period	Three-year-old Steers	Two-year-old Steers	Yearlings	Calves
	lbs.	lbs.	lbs.	lbs.
1st 100 Days...				
Corn........	586	597	534	431
Alfalfa.......	363	346	304	221
2nd 100 Days				
Corn........	1282	1085	916	623
Alfalfa.......	320	272	219	148
Total 200 Days				
Corn........	835	798	702	529
Alfalfa.......	350	314	266	186

* Nebraska Bulletin 229, 1928.

than older cattle. If necessary they can be held for a considerable length of time awaiting a favorable market, and all the while they will be making fair gains at not too great a cost. Mature steers, on the other hand, are held at great expense. After being on full feed for 150 or 160 days they gain very slowly, and the additional weight is achieved only by a very wasteful and extravagant use of feed.

Effect of Age upon Length of Feeding Period. Enough has already been said to indicate that young cattle can be fed longer with profit than old cattle. If feeder steers of different ages are started on feed

in approximately the same state of flesh or condition, the time required
to make each lot prime will vary inversely with the age of the cattle.
When cattle are fat and well finished they should be marketed as soon
as possible. To hold them longer will require both feed and labor, for
which little will be realized, either from increased weight or enhanced
killing merit. On the basis of many experiments that have been
carried on by different investigators, as well as the experiences of
practical feeders, it may be stated that 5 to 6 months of heavy feeding
are required for 2-year-old feeder steers to be put in choice to prime
condition; from 6 to 7 months for yearlings; and from 8 to 9 months for
calves. It should, of course, be understood that large numbers of cattle
are marketed after a relatively short feed before they are really
finished.

Effect of Age upon Total Gain Required to Finish. There is not a
great deal of difference in the increase in weight that must be realized
by feeder steers of different ages to attain the same degree of finish.
If the cattle are in equal condition when put on feed, the total gain
necessary to finish will decrease slightly with advanced age. In general, this gain will be approximately as shown in the tabulation.

Age	Total Gain Necessary to Finish
Two-year-olds	300–400 lb.
Yearlings	400–500 lb.
Calves	450–550 lb.

When stated in terms of initial weight as feeders, however, the
differences in total gains are significant. Calves practically double
their weight while in the feed lot; yearlings increase in weight approximately 70 per cent, and 2-year-olds are from 30 to 40 per cent
heavier at the end of the fattening period than they were at the beginning. Obviously, these percentages will be greatly affected by the
condition of the steers when started on feed.

Effect of Age upon Total Feed Consumed. The age of the cattle
has comparatively little effect upon the amount of feed required to
attain a given degree of finish, provided all ages are given a full feed
of grain and a reasonable amount of high-quality roughages throughout the feeding period. The longer feeding period of the younger
animals tends to make up for their smaller daily consumption of feeds,
so that by the time they have attained the desired finish they have
eaten about as much corn, protein concentrate, hay, and other feeds
as older cattle would have eaten in a shorter time. Consequently, the
age of the cattle has relatively little effect upon the number of animals
that should be purchased to utilize a given amount of feed, assuming,

of course, that the feed supply is equally well suited for fattening calves, yearlings, and 2-year-old steers.   (See Table 88.)

TABLE 88

EFFECT OF AGE OF CATTLE UPON THE AMOUNTS OF FEED
REQUIRED TO ATTAIN "CHOICE" FINISH*

	Calves		Yearlings		Two-Year-Olds	
Feed	Pounds	Bushels or Tons	Pounds	Bushels or Tons	Pounds	Bushels or Tons
Shelled corn	2735	48.8	2696	48.1	2811	50.2
Protein concentrate	452	0.23	405	0.20	372	0.19
Dry roughage	1139	0.57	1183	0.59	1203	0.60

* Average of the 7 trials which appear in Table 85.

Effect of Age upon Quality of Feeds Used.   Although the age of the cattle has little effect upon the amounts of shelled corn, protein concentrate, and good-quality hay required to attain a good or choice finish, it exercises much influence upon the possibility of limiting the grain ration to something less than a full feed and supplying more roughage to take its place.   Such a practice may be done fairly satisfactorily with long yearlings and 2-year-olds but not with calves, which lack the digestive capacity for large amounts of bulky feeds. Two-year-old steers may be fed large amounts of silage or given free access to good-quality hay without depressing their consumption of corn below that required to produce a satisfactory finish, whereas such a practice with calves would be almost certain to affect the finish adversely.   Calves usually are fed at least 2½ times as much grain as roughage after attaining a full feed.   Two-year-olds and yearlings, on the other hand, frequently eat only 1½ to 2 times as much corn, respectively, as the weight of roughage consumed.

This fact is of much importance from a practical standpoint.   Where it is desired to utilize considerable roughage, such as silage or corn fodder in fattening, 2- or 3-year-old feeders should be purchased rather than calves or yearlings.   It is often possible to put a fair "kill" on mature cattle by feeding roughage alone.   Calves fed on such a ration would not be likely to improve noticeably in condition.   The small size of their digestive systems would limit their consumption of such feeds to but little more than the amounts necessary for maintenance and normal growth.

The greatest difficulty experienced in feeding calves is getting them to eat a sufficient amount of feed to enable them to grow and fatten at the same time.   Older cattle do not have this growth factor to meet; consequently, a greater percentage of their food is available for the production of fat. Moreover, calves are much more likely to develop peculiar eating habits than older cattle. Musty or slightly spoiled feed that would be eaten readily by older cattle is often rejected by calves. Likewise, when coarse or stemmy hay is fed to calves a considerable portion is refused. No attempt should be made to feed calves unless the feeds at hand are of good quality. A somewhat more elaborate preparation of their ration is advisable in order to render it more palatable, and thereby increase its consumption.

Fig. 40. A drove of choice feeder calves. The economical gains made by young cattle and their flexibility of feeding and management have greatly increased the number of well-bred calves and light yearlings in Corn Belt feed lots.

It should be realized that calves are "babies" and, hence, have to be better sheltered, more kindly treated, and fed with a little more care than older animals. This does not mean that they should be "coddled" along or fed highly expensive feeds, but that due appreciation should be had for the inexperienced appetite and lack of hardiness that naturally attend their youth.

Effect of Age upon the Utilization of Pasture. Because of their limited capacity for feed, yearlings fatten less rapidly on pasture than older cattle.[1] Fresh grass is a bulky feed with a high moisture content. Therefore, yearlings are able to get little more digestible nutrients from pasture than they need for maximum growth, leaving but little for the improvement of condition. Two- and 3-year-old steers, on the other hand, have little additional growth to make. Consequently, nearly all the nutrients consumed above maintenance requirements are available for the production of fat. For this reason

[1] There are relatively few *calves* available for grazing in the spring, as most of the calves born the previous year are now *yearlings*.

older cattle are more popular than yearlings in the better grazing areas of the country, where many cattle are sold for slaughter directly off grass without the feeding of any grain. Even when grain is fed on pasture, yearlings will fatten less satisfactorily than 2-year-olds because they tend to eat too much of the green pasture forage to enable them to attain maximum finish. This does not mean that yearlings will not make more gain per acre on pasture than 2-year-olds, but that their gain is in the form of growth rather than fat.

Effect of Age upon Capital Investment. Although feeder calves usually cost from $2 to $4 a hundred more than yearling feeders of the same grade and from $3 to $5 a hundred more than 2-year-olds, they cost much less per head because of their lighter weight. This is a factor of great importance when feeder cattle are high in price. For example, a 400-pound calf at 25¢ a pound will cost $100, whereas a 650-pound yearling at 22 cents will cost $143 and a 900-pound 2-year-old at 20 cents will cost $180. Consequently, $9000 would be required to buy fifty 2-year-old cattle, but only $5000 would be needed for the same number of calves.

Calves, on the other hand, will tie up capital in cattle and feed for a longer period, since they must be fed for a longer time. They also require a slightly higher capital investment in buildings and equipment, since they require somewhat better shelter than older cattle.

Effect of Age upon the Flexibility of Feeding and Management. Young cattle have a marked advantage over older cattle from the standpoint of their suitability for different methods of feeding and management. Calves may be put on feed immediately or carried on roughage and pasture for 5 to 12 months before being started on a fattening ration. Yearlings, too, may be roughed through the winter but are less satisfactory than calves for such a plan of feeding for the reason that their gains are relatively slow and expensive.[2] Two-year-old steers are usually started on feed soon after their arrival at the farm, since they will make little gain on feeds that provide only enough digestible nutrients for maintenance and growth. Because calves have a long growing period, they may be held beyond the date of marketing originally selected more safely than older cattle, if such a change in feeding plans seems advisable.

Effect of Age upon Amount of Pork Produced. It is evident that since younger cattle make better use of their feed than older steers, the amount of gain made by hogs from the undigested feed should vary directly with the age of the cattle. This conclusion is fully borne out by experimental results. In the Nebraska experiments cited above, the hog gains per steer over a 200-day feeding period averaged 90, 70,

[2] *Cf.* p. 189.

59, and 44 pounds for 3-year-old, 2-year-old, and yearling cattle, and for calves, respectively. In terms of amount of hog gains per bushel of corn fed the steers, the results were 1.06, 0.88, 0.86, and 0.79 pounds, after making due allowance for the extra feed given the hogs.

By averaging a large number of lots receiving shelled corn and various other feeds, the author obtained the following figures for the amount of gain made by hogs per bushel of corn fed to cattle of different ages:

Age of Cattle	Number of Lots Averaged	Gain of Hogs per Bushel of Shelled Corn Fed to Cattle
Two-year-olds	131	1.58
Yearlings	23	1.01
Calves	48	0.76

Deciding on the Age of Cattle to Feed. It should be apparent after reading the foregoing discussion that age is often a very important factor in the purchase of feeder cattle. For example, calves are very unsatisfactory for a short feed and should not be bought by the farmer who plans to market his cattle after feeding them only 4 or 5 months. Similarly, 2-year-old steers should not be bought in the fall by the man who expects to carry his cattle into the late summer or fall of the next year, for their gains will be very expensive if fed for so long a period.

Two-year-old steers are much better than calves or yearlings for utilizing large quantities of roughage like silage and shock corn, because they have more digestive capacity. On the other hand, yearlings are better than either calves or 2-year-olds for utilizing stalks fields and late fall pastures, since they are old enough to use such feeds to advantage, yet not too old to make gains in the form of growth while on rations that are not sufficiently abundant or nutritious to permit the formation of fat.

Frequently men buy cattle of the age and weight that can most easily be made ready for market by the time they expect the highest prices for fat cattle the following year. Such a course of action is ideal in theory, but often too many cattlemen make the same "guess" as to when the market will be high, with the result that prices at that time are not very satisfactory. As a rule, the better plan is to purchase cattle of the age which is most able to utilize the feeds available and which will be in condition to sell to advantage when the feed supply is gone or when it is necessary to market them to avoid a shortage of labor in the fields.

16 ——————— The Importance of Grade and Sex in Feeder Cattle

What age cattle to buy is only one of the many questions that confront the man needing feeder cattle. In addition, he must decide between steers and heifers; between animals of one breed and those of another; and between high-class feeder steers, which will cost perhaps 30 cents per pound, and nondescript, trashy cattle, which can be purchased at almost half this figure. At most seasons of the year feeder cattle of all kinds are available in fairly large numbers at any of the larger markets. Naturally, certain markets have a reputation for affording unusually good selections of cattle of a certain breed or grade. Kansas City, for example, is recognized as probably the best market at which to buy high-grade Hereford calves; Omaha, as a good place to buy, in late summer and early fall, heavy, grass steers suitable for a short feed; East St. Louis, as a place where cheap, low-grade feeders are found in large numbers. If a large number of cattle of a given kind are to be bought, it will usually prove best to go to that market where the supply is likely to be the largest. However, if only a carload or two is wanted the market nearest at hand will usually be able to furnish them at the lowest cost, freight and other expenses considered.

Kind of Cattle to Buy. No hard and fast rule can be laid down as to what kind of cattle is best to feed. Many factors must be taken into account in deciding this question. Without doubt, the strength of the demand, in relation to the supply, both for the feeder animals and for the finished beeves, is likely to be the chief factor in determining the profit made from the feeding operation. Low-grade cattle may prove just as profitable, or more so, than choice or selected feeders, if they are purchased at a time when the supply of such animals is greater than the demand, and sold when the supply of cheap beef is relatively small. On the other hand, it frequently happens that the supply of prime, well-finished steers is so small that they enjoy a market all their own. Under such conditions the profit made on such cattle is relatively large, even though the price paid for them as feeders seemed at the time unreasonably high compared with quotations for plainer cattle.

The conditions under which the cattle are to be fed and the way

237

they are to be handled should receive first consideration in deciding on the kind of cattle to buy. For a long feed in which a liberal allowance of grain will be furnished, only the better grades of feeders should be purchased. Cattle of good breeding and of the proper type will, under such conditions, be prime when marketed and command the highest market price. Medium or common feeders, on the other hand, can never be made into "market toppers," no matter how long they are fed nor how excellent the ration. To feed such cattle a lot of expensive feed is likely to prove a wanton waste of money. As a rule, they should be fed for a comparatively short time, and the cost of the ration held at a low figure by the use of considerable roughage.

Importance of Sex. On the basis of sex differences, feeder cattle may be either steers, cows, heifers, or bulls. From the standpoint of numbers, steers are of more importance than the other three classes put together, and are the only kind of cattle that can be found in fairly large numbers throughout the entire year. The trade in feeder cows and heifers assumes considerable volume only during the fall and early winter months, and feeder bulls have become so scarce that commission men usually ask for at least a week in which to get together a truckload.

Heifers, other than heifer calves, and cows are better suited for a short than a long feed. Older heifers have probably been bred previously to their appearance on the market and will be likely to show unmistakable signs of pregnancy if kept longer than 90 to 120 days. Even though evidence of pregnancy were not to be feared, it is seldom a profitable practice to feed cows and heifers for as long as steers of the same condition and quality, since the market does not require that female beef be in such high condition as steer beef. The most attractive heifer carcasses are produced by animals weighing from 700 to 900 pounds, showing good condition and finish, but not so fat as to be wasteful. Heifers of this description sometimes sell for nearly the same price as steers, loads of mixed yearling steers and heifers often selling with no sorting. Animals in good condition at this weight are around 12 to 15 months old, at which age there is very little likelihood of the females' being pregnant.

Heifer calves mature a little earlier than steer calves, owing to their slower rate of growth. This, together with the fact that heifers need not be so fat as steers, results in heifers being ready for the market some 6 to 10 weeks before steers, started on feed at the same time, would ordinarily be sold. However, with only a single load of calves on feed, a common practice is to send all to market together, even though the heifers may be a little too fat or the steers a little underfinished. Usually better prices will be received if they are sold separately, when each has attained the finish desired for yearling cattle of that age and sex.

The gains made by heifers while on feed are somewhat smaller and more costly than those made by steers. This is due to the slower rate

TABLE 89

COMPARATIVE FEEDING QUALITIES OF STEER AND HEIFER CALVES
WHEN BOTH ARE FED THE SAME LENGTH OF TIME

| | Minnesota Bulletin No. 300 1925–26 | | Missouri Bulletin No. 314 2-year Average, 1925–27 | | | |
| | | | Full-fed in dry lot | | One-half grain ration in winter; full-fed on grass in summer | |
	Steer Calves	Heifer Calves	Steer Calves	Heifer Calves	Steer Calves	Heifer Calves
Days fed..............	217	217	182	182	322	322
Initial weight, lbs.......	451	449	359	358	358	354
Av. daily gain.........	2.35	2.27	2.16	1.94	1.84	1.64
Av. daily ration:						
Shelled corn.........	12.1	12.1	8.0	8.0	8.3	8.0
Prot. conc..........	2.0	2.0	1.1	1.1	1.2	1.1
Alfalfa hay.........	1.6	2.1	3.2	3.2	1.8	1.9
Corn silage.........	7.6	8.9	8.7	8.9	5.5	5.5
					(pasture)	(pasture)
Feed per cwt. gain:						
Shelled corn.........	517	535	369	410	452	483
Prot. conc..........	85	88	53	58	65	69
Alfalfa hay.........	69	93	115	162	97	118
Corn silage.........	322	391	400	450	297	336
Cost of cattle per cwt...	$8.00	$8.00	$10.40	$9.05	$10.40	$9.05
Selling price per cwt....	10.00	9.60	10.60	10.50	14.45	12.60
Return above cost of feed (ex. pork)..........	9.43	2.60	8.30	8.16	38.43	21.14
Dressing percentage....	....	....	57.3	59.1	59.5	60.3

of growth of heifers. As explained in the preceding chapter, the largest and cheapest gains are secured during that period of life when the rate of growth is most rapid. From this one would expect that, as between two animals, the one having the higher rate of growth would show both more rapid and more economical gains. However, this point is of little practical importance for the reason that steers are usually fed several weeks longer than heifers. Consequently, any advantage they may have over heifers in rate and economy of gains at the time the heifers are marketed is likely to disappear during the remaining weeks they are continued on feed when their gains are both slow and expensive relative to those made earlier. Indeed it frequently happens that

TABLE 90

COMPARATIVE FEEDING QUALITIES OF STEERS AND HEIFERS WHEN EACH IS
MARKETED

WHEN THE FINISH REQUIRED FOR THE RESPECTIVE SEX IS ATTAINED*

	Iowa Exp. Station (av. of 3 tests, 1930–33)		Ill. Exp. Station 1926–27	
	Steer Calves	Heifer Calves	Steer Calves	Heifer Calves
Number of days fed	240	170	200	140
Av. initial weight, lbs	415	406	379	379
Av. daily gain	2.18	2.18	2.35	2.56
Av. daily ration:				
Shelled corn	10.7	9.1	10.1	9.3
Protein concentrate	1.5	1.5	1.5	1.4
Alfalfa hay	4.9	5.4	2.0	2.0
Corn silage	...	...	8.1	8.2
Feed per cwt. gain:				
Shelled corn	492	433	428	363
Protein concentrate	65	65	63	54
Alfalfa hay	226	247	85	78
Corn silage	...	...	343	319
Cost per cwt. in lots	$6.93[a]	$6.13[a]	$9.90	$9.28
Selling price at Chicago	7.95[a]	6.40[a]	12.85[b]	10.75
Date marketed	July 18	May 6	July 13	May 14
Return above feed cost per head (ex. hogs)	$11.70[a]	$0.78[a]	$23.98	$10.94

* Mimeographed Reports of Calf-feeding Experiments.
[a] Average of last 2 years; first year discarded because of abnormal market conditions.
[b] The estimated value of the steers was $10.65 per cwt. at the time the heifers were sold. The market advanced approximately $1 after this date; the additional $1.20 indicates enhanced killing merit acquired during the last 60 days of feeding.

heifers will make larger average daily gains and also cheaper gains during a period of 5 or 6 months than will steers during a feeding period which is 2 or 3 months longer. (See Illinois Experiment, Table 90.)

A factor of much greater importance than the relative rate and economy of the gains made by steers and heifers is their relative selling

price when marketed.   The marked preference of the butcher and consumer for steer beef is probably founded largely on the fact that in the
early days of the beef industry most heifers were retained for breeding
purposes and the only "she" stock marketed were old cows.   Later, the
heifers not needed for the breeding herd were allowed to remain on the
farms and ranches until they were 2 years old, as the marketing of
younger cattle was very uncommon.   Consequently, they had become
pregnant and were not satisfactory for further feeding.   Hence, they
were sold to the packer for slaughter despite their thin condition.
The carcasses of these heifers as well as those of the old cows were
purchased by butchers whose customers could buy only cheap beef.
Thus, it has come about that the sex of the carcass is regarded as an
index of its quality, and hotels, clubs, and the best butcher shops will
seldom buy heifer carcasses no matter how good or how cheap they may
be.   Consequently, the price of these carcasses cannot rise above the
relatively low "ceiling" at which the great majority will sell readily
to the consumers who buy their meat on the basis of price per pound
instead of quality.   This price is reflected to the live cattle, with the
result that heifers usually sell from $2 to $4 a hundred below the price
paid for steers of similar quality and finish.   Feeders, realizing that
the market will pay little premium for the finish required to make a
heifer grade "prime," usually market heifers as soon as they will grade
"high good" or a little better.   As a result the average price of
grain-fed heifers is frequently $3 to $5 a hundred below the average
price of grain-fed steers.

Mention has been made of the fact that heifers acquire a satisfactory
market finish more quickly than do steers.   This point favors their
purchase when a short feeding period is desired to permit selling the
cattle before a seasonal decline in prices is expected to occur, but will be
a disadvantage if they reach a satisfactory market finish at a time of
year when prices of fat cattle are relatively low.   For example, heifer
calves that are full fed during the winter are usually ready for market
in May and June, when cattle of the better grades command relatively
low prices, whereas steers of the same age and condition that were
started on feed at the same time will ordinarily be fed until August or
September, when prices are usually much higher.

Steers usually are preferred to heifers for roughing through the
winter and grazing on pasture the following summer, because they have
a stronger growth impulse and, hence, will make larger gains on non-
fattening feeds.   Moreover, yearling heifers, after a summer on pasture and a short period of grain feeding in the dry lot will command
lower prices than steers, because of the competition they encounter

from the large number of grass-fat heifers that are marketed in the fall. (See Table 91.) Short-fed steers do not experience serious competition from grass-fed steers, since most of the grass-fed steers are sold for further feeding rather than for immediate slaughter.

TABLE 91

COMPARISON OF STEERS AND HEIFERS FOR UTILIZING LARGE AMOUNTS OF
ROUGHAGE AND PASTURE, AFTER WHICH THEY ARE GIVEN A SHORT
FEED OF GRAIN IN DRY LOT*

	Steers (Dec. 14, 1948– Jan. 6, 1950)	Percentage of Total	Heifers (Dec. 14, 1948– Dec. 9, 1949)	Percentage of Total
Average initial weight, pounds....	544		475	
Average winter gain (Silage, hay, protein concentrate)...........	174	28	153	30.7
Cost of winter gain per cwt.......	$15.78		$16.46	
Average summer gain, pounds (Grass-legume pasture)........	215	34.6	199	39.9
Cost of pasture gain per cwt......	$ 5.30		$ 5.73	
Average fall gain, pounds (Fed in dry lot).....................	232	37.4	147	29.4
Cost of dry lot gain per cwt......	$21.37		$20.32	
Average total gain, pounds......	621	100	499	100
Cost of total gain per cwt........	$14.26		$13.12	
Cost price per cwt..............	$28.65		$26.25	
Date sold†	Jan. 6		Dec. 9	
Selling price per cwt............	$27.00		$22.75	
Dressing percentage............	58.8		56.9	

* Missouri, Livestock Day Progress Report 10, April, 1950.
† Both lots sold when it was believed they would grade "good" as slaughter cattle.

Effect of Pregnancy. Often producers criticize the alleged unjust discrimination against fat heifers. The packers reply by pointing to their inability to sell heifer carcasses to the select trade and by calling attention to the fact that a majority of the heifers are pregnant when purchased and, hence, yield a low percentage of dressed beef. Pregnancy, they say, is so common in female cattle that the buyer is forced to protect himself by buying all of them on a pregnancy basis. Thus producers have no scruples against breeding their heifers soon after starting them on feed, particularly since many feeders believe that pregnancy favors more rapid and more economical gains by lessening feed-lot disturbances caused by heifers which are in heat, and hastens the attainment of a satisfactory market finish by increasing their tendency to fatten.

TABLE 92

EFFECT OF PREGNANCY UPON THE DEVELOPMENT OF YEARLING HEIFERS*

Average difference noted between 5 pairs of bred and open heifers during the first 150 days of gestation

1. Increase in ht. at withers......	− .80 cm.	7. Wt. of green hide..........	− 9.6 lbs.
2. " " circ. of paunch.....	+2.50 "	8. Wt. of uterus....	+28.6 "
3. " " width of loin......	−1.55 "	9. Score of dressed carcass......	+2.75
4. " " length of body.....	−2.50 "	10. Wt. of carcass lean..........	−12.4 lbs.
5. Gain in weight..............	+4.0 lbs.	11. " " " fat..........	+27.7 "
6. Dressing percentage.........	−.17	12. " " " bone........	−5.3 "

* Illinois Experiment Station, Unpublished Data.

That pregnancy has an important effect upon the feeding and killing qualities of cattle has long been recognized. However, the precise nature and extent of this effect has been a matter of considerable disagreement. Some feeders have advanced the theory that the embryo

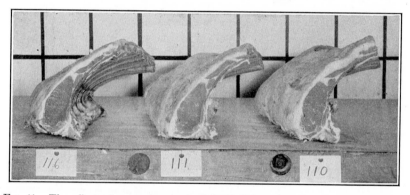

FIG. 41. The effect of sex and pregnancy upon the tendency of yearling cattle to fatten. No. 116, steer; No. 111, open heifer; No. 110, pregnant heifer. All were fed the same amounts of feed, and all were slaughtered on the 150th day after the pregnant heifer was bred. (*Courtesy Illinois Experiment Station.*)

imposes a tax upon the young mother, thereby interfering with her growth and development. Others have regarded the relationship between mother and fœtus as symbiotic, whereby the well-being of the mother is enhanced by the presence of the young *in utero*. Experiments carried on at the Illinois Station indicate that both these theories are in some respects true, as is shown by the following summary of the results of a paired comparison of open and bred yearling heifers fed equal quantities of feed for approximately 5 months. Each pair was slaughtered on the 150th day of the gestation period of the pregnant heifer.

1. *Activity:* Bred heifers were less active than open heifers, spending more time lying down and being more gentle and more easily handled and measured.
2. *Appetite:* Although both bred and open heifers were fed at the same level, the bred animals showed a desire for more feed than the open heifers could be made to consume.
3. *Growth:* Pregnancy exercised a noticeable inhibitory effect upon growth. This effect was apparent in the decreased development of the rear quarters and in the smaller size of the bones and internal organs.
4. *Rate of Gain:* Pregnancy had no appreciable effect upon the rate of gain in weight during the first 5 months of gestation.
5. *Apparent Slaughter Merit:* Pregnancy had an unfavorable effect upon the apparent slaughter merit of the heifers, as was indicated by consistently lower scores assigned to the bred heifers at the end of 150 days of gestation. These heifers were criticized severely on "straightness of lines" and "smoothness of finish."
6. *Dressing Percentage:* The dressing percentage of the bred and open heifers was practically the same when calculated on their weights after an overnight fast. Apparently the lighter hides, heads, shanks, stomachs, and other items of offal overcame a large part of the handicap imposed by the pregnant uterus, which averaged about 30 pounds at the time of slaughter.
7. *Appearance of the Carcass:* Pregnancy had a marked favorable effect upon the appearance of the dressed carcass. The carcasses of the pregnant heifers were noticeably better finished but not to the extent that they were criticized for being "wasty."
8. *Weight of Wholesale Cuts:* No effect of pregnancy upon the relative weight of the wholesale cuts was observed except in the flank, loin end, and round, all of which were significantly lighter in the bred than in the open heifers.
9. *Physical Composition of the Carcass:* The carcasses of the bred heifers contained approximately 5 per cent more fat but 3.5 per cent less lean and 1.5 per cent less bone than the carcasses of the open heifers.
10. *Color and Firmness of Fat:* Pregnancy had no significant effect on the color of either the fat or lean meat. However, the back fat of the bred heifers was slightly softer than that of their open mates.

The findings of this experiment apparently justify the breeding of full-fed yearling heifers 3 or 4 months before they are to be marketed. They also render untenable the claim of market buyers that fat yearling heifers, like cows, must be bought at a low price because of the probable losses due to pregnancy. However, as long as market buyers have this opinion, producers will do well to recognize it and market their heifers open or at least no later than the fourth month of gestation, as pregnancy is clearly apparent by the end of the fifth month.

Spayed vs. Open Heifers. One of the principal objections to feeding heifers is the disturbance caused by their coming in heat. When a carload or more of heifers are fed together hardly a day passes without one or more animals being thus affected, so that the herd is frequently in a state of excitement and unrest. Obviously such conditions are not conducive to rapid and economical gains.

TABLE 93

COMPARATIVE FEEDING QUALITIES OF STEERS, SPAYED HEIFERS, AND OPEN HEIFERS*

Average of Two Tests 1924–26	Yearlings			Calves		
	Steers	Spayed Heifers	Open Heifers	Steers	Spayed Heifers	Open Heifers
Av. initial weight, lbs....	635	589	570	382	386	390
Av. daily gain.........	2.10	1.89	2.15	2.07	1.66	1.92
Feed per lb. gain:						
Shelled corn........	702	723	665	502	619	544
Alfalfa hay.........	340	380	340	287	355	310
Initial value per cwt.....	$7.90	$6.40	$6.15	$7.60	$5.50	$6.25
Final value per cwt......	9.65	8.65	8.75	9.40	9.40	9.25
Dressing percentage.....	60.17	59.78	60.67	57.25	59.03	60.72

* Nebraska Bulletin 252, 1930.

In order to avoid the disturbances caused by in-heat heifers, spaying is sometimes resorted to. That more heifers are not spayed is due largely to the difficulty of the operation and the failure of the market to pay sufficient premiums for such heifers to cover the risk involved. The principal advantages claimed for spaying are a more tranquil disposition of the animals during the feeding period and a somewhat higher price for them when they are marketed. However, spayed heifers seldom have made as large or as economical gains or have attained as high a finish as open heifers in feeding experiments where they have been compared. Apparently the removal of the ovaries retards the growth and development of young heifers in much the same way that castration retards the growth and development of male calves.

As spayed heifers gain less rapidly than open heifers, spaying cannot be recommended on the ground that it will lessen activity in the feed lot and, hence, is conducive to faster gains. As a matter of fact, disturbances caused by in-heat heifers usually are most noticeable during the first few weeks of the feeding period and tend to become less and less frequent as the heifers approach market finish. Consequently, any advantage possessed by spayed heifers must lie in the certainty that they are not pregnant and, hence, may be purchased for a long feeding period without danger of their being far advanced in gestation by the time they are ready for market.

Feeding Cows. Large numbers of cows are marketed each fall by farmers and ranchers. Many of these cows have been suckling calves all summer and are very thin; consequently, they frequently are considered satisfactory for feeding, particularly if they can be bought for only about half the cost per pound of choice feeder calves and yearlings.

Although feeder cows often look worth the money when they are bought in the fall, they frequently prove to be a rather sorry bargain by the time they are marketed. Many misfortunes may happen to a drove of cows during the feeding period, which will reduce the profits materially. In the first place they are mature animals; consequently, all gains will be in the form of fat and will be very expensive. Gains made by cows are often 50 to 100 per cent more costly than those made by calves or yearlings. Such costly gains require a relatively large margin above the purchase price to prevent a financial loss. However, the price of fat cows is seldom very high, so that large margins are the exception rather than the rule. In fact, with ordinary price conditions, very skillful buying and feeding are necessary to realize a profit on a cow-feeding venture.

Another objection to buying cows for feeding is that most of them have been bred some 3 to 5 months before they were purchased. Consequently, some of them will probably calve before they are marketed, and a considerable percentage of those which do not will be sufficiently advanced in pregnancy to be penalized in price when they are sold. Not infrequently men who buy cows to feed will change their plans upon discovering that most of the cows appear to be pregnant, and will decide to keep them until fall and fatten them after the calves are weaned. Then, however, the grain already fed yields little return, as the flesh put on during the winter is lost to a large extent during the

TABLE 94

GAINS AND FEED CONSUMPTION OF FEEDER COWS WHILE BEING
FATTENED FOR MARKET

	Nebraska 66 days (1928–29)		Missouri 111 days (1929–30)	Illinois 154 days (1930–31)	
	Shelled Corn	Ground Ear Corn	Shelled Corn	1st 42 Days	Last 112 Days
Av. initial weight, lbs..........	1006	987	1004	713.5	
Av. daily gain................	1.34	2.09	2.24	1.32	2.44
Av. daily ration:					
Corn or grain mix...........	18.5	26.1	9.9	...	14.4
Protein concentrate..........	....	....	1.2	1.0	1.0
Corn silage.................	....	....	41.3	40.0	21.7
Legume hay................	8.9	8.1	6.7	2.0	2.0
Feed per cwt. gain:					
Corn......................	1384	1246	441	490	
Protein concentrate..........	....	....	55	47	
Corn silage.................	....	....	1843	1244	
Legume hay................	666	389	302	93	
Feed cost per cwt. gain........	$27.41	$19.47	$16.42	$9.04	
Cost per cwt. into feed lot.......	7.50	7.50	8.00	4.30	
Selling price per cwt...........	7.50	7.50	8.75	5.65	
Est. loss per head.............	23.50	23.38	3.75ᵃ	10.02	

ᵃ Estimated from reported data.

suckling period. Seldom do all the cows kept prove to be in calf.
These barren cows may be sold directly off pasture the following fall,
but if sold at this time of year they may not bring much more per
pound than they cost a year earlier.

Cows fed during a period of rising prices frequently return very
satisfactory profits and yield a high return on the amount of money
invested. Also, the return realized per bushel of corn fed may be
very high for the reason that cows usually are fed a limited grain ration
or a full feed for only a short time.

Importance of Type. Cattle feeders differ in their opinions as to
what type of steer is most profitable to feed. Some prefer small, compact, low-set animals, believing that they fatten more readily, have a
higher dressing percentage, and produce more shapely carcasses than
the conventional-type steer. Others favor large, growthy cattle with
plenty of bone and substance, believing that such animals make faster

and cheaper gains and will return more dollars per head because of their greater weight. Numerous tests have been made to obtain information on these points but few of them have disclosed significant differences between the two types. Although the large-type steers usually have gained somewhat faster, seldom has there been a signifi-

TABLE 95

EFFECT OF TYPE OF FEEDER STEERS UPON THE RATE AND
ECONOMY OF GAIN AND UPON THE CARCASS MERIT

	Calves Average of 3 Trials[a]		Yearlings Average of 9 Trials[b]		
	Small Type	Conventional Type	Compact Type	Medium Type	Rangy Type
Average initial weight, pounds...	338	412	722	752	785
Average total gain.............	351	438	350	360	373
Average daily gain.............	1.79	2.14	2.08	2.14	2.22
Percentage gain (gain ÷ initial weight)	104	106	48.5	47.9	47.5
Total feed consumed daily, pounds	12.5	15.1	....	....	....
Total feed consumed daily per 100 lb. av. live weight...........	2.43	2.42	....	....	....
Total feed consumed per hundred-weight gain.................	702	707	....	....	....
Dig. nutrients per hundredweight gain.......................	476	479	....	....	....
Feeder grade[c].................	5.1	4.4	....	....	....
Fat steer grade[c]...............	4.4	4.3	5.3	5.5	5.6
Carcass grade[c]................	4.5	4.4	5.1	5.1	5.1
Dressing percentage............	57.7	58.9	57.4	57.7	58.4

[a] Colorado Agricultural Experiment Station, Mimeograph Report, November, 1950.
[b] New Mexico Agricultural Experiment Station, Journal of Animal Science, Vol. 5, No. 4, 1946.
[c] Grading systems: (1) Colorado: 6 = fancy or prime, 5 = choice, 4 = good.
  (2) New Mexico: 4 = choice, 5 = low choice, 6 = high good.

cant difference between the amounts of feed eaten per hundredweight of gain. (See Table 95.)

Although the small and large types of cattle have not, as a rule, shown marked differences when both were full fed for the same length of time, it is possible that one type may be better suited than the other for a deferred system of feeding, in which young animals are carried on roughage and pasture for 6 months to a year before they are given a fattening ration. Such an experiment has been carried out at the Kansas, Ohio, and Oklahoma Experiment Stations under the auspices of the American Hereford Association. For this method of feeding the medium type was slightly more profitable than either the small or large type, if all calves were purchased at the same price per

TABLE 96

RELATIVE VALUE OF SMALL-, MEDIUM-, AND LARGE-SIZE HEREFORD CALVES FOR A DEFERRED SYSTEM OF FEEDING*

	Small	Medium	Large
Average initial weight, pounds	401	419	442
Wintering period 150 days			
Average gain	169	172	197
Summer grazing period 98 days			
Average gain	108	115	114
Late summer full-feeding period 101 days			
Average gain	228	233	231
Total gain 349 days	505	520	542
Final weight	906	939	984
Feed cost per head			
Winter period	$28.54	$28.40	$29.51
Summer grazing period	$11.00	$11.00	$11.00
Full-fed period	$47.20	$48.02	$49.43
Total feed cost per head	$86.74	$87.42	$89.94
Feed cost per cwt. gain	$17.18	$16.81	$16.59
Selling price per cwt.	$25.53	$25.78	$24.87
Dressing percentage	57.8	58.1	57.7
Average carcass grade	Low choice[a]	High good[a]	High good[a]

* The American Hereford Journal, March 15, 1951.
[a] New grading standards.

pound. If, however, they had been bought at the same price per head, the large and medium types would have returned the same profit, since the market value per head less the feed cost would have been nearly the same. (See Table 96.)

Importance of Beef Type. It is a well-recognized fact that cattle of pronounced beef type are more satisfactory to feed than cattle of dairy type. It is commonly held that the greater width and more compact form of the beef steer are conducive to more rapid and more economical gains than can be obtained from a dairy steer fed under similar conditions. Feeding trials do not bear out these contentions. Instead, they show comparatively little difference between the rate and cost of gains made by animals of these two types. Feeding experiments do emphasize, however, the advantages possessed by the steer of beef type in regard to the nature of gains, the quality of flesh, distribution of fat, and dressing percentage. As a result of these advantages, the selling price per pound of the beef-bred animal is very much higher than that of the dairy-bred animal. Unless the latter can be bought

TABLE 97

COMPARATIVE FEEDING QUALITIES OF BEEF AND DAIRY STEERS*
(Weighted average of 3 trials)

Average Time Fed — 217 Days	Beef-Type Angus	Cross-Bred Angus-Holstein	Dairy-Type Holstein
Initial weight....................	475 lbs.	535 lbs.	405 lbs.
Final weight.....................	950	980	915
Average daily gain...............	2.19	2.05	2.37
Average daily ration:			
Shelled corn and oats............	10.4	10.7	10.5
Nit. concentrate................	1.7	1.7	1.6
Corn silage....................	11.8	11.9	11.2
Alfalfa hay....................	2.9	3.0	2.9
Feed cost per cwt. gain.............	$12.20	$13.25	$11.15
Initial value per cwt.	10.40	10.00	7.40
Final value per cwt................	13.00	12.15	10.10
Return per head over feed cost.......	15.75	6.30	5.55
Dressing percentage...............	61.1	61.7	58.4
Grade of carcasses			
(Total of 3 trials)...............	8 prime	12 choice	1 good
	12 choice	8 good	22 medium
	4 good	2 medium	1 fair
Color of Carcass Fat...............	White	White	Bluish White

* Wisconsin Mimeographed Report, 1929.

so low as practically to preclude any profit from growing him to feeder age, there will be small chance to fatten him without incurring a loss.

During three consecutive years the Wisconsin Station carried on some feeding experiments involving the feeding of Aberdeen Angus, Holstein, and cross-bred Angus-Holstein calves of approximately the same age. Although some differences were found in the rate and economy of gains made by the various lots, more important differences were noted in the killing qualities of the cattle and in the grade of the beef produced. Whereas the carcasses of the Angus steers were "uniformly blocky, thick, with short shanks; smooth, thick and well covered throughout with a relatively small amount of kidney fat," the carcasses of the Holstein steers were "angular and long, loin weak, forequarters heavy and shanks long; lacking uniform thickness, thin exterior covering; kidney fat heavy in proportion to exterior fat." As was to be expected, the carcasses of the cross-bred steers "closely resembled those of the Angus in shape with a tendency toward heavier forequarters and longer shanks. In finish and covering they were not as smooth with a tendency toward heavier kidney fat." However, the carcasses of these Angus-Holstein steers were rated relatively high by expert meat judges, and it would seem that this kind of crossbreeding might well be considered by dairymen during periods of unsatisfactory milk prices or during a temporary shortage of labor.

Although the Wisconsin experiments are valuable to the farmer who raises his own feeders and who can raise either beef or dairy calves in the same way if he so chooses, they are of little practical value to the farmer who is contemplating the purchase of feeder cattle on the open market, where their previous management is largely an unknown quantity. Under such circumstances dairy steers are almost always older and noticeably thinner than beef steers of the same weight.

TABLE 98

FEEDING DAIRY AND BEEF STEERS*

(154 days. Six Steers per Lot. Figures on Single Steer Basis)

	Dairy Steers Holstein	Beef Steers Aberdeen-Angus
Average Age	11.5 mos.	10.5 mos.
Condition at Start of Trial	Thin	Fair market condition
Initial Weight	626 lbs.	632 lbs.
Daily Gains	2.57	2.21
Daily Ration		
Concentrates	16.50	14.80
Dry Roughage	6.60	3.80
Feed per Pound Gain		
Concentrates	6.42	6.70
Dry Roughage	2.57	1.72
Initial Value per cwt	$4.25	$7.00
Selling Price in Pittsburg	$8.50	$9.75
Shrinkage during Shipment	4%	5.8%
Dressing Percentage (Cold)	56.90%	60.72%

* Ohio Monthly Bulletin, Nov.-Dec., 1922.

Because of these facts, they may make larger gains, particularly during a short feeding period. Their low condition may also make for cheaper gains than those made by steers of beef breeding which are in much better flesh. Table 98 illustrates what is likely to happen under such conditions. The trial was in reality a comparison of thin dairy steers with beef steers "already in fair market condition." With this advantage the dairy steers would be expected to excel the beef steers in rate and economy of gain.

Importance of Grade. The cattle markets of the country do not recognize "type" as such. Instead they recognize "grade." Cattle intended for a particular purpose are classified as choice, good, medium, or common, depending on their desirability for the use to which they are to be put. The well-bred steer in thin flesh is classed as a "choice feeder," since he gives every indication of developing into a very desirable fat animal in a comparatively short time with a reasonable amount of feed. Steers noticeably lacking in improved beef blood, as evidenced by their rangy conformation, deficient quality, and lack of uniform color and size, are termed "common feeders," as they give no promise whatever of being very acceptable to the butcher at the close of their feeding period. Between these extremes we find steers that represent the intermediate grades of "good" and "medium." Detailed descriptions of the different grades of feeder steers may be found in a number of textbooks and bulletins. Brief descriptions of the principal grades are given below.

Choice Steers: Choice-grade feeders are markedly superior in conformation, finish, and quality. They are compact, wide, and deep, with legs short in proportion to depth of body. Top and underlines are approximately straight; the tail head is even with the back line, and the belly is wide and deep but not paunchy. Animals of this grade have a moderate covering of fat and show considerable refinement and quality. Their color indicates that they are high-grade and purebred individuals of strictly beef type.[1]

Good Steers: Steers of this grade must show the presence of considerable beef blood, have fairly straight lines, and should not be staggy. They are not so deep, low set, or well fleshed, nor do they show the uniform beef breeding that is characteristic of choice feeders.[2]

Medium Steers: Steers of this grade lack noticeably the blocky type of conformation of the good steers, are more uneven in their top lines,

[1] Extracts from U. S. D. A. Dept. Bull. 1464, 1927, pp. 67–68.
[2] Pennsylvania Bulletin 329, 1936, pp. 3–4.

tend to be more prominent in the hips and lighter in the hind-quarters, and show less uniformity than the good grade. They have many of the color characteristics of the beef breeds.[2]

TABLE 99

Comparison of Quality and Plain Feeder Steers
When Both Grades are Fed the Same Length of Time

	Kansas Circular 92, 1921 178 Days		Nebraska* Trial for the Year 1921–22 150 Days		Univ. of Alberta* Trial for Year 1921–22 140 Days	
	Quality Steers	Plain Steers	Quality Steers	Plain Steers	Good and Choice Feeders	Common Feeders
Estimated Age	3 yrs.	3 and 4 yrs.	....	....	2 yrs.	2 yrs.
Initial weight, pounds	1036	1199	955	925	907	879
Daily Gain	1.94†	1.90†	2.31	1.95	2.24	2.10
Feed per lb. gain						
Grain, pounds	6.70	7.37	7.75	8.68	5.01	5.38
Dry roughage	1.02	1.05	4.55	6.45	7.91	8.49
Silage	16.09	17.83	....	....	....	....
Pork per steer	....	....	72	83	....	....
Initial value per cwt	....	....	$6.20	$4.70	$4.00	$2.75
Selling price per cwt	$8.75	$8.25	$8.00	$7.15	$5.71	$5.06
Per cent shrinkage in shipping	2.63	3.5	....	....	....	....
Dressing percentage	61.8	60.6	....	....	....	....

* Mimeographed Report of Steer Feeding Experiments.
† Based on Market Weights.

Common Steers: Common feeder steers show a marked lack of constitution and only a semblance of the beef qualities found in the good feeders. They have rather prominent shoulders, long necks, and shallow chests, and are decidedly prominent in the hips. The tail head is sharp, the rump steep, and the body is generally narrow and lacking in depth. They have some of the color markings of the beef breeds but show many of the dairy characteristics.[2]

Numerous experiments have been conducted to ascertain the relative feeding qualities of the different grades of feeder steers, but many are of doubtful value to the practical feeder because all grades were fed for the same length of time. Consequently, either the better grades were fed too short a period to give them enough finish to sell to the best advantage or the lower grades were fed much longer than their breeding and quality warranted. Another serious criticism that may be made of most "grade" comparisons is that all grades were marketed on the same date, whereas each grade should be so fed as to insure its sale at the season of the year when prices are most favorable for cattle of that particular grade. However, these criticisms do not apply

Fig. 42. A drove of prime yearling steers. The better grades usually return the most profit when they are fed until they are prime. Their quality and breeding entitle them to sell at the top of the market if they are sufficiently well finished to command the top price.

to the Ohio experiments reported in Table 100. Consequently, the figures in that table deserve careful study.

Unfortunately, the Ohio experiments were conducted during a period of rapidly falling prices. During both years cattle fed during the winter and marketed in the spring and early summer were very unprofitable. However, it will be noted that the common-grade steers made a much better financial showing than either the medium or choice grades. In fact in the second test the common steers showed a profit of approximately $6 a head, whereas the medium-grade steers barely broke even and the choice steers suffered a loss of about $2 apiece. On the other hand, with the normal margins obtained on common, medium, and choice steers sold in April, May, and June, respectively, the financial outcome will usually favor the better grades. This is shown in the right-hand columns of the table. On a rising market the better grades will have a still greater advantage, since low-grade steers, like cows and heifers, will not rise above the relatively low price "ceiling" fixed by the limited purchasing power of consumers who will not buy beef if the price gets too high.

TABLE 100

A Comparison of Choice-, Medium-, and Common-grade Feeder Steers When Each Is Fed to the Degree of Finish Appropriate for the Grade

Ohio Experiments, Average of 2 years, 1930–31, 1931–32 Bimonthly Bulletins Nos. 152 and 158	Summary of Experiments with Actual Buying and Selling Prices[a]			Financial Results Based upon More Nearly Normal Prices[b]		
	Choice Steers	Medium Steers	Common Steers	Choice Steers	Medium Steers	Common Steers
Number of days fed.....	196	168	140	.....	.....	.....
Av. initial weight, lbs....	625	635	580	.....	.....	.....
Av. total gain.........	435	407	325	.....	.....	.....
Av. daily gain.........	2.22	2.42	2.32	.....	.....	.....
Av. feed per cwt. gain:						
Corn and cob meal....	633	599	612	.....	.....	.....
Protein supplement...	68	62	65	.....	.....	.....
Corn silage..........	450	412	431	.....	.....	.....
Legume and mixed hay	111	107	112	.....	.....	.....
Feed cost per cwt. gain..	$8.21	$7.85	$8.00	.....	.....	.....
Cost price per cwt. in lots	8.12	6.37	4.62	$8.50	$6.50	$4.50
Selling price per cwt. out of lots..............	7.17	6.24	6.05	10.00	8.00	6.50
Profit per steer (ex. pork)	−10.46	−7.37	1.95	17.16	10.14	6.73

[a] Cattle prices experienced a severe decline during the period covered by these tests. The average price of stocker and feeder steers at Chicago in October, 1930, was $7.30 and the average Chicago price of fat cattle in April, 1931, was $7.90. Similarly good to choice feeders were quoted at $6.75 in October, 1931, and good to choice corn-fed steers at $7.25 in May, 1932.

[b] The Chicago Daily Drovers' Journal of May 4, 1931, states that the average margin between October feeder cattle prices and fat cattle prices the following April for the previous 8 years was $3.15. This margin has been reduced approximately 50 per cent to cover shipping expenses to and from the farm.

It has already been stated that the best kind of cattle to buy depends upon the conditions under which they are to be fed and handled and the relative market price of the different grades. No hard and fast rule can be laid down for feeders to follow year after year in the purchase of their cattle. The majority of feeders should and do follow the conservative plan of handling cattle of average quality as represented by the good and medium grades, leaving to the more experienced and venturesome men the choice and common grades. However, this statement does not apply to steer calves, the lower grades of which, if full fed until they are sufficiently well finished for their grade, will be ready for market in the late spring or early summer when their selling price may be $3 to $5 a hundred lower than that of choice yearlings fed to prime condition and marketed in late summer or early fall. Consequently, the purchase of feeder calves falling below the good grade should be avoided unless they can be purchased at an unusually low price. It should also be realized that losses from death are much larger with low-grade calves than with low-grade animals of more maturity.

The comparative advantages of the different grades of yearling and 2-year-old steers are well set forth in Illinois Bulletin 90. extracts from the summary of which are quoted below:

1. A ration with a wide nutritive ratio and shorter feeding period tends to favor the feeding of the lower grades.
2. Well-bred steers possess greater capacity for consuming large quantities of feed than steers of a more common grade, especially in the later weeks.
3. The greater the cost of feed used, the greater the advantage in favor of the better grades.
4. As a rule, the better the quality and condition, the younger the cattle.
5. Opportunities for larger profits, and losses as well, lie with the better grades of feeders.
6. The grade of cattle on which the finishing will return the greatest profit will depend upon the following considerations:
   a. The relative cost of the various grades per hundredweight.
   b. The cost of feed.
   c. The method of feeding and time of marketing.
   d. The range in prices between the different grades of fat steers at the time the cattle are sold.
7. The better the grade of cattle, the higher the percentage of dressed beef.
8. Low-grade cattle carry larger percentages of internal fat than the better-bred ones, and there appears to be a more abundant and more evenly distributed layer of surface fat on the better-bred steers.

Data gathered by the United States Department of Agriculture and the University of Illinois in De Kalb County, Illinois, throw further light upon the feeding qualities of plain and well-bred cattle. These figures are the result of records kept on the feeding operations of some forty practical cattle feeders, who handled their cattle according to their usual methods of management. It will be observed that the good steers were on feed a full month longer than those grading common, but that, notwithstanding this fact, the gains of the good steers were both larger and cheaper for the entire time they were fed. These results tend to refute the claim sometimes made that the

gains made by common steers during a short "warming up" feed
are as large and as economical as those made by better animals over a
longer period. (See Table 101.)

TABLE 101

COMPARISON OF GOOD AND COMMON STEERS UNDER ACTUAL FARM CONDITIONS*

	Good Steers	Common Steers
Number of Droves	15	26
Number of Cattle	703	1785
Number of Days on the Farm	174	143
Purchase Weights	888 lbs.	824 lbs.
Sales Weights	1186	1013
Gain in Weight	298	189
Average Daily Gain	1.71	1.32
Feed per cwt. Gain		
Grain and other Concentrates	695	724
Silage	1261	1871
Dry Roughage	327	467
Pasture Days	9	8
Purchase Price per cwt	$7.00	$5.13
Sale Price per cwt. (at farm)	9.07	7.16
Necessary Margin to Break Even	1.52	1.99

* U. S. D. A. Mimeographed Leaflet, " Two Steers on the Same Trail." November, 1924.

Effect of Grade upon the Time Required to Attain a Given Finish.
Usually cattle representing a certain feeder grade are fed until they
are fat enough to qualify for the next higher slaughter grade. For
example, *good* feeder steers are fed until they are fat enough to be
graded as *choice* slaughter steers. However, they may be marketed
sooner, when they possess only enough finish to qualify for the
good grade, or they may be fed 2 or 3 months longer in the hope
that they will be graded and sell as *prime* slaughter steers.[3] From
the results of the experiments reported in Table 102 it is evident that
the higher the grade of feeder cattle, the less time and feed are
required to attain a given slaughter grade. This is due to: (1) the
better condition usually shown by the higher grades when started on
feed, and (2) the consideration given to form, quality, and breeding
as well as condition in determining the slaughter grades. Since the
lower grades of feeders are noticeably deficient in respect to nearly
all these characteristics, they must be above criticism in respect to

[3] Grade terms refer to new market grades authorized by the U.S.D.A.

finish if they are to qualify for a grade in which cattle of their conformation and breeding are not usually found.

TABLE 102

EFFECT OF THE GRADE OF FEEDER STEERS UPON THE TIME AND FEED
REQUIRED TO ATTAIN A GIVEN MARKET FINISH*

(Two-Year-Old Steers)

Grade of Finish Attained	Choice		Good			
Feeder Grade at Start of Test	Good	Choice	Common	Medium	Good	Choice
Fat in carcass, per cent.......	34.5	33.2	25.9	28.0	28.7	25.8
Days required to attain desired finish..................	204	148	166	134	130	79
Total gain, pounds..........	406	305	296	298	297	183
Average daily gain..........	1.99	2.06	1.78	2.22	2.28	2.32
Total feed consumed						
Shelled corn, bushels......	55.8	40.2	41.4	35.2	35.1	19.8
Clover hay, pounds........	1348	1003	1087	917	900	571
Feed consumed per cwt. gain						
Shelled corn..............	769	738	783	662	662	606
Clover hay..............	332	329	376	309	303	312
Cost of feed per cwt. gain[a]....	$18.85	$18.21	$19.67	$16.50	$16.43	$15.49

* Illinois Experiment Station Bulletin 501, 1944.
[a] Feed prices: shelled corn, $1.07 per bushel; clover hay, $25 per ton.

The Feeding of Inferior or Scrub Cattle. As a rule, the common grade represents the cheapest class of cattle regularly taken out into the country for feeding purposes. Although noticeably lacking in form, quality, and breeding, these common feeders do not usually show pronounced scrub or dairy blood. Instead, they are animals of rather nondescript breeding, usually in very thin flesh but still possessing a fair degree of thrift and vigor. As a rule, one would not say that they had been badly stunted, although, of course, the age of any individual steer of low grade is largely a matter of conjecture.

Ordinarily, steers that will not qualify for the common grade are classed as "canners" and are sold to the packers for slaughter. They appear on the market in greatest numbers in the late fall and early winter when the shortage of pasture necessitates the sale of all cattle for which winter feed is not available. Coming to market at the time of year when there is an abundance of cheap grass beef, these "trashy," "dogie" cattle sell for an extremely low price. This low price often results in their being purchased in large numbers by experienced feeders and canning companies for a short feed on corn silage, cannery refuse, and other cheap feeds.

The demand for steers wholly lacking in beef type for feeding purposes is not large, and it occasionally happens that they can be bought for a price as low as 40 or 50 per cent of the cost of good to choice feeders. When they are purchased on such a basis and are returned to market during the late winter and early spring when the supply of cheap beef is of much smaller volume, the profit made from their feeding may be even greater than that made from feeding the higher-priced cattle. Particularly is the return per dollar invested likely to be higher.

There are, however, some objections to handling "cull" steers that should not be overlooked. In the first place, such cattle bought on the open market vary greatly in age, feeding habits, and previous methods of management. Some of them will be steers 4 or 5 years of age that have been permanently stunted; others will be yearlings in very thin flesh. Some will be accustomed to eating corn; others will never have tasted it. Some will be cattle of poor breeding that have had fairly good feed conditions; others will be better-bred animals that have been almost starved. Naturally, all will not do equally well or finish evenly when placed in the same feed lot.

The general thrift and health of such cattle is relatively low. Death losses are apt to be considerably higher than in ordinary stock. Most of these animals are horned, and dehorning further increases the death risk. The death loss in handling ordinary feeders seldom exceeds 1 per cent, but it frequently is twice or three times this amount with cheap "dogie" steers. More than ordinary skill is required in handling and feeding cattle of this sort if good results are to be obtained. As a rule, they are not a safe proposition for the inexperienced feeder.

One of the chief objections to feeding low-grade and cull steers is the effect they have on the morale of the owner. Most livestock farmers take a great deal of pride in the appearance of their animals and derive considerable satisfaction from seeing them develop into acceptable market beasts. To top the market with a load of prime steers is frequently more gratifying to the real cattle feeder than the realization of a larger profit made from a drove of inferior cattle. The presence of the latter animals in the feed yards is regarded as an "eyesore" to the farm. Not infrequently, men who consider cheap cattle more profitable than the better grades also feed out each year a load or two of as good steers as they can buy, possibly for the purpose of maintaining their reputation as good cattlemen who know a superior beast when they see it.

Importance of Selection of Feeder Cattle. The ability to estimate quickly the relative merits of different droves of feeder cattle and

TABLE 103

RESULTS OF SELECTING FEEDER CALVES FOR FACTORS INDICATING RAPID AND ECONOMICAL GAINS

Selected to be	First Test, 1946–1947, 209 Days*		Second Test, 1947–1948, 224 Days†		Third Test, 1948–1949, 190 Days‡	
	Probable Good Gainers	Probable Poor Gainers	Probable Good Gainers	Probable Poor Gainers	Probable Good Gainers	Probable Poor Gainers
Average initial weight, pounds	454	383	455	373	492	403
Average final weight, pounds .	825	706	888	757	874	788
Average total gain, pounds. . .	371	323	433	384	382	385
Average daily gains, pounds. .	1.77	1.54	1.93	1.71	2.01	2.03
Average daily ration, pounds						
Ground shelled corn	9.5	9.1	9.4	8.7	9.9	9.3
Cottonseed meal	1.3	1.3	1.2	1.2	1.8	1.8
Atlas sorgo silage	10.5	7.6	13.5	7.5	8.9	8.0
Hay (alfalfa and prairie) . . .	1.3	0.9	3.1	2.6	2.5	2.5
Feed per cwt. gain, pounds						
Ground shelled corn	534	591	488	510	491	457
Cottonseed meal	74	85	63	72	91	90
Atlas sorgo silage	592	489	700	436	444	394
Alfalfa hay	71	56	161	153	126	126
Selling price per cwt	$31.00[a]	$30.50[a]	$31.00[a]	$30.50[a]	$26.00	$25.00
Margin per head above feed costs	$73.02[a]	$53.05[a]	$73.02[a]	$53.05[a]	$24.20	$20.59

* Kansas Experiment Station, Mimeographed Report, 1948.
† Kansas Circular 250, May 7, 1949.
‡ Kansas Circular 265, May 6, 1950.
[a] Average of 1946–1947 and 1947–1948 tests.

the skill in selecting thrifty, healthy animals that will make rapid and economical gains can be acquired only by experience and practice. That such ability pays off in dollars and cents may be seen from the Kansas experiments reported in Table 103. In these experiments the steer calves that were selected as probable good gainers made larger and cheaper gains and sold for a higher price when marketed than the calves that showed less promise at the time they were started on feed. As a result they were much more profitable. The buyer who can go into a drove of 100 steers and sort out the best 50 or 60 head has a big advantage over the man who is satisfied with a "gate cut" of the number he desires to buy. Most unfortunate is the man who arrives on the scene after the selected cattle have been shipped and, in the absence of no better cattle in the yards, buys the "culls" at a price only a little below that paid for the top end of the drove.

So difficult is it to select feeder cattle, especially when one buys only one or two droves a year, that few feeders trust their own ability to buy the cattle they need. Instead they place their orders with a commission company at the market where cattle of the weight and grade desired are most likely to be available and leave the details of selection to men who are experts both in the selection of feeder cattle and in beating down price quotations that are clearly too high. The skill of such men in recognizing unthrifty steers by the carriage of the ears or the expression of the eyes usually will result in culling 2 or more animals from the drove, which would be poor-doers if purchased. Often the ability of a buyer in detecting cattle that have taken on an abnormal "fill," and his insistence on a substantial reduction in price to offset the excess weight, will save his client several times the modest fee charged for his services.

17 —————— The Use of Grain in Fattening Cattle

Except for odd lots of cows and heifers that are culled from breeding herds, nearly all cattle marketed from the Corn Belt have been fed at least enough grains to permit them to qualify as grain-fed cattle. Such cattle are valued considerably higher than grass-fattened animals by market buyers; consequently, it usually is profitable to give cattle at least a short feed of corn or other grains before they are shipped. The amount of grain to feed a particular drove of cattle depends upon the prevailing prices of corn and roughage (including pasture) and upon the premium being paid for additional finish on the grade of cattle being fed.

Full Feed Defined. Most of the cattle fattened in the Corn Belt are given a full feed of grain during part of the feeding period. On some farms the cattle are placed on a full feed as quickly as possible, perhaps within 2 or 3 weeks after they are put into the feed lot; on others a full feed of grain is fed during only the last month before they are sold.

Opinions differ as to what constitutes a full feed of grain. Most farmers consider cattle to be on a full feed when they are fed all the grain they want to eat. Yet, if they are also fed all the good-quality legume hay and corn silage they want, they can be induced to eat still more grain by limiting the roughage to what they will clean up readily. A good example of such a ration is that of the full-fed lot in Table 108. Many feeders would not consider 12 pounds of shelled corn to be a full feed for 2-year-old cattle that averaged 950 pounds when they were put into the feed lot. Yet it was as much corn as the Indiana steers would eat along with 31 pounds of silage and approximately 3 pounds of hay. Had the silage been limited to 20 pounds a day, their average daily consumption of shelled corn probably would have been 16 or 17 pounds. Or if no silage at all had been fed, but only 6 or 7 pounds of hay, they probably would have eaten 18 or 19 pounds of shelled corn as an average for the whole feeding period. If only 12 pounds of corn is considered a full feed, in the Indiana experiment, what term should be given to the larger amounts the cattle would have eaten if less roughage had been fed?

It, therefore, is highly desirable that the term "full feed"[1] be defined more accurately than by saying simply that it is the amount of grain that cattle will eat. This amount varies much too widely for the term to have much value to the inexperienced feeder who is attempting to feed his cattle in accordance with approved practices. A much better way to define it would be to state the amount of grain they *should eat* if they are to be regarded as full-fed cattle. With this thought in mind we shall define a *minimum full feed of grain* (MFFG) to be 1.5 pounds daily per 100 pounds live weight, including the grain in any corn silage that is fed. Anything over this amount is, of course, a full feed without qualification. However, the feeding of more than 1.75 pounds of grain daily per 100 pounds live weight is a practice of doubtful merit, except for short-fed cattle, since a very heavy consumption of concentrates during the early and middle parts of the feeding period is likely to "burn out" the cattle and result in sluggish appetites and very low gains toward the end. The Iowa calves in Table 104 are a good example of cattle that were fed too much corn during the first half of the feeding period. Whereas they averaged 10.2 pounds of corn per day during the third month and 13 pounds during the sixth, their average consumption was only 10.2 pounds during the eighth month and 11.2 pounds during the ninth.

After cattle have been gotten on a full feed they should be kept there until they are marketed. Consequently, it is highly important that they be so fed that their consumption of grain will not fall below 1.5 pounds per 100 pounds live weight even during the last month they are on feed. This can be achieved only if they are not placed on full feed too quickly and if the amount of grain consumed daily is not allowed to exceed 1.75 pounds per 100 pounds live weight by feeding enough good palatable roughage to keep the grain consumption at or slightly below this level.

How Much Feed Will Cattle Eat? The previous discussion about what constitutes a full feed of grain has brought out the fact that the amount of corn or roughage eaten can be controlled by increasing or decreasing the other components of the ration. If cattle are being fed principally to utilize roughage, the corn will be fed in limited amounts in order to induce the cattle to consume large quantities of roughage. But, if the purpose of feeding is to market as much corn

---

[1] The term "full feed" may be applied to the roughage part of the ration as well as the grain. If the grain and hay were limited but the cattle were fed all the corn silage they would eat, we would then say they were given a *full feed* of silage. However, when not otherwise indicated, the term refers to a full feed of grain.

TABLE 104

FEED EATEN PER 100 POUNDS LIVEWEIGHT BY CATTLE OF DIFFERENT AGES

	First Month	Second Month	Third Month	Fourth Month	Fifth Month	Sixth Month	Seventh Month	Eighth Month	Ninth Month	Average Total Period
Shelled Corn										
Calves										
Iowa[a]	1.6	1.8	1.8	1.8	1.8	1.6	1.4	1.2	1.2	1.6
Indiana[b]	1.3	1.5	1.5	1.6	1.8	1.7	...	...	...	1.6
Nebraska[c]	*	*	*	*	*	*	*	...	...	1.9
Morrison[d]	*	*	*	*	*	*	*	...	...	1.7
Yearlings										
Iowa	1.4	1.8	1.7	1.6	1.5	1.4	1.3	...	...	1.6
Indiana	1.3	1.7	1.7	1.7	1.6	1.6	...	...	...	1.6
Nebraska	*	*	*	*	*	*	*	...	...	1.8
Morrison	*	*	*	*	*	*	...	...	...	1.7
2-year-olds										
Iowa	1.3	1.9	1.7	1.7	...	...	...	...	...	1.7
Indiana	1.1	1.5	1.5	1.7	1.6	1.5	...	...	...	1.5
Nebraska	*	*	*	*	*	*	*	...	...	1.6
Morrison	*	*	*	*	*	...	...	...	...	1.6
Total air-dry feed										
Calves										
Iowa	2.6	2.6	2.6	2.5	2.4	2.4	2.1	1.9	1.8	2.3
Indiana	2.7	2.7	2.6	2.5	2.4	2.3	...	...	...	2.5
Nebraska	*	*	*	*	*	*	*	...	...	2.6
Morrison	*	*	*	*	*	*	*	...	...	2.5
Yearlings										
Iowa	2.7	2.7	2.6	2.4	2.2	2.1	1.9	...	...	2.4
Indiana	2.9	2.7	2.6	2.5	2.2	2.1	...	...	...	2.4
Nebraska	*	*	*	*	*	*	*	...	...	2.4
Morrison	*	*	*	*	*	*	...	...	...	2.5
2-year-olds										
Iowa	2.4	2.6	2.3	2.1	...	...	...	...	...	2.4
Indiana	2.6	2.5	2.4	2.4	2.2	1.9	...	...	...	2.3
Nebraska	*	*	*	*	*	*	*	...	...	2.2
Morrison	*	*	*	*	*	*	...	...	...	2.4

[a] Iowa Bulletin 271, 1930.
[b] Indiana Bulletin 136, 1909.
[c] Nebraska Bulletin 229, 1928.
[d] Morrison Feeds and Feeding, 21st edition, 1948, p. 799.
* Monthly amounts not reported.

through cattle as possible, it will be roughage that is limited. This leads to the questions how much total feed will cattle eat and what is the replacement value of roughage in terms of grain.

A study of the lower half of Table 104 will disclose that the total air-dry feed eaten per 100 pounds live weight decreases gradually during the feeding period. During the first quarter it is about 2.7 pounds; during the last quarter it is often little more than 2.0 pounds per 100 pounds live weight. However, this does not mean that the daily consumption of feeds has declined. Rather it has constantly increased, for the cattle have increased in weight faster than their feed intake per unit of weight has diminished.

Between cattle of different ages, the differences in the feed consumption per 100 pounds live weight are too small to be of practical importance. It will be noted in Table 104 that the Iowa calves were fed for 9 months, which is about 1 month longer than most calves

TABLE 105

AVERAGE AMOUNTS OF FEED CONSUMED BY FULL–FED CATTLE
DURING DIFFERENT PARTS OF THE FEEDING PERIOD*

Feed per 100 Pounds Live Weight

Quarter of Feeding Period	Total Air-Dry Feed (pounds)	Grain (pounds)	Air-Dry Roughage (pounds)
1. First	2.7	1.5	1.2
2. Second	2.5	1.7	0.8
3. Third	2.3	1.6	0.7
4. Last	2.1	1.5	0.6
Average for entire period	2.4	1.6	0.8

* Average length of feeding period: 2-year-old steers, 150 days; yearlings, 200 days; calves, 250 days.

are fed. Had they been marketed after 8 months, their average daily consumption of feed for the total period would have been 2.4 pounds. On the other hand, the Indiana calves were fed for only 6 months. Had they been fed 2 months longer, 2.4 pounds probably would have been about their daily consumption of both corn and hay per 100 pounds live weight. In referring to the 2-year-old steers, we note that both the Indiana and Nebraska steers were fed somewhat longer than most cattle of this age. Had they been fed only 5 months, it seems reasonable to believe that their average total feed consumption per 100 pounds live weight would also have been close to 2.4 pounds. Consequently, 2.4 pounds per 100 pounds live weight appears to be a good figure to use in estimating the average daily total feed consumption of cattle that are fed a full feed of grain after about the first month or 6 weeks of the feeding period. The approximate consumption during different parts of the feeding period may be

TABLE 106

REPLACEMENT VALUE OF GRAIN AND ROUGHAGE IN THE
DAILY RATION OF FATTENING CATTLE

Replacement Made	Average Weight During Experiment (pounds)	Average Daily Ration			Average Total Air-Dry Feed per Day (pounds)[a]	Time Fed (days)	Air-Dry Feed per 100 Pounds Live Weight (pounds)
		Grain (pounds)	Hay (pounds)	Silage (pounds)			
1. Grain replaced by hay							
Nebraska Bull. 116							
Heavy feed of grain	1200	19.9	8.8	....	28.7	84	2.50
Medium feed of grain	1156	17.2	9.7	....	26.8	84	2.33
Light feed of grain.	1124	12.0	14.0	....	26.0	84	2.31
Nebraska Bull. 355							
Heavy feed of grain	1028	16.4	9.7	....	26.1	140	2.54
Medium feed of grain	1039	14.0	12.6	....	26.6	140	2.56
Light feed of grain.	1042	12.1	15.5	....	27.6	140	2.65
Ohio Bull. 198							
Full feed of corn...	923	13.3	3.2	13.7	22.0	240	2.38
¾ feed of corn......	914	10.1	6.2	14.1	21.7	240	2.38
½ feed of corn......	889	6.7	8.7	14.2	21.1	240	2.37
2. Grain replaced by silage							
Kansas Mimeo. 45-B-1							
Full feed of barley .	936	14.0	....	17.8	21.2	180	2.27
⅔ feed of barley....	916	9.4	....	33.6	22.8	180	2.49
⅓ feed of barley	909	4.7	....	41.8	21.4	180	2.36
Iowa Mimeo. AH 162							
Full feed of corn...	900	13.2	1.1	17.7	21.4	175	2.38
½ feed of corn......	862	6.4	1.1	32.3	20.4	175	2.37
Indiana[b]							
Full feed of corn...	1115	11.9	3.0	31.5	27.5	139	2.46
½ feed of corn......	1093	6.1	3.5	39.9	25.6	139	2.34

[a] Air-dry weight of silage assumed to be 40 per cent of weight of silage fed.
[b] See Table 108 for Indiana results in more detail.

obtained by assuming the total air-dry feed to be 2.7, 2.5, 2.3, and 2.1 per cent of the live weight for the first, second, third, and last quarters of the feeding period, respectively. This, of course, is on the assumption that calves are fed approximately 250 days, yearlings 200 days, and 2-year-old steers 150 days. For cattle fed a shorter time, the estimates for the last quarter should be disregarded; and for a feeding period of only one-half the usual length, only 2.7 and 2.5 will apply. If it is desired to make month-by-month estimates of the grain or total feed consumed daily, the monthly averages given in Table 104 may be used.

It will be noted that in discussing a full feed of grain and the total feed consumed daily no mention has been made of the amount of protein concentrate fed. This item of the ration has been intentionally omitted from the discussion, since the feeding of 1 to 2 pounds of protein supplement has no significant effect upon the amount of grain and roughage consumed (see Table 132); consequently, it may be ignored in estimating the amount of grain required for a full feed and the total air-dry feed required to satisfy the appetites of full-fed cattle.

Replacement Value of Roughage. It appears that grain and air-dry roughage are interchangeable on a pound-for-pound basis for cattle that are fed at least half of a minimum full feed of grain. (See Table 106.) The replacement value of silage in terms of grain is more difficult to determine for the reason that it varies greatly in moisture content. However, if we assume that the air-dry roughage equivalent of silage is 40 per cent of the weight fed, we find that grain and silage will replace each other on an air-dry basis within the limits of practical error.

Estimating Feed Requirements of Fattening Cattle. The factors that have been developed in the preceding paragraphs in regard to the feed consumption of fattening cattle have much value in estimating the amount of grain and roughage required to fatten a given drove of cattle and in checking the ration at different stages of the feeding period to see whether grain and roughage are being fed in about the approved amounts. The following example will show how they are used.

Given: 30 steers, weighing 700 pounds when purchased, which are to be fed to choice finish. How much shelled corn and legume hay will be needed?

Solution:

   Estimated time fed, 180 days.
   Estimated average daily gain, 2.25 lb.
   Calculated final weights (700 + 180 × 2.25) lb. = 1105 lb.
   Calculated average weight (700 + 1105)/2 = 900 lb.
   Total feed required daily per 100 lb. live weight = 2.4 lb.
   Total feed required daily per head, 2.4 lb. × 9 = 21.6
   Total feed required daily by 30 steers, 30 × 21.6 = 648 lb.
   Average grain eaten daily per 100 lb. live weight by cattle on full feed, 1.6 lb.
   Average grain eaten daily by 900-lb. cattle, 9 × 1.6 = 14.4 lb.
   Average grain eaten daily by 30 cattle = 432 lb.

Average hay eaten daily by 30 cattle = 648 — 432 = 216 lb.
Estimated total grain needed for 180 days = 180 × 432 = 77,760 lb. = 1400 bu. corn.
Estimated hay needed for 180 days = 180 × 216 = 38,880 lb. = 20 tons.

Similarly, if it is desired to know how much corn and hay will be needed during the last month of the feeding period, a close estimate may be made by assuming that approximately 2 pounds of grain and hay combined will be eaten daily per 100 pounds live weight. About 1.5 pounds of this amount will be grain and 0.5 pound will be hay. (See Table 105.) Multiplying these quantities by the estimated weight of the cattle and dividing the results by 100 will give the approximate average daily consumption of corn and hay during the last month of the feeding period.

Getting Cattle on Feed. Comparatively few of the feeder cattle shipped into the Corn Belt from the Range states have been fed any grain. Consequently, they must be taught to eat it. This can be done easily by putting about a pound of corn per head in the feed trough and feeding 4 to 6 pounds of hay on top of it. In eating the leaves and chaff from the bottom of the trough the cattle will also pick up the corn and will quickly learn to eat it. If it is desired to get the cattle on a full feed of grain rather promptly, the corn should be increased by about 1 pound per head daily until they are eating 1 pound of corn per 100 pound live weight, after which time increases of 1 pound a head every third day for 2-year-old steers, ½ pound every third day for yearlings, and ¼ pound every third day for calves are recommended. (See Table 107.) All this time, of course, the cattle should have as much roughage in the form of hay or silage as they will eat. If all the cattle do not appear hungry when they are fed, the hay or silage should be reduced enough to insure that all animals come to the feed trough promptly and begin eating when the grain is fed.

If the grain ration is increased gradually as suggested above, 2-year-old cattle will attain a minimum full feed of grain (1.5 per cent of their live weight) about 30 days after they have been started on feed, yearlings in about 40 days, and calves in about 50 days. In other words, each will have reached a minimum full feed at about the end of the first fifth of the feeding period. Further increases, of course, should be made as the cattle increase in weight and become better adjusted to a heavy feed of grain.

Obviously, the weight of the cattle will increase more rapidly than their capacity for feed. Consequently, it usually will be necessary to reduce the roughage from time to time in order to maintain the level

TABLE 107

Day	2-Year-Olds			Yearlings			Calves			Actual Record of 373-Pound Calves*	
	Shelled Corn (lb.)	Average Weight (lb.)	Corn per 100 (lb.)	Shelled Corn (lb.)	Average Weight (lb.)	Corn per 100 (lb.)	Shelled Corn (lb.)	Average Weight (lb.)	Corn per 100 (lb.)	Shelled Corn (lb.)	Corn per 100 (lb.)
1	1	900		1	700		1	425		3.0	
2	2			2			2			4.4	
3	3			3			3			5.5	
4	4			4			4			6.4	
5	5			5			4			7.3	
6	6			6			4			7.5	
7	7			7			4.25			8.0	
8	8			7			4.25			8.25	
9	9			7			4.25			9.25	
10	9	930	0.97	7.50	725	1.0	4.50	450	1.0	9.50	2.4
11	9			7.50			4.50			9.25	
12	10			7.50			4.50			6.4	
13	10			8			4.75			2.5	
14	10			8			4.75			2.5	
15	11			8			4.75			5.6	
16	11			8.50			5			7.75	
17	11			8.50			5			8.38	
18	12			8.50			5			9.13	
19	12			9			5.25			9.75	
20	12			9			5.25			8.00	
21	13			9			5.25			8.00	
22	13	960	1.35	10.50	750	1.40	5.50	465	1.2	5.00	1.2

* Iowa Bulletin 271, 1930. These calves were gotten on feed too rapidly and went off feed badly on the twelfth day and again on the twenty-second day.

of grain consumption at at least 1.5 per cent of the live weight.[2] However, the reduction of the roughage to a weight below 0.5 per cent of the live weight is seldom justified, since further decreases in the roughage usually have little effect upon the consumption of grain. In calculating the consumption of roughage the cobs in corn-and-cob meal and the estimated dry weight of the stover in corn silage should, of course, be considered as air-dry roughage.

Full vs. Limited Grain Rations. Although the general practice among Corn Belt cattle feeders is to get their cattle on a full feed of grain within 30–50 days, it is sometimes decided to limit the grain

[2] Calves, because of their rapid growth, may increase in size sufficiently to permit appropriate increases of grain without reducing the roughage below the amount they were eating when they attained a minimum full feed.

to a smaller amount and feed more than the usual amounts of roughage. This plan of feeding is likely to be popular during years when corn is in short supply and high in price and roughage is plentiful and cheap, and also during periods when, because of an abnormally strong demand for beef, a narrow price spread prevails between well-finished cattle and those marketed in lower condition. Such a situation prevailed during both World War I and World War II, with the result that a large percentage of the cattle fed during the war years were given somewhat less than a full feed of grain.

The extent to which the grain ration is limited depends principally upon (1) the relative supply of grains and roughages, (2) the kind and quality of the roughage, and (3) the length of the feeding period. If plenty of corn silage is available, the grain may be limited to only the corn that is in the silage, since cattle will make fairly good gains on a full feed of corn silage, 2 to 4 pounds of legume hay, and about 2 pounds of a protein concentrate. If the principal roughage fed is hay or corn stover, at least one-half a full feed of grain must be fed if satisfactory gains and finish are to be secured.

Usually the most satisfactory way to employ limited grain rations in fattening cattle is to feed no corn during the first and second months except the corn in the silage, one-half a full feed during the third and fourth months, and a full feed during the last month. If the cattle are fed longer than 5 months, two-thirds or three-fourths of a full feed may be fed during the fourth month and a full feed thereafter.

Usually better results will be obtained by increasing the level of grain feeding from time to time than by maintaining the same level throughout the feeding period. For example, in an extensive series of experiments carried out at the Indiana Experiment Station, steers that were fed no corn during the first half of the experiment but a full feed during the last half gave better results than a lot that received one-half a full feed during the whole period. (See Table 108.)

Effect of Limiting the Grain. (a) *Upon Rate of Gain.* Obviously, the rate of gain will increase with the level of grain feeding. However, if the amount of corn is gradually increased, so that a full feed is supplied during the last few weeks, the decline in gains usually observed in full-fed cattle may not occur. Such a decline in gains is especially likely to occur in cattle full fed longer than 200 days, which often show sluggish appetites during the latter part of the feeding period.

(b) *Upon Cost of Gains.* Unless cheaper gains are secured from limiting the grain ration, there can be no advantage from doing it, since it is almost certain that the cattle will sell for less per hundred than they would bring if they were full fed. The fact that the cost of the daily ration is less does not necessarily mean that the gains are cheaper, since the daily gains too are smaller than those of full-fed cattle. Consequently, the cost of the gain per hundred made by limited-fed cattle should be checked frequently during the feeding period to see whether the saving in cost of gains during the remainder of the period will be enough to offset the mark-down in selling price which will probably be encountered by the cattle because of their having been fed less than a full feed of grain.

(c) *Upon Profit Realized.* Cattle fed a limited feed of grain are not always more profitable than those that have been full fed. Indeed, if anything, the reverse is true. Only when the price spread between well-finished steers and those carrying only a moderate amount of flesh is unusually small will the profit realized per head be larger from limited grain feeding. However, the practice may be justified on the basis of numbers fed. For example, if only enough corn is available to supply 30 cattle with a full feed, it will furnish a half feed to 60 head, if there is enough roughage for the larger number. Consequently, limiting the corn would be more profitable than full feeding even though the profit realized per head on them was only 60 per cent that made from those that were full fed. Moreover, a cash return has been obtained for a considerable quantity of roughage which would not have been utilized if only 30 cattle had been fed instead of 60.

The Indiana Experiments. Although almost every Corn Belt station conducted feeding trials involving the use of limited grain rations during the period 1916–1921, those carried on by the Indiana Station are so exhaustive as to make a careful study of their results highly desirable. Altogether, the Indiana tests covered 7 years' work, involving the use of some 26 different lots of cattle or over 250 head in all. The work was begun in the winter of 1915–1916 and continued each year without interruption until the completion of the 1921–1922 test. Except for the first year, when only 2 lots were used, each trial involved the use of 4 lots of cattle, fed corn as follows:

1. Full feed during entire period.
2. One-half feed, based upon consumption of Lot 1.
3. No corn during first part of feeding period; full feed during last part (approximately last half).
4. No corn at all.

In addition to the corn ration, fed as stated above, all lots received cottonseed meal, clover hay, and corn silage. The cottonseed meal was

fed at the rate of 2.5 pounds per day per 1000 pounds live weight, and
the clover and silage were supplied according to the appetites remaining

TABLE 108

COMPARISON OF RATIONS CONTAINING DIFFERENT AMOUNTS OF CORN FOR
FATTENING STEERS*

Two-year-old Steers

Average of Seven Years' Work 1915-16 to 1921-22, inclusive	Full Feed of Corn	One-half Feed of Corn	Full Feed of Corn During Last Half of Period	No Corn
Number of Lots Averaged†	7	7	6	6
Length of Feeding Period (days)	139	139	136.6	136.6
Initial Weight	951 lbs.	951 lbs.	964 lbs.	964 lbs.
Total Gain	327.5	283.5	299	259.5
Daily Gain	2.37	2.05	2.17	1.90
Total Feed Consumed (lbs.)				
Shelled Corn	1650	850	745	....
Cottonseed Meal	370	365	365	365
Clover Hay	410	448	525	550
Corn Silage	4350	5515	5665	6680
Average Daily Feed				
Shelled Corn	11.89	6.13	5.42	....
Cottonseed Meal	2.66	2.64	2.67	2.66
Clover Hay	2.97	3.48	3.81	3.98
Corn Silage	31.54	39.91	41.58	48.99
Feed per lb. Gain				
Shelled Corn	5.05	3.05	2.53	....
Cottonseed Meal	1.14	1.32	1.27	1.44
Clover Hay	1.28	1.73	1.85	2.16
Corn Silage	13.43	19.92	19.91	26.43
Cost per cwt. Gain	$18.67	$18.19	$17.47	$15.63
Initial Value per cwt.	9.03	9.03	9.03	9.03
Necessary Selling Price (in lots)	11.40	11.00	10.86	10.34
Actual Selling Price (in lots)	11.62	11.08	11.125	10.85
Profit per Steer (excluding pork)	3.25	1.13	3.38	6.47
Pork Produced per Steer	45.17	29.41	31.67	−1.43
Profit per Steer, Pork Included	13.87	8.08	9.91	7.95

* Compiled from Indiana Bulletins 191, 206, 220, 240, 249, 255, 265.
† Six lots used in averaging financial results.

after the consumption of the desired amounts of corn. In no test did
the full-fed cattle receive an excessive amount of corn, such as is sometimes fed by feeders of the old school. The average ration varied dur-

ing the 7 years from 9.81 to 13.25 pounds of shelled corn per day for the entire period, the average consumption for the 7 trials being 11.89 pounds. As the cattle used in all trials were 2-year-olds, the limited grain-fed lots were checked, not against a largely obsolete method of feeding old-fashioned, matured steers, but against a very modern, up-to-date method of fattening cattle of the type and age very popular with present-day feeders. Consequently, the results obtained should have considerable significance for the man who handles cattle of this kind. (See Table 108.)

While some variation existed in the Indiana trials during the different years in the effect of the amount of corn fed upon the daily gains secured, in no year did the full-fed lot fail to make the largest, and the no-corn lot the smallest, daily gain. The greatest difference was observed in the winter of 1916–1917, at which time the full-fed lot made 2.50 pounds, and the no-corn lot 1.63 pounds, gain per day. The least difference was shown in 1918–1919, when the lots referred to made 2.36 and 2.07 pounds, respectively.

Note should be made of the fact that, as the feeding period progressed, the gains made by the no-corn cattle fell off much more rapidly than those for the full-fed lot. The same statement applies to the cattle receiving half a feed of corn, though with hardly the same force. Such a condition is to be expected with limited grain rations, since the withholding of the grain results in a relatively unpalatable ration of which the cattle will in time grow tired. In the full-fed lots the gains were kept up largely by decreasing the roughage component of the ration and increasing the concentrates. Similar results were obtained by feeding corn during only the latter half of the feeding period.

The Ohio Experiments. The Ohio Experiment Station began, in the fall of 1928, a series of feeding experiments that demonstrated the importance of limited grain rations for farmers who do not have enough corn to supply a full feed to the number of cattle required to utilize the available roughages. The most noteworthy fact disclosed by these tests is that nearly twice the number of cattle may be fed for a given number of days on a field of corn put into the silo than could be fed if the corn were cut and shocked and fed as shelled corn and stover. Whereas cattle fed silage and no additional grain often show a smaller profit per steer, they usually will return a larger profit per acre because of the greater number fed. Consequently, this method of feeding has a real advantage for the farmer who is seeking a way to market a field of corn so that it will add most to the total farm income. Moreover, many small farmers who are able to feed a limited grain ration to a carload of steers would have sufficient corn to full-feed only half that number. The greater number will benefit the farm by utilizing a much larger supply of unmarketable roughages and by producing a larger amount of manure for the cultivated fields. (See Table 109.)

TABLE 109

EFFECT OF LIMITING THE GRAIN RATION UPON THE RETURN REALIZED PER STEER AND PER ACRE OF CORN FED*

Corn Component	1928–29 174 Days		1929–30 177 Days		1932–33 183 Days	
	Corn Silage	Shelled Corn Stover	Corn Silage	½ Feed Silage Sh. Corn Stover	Corn Silage	½ Feed Silage Ground Oats
Initial weight, lbs........	622	607	662	662	630	632
Av. daily gain...........	2.01	2.24	2.11	2.51	1.85	2.15
Av. daily ration.........						
Shelled corn..........	....	16.3	....	11.9	....	11.2†
Prot. conc.............	2.0	2.0	2.0	2.0	2.0	...
Corn stover..........	....	9.5	....	7.7	....	...
Mixed hay...........	1.2	1.6	2.8	2.1	2.9	2.8
Corn silage..........	47.4	....	49.4	24.9	42.0	21.0
Gain of cattle per acre of corn................	752	372	712	515	712	236[a]
Steer days per acre of corn.	375	166	337	205	385	110[a]
Selling price of cattle.....	$14.00	$14.75	$10.60	$11.25	$5.25	$5.50
Profit per steer.........	8.58	3.46	11.79	13.69	−5.86	−4.83
Return per acre of corn...	71.65	50.80	56.66	57.06	....	...
Yield per acre						
Silage, tons..........	8.8	....	8.8	8.8	8.3	8.3
Grain, bushels........	(48)	48	(63)	63	(40)	45[b]

* Ohio Bimonthly Bulletins Nos. 139, 146, 164.
† Ground oats.
[a] Per acre of land in both silage and oats.
[b] Yield of oats.

A second series of limited grain experiments were begun by the Ohio Station in 1935. They differed from previous tests in that large quantities of hay instead of silage were fed to take the place of the corn withheld from the cattle. These tests are of particular value to farmers who are increasing their acreage of alfalfa and other legume hays. Large amounts of hay can be utilized only by limiting the grain to considerably less than a full feed, so that the cattle will be induced to eat it.

TABLE 110

LIMITING THE CORN AND INCREASING THE AMOUNT OF LEGUME HAY IN
RATIONS FOR FATTENING YEARLING STEERS*

(Average of 3 tests)

Av. Time Fed, 240 Days	Full Feed of Corn	Three-fourths Full Feed of Corn	One-half Full Feed of Corn
Av. Initial Wt. lbs....	694	694	686
Av. Final Wt. lbs....	1152	1133	1091
Av. daily gain....	1.91	1.78	1.69
Av. daily ration			
Corn-and-cob meal....	13.3	10.1	6.7
Prot. conc....	1.5	1.5	1.5
Corn silage....	13.7	14.1	14.2
Clover or alfalfa hay....	3.2	6.2	8.7
Feed per cwt. gain			
Corn-and-cob meal....	696	564	399
Prot. conc....	78	83	88
Corn silage....	719	790	843
Clover or alfalfa hay....	169	347	517
Selling price per cwt....	$12.62	$12.20	$11.83
Acres of feed eaten per head			
Ear corn....	.91	.69	.46
Corn silage....	.17	.17	.17
Legume hay....	.19	.37	.52
Total acres....	1.27	1.23	1.15
Ratio of Corn Acreage to Hay Acreage....	5.5:1	2.3:1	1.2:1
Cattle gains per acre....	367	350	354
Hog gains per acre....	20	19	14
Total gains per acre....	387	369	368

* Ohio Bimonthly Bulletin 198.
† Yields used in computing returns per acre: Corn, 50 bu.; silage, 10 tons; legume hay, 2 tons.

A comparison of Table 110 with Table 109 brings out the great advantage which corn silage has over legume hay in limited grain rations. Whereas the substitution of silage for part or all the grain greatly increased the number of cattle that could be fattened on a given area, the substitution of legume hay for the grain increased the number only slightly. Of still more importance is the fact that the total gain realized per acre of crops fed to cattle greatly increased with the amount of silage fed, whereas it decreased slowly but steadily with the amount of hay fed. Of course, it should be said that legumes must be grown to keep up the fertility of the soil, and also that a large part of the corn grown on many farms is fed to hogs, leaving a limited amount of corn but large quantities of hay to be utilized by beef cattle. Where this condition exists, better returns will usually be realized if all the corn available for the cattle is made into silage and a sufficient number of cattle are purchased to be fed a full feed of silage and 3 or 4 pounds of hay for approximately 150 days. Legumes not needed for hay under this system of feeding may well be plowed under to enrich the soil, thereby saving the expense of harvesting.

Fig. 43. A pair of steers suitable for limited grain feeding. Thin yearling or 2-year-old steers of medium grade are usually the best kind of cattle to fatten on a limited feed of grain. (*Courtesy Illinois Experiment Station.*)

Practical Use of Limited Grain Ration. The results of any experimental feeding trial with limited grain rations should not be applied directly to practical feeding operations. In studying them it should be kept in mind that the different rations were fed to the same grade of cattle and for the same length of time. That these items be identical in the different lots is highly necessary from an experimental standpoint, since in an experiment only one factor may vary. However, great variations exist in these respects in actual feeding operations. Farmers who plan to feed but little or no corn seldom, if ever, buy as good a class of feeder cattle as those men who full feed from the start. To do so would, as a rule, be a waste of money. Cattle fattened largely on roughage cannot hope to "top the market." Realizing this, most cattlemen refrain from buying choice or fancy feeders to utilize large quantities of roughage and but little corn. Since cattle so fattened furnish a comparatively low grade of beef, it is manifestly good practice to start with comparatively low-priced steers.

As limited grain rations cannot be counted upon for satisfactory gain after about 150 days, few feeders use such rations for longer periods. Indeed, the more usual practice is to feed for only 90 to 120 days. With such a short feeding period, it is desirable that the cattle have considerable age and size, so that they will be likely to make a rapid improvement in condition. Fully matured steers, lacking somewhat in quality and decidedly thin in flesh, but having large frames and good deep middles, are the ideal kind for limited corn rations. Because of their deficient quality and condition they can be bought cheap. Moreover, their size and maturity will insure a rapid gain in weight and a marked improvement in condition from the large quantities of roughage that they will consume.

Another point to be kept in mind in connection with limited grain rations is that such rations are most likely to prove satisfactory during the winter months when the appetites of the cattle are unusually keen because of the prevailing cold weather. At other seasons of the year the consumption of bulky feeds like silage and hay is not likely to be sufficiently large to produce satisfactory gains in the absence of a liberal amount of grain. Also, the market for plain, half-fat steers, such as are produced by the use of such rations, is usually much better in the late winter and spring than at any other time of year.

18

Carbonaceous Concentrates and Their Use in the Fattening Ration

From the standpoint of their source, concentrates are of two kinds: (1) the grains of farm-grown crops; and (2) commercially manufactured feeding stuffs. According to their composition, concentrates may be divided into two groups: (1) carbonaceous feeds, or those containing a relatively low percentage of protein; and (2) nitrogenous feeds, or those that are especially rich in protein. In general, the farm-grown grains belong in the carbonaceous class, whereas a majority of the commercial feeding stuffs are nitrogenous.

Carbonaceous feeds, as their name implies, are rich in chemical compounds that contain a relatively large amount of carbon. The more important of these compounds are starches, sugars, and fats. All these materials, when consumed by animals, are utilized chiefly for the production of muscular energy and for the manufacture of fat, which is stored in various parts of the body, but especially in the superficial layers of muscles found just beneath the skin. To promote such a storage of fat is, of course, the object sought in cattle feeding. Consequently, carbonaceous feeds are of prime importance in fattening cattle for the market.

Carbonaceous concentrates are not only highly efficient in the production of fat; in addition, they are produced in great abundance by the farmers themselves and, consequently, are relatively cheap. Because of these facts they should, and usually do, form the bulk of the fattening ration.

The important carbonaceous concentrates used in cattle feeding are corn, oats, barley, wheat, the grain sorghums, beet pulp, and molasses. Although the use of some of these feeds is limited to certain sections, a brief discussion of all of them will be attempted.

Corn. In corn is found the explanation of the wonderful development attained by the beef cattle industry of the United States. Other countries have cattle of as good or better breeding; other regions have as good or more favorable climate; other nations have more and better grass lands; but no other country has such a great supply of corn available for cattle feeding. So long as our country holds this important

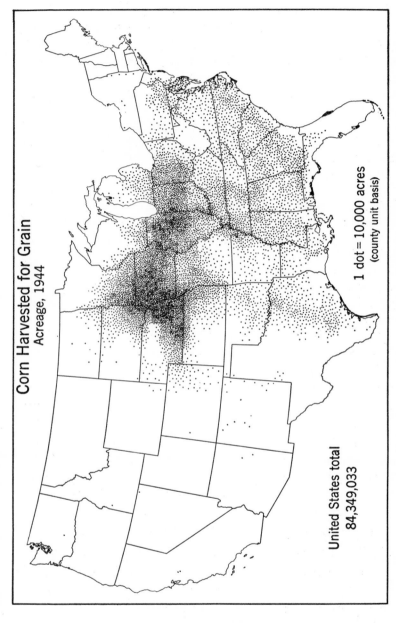

Corn Harvested for Grain
Acreage, 1944

1 dot = 10,000 acres
(county unit basis)

United States total
84,349,033

FIG. 44. Corn acreage harvested for grain. The number of cattle fattened for market in a county or district usually depends largely upon the amount of corn produced there. (*Courtesy Bureau of the Census.*)

advantage, just so long will her beef enjoy an enviable reputation and command a distinct premium in the large meat markets of the world.

As a feed for fattening cattle, corn is unsurpassed. It is highly palatable, being eaten readily by cattle of all ages. It is very fattening, being high in digestible carbohydrates and fat, the two nutrients out of which fat is most readily formed. It is easily stored and easily prepared for consumption. It is produced in great abundance and, consequently, is relatively cheap. In fact, corn may be said to combine all the essentials of a valuable cattle feed, save one. It is noticeably deficient in protein. For this reason it should not be fed alone, but should be supplemented with feeds that are high in protein, such as cottonseed meal and alfalfa hay.

In all sections where corn is extensively grown it should, and normally does, form the bulk of the fattening ration. Seldom is it possible for Corn Belt feeders to use other carbonaceous concentrates to any great extent without materially increasing the cost of the ration, lowering its efficiency, or possibly doing both.

New vs. Old Corn. In view of the large amount of corn placed in storage under the government loan and purchase agreement, some of which is carried over for 2 or more years, the question arises of the feeding value of such corn relative to corn that has been recently harvested. Obviously, old corn contains less moisture than new corn and, consequently, is a more concentrated feed. On the other hand, its low moisture content makes it less palatable, both because it is harder to chew and because it probably has lost much of the flavor and aroma possessed by new corn. Vitamin A assays of corn of different ages show a serious loss of this important nutrient, which varies with the time. This point is probably of little significance if plenty of high-quality legume hay is fed with the corn, but it might be of great importance if the corn were the principal source of Vitamin A. Feeding tests comparing corn stored for one or more years and that which has been only recently cribbed show no significant difference between old and new corn for fattening cattle. (See Table 111.)

Farmers who full-feed cattle during the summer for the late fall market frequently run out of old corn before the cattle are fat enough to sell. When this happens they are faced with the question of finishing the cattle on new corn or buying old corn at a much higher price per bushel than the prevailing price offered for the new crop. Sometimes the supply of old corn is exhausted by mid-September or even in late August, several weeks before new corn will be mature enough to husk and possibly 2 months before it will be dry enough to shell. In this situation there is a strong temptation to substitute,

TABLE 111

THE RELATIVE VALUE OF OLD AND NEW CORN FOR FATTENING CATTLE

	Iowa AH Leaflet 160 (210 days)					Illinois Mimeo. Report, April 26, 1940 (162 days)	
	4-year-old Corn (1937)	3-year-old Corn (1938)	2-year-old Corn (1939)	1-year-old Corn (1940)	New Corn (1941)	2-year-old Corn (1937)	New Corn (1939)
Relative hardness of kernels .	164	160	174	150	100	132	100
Moisture (percentage).......	10.4	10.9	12.4	12.9	16.7	11.0	16.2
Vitamin A, units per pound of corn.................	821	809	869	1330	1720	.....	.....
Crude protein (14% moisture basis) (percentage)........	9.8	8.5	8.6	8.3	8.0	.....	.....
Average initial weight, pounds	735	736	732	732	738	805	802
Average daily gain, pounds..	2.20	2.15	2.10	1.97	2.15	2.49	2.53
Average daily ration, pounds Shelled corn (14% moisture).................	16.3	15.0	16.1	15.7	14.9	13.7	13.9
Protein supplement.......	1.0	1.0	1.0	1.0	1.0	1.4	1.0
Alfalfa hay..............	4.0	4.0	4.0	4.0	4.0	2.1	2.1
Corn silage.............	.....	.....	.....	.....	.....	18.9	18.9
Feed per cwt. gain, pounds Shelled corn (14% moisture).................	741	696	766	799	693	552	550
Protein supplement.......	45	47	48	51	47	55	58
Alfalfa hay..............	181	187	190	203	186	86	84
Corn silage.............	.....	.....	.....	.....	.....	762	745
Selling price per cwt........	$14.10	$13.75	$13.60	$13.70	$13.70	$10.25	$10.40
Shrinkage (percentage)......	2.0	1.4	3.2	2.3	1.9	2.5	1.3
Dressing percentage.........	63.7	63.8	63.9	63.5	62.8	61.3	61.8

for part of the old corn, freshly cut "stalk-and-all" gathered daily with a field harvester or new ears broken or sliced by hand or with a mechanical slicer. Most experienced feeders are strongly opposed to such a change in the ration of cattle approaching market condition, on the ground that the new corn is too bulky and too laxative to supply the energy to which the cattle have become accustomed. Consequently, the gains will be noticeably less than those obtained if the cattle were continued on old corn.

The few feeding tests made with corn fed before it is dry enough to crib indicate that its higher palatability and probable higher digestibility largely offset its higher moisture content and lower energy value. In a test made at the Illinois Station with yearling steers that had been full fed in the dry lot since April 27, the cattle that were changed gradually to new corn, beginning September 6 and were fed only new corn after September 30, gained as rapidly during the period September 6 to November 4 as the check lot fed old shelled corn. During the first 8 days of the test the new corn was fed in the form of green stalks cut with a field harvester; during the next 37 days it was fed as sliced ears; and during the last 14 days of the test it was fed as shelled corn. The original plan of the experiment provided for feeding a half feed of old corn until the new corn was dry enough to shell, but the cattle showed such a dislike for the old corn that it was discontinued after 24 days, after which time only now corn was fed.

In another test, also made at the Illinois Station, equally good gains were made by yearling steers that were fed old corn throughout the test, and steers that were fed new oats from July 24 until August 21, decreasing amounts of oats and increasing amounts of chopped new ear corn from August 21 until October 2, and new shelled corn from October 2 until November 11, when the cattle were marketed. The moisture content of the corn kernels was 59 per cent when the feeding of new corn was begun on August 21, and 24 per cent on October 2, when the change from sliced ears to shelled corn was made. In this second test the steers fed old corn sold for 50 cents per hundred more than those fed new corn and returned, as a result of the higher selling price, approximately $5 per head more profit, despite the fact that new and old corn were valued at 56 and 65 cents a bushel, respectively.

Value of Soft Corn. Often a field of late-planted corn fails to mature before the first killing frost, and about once in 8 or 10 years, an unusually early frost will damage a considerable percentage of the crop over a large portion of the Corn Belt. Frost destroys the life in the green, growing stalk, resulting in the stoppage of the translocation of the food nutrients from the stalk to the ear and the transfer of water from the ear to the stalk, where it normally would evaporate through the leaves. As a consequence the ears fail to dry out and they contain an abnormally high percentage of moisture. Such corn is commonly termed "soft." In practice, soft corn is corn that contains too high a percentage of moisture to be stored in the ear without danger of heating. Heating is likely to occur when the amount of moisture exceeds 25 per cent.

As soft corn is unmarketable, it is retained on the farm and fed. The feeding value of such corn has long been a matter of controversy. That it is inferior to sound corn, none will deny. However, results obtained at experiment stations where the two feeds have been compared indicate that soft corn is a better feed for fattening cattle than has commonly been supposed. On the basis of dry-matter content, soft corn is as efficient as mature corn in producing gains. However, the gains from soft corn are somewhat less rapid because its greater bulk results in a smaller consumption of dry matter.

TABLE 112

THE VALUE OF SOFT CORN FOR FATTENING CATTLE*

Two-year-old Steers, Fed 80 Days	Soft Corn			Mature Corn from Previous Year
Form of Corn Fed	Shock Corn	Broken Ears	Ear-corn Silage	Broken Ears
Average per cent moisture.....	31.75	35.82	59.65	13.61
Average daily gain..........	3.20 lbs.	3.20 lbs.	3.35 lbs.	3.52 lbs.
Average daily ration				
Ear corn.................	26.40	31.48	....	25.59
Linseed meal.............	1.88	1.89	1.89	1.89
Ear-corn silage...........	....	....	45.43	....
Alfalfa hay..............	2.46	2.70	2.35	2.70
Feed per lb. gain				
Ear corn.................	8.25	9.84	....	7.27
Linseed meal.............	.59	.59	.56	.54
Ear-corn silage...........	....	....	13.56	....
Alfalfa hay..............	.77	.84	.70	.77
Dry matter in corn (ears only) per lb. gain..............	5.55	6.42	5.34	6.28
Selling price per cwt.........	$9.65	$9.35	$10.00	$9.85
Dressing percentage.........	60.5	60.0	60.7	60.6
Cattle and hog gains per acre .	273 lbs.	247 lbs.	292 lbs.	....

* Illinois Bulletin 313, 1928.

Corn containing an abnormal amount of moisture will freeze so hard during severe weather that cattle can scarcely eat it. Hence, soft corn should, if possible, be fed during the fall and early winter. In order to obtain as great a consumption of corn as possible, the roughage allowance should be limited to 4 or 5 pounds per 1000 pounds live weight. Silage is not as satisfactory a roughage as hay for cattle fed on soft corn.

One of the problems connected with the utilization of soft corn is the matter of storage. Ordinarily, the corn is cut and shocked, or is left in the field to be gathered as it is needed. Both these methods are likely to prove inconvenient during bad weather when the fields are soft and muddy or are covered with deep snow. This difficulty can be avoided by snapping the ears soon after the first killing frost and making them into ear-corn silage.

Ear-Corn Silage. Results secured from feeding soft corn in the form of ear-corn silage have compared so favorably with those ordinarily obtained from feeding sound, mature corn that it may be asked why this method of harvesting and feeding corn need be limited to those occasional years when corn fails to mature. If a given area of corn made into ear-corn silage will produce as much gain when fed to cattle as it would if it were allowed to ripen and were fed as ear or shelled corn, there would seem to be several advantages to be gained by this novel method of harvesting. In the first place, it permits the harvesting of a considerable portion of the corn crop during favorable autumn weather. Second, it stores the corn in a form suitable for feeding cattle of all ages without further preparation, thereby eliminating the expense of grinding or shelling, with the extra handling of feed involved in these operations. Third, it makes possible the pasturing of stalk fields while they are still green and palatable, or the making of the green stover into green stover silage;[1] or, if the green stover is not needed, the stalks may be plowed under and the field sown to wheat.

The method of making ear-corn silage is relatively simple. The ears, together with the attached husks, are gathered either by hand or with a mechanical picker,[2] hauled to the silo, and shoveled onto the feed table of a silage cutter. No feeder is required, as in making ordinary silage, as the ears go through the rollers into the cutter of their own accord. Neither is it necessary to tramp the silage in the silo, as the weight of the corn and the absence of much bulky material cause the silage to settle almost as rapidly as it is made. However, it is necessary to have someone in the silo to see that the silage is evenly distributed. Otherwise, the cut corn will tend to pile up in the center while the husks accumulate along the walls.

If the corn is too ripe and contains insufficient moisture to insure thorough packing, a small amount of water should be added by introducing a pipe or hose into the blower of the cutter. When the job is finished the silo should be sealed by running sufficient green stover through the cutter to make a layer approximately 3 feet deep on top of the ear corn. Considerable water should be added to this stover to insure thorough packing. When ear-corn silage is so sealed, little spoilage will occur.

[1] *Cf.* p. 157.

[2] If a picker is used, the husking rolls should be removed or covered with sheet iron to prevent the removal of the husks from the ears.

As ear-corn silage is very heavy in proportion to its volume, a relatively small silo will hold sufficient silage to feed a carload of cattle even though they receive little other feed. If the silo is too large in diameter, insufficient silage will be removed daily to prevent spoilage in warm weather. A silo 12 × 40 feet will hold approximately 120 tons of ear-corn silage, or enough to fatten 40 to 50 head of cattle during the usual length feeding period.

TABLE 113

EAR-CORN SILAGE FOR FATTENING CALVES*

Equal Areas of Corn Harvested and Fed	Ear-Corn Silage	Ear-Corn Silage	Mature Corn (C. and Cob meal)
Date harvested........................	Sept. 4–9	Sept. 24–25	Oct. 25–30
Moisture in grain when harvested.....	53.4%	37.5%	Under 25%
Average daily gain...................	2.23 lbs.	2.12 lbs.	2.10 lbs.
Average daily ration:			
Corn component....................	29.4	27.3	13.3
Cottonseed meal...................	1.6	1.6	1.6
Alfalfa hay.......................	2.0	2.0	2.0
Oat straw........................	....	....	2.9
Total days feed from area............	3,018 days	3,153 days	3,329 days
Calc. total gain to be credited area....	6,721 lbs.	6,686 lbs.	6,987 lbs.
Selling price per cwt.................	$15.70	$15.65	$15.35
Dressing percentage.................	61.1	61.4	60.4
Return per bushel of corn obtained from the area allowed to mature....	$1.19	$1.11	$1.07

* Illinois Experiment Station, Mimeographed Report, 1928–29, Calf Feeding Experiments.

Effect of Variety of Corn upon Feeding Value. During the period 1930–1940, when hybrid corn was rapidly displacing the open-pollinated varieties, the relative feeding value of the different hybrids was widely discussed. Some hybrids were claimed to be so hard that they were eaten with difficulty and, hence the kernels were swallowed with but little chewing and were poorly digested. Other varieties were believed not only to be softer but also to possess an aroma and flavor that made them more palatable. In order to ascertain the validity of these statements several feeding trials were carried out at the experiment stations of the Corn Belt states, in which the more popular hybrids, as well as open-pollinated varieties of corn, were fed to both cattle and hogs. In most of the tests the relative hardness of the varieties used was determined by measuring the force required to crush the kernels in a vice-like screw press.

In most of the tests reported, the open-pollinated corn fed proved to be somewhat superior to the hybrid varieties in palatability, rate of gain, and finish produced, as measured by selling price per hundredweight and dressing percentage of the finished cattle. Also, in tests in which two or more hybrids were compared, differences in these respects were noted between the different hybrids. Both corn consumption and hog gains usually were noticeably affected by hardness of

TABLE 114

EFFECT OF VARIETY OF CORN UPON ITS FEEDING VALUE FOR BEEF CATTLE

	Nebraska 1939–1940 (193 days)		Iowa 1939–1940 (210 days)				Illinois 1939–1940 (162 days)	
	Open-Pollinated	U.S. 44	Open-Pollinated	Iowa 13	Pioneer 307	U.S. 44	Open-Pollinated	Illinois 784
Relative hardness........	...	...	100	106	122	111	100	112
Average initial weight, lb..	396	396	722	727	725	729	802	802
Average daily gain, lb.....	2.09	1.92	2.17	2.02	1.97	1.80	2.53	2.43
Average daily ration, lb.								
Shelled corn...........	11.7	10.7	12.3	12.0	12.9	11.9	14.3	13.2
Protein concentrate....	1.5	1.5	1.5	1.5	1.5	1.5	1.5	1.4
Corn silage...........	9.0	9.4	12.5	12.5	12.5	12.5	18.9	18.9
Legume hay..........	...	...	1.7	1.7	1.7	1.7	2.1	2.1
Feed per cwt. gain, lb.								
Shelled corn...........	560	558	567	595	653	658	564	543
Protein concentrate....	72	78	69	74	76	83	58	56
Corn silage...........	430	489	577	622	637	696	745	779
Legume hay..........	...	...	77	83	85	93	84	87
Corn saved by hogs per bushel of corn fed....	...	...	3.1	4.4	3.2	7.8	1.48[a]	1.44[a]
Selling price per cwt......	$9.90	$9.40	$9.40	$9.10	$9.15	$9.15	$10.40	$10.60
Dressing percentage......	62.1	61.2	...	...	...	...	61.8	62.0

[a] Gain of hogs per bushel of corn fed.

kernel, supporting the belief that hard kernels are less palatable and less digestible than those which are more easily masticated.

Since cattle feeders are likely to know more about the yield per acre than about the relative feeding value of the different varieties of corn, they are likely to grow those hybrids which have the reputation for producing the most bushels per acre. To select on yield alone is a serious error, since the higher production may be more than offset by slower gains and a lower price for the finished cattle, if the corn is too hard to be palatable and well digested. For example, in the Nebraska experiment reported in Table 114, 60 bushels of open-pollinated corn were as valuable as 75 bushels of the hybrid variety on the basis of the net returns realized from the two lots of cattle.

Feeding Corn to Breeding Animals. Although corn ranks high as a feed for fattening cattle for market, its use as a feed for breeding animals is often severely criticized. It is stated that, owing to its high starch and fat content, it is likely to produce such an accumulation of fat around the reproductive organs that their normal function will be impaired. Also, it is thought that the great strain put upon the digestive system by the digestion and assimilation of such a highly concentrated food, and upon the excretory system by the elimination of the oxidized products, may result in a serious and perhaps permanent derangement of some of the organs of these systems. This latter condition, commonly referred to as "burnt up by too much corn," is regarded as particularly likely to occur in young bulls and heifers.

That breeding animals should not be kept in too high condition, no one will deny. Also, the feeding of a highly concentrated, fattening ration to young stock intended for the breeding herd is likely to result in extremely early maturity gained at the expense of size. But that it is necessary to withhold corn from breeding animals to avoid these effects is by no means an established fact. Rather, the general use of corn in moderate quantities for cattle of all ages and descriptions by many successful breeders would indicate that corn, when properly supplemented and wisely fed, has an important place in the ration of the breeding herd. However, its low percentages of protein, minerals, and vitamins make the need of proper supplementary feeds more urgent for breeding cattle than for fattening steers.

Oats. Formerly oats were not of great importance in beef cattle feeding, but, with the loss of the market for oats for feeding horses, they are now used rather extensively for cattle in many parts of the Corn Belt. For fattening purposes they are rather too high in crude fiber and too low in digestible nutrients to be fed alone; but when mixed with other grains like corn and wheat, which are higher in energy and less bulky, they give very satisfactory results. The tough, fibrous hull and the small size of the kernel make grinding oats advisable for older cattle, which swallow a considerable percentage of the kernels without much chewing if the oats are fed whole. Grinding oats, as a rule, is not advisable for calves, unless the grain with which the oats are fed is also ground, in which case grinding will insure a better mixture of the two feeds.

That both whole and ground oats are more palatable than corn for calves is indicated by the relative amounts eaten in the Kansas experiment reported in Table 115, where the two grains were fed free-choice in separate self-feeders. This slight difference in palatability was probably due to the fact that the oat grains were softer and more easily chewed than the kernels of corn.

TABLE 115

RELATIVE PALATABILITY OF SHELLED CORN AND
OATS WHEN FED FREE–CHOICE TO BEEF CALVES*

| | Lot 1 | | Lot 2 | |
	Shelled Corn	Whole Oats	Ground Shelled Corn	Ground Oats
Average daily consumption, lb.				
1st 28 days	1.96	3.18	1.83	3.45
2nd 28 days	1.96	5.85	2.50	5.02
3rd 28 days	4.56	4.57	4.96	4.35
4th 28 days	4.70	6.32	6.48	5.46
Last 26 days	2.44	8.53	4.80	7.33
Average 138 days	3.14	5.65	4.10	5.09
Average initial weight, lb.	412		409	
Average final weight	738		729	
Average daily gain	2.36		2.32	

* Kansas Cattle Circular 38B, May 7, 1938.

Feeding experiments indicate that oats more nearly approach the value of corn for feeding mature cattle than for feeding calves. In tests conducted at the Indiana Station with 2-year-old steers the substitution of ground oats for one-third of the corn ration decreased slightly the feed required per 100 pounds of gain. However, in none of the 7 experiments with calves shown in Table 116 did oats have as high feeding value as corn. On the average 118 pounds of oats replaced 100 pounds of corn, or 2 bushels of oats replaced approximately 1 bushel of shelled corn. One objection to feeding oats to young cattle is that oats tend to make the cattle grow rather than fatten. This fact is substantiated by the lower prices received for most of the oat-fed lots when they were marketed.

Oats may constitute as much as one-half or two-thirds of the grain ration while the cattle are becoming accustomed to a full feed. Since oats contain less energy and are more bulky than corn, their use at this time will lessen the danger that some of the steers will overeat and become foundered. However, the oats should gradually be reduced in amount as the feeding progresses, so that they will form only 20 to 30 per cent of the grain ration, or possibly be eliminated altogether, during the last third of the fattening period. Obviously, the relative prices of corn and oats should be considered carefully in determining the extent to which oats should be used in the fattening of cattle for market.

As stated above, the feeding of large amounts will not be profitable unless the price of oats per bushel is less than one-half that of corn. Hogs following cattle in the feeding lot appear to make almost no use of the oats which the cattle fail to digest. Consequently, the substitution of oats for a considerable part of the corn ration will result in much smaller hog credits.

TABLE 116

COMPARISON OF CORN WITH CORN AND OATS FOR FATTENING CATTLE

	Shelled Corn			Shelled Corn and Oats			
	Daily Gain	Grain per cwt. Gain	Selling Price per cwt.	Ratio of Corn to Oats	Daily Gain	Grain per cwt. Gain	Selling Price per cwt.
	lbs.	lbs.			lbs.	lbs.	
Two-year-old steers							
Indiana Bulletin 371....	2.50	593	$12.90	2:1ᵃ	2.60	564	$13.00
Indiana Bulletin 371....	1.88	584	11.50	2:1ᵃ	2.16	508	11.75
Indiana Bulletin 371....	2.15	592	7.45	2:1ᵃ	2.18	586	7.50
Calves							
Illinois, 1912–13........	2.00	594	8.50	4:1	1.96	603	8.55
Illinois, 1935–36........	2.06	447	8.65	2.5:1	2.02	472	8.65
Nebraska, 1922–23......	2.47	453	9.50	2:1	2.40	494	9.25
Minnesota Bull. 237....	2.32	580	9.60	4:1	2.19	602	9.40
Oklahoma, 1937–38.....	1.95	469	8.75	1ᵃ:1ᵃ	1.95	495	9.00
Kansas, 1932–33........	2.11	444	6.75	0:1ᵇ	2.02	442	6.00
Kansas, 1933–34........	2.14	476	7.00	1.3:1	2.13	516	6.75
Average of 7 lots of calves	2.15	495	$8.40	....	2.09	518	$8.25

ᵃ This grain fed ground.
ᵇ Whole oats alone fed first 100 days and shelled corn alone last 100 days.

Oats are somewhat higher in protein and minerals than corn, and for this reason they are especially valuable for breeding stock. When used in mixtures with other grains, they are highly regarded by Scotch herdsmen in fitting cattle for shows and sales. For such animals the hulls are in no way objectionable, since they give bulk and lightness to the grain ration.

Barley. Large amounts of barley are used in cattle feeding in the northern states and in Canada. At these latitudes corn cannot be expected to mature, and barley, with a shorter growing season, is raised to take its place. Barley is also grown to a limited extent along the western edge of the Corn Belt, where a grain crop is desired which will mature before the arrival of hot, dry weather.

TABLE 117

BARLEY VS. CORN FOR FATTENING CATTLE

	Steer Calves*		Yearling Steers†		Steer Calves†	
	Ground Shelled Corn	Ground Barley	Shelled Corn	Ground Barley	Shelled Corn	Ground Barley
Daily gain, lb...........	2.11	1.96	2.49	2.25	2.34	2.21
Feed per cwt. gain						
Grain...............	570	613	577	554	476	476
Protein concentrate ...	47	51	79	87	64	68
Corn silage..........	....	....	511	542	414	431
Hay................	176	199	173	188	119	114
Selling price per cwt.....	$7.75	$7.60	$13.50	$13.20	$11.25	$11.00
Pork credits per steer, lb..	....	....	43	8	....	....

* Kansas Mimeographed Cattle Circular 36A, 1936.
† Minnesota Bulletin 300, 1933.

Barley, like oats, has its kernel surrounded by a tough, heavy hull which materially lessens its digestibility and renders it somewhat unpalatable unless it is ground. The kernel itself is rather hard and flinty in texture and does not "chew up" as easily as corn. This fact makes the grinding or crushing of barley all the more necessary if satisfactory results are to be obtained from its use. The feeding of whole barley is a very wasteful practice, as a high percentage of the kernels are not chewed sufficiently well to permit them to be thoroughly digested. Undigested kernels of barley, like those of oats, are not utilized very well by the hogs which are kept in the feed lot.

In chemical composition, barley falls midway between oats and corn. Because of its higher protein and mineral content, it is a somewhat better-balanced feed than corn, but its lower percentage of fat and greater amount of fiber make it less fattening. Many comparisons have been made between shelled or ground corn and ground barley as feeds for fattening cattle, the results of which show considerable disagreement. It is likely that in at least some of the experiments the grains fed were not of the same quality. That this factor may be highly important is shown by the daily gains of 3 lots of steers fed

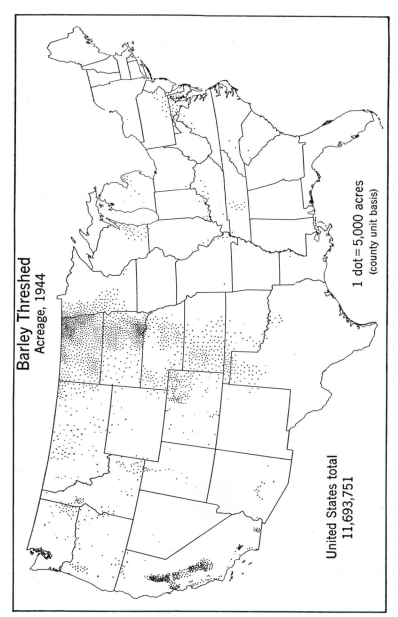

Barley Threshed
Acreage, 1944

United States total
11,693,751

1 dot = 5,000 acres
(county unit basis)

Fig. 45. The principal barley-producing areas of the United States. Most of the barley is grown north and west of the best corn-producing regions. (*Courtesy Bureau of the Census.*)

shelled corn, native barley, and northern-grown barley by the Illinois Station, which were 3.08, 2.81, and 3.35 pounds a head, respectively. Since weather conditions for the production of a high grade of barley are almost the opposite of those required for a good grade of corn, it is not surprising that there is much variation in the results obtained on the relative value of these two grains.

Although feeding tests show considerable variation in the relative value of corn and barley for fattening cattle, most of them indicate that ground barley is less palatable than shelled corn, that it has a tendency to cause bloat, and that barley-fed cattle usually sell for less than corn-fed cattle when marketed. In view of these facts the feeding of barley alone is confined largely to those sections of the country where barley is extensively grown and consequently is relatively cheap.

In the Corn Belt proper, barley should always be fed mixed with corn or corn and oats to lessen the frequency of bloat. In such mixtures barley has a feeding value fully equal to that of corn, but fed alone its value is only about 90 per cent that of corn on a pound basis. Or we may say that 5 bushels of barley have about the same feeding value for fattening cattle as 4 bushels of shelled corn.

Barley for Breeding Animals. Barley stands high in the estimation of feeders of breeding animals. Also, in the fitting of animals for the show ring it is regarded with much favor. Lower in the fat-forming compounds than corn, it is less "heating" and is conducive to the formation of a mellowness of flesh that is seldom attained by the use of corn. The barley-fed steers of the Northwest and the Pacific Coast have long been noted at the International Live Stock Exposition for their wonderful handling qualities and "touch." Several grand champion steers have been developed in these regions with the use of scarcely any corn, barley being the principal concentrate fed. Nearly all experienced feeders agree that there is nothing superior to barley to "mellow up" an animal that has become a bit hard in his flesh or to prevent a highly finished beast from becoming rough and patchy.

Wheat. Wheat is fed to beef cattle only when its price is abnormally low, so that its cost per pound is comparable to that of corn. Owing to the small size of the kernels, it must be ground to insure its thorough digestion. Wheat should not be fed alone, since the starch becomes sticky when mixed with saliva and is not greatly relished by the cattle. However, this objection is easily overcome by mixing ground wheat with other grains, such as shelled corn or ground oats. Such a mixture is sufficiently more valuable than corn alone to justify the feeding of wheat when corn and wheat are the same price per pound, even though the cost of grinding is 4 or 5 cents a bushel.

Results secured at the Kentucky[3] and Kansas Experiment Stations[4] indicate that ground wheat may be fed alone successfully if it is spread evenly over a rather liberal feed of corn silage. Evidently the silage reduces the sticky nature of the ground wheat by supplying more bulk and by compelling the cattle to eat the wheat more slowly.

Rye. Rye is usually regarded as a feed for hogs and as a rule is fed to beef cattle only when its price per bushel is considerably below that of corn. The grains are small and hard and, of course, should be ground. Like wheat, rye gives much better results when fed with corn than when fed alone. When so fed ground rye may be considered to be equal to ground wheat. (See Table 118.)

Grain Mixtures. Experienced feeders of purebred cattle greatly prefer a mixture of several grains to corn alone for fitting cattle for the show and sale ring. On the other hand, the men who feed steers for the market usually feed only corn unless corn is scarce and high in price compared with other grains. Feeding experiments indicate that grain mixtures usually are sufficiently better than single grains like corn or barley to justify their use, even though additional labor is required in their preparation. An exception to this statement appears to be a mixture of corn and oats for calves, which, as shown in Table 116, usually produces smaller gains and less finish than corn alone. An exception also is a mixture of ground oats and barley, which probably contains too much fiber and is too bulky for young animals.

Hominy Feed. Most of the by-products of the milling industry which are fed to beef cattle are relatively high in protein and are classed as nitrogenous rather than carbonaceous concentrates. An important exception is hominy feed, which is a by-product of the dry-process method of milling corn. Hominy feed consists of the corn germ, the outer coating or bran, the tips of the kernels, and small particles of starch from the endosperm which are formed in the removal of these parts. Since most of the oil of the corn kernel is found in the germ, hominy feed contains considerably more oil than shelled corn. It is also somewhat higher in protein and minerals, owing partly to the presence of the corn bran but principally to the fact that the percentage of moisture is considerably lower because of the kiln-drying of the corn before milling.

Hominy feed has proved to be a satisfactory substitute for shelled corn in the few experiments where it has been fed. However, it is too bulky to be fed alone successfully but may constitute up to 50 per cent

[3] Kentucky Bulletin 332, 1932.
[4] Kansas Bulletin 261, 1932.

TABLE 118

COMPARISON OF SINGLE GRAINS WITH GRAIN MIXTURES FOR FATTENING CATTLE

	Corn and Ground Oats — Indiana Bull. 371 (2-Year-Old Steers)			Corn and Ground Barley — Illinois Report, 1928 (2-Year-Old Steers)			Corn, Ground Wheat, and Ground Oats — Illinois Report, 1930 (2-Year-Old Steers)				Ground Oats and Ground Barley — Minnesota Bull. 300 (Calves)			Corn and Ground Wheat, and Corn and Ground Rye — Nebraska Bull. 295, 1935 (Calves: 3 Years. Average)	
	Corn	Oats	Corn 2 and Oats 1	Corn	Barley	Corn 1 and Barley 1	Corn	Corn 1 and Wheat 1	Oats 1 and Wheat 1	Corn 1 Oats 1 Wheat 1	Oats	Barley	Barley 2 Oats 1	Shelled Corn 1 and Ground Wheat 1	Shelled Corn 1 and Ground Rye 1
Av. daily gain, lb...	2.18	2.19	2.31	3.08	2.81	3.16	2.32	2.42	2.36	2.58	2.09	2.24	2.15	2.28	2.28
Av. daily ration															
Grain...........	12.8	12.1	12.7	15.6	16.0	15.6	15.8	15.8	15.0	15.7	10.2	10.7	10.5	10.7	10.8
Prot. conc.......	2.6	2.6	2.6	2.2	2.3	2.2	2.2	2.2	2.1	2.2	1.5	1.5	1.5	....	....
Silage..........	29.3	29.2	28.9	19.2	19.6	19.3	....	....	....	....	7.2	7.9	7.1	....	....
Hay............	3.4	2.5	3.1	2.0	2.0	2.0	5.2	5.2	5.2	5.2	2.1	2.5	2.1	5.9	5.6
Feed per cwt. gain															
Grain...........	590	555	554	507	571	495	680	653	634	609	489	478	487	473	474
Prot. conc.......	120	118	113	72	82	71	95	91	88	85	69	65	67	....	....
Silage..........	1350	1336	1260	622	699	611	....	....	....	....	344	354	328	....	....
Hay............	158	114	134	65	71	63	223	213	219	200	102	111	98	261	246
Selling price per cwt.	$10.62	$10.40	$10.75	$13.75	$13.75	$14.00	$9.15	$9.70	$9.70	$9.70	$12.75	$13.75	$13.50	$6.92	$6.87
Pork credits, lb.....	86	66	72	32	8	17	31	34	9	14	....	....	....	....	....

of the grain ration when mixed with non-bulky feeds like corn and wheat.

The Grain Sorghums. The growing of the non-saccharine sorghums as grain crops is limited to the southwestern states. Here the prevalence of dry, hot winds during the summer months renders a satisfactory corn crop a thing of considerable uncertainty. Grain sorghums, being drought-resistant, are less affected by such weather conditions. Consequently, they have, in a measure, replaced corn over a considerable portion of the Southwest, particularly in western Kansas, Oklahoma, and Texas. As these are important cattle states, these feeds are utilized largely by beef cattle.

The principal varieties of grain sorghums grown in the United States are kafir (often called kafir corn), milo maize, and hegari. In general, they are similar in character, all being rather short, heavy-stemmed, broad-leaved plants with the seeds borne on a large, thick panicle at the very top of the stalk. The most important difference between the three varieties is found in the relation between the yield of grain and stover. Hegari, having the most leaves, is highly valued both as a forage and a grain crop. Milo, on the other hand, has relatively few leaves but produces a considerable yield of grain from its large, thick heads. Kafir resembles hegari more closely than it does milo, in that it has stout, thick stems and broad leaves and is rather late in maturing.

There are several different strains of each variety of the grain sorghums, each of which differs from the others in respect to height of stalk, shape of panicle, color of seeds, and average date of maturity. Several low-growing strains of the important grain-producing types have been developed, which may be harvested successfully with a combine. Yields of 50 to 60 bushels an acre are frequently obtained on fertile soil with favorable weather conditions, but yields of 25 to 35 bushels are considered satisfactory for an average year.

In chemical composition, the grain sorghums are very similar to corn. They are a little lower in their percentage of fat, but otherwise are practically the same. The threshed grain corresponds very closely to shelled corn, and the whole heads have approximately the same chemical composition as ear corn.

Like Indian corn or maize, the grain sorghums are used in cattle feeding in several different forms. The usual method of harvesting the crop is to cut it with a combine when the seed is fully mature and can be stored without danger of heating. The taller-growing strains are cut with a binder and shocked in the field, and the bundles are threshed when they are thoroughly dry. Frequently when the seed crop is light

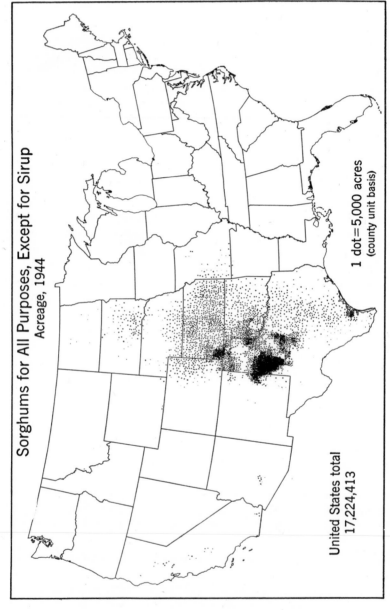

Fig. 46. Areas in which grain sorghums are extensively grown. The grain sorghums are noted for their drought-resistant ability; hence, they are popular in the semi-arid Southwest. (*Courtesy of the Census.*)

TABLE 119
COMPARATIVE VALUE OF GRAIN SORGHUMS FOR FATTENING CATTLE

	Daily Ration			Average Daily Gain	Feed per Cwt. Gain		
	Grain	Protein Concentrate	Roughages (Dry Basis)		Grain	Protein Concentrate	Roughage (Dry Basis)
I* Cracked shelled corn......	17.1	1.1	6.0	2.86	598	37	211
Cracked white kafir.......	16.5	1.1	5.9	2.49	662	42	236
II* Cracked shelled corn......	10.6	1.5	3.2	1.94	546	77	167
Cracked Atlas sorghum...	12.0	1.5	3.6	2.08	575	72	172
III* Cracked shelled corn......	11.1	1.5	3.4	2.01	553	74	170
Cracked Sooner milo......	11.7	1.5	3.4	2.03	573	74	169
IV* Cracked shelled corn......	11.2	1.5	3.7	2.07	541	73	180
Cracked early kalo........	12.1	1.5	3.8	2.04	594	74	187
V† Ground shelled corn......	7.4	2.5	4.1	2.05	370	110	200
Ground darso...........	7.8	2.6	4.1	1.80	437	145	228
VI‡ Ground shelled corn......	14.6	1.9	4.8	2.10	695	89	227
Ground Wheatland milo...	17.0	1.9	4.8	2.41	706	78	199
Ground Blackhull kafir...	16.3	1.9	4.7	2.29	711	82	207
Ground Westland milo...	16.8	1.9	4.8	2.19	770	86	219

* Nebraska Bulletin 347, 1943.
† Oklahoma Bulletin 237, 1939.
‡ Kansas Mimeo. Report 42-B-2, July 10, 1942.

the bundles are left standing in the shock until winter, when they are hauled and fed to the cattle, either on the ground or in large racks. In this form it corresponds to ordinary shock corn (maize). Sometimes the heads are cut from the stalks and either fed entire or run through a chopper to reduce them to a feed similar to broken or chopped ear corn. However, grinding is much more widely practiced than chopping and results in a product very much like corn-and-cob meal. The threshed grain, like shelled corn, may be fed either whole or ground. Grinding is generally practiced, since the grains are so small and hard that they are poorly digested if fed whole.

Many feeding trials have been conducted by the experiment stations of the southwestern states to compare the grain sorghums with each other and also with corn. The results secured from these feeds have been very satisfactory. In a few cases the grain sorghums have been equal to or slightly superior to corn. Kafir has given somewhat better results than milo maize, both in rate and in economy of gains.

Beet Pulp. In the manufacture of sugar from beets, great quantities of wet beet pulp result as a residue of the sugar-extraction process. Thousands of cattle and tens of thousands of sheep and lambs are fattened annually on this material in the beet-growing sections of the West. Because of the large amount of moisture that it contains— approximately 90 per cent—wet beet pulp should be regarded as a diluted carbonaceous roughage similar to corn silage. Consequently, it will be discussed in connection with that subject.[5]

A considerable quantity of the beet pulp produced at the sugar factories is dried with waste steam to produce "dried beet pulp." This dried pulp may be bagged and sold as *plain beet pulp,* or it may be mixed with molasses to produce *dried molasses beet pulp.* Approximately 100 pounds of plain dry pulp are obtained from each ton of sugar beets processed. Five hundred pounds of molasses are mixed and dried with about 1600 pounds of dried pulp to make a ton of dried molasses beet pulp.[6]

In chemical composition dried beet pulp is a carbonaceous concentrate. Because of its bulk it produces slightly faster gains when mixed with corn or ground barley than when it is fed alone. Mixtures of 1 part of dried beet pulp and 2 parts of corn, or equal parts of dried pulp and shelled corn, were equal in all respects to a full feed of shelled corn in three tests carried out at the Nebraska Station. Plain dried pulp gave as good results as dried molasses pulp when fed with ground barley in two tests made at the Colorado Station. (See Table 120.)

[5] *Cf.* p. 421.
[6] Colorado Bulletin 422, 1936, p. 24.

TABLE 120

VALUE OF DRIED BEET PULP FOR FATTENING CATTLE

	Colorado Bull. 422, 1936		Colorado Bull. 422, 1936		Nebraska Bull. 359, 1944		
	Ground Barley	Dried Molasses Beet Pulp	Ground Barley and Plain Beet Pulp	Ground Barley and Dried Molasses Beet Pulp	Ground Shelled Corn	Ground Shelled Corn 2 and Dried Beet Pulp 1	Ground Shelled Corn 1 and Dried Beet Pulp 1
Average initial weight, pound	713	723	348	349	549	550	546
Average final weight	1120	1120	746	746	1064	1059	1060
Average daily gain	2.26	2.20	2.04	2.03	2.19	2.17	2.19
Average daily ration							
Grain	10.6	....	3.6	3.6	10.9	7.2	5.4
Dried beet pulp	....	10.7	3.4	3.4	....	3.6	5.4
Protein concentrate	2.1	2.1	1.0	1.0	1.0	1.0	1.0
Silage	15.7	15.6	9.2	9.2	21.2	17.3	16.6
Legume hay	7.3	7.7	4.2	4.2	1.9	1.9	1.9
Selling price per cwt	$10.14	$10.35	$9.86	$9.84	$15.35	$15.35	$15.35
Dressing percentage	63.0	63.8	62.5	62.5	59.9	60.5	60.2

Usually the cost of beet pulp is considerably higher than that of corn or barley; consequently it is not fed to beef cattle to any extent, except in the vicinity of sugar factories where it is purchased direct from the mills. Frequently small amounts are used in fitting cattle for show. One quart of dried beet pulp moistened with 1 quart of water will overnight swell up to about 2 quarts of soft, succulent feed, which may be fed alone or mixed with other concentrates.

Molasses. A large amount of low-grade molasses is produced each year as a by-product of the sugar-refining industry. Besides our own domestic supply, large quantities are imported, principally from Puerto Rico and Cuba. Frequently it is shipped in tank cars to the locality where it is to be fed and drawn off into wooden or steel barrels holding from 500 to 600 pounds each.

Feeding molasses is of the three kinds—cane, beet, and corn, depending upon the plant from which it is made. Most of the cane molasses is made in the South, where it is commonly called "blackstrap." Beet molasses is produced principally in the sugar-beet areas of Michigan and Colorado. Corn molasses, called "Hydrol," is available in relatively small amounts for feeding purposes. It is a by-product of the corn-milling industry in the manufacture of corn sugar. Formerly, cattle feeders showed a strong preference of cane molasses, claiming that the beet variety was less palatable and much more laxative. A more extensive use of beet molasses, however, has convinced feeders that there is very little difference between the two kinds. The use of corn molasses in beef-cattle feeding has been too limited to permit a definite statement about its feeding value. However, in three tests in which it was used at the Illinois and Nebraska Stations[7] no superiority over "blackstrap" was disclosed. Because of its very high viscosity it is very difficult to handle during cold weather.

Apparently, many erroneous opinions are held regarding the value of molasses as a feed for fattening cattle. Occasionally farmers are encountered who consider molasses a possible substitute for cottonseed meal. Nothing could be farther from the truth. It is exceedingly low in protein, and its use will require the feeding of more rather than less protein concentrate. Because of its sweet taste, pronounced odor, and syrup-like appearance, it is almost universally considered to be highly palatable yet it has been shown that sprinkling molasses diluted with water on cottonseed hulls or good-quality wheat straw does not always increase the consumption of these roughages.[8] It is true that when cattle are first fed molasses they show a pronounced liking for it, but it

[7] Illinois Mimeographed Report, 1937, and Nebraska Bulletin 355, 1944.
[8] Kansas Station Biennial Report, 1934–1936, p. 62.

is also true that when it is self-fed its consumption usually declines steadily and is only 2 or 3 pounds per day during the last part of the feeding period. Lastly, the claim is made that molasses intensifies thirst, causing the cattle to drink abnormally large amounts of water. Experiments substantiate this claim in so far as it refers to such large quantities of molasses as 5 or more pounds per day. However, the effect of only 1 or 2 pounds daily upon the consumption of water is negligible. Moreover, there is no basis for believing that cattle obtain any benefit from drinking unusually large amounts of water.

Feeding experiments indicate that 1 or 2 pounds of molasses usually can be supplied to full-fed cattle without appreciably affecting the consumption of the other feeds. In theory this intake of additional nutrients should result in an increase in the rate of gain, but in only a few of the experiments where small amounts of molasses have been fed has the increase been significant. In fact, in 10 out of 25 experiments where not more than 5 pounds of molasses were fed daily the average gains were no larger than those of the check lots. Since molasses increased the cost of the ration and on the average lessened instead of increased the selling price, the use of small quantities for the purpose of accelerating gains and producing a quick finish is hard to justify. (See Table 121.)

TABLE 121

THE VALUE OF SMALL AMOUNTS OF MOLASSES FOR FATTENING CATTLE

Age of Cattle	Calves		Yearlings		2-year-olds		All Tests	
Number of Tests	12		6		7		25	
	Check	Mo-lasses	Check	Mo-lasses	Check	Mo-lasses	Check	Mo-lasses
Av. molasses fed, lbs..........	.....	1.4	.....	2.6	.....	3.0	.....	2.2
Av. grain eaten (all lots).......	9.9	10.1	13.8	12.1	15.9	13.5	12.5	11.6
Av. grain eaten.............. (unrestricted lots)	9.9	10.1	15.1	14.8	17.6	15.2	12.6	12.1
Av. daily gain...............	2.02	2.15	2.53	2.42	2.79	2.72	2.36	2.38
Water drunk daily...........	54.0	56.3	.....	.....	48.8	47.2	52.3*	53.6*
Feed consumed per cwt. gain								
Grain...........	491	471	547	496	567	496	509	484
Prot. conc.................	98	92	77	80	108	110	96	95
Corn silage...............	333	311	201	256	840	852	553	549
Hay......................	90	86	215	215	118	125	129	137
Molasses..................	.....	55	.....	124	.....	115	.....	88
Selling price per cwt..........	$10.72	$10.65	$10.86	$10.67	$10.48	$10.60	$10.69	$10.64

* Average of 17 comparisons made of water consumption.

Molasses has a definitely useful place in cattle feeding during times of grain scarcity. By feeding molasses in amounts large enough to replace from one-third to two-thirds of the usual grain ration a suf-

TABLE 122

VALUE OF MOLASSES AS A SUBSTITUTE FOR A CONSIDERABLE PART
OR ALL OF THE GRAIN RATION*

Yearling Steers — 150 days

Grain fed to molasses lots was ground to absorb the molasses	Shelled Corn	Cane Molasses	Ground Corn 25% Ground Oats 25% Molasses 50%	Gr. Corn 50% Gr. Oats 50% Molasses
Method of Feeding Molasses		Poured on Silage	Poured on Grain and Silage	All Feeds except Silage Machine Mixed	Self-Fed
Av. initial weight, lbs..........	753	754	753	750	752
Av. daily gain...............	2.51	2.08	2.57	2.51	2.24
Av. daily ration					
Corn or corn and oats.......	13.9	......	6 8	5.9	6.8
Molasses..................	......	14.3	7.2	6.1	5.6
Soybean-oil meal..........	1.9	2.9	2.6	2.2	2.6
Corn silage...............	20.0	22.7	20.0	20.0	20.0
Alfalfa hay...............	2.0	2.0	2.0	2.9ª	2.0
Feed per cwt. gain					
Corn or corn and oats.......	516	......	265	234	278
Molasses..................	......	642	282	243	251
Soybean-oil meal..........	74	129	100	88	104
Corn silage...............	796	1021	778	796	893
Alfalfa hay...............	80	96	78	117	89
Cost of gain per cwt.........	$15.09	$14.85	$13.64	$13.25	$14.76
Selling price per cwt.........	18.25	16.00	17.25	16.75	16.50
Shrinkage in shipment, lbs.....	41	66	54	72	59
Return above cost of cattle and feed....................	$69.35	$41.09	$61.88	·$54.50	$47.73
Price per ton at which molasses would have been as profitable as corn at $1.12 and oats at 40 cents a bu.............	.. ...	−$3.25	$11.20	−$7.42	−$26.20
Water drunk daily					
Aug. 5–19, lbs.............	92	108	....	....	.........•
Aug. 22–Sept. 6...........	86	......	....	119	.........•

* Illinois Experiment Station, Mimeographed Report, 1937.
ª Hay ground and mixed with grain to help absorb the molasses.

ficient number of cattle may be fattened to utilize the farm roughage supply to the best advantage. Although cattle fed only corn during such a year probably will return a higher profit a head than those fed a limited amount of corn and considerable molasses, the larger number it is possible to feed by using molasses will likely return larger profits to the individual farmer and to the industry as a whole.

Feeders who make large profits on molasses-fed cattle during a year of feed scarcity should not be misled as to its feeding value in terms of corn. When fed to the extent of one-third or more of the grain ration it is approximately 80 per cent as efficient as shelled corn in producing a given amount of grain. However, when the lower selling price of the molasses-fed cattle is taken into consideration, the actual money value of the molasses may disappear altogether. (See Table 122.)

Mixed Molasses Feeds. After all, comparatively little low-grade molasses is sold to cattle feeders. The greater percentage is purchased by the manufacturers of mixed feeds and is utilized by them in the preparation of their special products. On account of the large quantities of molasses that many of these concerns use, it can be shipped in tank cars at a very low freight and handling charge.

The principal use of molasses in mixed feeds is to sweeten the product and make it more palatable. Sometimes the materials entering into mixed feeds are of inferior grade and would not be consumed in quantity in their natural state. Although many of these feeds contain nothing but high-grade materials, a few are made up largely of mill screenings; chaffy, lightweight grains; oat hulls; coarse, stemmy, or discolored alfalfa; cottonseed hulls; and sometimes ground corn cobs and dried peat. Molasses added to a mixture of such materials not only increases its palatability but also tends to bind the several ingredients closely together, thereby making it difficult for the purchaser to determine their true nature and quality.

The exact composition of most of the prepared feeding stuffs is known only to the manufacturers. As a rule, they are sold under some high-sounding trade name which is thought likely will appeal to the cattleman. Except in those states that have no pure feed laws, the guaranteed composition printed on each bag can be taken as an index of the feeding value, and the price that one can afford to pay for the particular feed in question should be figured before purchasing. Careful attention should be given to the amount of fiber present, as well as to the percentages of protein and fat, as some mixed feeds run so high in fiber as to warrant their classification as roughages rather than as concentrates. This applied particularly to those feeds made up largely of "alfalfa meal."

Most mixed cattle feeds contain sufficient linseed or cottonseed meal to bring their total crude protein up to at least 15 per cent. When this is so, they are more properly classed as nitrogenous concentrates, and their detailed discussion will be reserved for the chapter that deals with this group of feeding stuffs.[9]

Root Crops. Root crops are not popular in the Corn Belt because of the large amount of hand labor required in their production. Moreover, summer temperatures are likely to be too high and moisture conditions too low for satisfactory yields. Farther north, growing conditions are more favorable for roots and less favorable for corn; hence, in this region, roots are used to some extent as a substitute for corn in fattening cattle.

Roots are very high in moisture, usually having but 10 to 15 pounds of dry matter per hundred. The principal reason for considering them as concentrates rather than as roughages is their small amount of fiber. Only 5 to 10 per cent of the dry matter of roots consists of fiber, whereas the corresponding figure for silage is from 20 to 30 per cent. Inasmuch as their nutritive ratio is approximately 1 : 8, roots are carbonaceous rather than nitrogenous feed materials.

Roots, especially those high in sugars, are highly prized as a feed for show cattle, and this constitutes their principal, if not almost their sole, use in the Corn Belt proper. Their succulence is of much value in cooling out animals that have been fed nearly "off their feet" and in keeping the digestive tract in good condition. Most experienced fitters prefer roots to silage for show cattle, as roots are more palatable and have a narrower nutritive ratio. Moreover, they can be taken along on the show circuits, a thing impossible with silage.

Farther north, where roots are more extensively grown, they have proved a valuable feed in fattening cattle for market. Wilson, of the South Dakota Station, in feeding three varieties of roots to yearling steers in moderate quantities, against a check lot getting silage, found two of the varieties superior to silage, whereas the third was somewhat inferior. (See Table 123.)

Potatoes. Of the 450 million bushels of potatoes harvested in the United States each year 5 to 10 per cent are culls which cannot be marketed profitably for human consumption. During years of abnormally large yields a considerable percentage of edible potatoes may be held off the market to prevent prices from falling to abnormally low levels. Cull and surplus potatoes constitute an important feed for cattle in the important potato-growing areas of the United States. Usually they are considered to be too bulky in relation to their feeding value to justify shipping them very far from where they were grown.

Raw potatoes, like other roots and tubers, should be considered a carbonaceous concentrate which is diluted with a large amount of

[9] See pp. 351–354.

water. Consequently, cattle must consume large amounts of potatoes
to get enough digestible nutrients to make satisfactory gains. They
are very low in protein, minerals, and vitamins and, therefore, must
be combined with other feeds that will supply adequate amounts of
these nutrients. High-quality alfalfa hay grown on phosphorus-rich
soil is a good source of these nutrients, but the hay must be limited in

TABLE 123

VALUE OF ROOTS FOR FATTENING CATTLE*

120 Days

Succulent Feed Fed	Lot I	Lot II	Lot III	Lot IV
	Corn Silage	Sugar Beets	Mangels	Stock Beets
Daily Gain................	2.54 lbs.	2.55 lbs.	2.61 lbs.	2.39 lbs.
Feed per lb. Gain				
Shelled Corn.............	7.68	7.56	7.48	8.03
Linseed Meal............	.67	.67	.65	.70
Prairie Hay.............	2.27	2.17	2.84	2.57
Corn Silage.............	2.77	....	....	....
Roots..................	....	2.48	3.43	3.74
Pork per Steer......	55	51	47	39

* South Dakota Bulletin 137, 1912.

amount in order not to interfere with a large consumption of potatoes.
Fairly satisfactory results have been obtained at the Northwest Branch
Station, University of Minnesota, from feeding potatoes and oat straw
according to appetite plus 1 pound of linseed meal per head daily.
Yearling steers fed this ration for 196 days made an average daily
gain of 1.90 pounds, compared with 2.33 pounds for similar steers given
a full feed of grain and alfalfa and brome-grass hay. Reducing the
potatoes somewhat during the last half of the feeding period and feeding from one-third to one-half a full feed of grain resulted in gains and
finish nearly equal to those of the check lot given a full feed of grain.
(See Table 124.)

In three experiments at the Northwest Branch Station, Crookston,
Minnesota, potatoes were worth from 25 to 70 cents per 100 pounds
based on the cost of gains, when grain, hay, and oat straw were valued
at approximately $40, $25, and $10 a ton, respectively. Slicing the
potatoes reduced their palatability and consumption slightly and, there-

fore, was of no value. Choking from eating whole potatoes was prevented by nailing a 2 inch by 6 inch plank about 30 inches above the feed bunk to compel the steers to keep their heads down while eating.

TABLE 124

THE VALUE OF POTATOES FOR FATTENING CATTLE*

	Yearling Steers, 1948–1949 (168 days)				Yearling Steers, 1950–1951 (196 days)		
	Check Lot: No Potatoes	Whole Potatoes, Hay	Sliced Potatoes, Hay	Whole Potatoes, Oat Straw	Check Lot: No Potatoes	Whole Potatoes, Oat Straw	Whole Potatoes, Oat Straw, Linseed Meal
Av. initial weight, lb.	744	754	748	736	689	701	689
Av. daily gain. . . .	2.12	2.00	1.72	1.99	2.33	1.57	1.90
Av. daily ration							
Grain mixture[a].	16.1	8.7[b]	9.2[b]	8.7[b]	15.6	. . .	. . .
Linseed meal. . .	. . .	. . .	. . .	. . .	1.0	. . .	1.0
Alfalfa hay. . . .	3.0	3.0	3.0	. . .	3.0	. . .	. . .
Brome-grass hay.	6.5	8.3	9.6	. . .	4.8	. . .	. . .
Oat straw.	. . .	. . .	. . .	10.7	. . .	8.1	6.6
Potatoes.	. . .	51.5	48.3	52.9	. . .	61.3	61.1
Feed per cwt. gain							
Grain mixture .	757	216	266	218	670	. . .	. . .
Linseed meal. . .	. . .	. . .	. . .	. . .	40	. . .	51
Hay.	448	565	728	. . .	340	. . .	. . .
Oat straw.	. . .	. . .	. . .	537	. . .	517	349
Potatoes.	. . .	2566	2795	2653	. . .	3907	3219

* Northwest School and Experiment Station, University of Minnesota, Crookston, Minnesota, Mimeo. Reports, unnumbered.
[a] Grain mixture: 1948–1949: 60% barley, 30% oats, 10% linseed meal; 1950–1951: 70% barley, 30% oats.
[b] Grain fed last 84 days.

Use of Root Crops in Great Britain. That roots possess considerable merit as a feed for fattening cattle is shown by their extensive use throughout the British Isles. There they are the main source of food nutrients, inasmuch as relatively small amounts of ordinary concentrates are fed, and the roughage supplied is largely chaff and straw.

British farmers usually do not put their cattle into the feed lot until they are 2 or 3 years old, at which ages they have considerable capacity and can handle large quantities of roots daily. It is by no means unusual to feed from 60 to 80 pounds of roots per day, while even greater amounts are sometimes used. Of 201 lots of cattle fed experimentally in Great Britain from 1833 to 1908, all but 16 received roots, 43 lots consuming 100 pounds or more per day. The average daily gain of the root-fed lots was 1.82 pounds, while that of the no-root lots was 1.51.[10]

Best results are obtained from heavy root rations when the feeding period is not too long. Roots are too bulky to sustain the rate of gain at a satisfactory figure after the cattle acquire a fair amount of flesh. In this respect, roots are like corn silage. As a matter of fact, these two feeds are similar in a great many ways. American farmers who wish to fatten cattle largely on roughage will do well to make a careful study of British methods, keeping in mind that corn silage is but little, if at all, inferior to roots when fed under similar conditions.

Miscellaneous Carbonaceous Carbohydrates. From time to time, especially when the price of corn is high, Corn Belt cattle feeders become interested in possible corn substitutes, which ordinarily are used only in the locality where they are produced. Among such feeds are dried citrus pulp and dehydrated potatoes.

Dried Citrus Pulp. The rapid increase in the production of canned and frozen citrus fruit juices since the early 1940's has made available large quantities of orange and grapefruit pulp for livestock feeding. Much of this pulp is fed in the fresh form in the vicinity of the canning establishments, but a considerable amount is dried and bagged for use elsewhere. It is estimated that 140,000 tons of dried citrus pulp and 60,000 tons of citrus molasses were produced in Florida during the canning season of 1947–1948.[11] Since the canning and freezing of citrus juice is a comparatively new industry, the present production of dried pulp may be but a fraction of the future supply.

Dried citrus pulp compares favorably with ground-ear corn in total digestible nutrients but is much lower in digestible protein. Although it has a slightly bitter taste, it is eaten readily by cattle and has proved to be a good concentrate for fattening when it is properly supplemented with a protein concentrate. In three trials conducted at the Florida Station during the period 1945–1948, yearling steers fed grass hay and cottonseed meal ate on the average 9 pounds of dried pulp and 2 pounds of ground snapped corn, compared with an average consumption of 11.8 pounds of ground snapped corn for the check lot. The average gains of the two lots were 2.55 and 2.37 pounds, respectively. In two

[10] Ingle, H., Cattle Feeding Experiments in Great Britain, Transactions of the Highland and Agricultural Society of Scotland, 1909.

[11] Florida Bulletin 454.

trials steers full-fed dried pulp without any corn consumed only about 1 pound of pulp per 100 pounds live weight and gained more slowly than the steers fed snapped corn or a mixture of snapped corn and dried citrus pulp.   (See Table 125.)

TABLE 125

THE VALUE OF DRIED CITRUS PULP AND DEHYDRATED
SWEET POTATOES FOR FATTENING CATTLE

	Florida Bull. 454 (Average 2 Trials)			Oklahoma Miscel. Publ. 11 and 13, 1947–1948 (Average 2 Trials)		
	Ground Snapped Corn	Dried Citrus Pulp	Ground Snapped Corn, 2 lb. Dried Citrus Pulp	Ground Shelled Corn	Dried Sweet Potatoes	Ground Corn 1, Dried Sweet Potatoes 1
Initial weight, lb.....	608	590	607	507	506	508
Final weight.........	892	850	883	862	825	877
Total gain..........	284	260	276	355	319	369
Av. daily gain.......	2.37	2.17	2.30	2.14	1.92	2.22
Av. daily ration						
Ground snapped or shelled corn.....	10.6	....	2.0	11.3	....	6.2
Corn substitute....	....	7.9	9.0	....	9.0	6.2
Protein concentrate	2.9	2.9	2.9	1.5	1.9	1.7
Sorgo silage.......	....	....	....	9.5	8.8	9.5
Hay.............	5.8[a]	5.7[a]	5.8[a]	1.0[b]	1.0[b]	1.0[b]
Feed per cwt. gain						
Ground snapped or shelled corn.....	455	....	87	528	....	279
Corn substitute....	....	365	322	....	478	279
Protein concentrate	124	135	127	71	100	79
Silage.............	....	....	....	445	478	430
Hay.............	245[a]	264[a]	250[a]	59[b]	53[b]	45[b]

[a] Carpet and Bermuda grass hay.
[b] Alfalfa hay.

Dehydrated Potatoes.   A considerable percentage of both the white and sweet potatoes grown commercially during an average year are cull tubers which are too small and misshapen to be sold for human consumption.   Many of them are fed raw to cattle and hogs in the vicinity where they are grown, but some are dried and sold as dehydrated potatoes, which are a much more valuable feed.   Dehydrated sweet potatoes are regarded more highly than dried white potatoes because they are more palatable. Neither are of much economic importance in the Corn Belt, but they may be purchased by Corn Belt cattle feeders when corn is scarce and its price is abnormally high.

Dehydrated potatoes, like dried citrus pulp, compare favorably with corn in total digestible nutrients but are noticeably lower in protein. They are less palatable than corn and when fed as the only concentrate are not eaten in sufficient amounts to produce a satisfactory rate of gain. In two tests made at the Oklahoma Station steer calves full-fed dried sweet potatoes ate considerably less feed and gained more slowly than the check lot fed ground shelled corn. However, a third lot fed equal parts of ground corn and dried sweet potatoes consumed more concentrates and made faster gains than the check lot. Even in this third lot the substitution of dried potatoes for half the corn ration reduced the net profit the first year because the dried potatoes cost $19 a ton more than corn, and the second year because the potato-fed cattle sold for 50 cents a hundred less than those fed ground shelled corn. (See Table 125.)

19 — Protein Requirements and How to Supply Them

One of the first discoveries made by early investigators of animal feeding was the need of the animal body for the complex organic compounds called proteins. The important thing about proteins is that they contain nitrogen, an element indispensable to all animal life. Nitrogen is necessary for the building and repair of practically all the tissues of which the animal body is composed. As a matter of fact, the lean portions of the body, the skin and its modifications, and the connective tissues consist almost entirely of protein materials, which have been elaborated and built up from the protein compounds in the feeding stuffs consumed by the animal. Not only do protein feeds contain nitrogen, but they also are rich in phosphorus, an element that is highly necessary for the growth of the bones.

Although the principal use made by animals of the proteins in their rations is to build new protein materials and to repair old tissues within their bodies, any excess consumed beyond the amount needed for these purposes can be converted into energy to be used in performing the normal body functions, or it can be converted into glycogen[1] and fat and stored. Apparently it is impossible for any protein in excess of the immediate body requirements to be stored as protein until needed. Instead, after the immediate needs for this material are satisfied, any excess is converted into non-protein substances or is got rid of by oxidation in the tissues. Fat and energy are the two important products of these processes; the others are useless and are eliminated through the organs of excretion. Since protein feeding stuffs are relatively high in price, it is evident that their use for the production of fat and energy is not economical. Hence, it is important that the protein requirements of animals of different ages kept under different conditions be understood, in order that the proper amount of this nutrient may be supplied.

Protein Requirements of Cattle. Although the protein requirements of animals have received much attention from animal nutrition

---

[1] Glycogen is the term given to animal sugars, the greater part of which are found in the liver. The storage of glycogen by the fattening animal is of no practical importance to either the feeder or the butcher.

investigators, considerable work still remains to be done before we can say definitely just what these requirements are. Indeed, it appears in the light of numerous experiments that proteins are even more complex substances than was formerly supposed. Instead of being chemical compounds made up of elements, they are in reality groups of compounds. These simpler compounds are called amino acids. Inasmuch as proteins differ considerably in the amino acids that they contain, and since certain amino acids are indispensable to the animal organism whereas others are not, proteins vary greatly in their feeding value. More study must be done before the relative importance of the different proteins, based upon their amino acid content, can be definitely stated. Fortunately, beef cattle are usually fed a combination of 3 to 5 feeds, each of which furnishes a different assortment of amino acids. Moreover, much information is available which indicates that a considerable portion of the protein consumed by cattle is elaborated into new nitrogenous compounds by the bacteria in the paunch, which in turn are digested and utilized by the cattle. Consequently, the feeding of complex protein mixtures for the purpose of supplying all the essential amino acids does not seem to be as important in feeding cattle as in feeding the non-ruminant species of livestock.

Practically all textbooks on animal feeding contain tables giving the protein requirements, in pounds of digestible crude protein per 1000 pounds live weight of animal, for cattle of different ages, kept under different conditions. Although the figures in such tables cannot be regarded as absolutely correct, they do serve as a valuable and useful guide in determining the approximate amount of protein that should be supplied in the ration. Among their valuable features is the "nutritive ratio" that is given for cattle of different ages. Some of these ratios were worked out under European conditions and are, therefore, somewhat higher than will ordinarily be possible to maintain in this country. However, they form a good guide as to the relative amounts of protein needed by cattle of different ages and at different stages of the fattening process.

A study of Table 126 discloses the fact that older animals require less protein in proportion to their live weight than do young animals. This is to be expected, since the rate of growth decreases with age and protein is used primarily for growth. Theoretically, 2-year-old steers on full feed should require still less protein per thousand pounds live weight than younger animals on somewhat limited rations. However, experimental feeding trials have shown that if the nutritive ratio becomes too wide the efficiency of the entire ration is noticeably lowered. Consequently, an increase in the carbohydrate part of the ration re-

TABLE 126

PROTEIN REQUIREMENTS OF BEEF CATTLE

	Daily Requirements per Head*		Calculated Digestible Protein Required†	
	Digestible Protein (pounds)	Total Digestible Nutrients (pounds)	Daily per 1000 Pounds Live Weight	Ratio of Protein to Carbohydrates (Nutritive Ratio) 1:
1. Calves fattened for baby beef				
400 pounds............	1.05–1.15	7.4– 8.6	2.6–2.9	6.1–6.5
600 pounds............	1.26–1.37	10.2–11.8	2.1–2.3	7.1–7.6
800 pounds............	1.52–1.68	12.6–14.4	1.9–2.1	7.3–7.6
2. Fattening yearling cattle				
600 pounds...........	1.18–1.32	10.7–12.3	1.9–2.2	8.0–8.3
800 pounds...........	1.52–1.68	14.1–15.9	1.9–2.1	8.3–8.6
1000 pounds...........	1.71–1.91	16.0–18.0	1.7–1.9	8.4–8.6
3. Fattening of 2-year-old steers				
800 pounds...........	1.46–1.62	14.1–15.9	1.8–2.0	8.6–8.8
1000 pounds...........	1.65–1.85	16.5–18.5	1.6–1.8	9.0
1200 pounds...........	1.70–1.90	17.0–19.0	1.4–1.6	9.0

* From Morrison, Feeds and Feeding, 21st edition, 1948, p. 1149.
† Calculated from columns 1, 2, and 3.

quires an accompanying increase in the protein component. Apparently a deficiency of protein in the ration tends to depress the digestion of non-protein substances, probably partly through a lack of sufficient protein for the growth of the fermenting bacteria of the digestive tract. Steers fed shelled corn and timothy hay at the Ohio Station digested only 48.4 per cent of the dry matter in the timothy hay but 54.6 per cent when the ration was supplemented with 2.4 pounds of soybean oil meal. In the same series of experiments the apparent digestibility of the dry matter of corn cobs was raised from 58.9 per cent to 66.7 per cent by adding a protein concentrate to the ration.[2]

Sources of Protein. While all ordinary feeding stuffs contain some protein, the amount furnished by the cereal grains, usually the principal component of fattening rations, is so small that other feeds containing a relatively high percentage of protein must be supplied if satisfactory

[2] *Journal of Animal Science*, 1949, Vol. 8, No. 1.

results are to be obtained. Because of their nitrogen content, protein feeding stuffs are spoken of as "nitrogenous feeds" and are divided according to their nature into nitrogenous concentrates and nitrogenous roughages. In the main, the concentrates consist principally of the by-products that result from the milling of cereal grains and from the extraction of oil from seeds that have a high percentage of fat. The more commonly known feeds of this class are linseed meal (flaxseed),

TABLE 127

RELATIVE COST OF PROTEIN IN PURCHASED FEEDS
AND FARM-GROWN LEGUME HAY*

	Digestible Nutrients per Ton		Approximate Farm Value per Ton	Approximate Value of Carbohydrates and Fat†	Net Cost of Digestible Protein	Net Cost of Digestible Protein per Pound (cents)
	Protein (pounds)	Carbohydrates and Fats (pounds)				
Cottonseed meal (41%).........	565	756	$90	$15.12	$74.88	11.4
Soybean oil meal (43%).........	750	822	80	16.44	63.56	8.5
Linseed meal (37%)	662	886	80	17.72	62.28	9.4
Wheat bran.......	274	1070	50	21.40	28.60	10.4
Clover hay........	142	902	20	12.03‡	7.97	5.6
Alfalfa hay........	210	796	25	10.61‡	14.39	6.9

* Calculated from Tables of Digestible Nutrients in Morrison's Feeds and Feeding, 21st edition, 1948.

† In determining the money value of the digestible carbohydrates, an arbitrary value of 2 cents a pound was assumed. This is the approximate cost of the digestible carbohydrates in corn at $1.12 per bushel:

> 1 bushel (56 lb.) corn contains:
> 3.7 lb. digestible protein @ 8 cents   = $0.296
> 41.1 lb. digestible carbohydrates @ 2 cents =   0.822
>   Total value of nutrients in 1 bushel of corn $1.118

‡ Arbitrarily decreased one-third because of the higher percentage of fiber in roughages.

cottonseed meal, soybean meal, gluten meal (corn), and wheat bran. The nitrogenous roughages are represented by the different legume hays and are, of course, entirely farm-grown. Clover, alfalfa, soybean, cowpea, and lespedeza are the principal legume hays used in cattle feeding. In connection with nitrogenous roughages should be mentioned green legume forage such as red, alsike, and sweet clover pastures. Steers with access to such grazing will obtain a large percentage of the protein needed from these pasture crops. For mature cattle, no additional protein is likely to be required.

The Use of Protein Feeding Stuffs in the Fattening Ration. So far as possible, the major portion of the protein needed by beef cattle should be furnished in the form of legume hay grown on the farm where the cattle are fed. Only in this way is it possible to realize one of the purposes for which cattle are kept, viz., to furnish a means of marketing legume crops without losing the nitrogen that they secure from the air. Moreover, a pound of protein can be produced more cheaply in the form of legume hay than it can usually be bought in the form of a commercial nitrogenous concentrate. This is particularly true if the value of the carbohydrates in each material is subtracted from the price of the feed before calculating the net cost per pound of protein. Lastly, the supply of nitrogenous concentrates available for cattle feeding is decidedly limited.

Despite the large amounts of high-protein feeds produced in this country they fall far short of being enough to balance the enormous tonnage of grains, straw, stover, and low-protein mill feeds that are used annually in meat, eggs, and dairy production. Hogs and poultry are unable to use legume roughages to any extent; hence, high-protein feeds must be included in their rations, regardless of the price, if a satisfactory level of production is to be maintained. Beef cattle, on the other hand, can utilize large amounts of roughage and often derive the major portion of their protein requirements from legume hay and pasture. These farm-grown sources of protein enable beef producers to fatten their cattle successfully with relatively little purchased protein concentrate if they keep the recommended percentage of their farm acreage in legume crops.

Need for a Protein Concentrate. 1. *Where the Roughage is Legume Hay.* Many feeders consider that cattle receiving a ration of corn and alfalfa or clover hay have little or no need for a protein concentrate. However, most experimental feeding trials show that the addition of a small amount of cottonseed or linseed meal to such a ration usually results in a noticeable increase in the average daily gains, proving that from the standpoint of the cattle such a ration is somewhat deficient in protein. Whether the use of such material will prove to be profitable from a financial point of view will depend upon the relative costs of the nitrogenous concentrate and the feeds that it displaces or saves, as well as upon the amount of premium that highly finished cattle command on the market. Under normal conditions its use would not be justified during the first half of the feeding period, while the cattle are consuming large amounts of legume hay. During the last half, however, a small amount of protein concentrate usually is advisable, since the amount of hay eaten at this time is seldom enough to furnish the amount of protein required to maintain the proper ratio between protein and carbohydrates for the most effective action of the rumen bacteria.

TABLE 128

EFFECT OF ADDING A PROTEIN CONCENTRATE TO A RATION OF CORN AND
LEGUME HAY FOR TWO-YEAR-OLD STEERS

	Iowa Mimeo. Report, 1922–1923		Nebraska Bull. 345, 1943		Nebraska Bull. 345, 1943 (Average 2 Trials)	
Legume Hay Fed	Clover Hay		Alfalfa Hay		Alfalfa Hay	
Supplement Fed	None	Linseed Meal	None	Linseed Meal	None	Cottonseed Meal
Av. daily gain, lb.	2.33	2.56	2.31	2.26	2.32	2.57
Av. daily ration						
Shelled corn	19.9	22.0	17.9	17.6	17.2	17.7
Protein concentrate	....	1.5	....	1.7	....	1.7
Legume hay	8.9	7.1	10.5	8.7	11.0	10.4
Feed per cwt. gain						
Concentrates	857	919	775	856	735	732
Legume hay	381	278	455	388	496	422
Feed cost per cwt. gain	$12.74	$13.44	$8.08	$9.68	$12.91	$13.02
Selling price per cwt.	9.75	10.00	8.00	8.00	10.75	10.95
Net return per head (including hog gains)	3.48	5.48	13.71	7.44	23.02	26.63

Apparently one of the benefits derived from adding a protein concentrate to a ration of corn and alfalfa hay during the last half of the feeding period is its effect upon the appetites of the cattle, which tend to become sluggish as the cattle approach market finish. Most of the protein concentrates are highly palatable; consequently, not only is the protein concentrate itself consumed, but the cattle often eat more corn and hay than they would eat if the protein feed were omitted. As a result the daily gains are, of course, increased.

The results usually obtained from adding a protein concentrate to a corn-legume hay ration are well illustrated by two of the three experiments reported in Table 128. In these trials the use of the protein feeds brought about a slight increase in the consumption of corn and produced slightly larger daily gains. In all three trials, however, the feed costs were increased to the extent that the use of the supplement would have been unprofitable had not the cattle receiving it sold for approximately 25 cents a hundred more than those which were fed only corn and legume hay.

Somewhat better results may be expected in calves and yearlings,

TABLE 129

NEED OF CALVES FOR A PROTEIN CONCENTRATE WITH CORN AND ALFALFA

Supplement Fed	Illinois Mimeographed Report (1914)		Kansas Mimeographed Report (1918)		Nebraska Bull. 345, 1943	
	None	Cottonseed Meal	None	Linseed Meal	None	Cottonseed Meal
Av. daily gain, lb.......	1.97	2.17	2.29	2.37	2.41	2.54
Av. daily ration						
Shelled corn.........	12.4	11.0	10.5	9.9	11.1	10.6
Protein concentrate...	....	2.2	....	1.7	....	1.8
Hay...............	6.2	6.1	10.3	9.8	4.4	4.6
Feed per cwt. gain						
Concentrates........	621	605	457	488	460	486
Hay...............	319	283	450	413	182	180
Feed cost per cwt. gain..	$9.14	$9.07	$16.72	$17.40	$7.12	$7.78
Selling price per cwt....	9.80	10.00	16.00	16.25	10.25	10.50
Net return per head....	7.41	8.86	28.89	27.13	12.07	13.33

since their need for protein is greater. Also, younger cattle have less capacity than older animals and hence will not ordinarily eat enough legume hay to secure as much protein from that source as they need.

Despite these facts, however, it should not be inferred that the profit realized from feeding calves will always be increased by the use of purchased concentrates. The gains made will be larger, but probably more costly. However, under normal market conditions, the superior condition and finish produced by the protein concentrate will result in an advance in selling price sufficient to cover the increased cost of gains with something left over to add to the profit.

2. *Where No Legume Hay is Fed.* No informed progressive cattleman considers it wise to try to fatten cattle without some kind of nitrogenous feeding stuff in the ration. However, there are hundreds of men who, finding themselves without legume hay of any kind, still attempt to make cattle ready for market using only such feeds as corn, corn silage, prairie hay, and straw. With the unbalanced rations that are bound to result from these wholly carbonaceous materials, it is not surprising that the cattle put on weight very slowly and with a very wasteful use of feed. So inefficient is a ration of this kind that its use can never be recommended except at such times as the price of nitrogenous feeding stuffs is extremely high compared with corn; and then only for mature, low-grade steers or cows that are being given a short

feed. With such a ration it is almost impossible to put yearling or 2-year-old cattle in choice or prime condition unless the feeding period is unduly prolonged. If it is impossible or impracticable to purchase a nitrogenous feeding stuff to supplement these farm-grown feeds, the grain had better be sold and the straw and stover returned to the land

TABLE 130

EFFECT OF ADDING A PROTEIN SUPPLEMENT TO A RATION
CONTAINING NO LEGUME HAY

| | Indiana Bull. 115, 1906 | | Illinois Station Mimeo. Rpt., 1928 | | Oklahoma Station Mimeo. Rpt., 1930 | |
| | Corn Stover and Oat Straw (2-year-olds) | | Corn Silage and Oat Straw (Calves) | | Prairie Hay (Calves) | |
	No Supplement	Linseed Meal	No Supplement	Cottonseed Meal	No Supplement	Cottonseed Meal
Av. daily gain, lb.......	1.30	1.78	1.51	2.44	1.40	2.22
Av. daily ration						
Corn...............	17.6	20.5	9.32	11.34	8.70	9.33
Protein supplement..	....	1.5	....	1.64	....	1.46
Corn stover or silage..	....	....	6.9	8.1	....	....
Hay or straw........	....	....	.63	2.0[a]	3.47	5.30
Limestone..........	....	....	.10	....	.17	.19
Feed per cwt. gain						
Concentrates........	1345	1148	618	528	615	486
Roughage..........	586	393	497	415	245	233
Feed cost per cwt. gain..	....	....	$10.78	$10.31	$9.37	$8.17
Selling price per cwt....	$5.00	$5.35	$12.60	$13.65	$10.00	$11.50

[a] Alfalfa hay.

and plowed under. However, if a sufficient amount of a nitrogenous concentrate is fed to supply the necessary protein, the results secured from corn stover and straw are not greatly inferior to those from legume hay.

A study of Table 130 shows the following advantages of adding a nitrogenous concentrate to a badly unbalanced ration:

1. A larger consumption of feed is realized.
2. Larger daily gains are made by the animals.
3. The amount of feed required per pound of gain is materially reduced.
4. A higher price is obtained for the finished cattle.

3. *Where but Part of the Roughage is Legume Hay.*   Unless nearly all the roughage ration consists of a good grade of legume hay, the feeding of a nitrogenous concentrate will usually be advisable.   Although it will sometimes happen that an unusual demand for the common protein feeding stuffs will force their price so high that their use will materially increase the cost of gains, the increase in selling price

TABLE 131

Need for a Protein Concentrate When Only Part
of the Roughage is Legume Hay

	Indiana Bull. 429, 1938* (Calves)		Minnesota Bull. 300, 1933 (Calves)		Indiana Bull. 330, 1929, and 396, 1935* (2-Year-Olds)	
Roughages Fed	Corn Silage and Clover Hay		Corn Silage and Alfalfa Hay		Corn Silage and Soybean Hay	
Supplement Fed	None	Cottonseed Meal	None	Linseed Meal	None	Cottonseed Meal
Av. daily gain, lb.......	1.78	2.17	2.02	2.32	2.35	2.46
Av. daily ration						
Shelled corn.........	10.8	9.7	13.3	13.5	14.3	12.7
Protein concentrate...	....	1.5	....	1.9	....	2.3
Corn silage..........	9.0	10.2	4.8	4.3	24.1	23.6
Legume hay.........	2.8	2.9	1.8	1.3	4.4	4.5
Feed per cwt. gain						
Shelled corn.........	626	467	660	580	611	518
Protein concentrate...	....	72	....	80	....	95
Corn silage..........	510	484	215	187	1030	961
Legume hay.........	163	138	91	57	198	183
Feed cost per cwt. gain..	$6.88	$6.27	$8.95	$9.61	$7.85	$8.35
Selling price of cattle...	$7.21	$7.60	$9.45	$10.10	$7.05	$7.08
Net return per steer....	$7.93	$14.49	$10.72	$13.36	$8.68	$6.66

* Average of 3 experiments.

that results from the better condition and finish of the cattle will usually be sufficient to increase the net profit.   Obviously, somewhat less cottonseed or linseed meal is needed where clover or alfalfa makes up a considerable part of the roughage ration than where carbonaceous roughages, such as silage and straw, predominate.

In all the experiments reported in Table 131 to illustrate the feeding situation under consideration, the amounts of clover and alfalfa eaten were small. This is usually the situation when silage is fed, but very often it is not true when legume hay and corn stover or oat straw are the roughages used. Should the consumption of legume hay equal 6 or 8 pounds per day, the amount of cottonseed meal needed would be materially less than the quantities indicated in the table.

The Use of Nitrogenous Concentrates as Conditioners or Appetizers. In addition to supplying much-needed protein, nitrogenous concentrates have a certain value as appetizers and conditioners. By this is meant that their use stimulates the appetites of the cattle, causing them to eat more feed than they would otherwise consume, and that the cattle take on a sleek, thrifty appearance not altogether accounted for by the more rapid gains made. Nearly all the common nitrogenous concentrates are highly palatable. Not only will the introduction of 1 or 2 pounds of linseed or cottonseed meal into a ration usually cause no diminution in the amounts of the other feeds eaten, but it will often result in a noticeable increase in the consumption of the other components, particularly of those materials with which the nitrogenous supplement is fed. In this respect the protein supplement acts as a "seasoner" or appetizer, much like salt and sugar in the human diet. Naturally, the greater consumption of all feeds results in a substantial increase in the rate of gains.

TABLE 132

EFFECT OF PROTEIN CONCENTRATE UPON CONSUMPTION OF OTHER ITEMS OF THE RATION

(Average of 25 Experiments)

		Average Daily Ration		
	Corn (pounds)	Protein Concentrate (pounds)	Dry Roughage (pounds)	Corn Silage (pounds)
Lots fed no protein concentrate	14.3	...	5.5	8.6
Lots fed protein concentrate	14.2	2.0	5.3	8.9

The conditioning effect of these feeds is probably due largely to their beneficial effect upon the digestive tract. Nearly all the common nitrogenous concentrates have a mild laxative effect and serve to keep the digestive system in good order, thereby adding much to the health and well-being of the animals. Moreover, the balanced ration that results from their use makes for more effective nutrition, which soon gives rise to an improvement in the general appearance of the cattle.

Amount of Nitrogenous Concentrate to Feed. From the standpoint of good nutrition young cattle need a somewhat narrower ration at the beginning of the feeding period than they do at the close, since they are younger at the beginning, and consequently need more protein for growth than is required later on.   But the need for a nitrogenous concentrate as an appetizer and conditioner increases as the feeding period progresses, as it is only by the introduction of more and more of this highly palatable "seasoning" material that the cattle are induced to maintain and even increase their consumption of grain and thus attain a high degree of finish.   So important do practical cattlemen consider this latter use of nitrogenous concentrates that most feeders with only a limited amount of linseed or cottonseed meal at their disposal will save it until the last half of the feeding period, when, starting with a small amount, they will gradually increase the quantity fed until they are feeding 2 or 3 pounds per head daily the last few weeks before marketing.

Most rules for feeding protein concentrates state the approximate amount of digestible protein required per 1000 pounds live weight or specify different amounts of protein per head for cattle of various weights and ages.   Reference to Table 126 will disclose that 2-year-old steers require 30 to 40 per cent less digestible protein than calves per 1000 pounds live weight, and from 15 to 25 per cent less than yearling cattle.   This, of course, is due principally to the fact that the older cattle are growing less rapidly and consequently need less protein for the formation of new tissues.   On a head basis, however, the protein requirements increased with age, being 30 to 40 per cent larger for 2-year-old steers than for calves and 10 to 20 per cent larger for 2-year-olds than for yearlings.   This is due partly to the larger maintenance requirements of the older animals and partly to the larger amounts of carbonaceous nutrients that are consumed and that require correspondingly larger amounts of protein for their effective digestion.

Let us apply the standards given in Table 126 to some common Corn Belt rations and see how much of the common protein concentrates is needed to furnish the amount of digestible protein required.

First we shall take a ration of corn and carbonaceous roughages, such as corn silage and oat straw.   An 800-pound yearling steer on full feed will consume daily approximately 12 pounds of shelled corn, 15 pounds of corn silage, and 2 pounds of oat straw.

12.0 lb. corn @ 6.6% digestible protein[3]	=	0.792 protein
15 lb. corn silage @ 1.3% digestible protein	=	0.195
2 lb. oat straw @ 0.7% digestible protein	=	0.014

1.001

[3] Percentages taken from Morrison, Feeds and Feeding, 21st edition, 1948.

Digestible protein required by a 800-pound yearling steer: 1.52 to 1.68 pounds; shortage: 0.52 to 0.68 pound. Digestible protein in 41 per cent cottonseed meal: 32.4 per cent. Cottonseed meal required to balance the ration:

$$(0.52 \div 32.4\%) \text{ to } (0.68 \div 32.4\%) = 1.6 \text{ to } 2.1 \text{ lb.}$$

Hence, we can say that 1.5 to 2.0 pounds of 41 per cent cottonseed meal are required by an 800-pound steer which is fed a full feed of shelled corn and no legume hay.

Next we shall calculate the amount of protein concentrate required in a ration consisting of shelled corn and alfalfa hay.

14 lb. corn @ 6.6% digestible protein	= 0.924 lb. protein
6 lb. alfalfa hay @ 10.5% digestible protein	= 0.63
	———
	1.55

Shortage: none to 0.13 lb. digestible protein.

$$13 \div 32.4\% = 0.4$$

Cottonseed meal required: none to 0.4 pound.

In the same way, with a ration of 14 pounds shelled corn and 6 pounds red clover hay, we get a deficiency of 0.21 to 0.33 pound of digestible protein, which can be overcome by the addition of 0.6 to 1 pound of 41 per cent cottonseed meal.

The method described in the preceding paragraphs suggests how it is possible to calculate the amount of protein concentrate one should feed on the basis of published feeding standards. However, the method is rather too complicated for the practical feeder. Moreover, the accuracy of the feeding standards is only approximate, as is suggested by the fact that the protein requirements are stated in terms of limits which vary as much as 15 per cent in some cases. Lastly, the protein content of a nitrogenous supplement is not always a true index of its feeding value. For example, linseed meal nearly always gives better results than cottonseed meal, although it contains only about 80 per cent as much protein. For these reasons few cattle feeders are guided in their feeding practices by feeding standards and the chemical composition of feeds. Instead they rely principally upon the results obtained from feeding experiments in which different protein feeds or different amounts of the same feed have been fed under conditions similar to those prevailing on their own farms. Literally scores of such experiments have been carried out during the present century, and a large amount of data is available bearing on the relative value of the different kinds and amounts of protein concentrates for fattening beef cattle.

Different Amounts of Protein Concentrate Compared.   In the early years of experimental beef-cattle feeding, the practice was to feed from 2 to 3 pounds of protein concentrate per head daily to 2-year-old steers after they were on full feed, even though they were fed considerable legume hay.   For example, the average daily ration of a drove of 2-year-old steers fed at the Indiana Station during the winter of 1910–1911 was approximately 23 pounds of shelled corn, 3⅓ pounds of cottonseed meal, and 10 pounds of clover hay after the first 60 days. Such amounts of protein concentrates were soon found to be too large for the most economical gains, and they were gradually reduced.   In fact, the results of many feeding experiments subsequently carried on have indicated the need for less and less protein concentrate in the ration of fattening cattle, until now, when less than half the amount fed in the Indiana experiment mentioned above is the amount recommended for mature steers fed a liberal amount of legume hay.

It has, of course, long been known that young cattle require more protein concentrate in proportion to their weight than older cattle. However, feeding experiments show that there is very little difference in the requirements per head of cattle of different ages when all are fed appropriate amounts of roughage of the same type, i.e., legume or non-legume.   Knowledge of this fact has greatly simplified the feeding of cattle, since the same rules for supplying protein may be applied to cattle of all ages.

Another discovery has been made which still further simplifies the feeding of protein concentrates.   Experiments carried out at the Ohio[4] and Kansas[5] Stations have shown that the feeding of a constant amount of protein concentrate throughout the feeding period gives better results than either gradually increasing or decreasing the amount as the feeding period progresses.   Although the experiments were performed with calves, it seems reasonable to believe that this method of feeding is even better suited to older cattle, the protein requirements of which are more nearly constant because their rate of growth changes less and their feeding period is much shorter.

In the Ohio tests, with constant, increased, and decreased amounts of protein, silage was the variable roughage fed and the legume hay was fed at a constant level during the feeding period.   It appears highly probable that, had legume hay been the only roughage fed with large amounts at the beginning and relatively small amounts at

[4] Ohio Bimonthly Bulletin 192, 1938.

[5] Kansas Mimeo. Report, May 24, 1934

TABLE 133

Value of Different Amounts of Protein Concentrates for Fattening 2-Year-Old Steers

	Indiana* (Average of 3 Tests)				Illinois Mimeo. Report, April 18, 1947		Iowa Mimeo. Report D-86, 1922–1923			
	Cottonseed Meal, Clover Hay		Cottonseed Meal, Oat Straw, Corn Silage		Soybean Oil Meal, Clover Hay		Linseed Meal, Clover Hay		Linseed Meal, Clover Hay, Corn Silage	
Av. protein concentrate per day...	1.25	2.5	2.5	4.0	2.3	3.9	1.5	3.0	1.5	3.0
Av. daily gain, lb...	2.31	2.36	2.48	2.37	2.75	2.93	2.56	2.36	2.61	2.56
Feed per cwt. gain										
Concentrates...	839	881	676	707	680	667	919	951	857	901
Dry roughage...	501	484	36	33	150	141	278	330	163	202
Corn silage...			1062	1073					526	300
Feed cost per cwt. gain...	$9.66	$10.35	$8.99	$9.73	$11.18	$11.10	$13.44	$15.22	$13.45	$14.42
Selling price per cwt...	6.35	6.60	8.60	8.60	15.00	15.25	10.00	9.75	10.00	10.00
Net return per head...	9.01	9.00	16.70	12.72	14.08	18.72	5.48	2.28	5.94	2.37
Feed cost per unit										
Shelled corn per bushel...	$ 0.46		$ 0.50		$ 0.80		$ 0.63			
Protein concentrate per ton...	31.50		31.00		36.00		51.90			

*Indiana Bulletins 163, 167, 178.

the end, the lot of calves fed increased amounts of protein concentrates would have made the best showing. At any rate, such a plan of feeding would be necessary to insure a constant supply of protein to cattle that are fed legume hay as the only roughage.

In the light of the facts discussed in the foregoing paragraphs and the information presented in the accompanying tables, it appears that a rule for feeding protein concentrates to full-fed cattle need take into account but one factor, viz., the amount of legume hay consumed daily. Since 4 pounds of legume hay contain approximately the same amount of digestible protein as 1 pound of high-quality protein concentrate, the following simple rule should be sufficiently accurate for practical feeding operations:

> To cattle fed no legume hay
> Feed 2 pounds of protein per day;
> But for each pound of hay you feed
> One-fourth pound less of meal they'll need.

The application of this simple rule to full-fed steers will nearly always result in their getting an amount of digestible protein well within the limits of the requirements given in Table 126.

Example: A 600-pound baby beef steer is fed 3 pounds of clover hay and a full feed of shelled corn.

Estimated daily ration:

10	lb. shelled corn @ 6.6%	= 0.66 lb. digestible protein
3	lb. clover hay @ 7.1%	= 0.21
1.25	lb. soybean oil meal @ 37.5%	= .47
		1.34

Limits, Table 126, 1.26 to 1.37 lb. of digestible protein.

Since calves on full feed consume less legume hay per head than older cattle, they will be fed more protein concentrate, if fed by this rule, than yearlings or 2-year-olds. This is a merit rather than a fault of the rule, as calves need more palatable rations than mature cattle.

Protein Concentrates More Necessary toward End of Feed. It should be understood that the rations given in the accompanying tables are the approximate amounts of feed eaten for the entire feeding period. With corn and alfalfa, or corn and clover, considerably more hay than the amounts stated would be fed during the first part of the fattening period and smaller amounts during the latter part. Consequently, the protein deficiency would really exist only during the latter half, at which period it would be somewhat greater than that calculated, especially if the need of the cattle for an appetizer is taken into account.   With either of these rations, undoubtedly the greatest benefit would be derived from feeding the nitrogenous concentrate during only the last 3 or 4 months, at which time the consumption of hay would be small.

TABLE 134

VALUE OF DIFFERENT AMOUNTS OF PROTEIN CONCENTRATES FOR FATTENING CALVES

Critical Feeds	Oklahoma*—Av. of 2 Years 1929–31 (Calves) Cottonseed Meal Prairie Hay			Ohio†—Av. of 2 Years 1934–36 (Calves) Mixed Supplement Mixed Hay, Silage			Kansas Circular 105, 1924 Cottonseed Cake—Alfalfa Hay			
Av. Prot. Conc. Per Day	1.5	2.5	3.5	0.8	1.6	2.4	0.5	1.0	1.5	2.0
Av. daily gain, lb........	2.21	2.27	2.22	1.99	2.20	2.21	1.98	2.06	2.07	2.12
Feed per cwt. gain										
Concentrates.........	495	484	501	609	593	599	515	519	539	550
Dry roughage........	235	230	237	85	77	77	101	97	97	94
Silage...............	....	....	....	351	319	317	462	442	438	432
Feed cost per cwt. gain..	$7.50	$7.59	$8.15	$10.42	$10.30	$10.60	$8.66	$8.91	$9.44	$9.79
Selling price per cwt.....	9.40	9.65	9.50	11.40	11.95	12.15	10.00	10.35	10.25	10.50
Profit per head.........	−.14	1.21	−.78	17.55	25.25	24.81	7.79	9.17	6.62	6.28

* Mimeographed Report.   † Ohio Bimonthly Bulletins 179 and 186.

Other Rules for Feeding.   The amount of nitrogenous concentrate, instead of being based upon the live weight of the animals, is frequently based upon the amount of corn fed.   In other words, a given ratio is maintained between the weight of corn and the weight of the protein feed used.   The advantage of such a method is its simplicity.   The feeder is much more likely to know how much corn he is feeding than he is to know how much the steers really weigh.   Its chief disadvantage is that the same ratio is likely to be maintained throughout the feeding period.   Hence, the ration is no more palatable toward the end than it was at the beginning.   This trouble, however, can be easily overcome by gradually narrowing the ratio as the feeding period progresses.   Based on such a plan, the ratios in Table 135 will be found fairly satisfactory.

The comparatively narrow ratio during the first part of the feeding period, when a non-legume roughage is used, is necessary because of the small amount of corn that is commonly fed at this stage of the fattening process. Where a legume roughage is used the condition is reversed, as the large amount of clover or alfalfa hay consumed during the first weeks furnishes an adequate supply of protein.

Still another rule for feeding the protein concentrate is simply to feed so many pounds daily per head. This is the simplest method of all, and is the one most widely followed. It is most frequently used by feeders who value the linseed or cottonseed meal chiefly as an appetizer

TABLE 135

RATIO BETWEEN NITROGENOUS CONCENTRATE AND CORN FOR FULL-FED STEERS

Ration	Period	Two-year-olds	Yearlings	Calves
Corn—Non-legume Roughage..	1st third	1:6	1:5	1:4
	2d third	1:8	1:7	1:6
	Last third	1:7	1:6	1:5
Corn—Legume Hay...........	1st third	None	None	1:10
	2d third	None	1:10	1:8
	Last third	1:10	1:8	1:7

and for the finish and "bloom" it produces. Such feeders usually start out with about ½ pound of the concentrate daily per 2-year-old steer, increasing the amount approximately ½ pound per month, until at the end of the fattening period the cattle are getting from 2 to 3 pounds of meal per day. Although steers fed according to this plan often suffer from a lack of protein during the first 2 months, the feed eaten at this period is largely roughage, and hence the waste resulting from a poor balancing of food nutrients entails no large loss. On the other hand, during the last part of the feeding period when the consumption of grain is large, the supply of protein is fully adequate for the needs of the cattle. With calves and yearlings, which have a longer feeding period, the increases should be made more slowly, so that each animal will be getting from 2 to 3 pounds daily during the last few weeks before going to market.

Protein Concentrates as Substitutes for Corn. It occasionally happens that cottonseed or soybean-oil meal is cheaper per pound than shelled corn. At such times farmers are likely to feed large amounts in an attempt to cheapen the ration by replacing part of the grain. A study of Tables 133 and 136 will disclose that protein concentrates fed in excess of the amount needed for their protein content will not as a rule replace their weight of corn in producing a pound of gain. Consequently, even with corn and protein feeds at the same price, the substitution of protein for part of the corn will result in more expensive gains. However, cattle fed a generous amount of protein often com-

TABLE 136

VALUE OF FEEDING AN EXCESS AMOUNT OF PROTEIN CONCENTRATE TO REPLACE PART OF THE CORN RATION OF FATTENING CATTLE

	Illinois Mimeo. Report, April 18, 1947* (2-Year-Old Steers)			Illinois Mimeo. Report, 1927–28 (Calves)		Oklahoma Mimeo. Circ. 58, 1940† (Calves)	
	Soybean Oil Meal			Cottonseed Meal		Cottonseed Cake	
Av. Protein Concentrate per Day	2.3	3.9	6.4	1.6	4.2	2.0	7.0
Av. daily gain, lb............	2.75	2.93	2.89	2.44	2.57	2.23	2.24
Feed per cwt. gain							
Shelled corn..............	595	534	442	461	324	451	225
Protein concentrate........	85	113	220	67	162	88	312
Dry roughage.............	150	141	143	82	317	515	514
Silage....................	....	....	....	333	78	....	....
Feed cost per cwt. gain.......	$11.18	$11.10	$11.36	$10.31	$10.65	$6.78	$7.71
Selling price per cwt..........	$15.00	$15.25	$15.40	$13.65	$13.60	$9.87	$9.83
Net return per head.........	$14.08	$18.72	$19.42	$29.52	$28.15	$20.67	$13.68
Feed cost per unit							
Shelled corn per bushel.....	$ 0.80			$ 0.84		$ 0.57	
Protein concentrate per ton..	36.00			50.00		29.00	

* 80-day trial.
† Average of 3 tests.

mand a sufficient premium when marketed to justify replacing 20 to 30 per cent of the grain ration with a protein concentrate, even though corn is slightly cheaper on a pound or ton basis. That under ordinary price conditions the feeding of an excess amount of protein to commercial cattle is not justified is indicated by the fact that in only 2 of the 9 trials reported in Tables 133 and 136 did the cattle fed the most protein return the largest profit.

In feeding cattle for show and sale, relatively large amounts of protein concentrates are recommended. Here economy is secondary to improvement in appearance; and where as much sleekness of hair and mellowness of flesh as possible are desired, 3 or more pounds of protein concentrates are sometimes fed.

20 ——— The Principal Nitrogenous Concentrates Used in Cattle Feeding

Practically all the common protein concentrates that are used in cattle feeding are by-products of the cereal and vegetable-oil milling industries. From the cereal mills, we obtain bran and gluten meal, and from the oil factories we obtain cottonseed meal, linseed meal, and soybean meal. In addition to these feeding stuffs, which must be purchased by farmers, we have the seeds of a few leguminous plants, which are used to some extent in supplying the protein needs of fattening cattle. Of these farm-grown protein concentrates, soybeans are by far the most important, especially in the North and South Central states. In the Gulf Coast region and in the South Atlantic states, the velvet bean bids fair to become an important source of protein for all classes of livestock, and especially for cattle.

I. COTTONSEED MEAL

Strange as it may seem, the diversified livestock farming of the northern states depends, in considerable measure, for its success, upon the single-crop system practiced in the Cotton Belt. Except for the large surplus of cottonseed products of the southern states, many Corn Belt feeders would experience considerable difficulty in supplying balanced rations for their cattle. If, as now seems probable, southern farmers, in the course of time, engage more extensively in livestock production, putting more and more of their present cotton acreage in hay and pasture crops, a considerable proportion of the reduced production of cottonseed will find a ready market in the South. Until that time, however, there will be a large amount of meal and cake to be used by the cattle feeders of the Corn Belt and by the ranchers of the Western Range.

Protein Content. Although cotton is not a legume, its seeds contain a relatively large amount of protein, normally about 20 per cent. With the removal of the hulls and the extraction of the oil, the protein content of the remaining meal is approximately double that of the whole seed. Although the percentage of protein varies somewhat according to the completeness with which the hulls are removed, the

TABLE 137

Supply of Protein Feedstuffs Suitable for Livestock Feeding*

Protein Feeds	Amount Fed in U.S. 1947	Amount Fed in U.S. 1948	Wholesale Price per Ton[a] Average 1940–1949
	tons (000)	tons (000)	
1. Mill products			
Wheat mill feeds	5540	4916	. . . .
Wheat bran	. . . .	. . . .	45.65
Gluten feed and meal	799	848	48.40
Rice mill feeds	177	190	. . . .
Brewers' dried grains	228	233	44.60
Distillers' dried grains	353	334	52.25
Dried and molasses beet pulp	311	340	. . . .
Alfalfa meal	1013	1122	52.50
Total	8421	7983	
2. Oil cakes and meals			
Cottonseed	1954	2271	58.70
Linseed	605	641	57.05
Soybean	3440	4140	64.25
Peanut	106	96	56.50
Copra	177	162	56.25
Total	6282	7310	
3. Animal proteins			
Tankage and meat scrap	822		90.55
Fish meal	200		108.90
Dried milk	90		
Total	1112		

* U.S.D.A. Agricultural Statistics, 1949, p. 73.
[a] Feed age, May, 1951.

better grades of cottonseed meal stand at the very top of the list of high-protein feeding stuffs fed to cattle.

Physical Properties. Cottonseed meal should be of a rather light yellowish-brown color and have a pleasant nut-like odor. A dark, dull color signifies a lower-grade product and is due to the presence of an abnormal number of hull particles or to overheating the seeds during the process of extracting the oil. Although the finely ground "meal" is the product commonly used in this country, it is by no means the only form into which the material is manufactured. When taken from the hydraulic presses that remove the oil, the product is in the shape of large, slab-like cakes about 1 inch thick, 1 foot wide, and 2½ feet long. These cakes are put through crushers that reduce them, first, to pieces about the size of a walnut. This product is called cottonseed "nut cake" and is the form commonly fed on the ground to cattle in the Southwest during periods of grass shortage. The nut size is very well suited for feeding on the ground and with broken ear corn, since it is easily mixed with the broken ears.

Additional grinding reduces the product to the so-called "pea size" cottonseed meal, a form particularly well adapted for feeding with shelled corn. Finally, the process of grinding may be continued until the resulting product is a fine meal, almost flour-like in texture. This is by far the commonest form used in this country. It is well suited for mixing with ground grain or for sprinkling over silage, but is less satisfactory than the pea or nut sizes for feeding with whole corn, especially when the feed is placed in bunks that are exposed to the weather. In many localities, however, it is the only form of product that can be purchased from retail feed dealers.

During recent years more and more cottonseed meal has been "pelleted" by forcing the finely ground meal through small steel openings to make "sticks" or "pellets," which resemble broken lemon stick candy in general appearance. These pellets vary from $\frac{1}{8}$ to $\frac{3}{4}$ inches in diameter and from $\frac{1}{4}$ to $1\frac{1}{2}$ inches in length. The small pellets are very satisfactory for feeding with shelled or coarsely ground corn. The larger sticks are very popular in the range area, where "cake" is frequently fed to cattle during the winter by scattering it upon the dry ground. Often the cottonseed meal is mixed with 10 to 20 per cent of its weight of ground alfalfa to obtain a cake that is a valuable source of vitamin A. Enough molasses is often added to the mixture to produce a pellet that will not crumble during shipment and handling.

Cold-Pressed Cottonseed Meal. Not all cottonseeds are hulled before the oil is extracted. A relatively small percentage goes directly from the gin into large hydraulic presses where as much of the oil is extracted as possible. The residue, consisting of the hulls as well as the kernels, is known as "cold-pressed" cottonseed cake. The high percentage of fiber resulting from the presence of the hulls makes the feeding value of the cold-pressed cake relatively low. As a rule, it is sold in either the nut or pea form, though it may be ground into a meal.

Cottonseed Feeds. Owing to the high prices that have prevailed for high-grade cottonseed meal, there have been manufactured and offered for sale cottonseed products of a relatively low feeding value. Because of the considerable amount of ground hulls that it contains, such material can be sold for a much lower price than choice or prime cottonseed meal. Cattle feeders should not be mislead into thinking that these "cottonseed feeds" are equal to the higher-priced meal in feeding value. When the cost per pound of digestible protein is taken into consideration, the higher-grade product will usually prove to be the more economical.

Cottonseed Meal as a Substitute for Corn. In the South, where cottonseed meal is abundant and relatively cheap, it is frequently fed in large amounts as a substitute for corn in fattening cattle for market. Occasionally its cost per pound in the Corn Belt is but little above that of corn, so that feeders are tempted to use it much more liberally than they do when normal prices prevail. In this connection it should be remembered that corn contains about 80 therms of net energy per hundredweight, whereas cottonseed meal contains but 74 therms.[1] Hence, one should not expect to obtain much advantage from substituting cottonseed meal for corn other than a possible saving in feed costs. However, the excess protein sometimes causes the cattle to take on a little more "bloom," which may increase their selling price sufficiently to justify feeding as much as 4 or 5 pounds of cottonseed meal per head daily. (See Table 136.)

Cottonseed Meal Poisoning. Occasionally cattle fed cottonseed meal over an extended period have become unthrifty in appearance, showing harsh staring coats and inflamed eyes; some animals even, in time, became blind. Such trouble formerly was rather common in the South, where large quantities of cottonseed meal were often fed along with cottonseed hulls or other low-grade roughages for rather long periods. Reports of such conditions caused some feeders to hold the belief that cottonseed meal was not a safe feed for cattle which were to be fed for several months. It has now been established that a number of cases of so-called "cottonseed meal poisoning" were due to a deficiency of vitamin A. The characteristic symptoms of the disease have been produced by feeding rations low in this vitamin, and they have disappeared entirely when an adequate amount of vitamin A was provided.

Under former methods of manufacture, cottonseed meal often contained an appreciable amount of an organic substance called "gossypol," which occasionally was toxic to cattle and often was fatal to hogs. However, improvements in the method of processing have resulted in almost eliminating this substance, making cottonseed meal a perfectly safe feed for cattle, and also for hogs, if it is mixed with other supplements like tankage and soybean oil meal.

II. LINSEED MEAL

Linseed meal, linseed oil meal, or simply oil meal, as it is sometimes called, is the product that results from the extraction of oil from flax-

[1] Morrison, Feeds and Feeding.

seed. Flaxseed resembles cotton in that it is not a legume but produces a seed containing a high percentage of protein and oil. When the oil is extracted the percentage of protein in the residue is still further increased. The average protein content of flaxseed is approximately 17 per cent, whereas that of the meal is slightly over twice this amount.

Flax is grown on a much smaller scale than cotton in the United States. Altogether, only 600 to 800 thousand tons of flaxseed are produced annually, over half of which are grown in Minnesota and North Dakota. This amount is not sufficient to meet the demand for linseed oil, and an additional 200 to 400 thousand tons of flaxseed are imported, principally from Argentina. Normally about 700 thousand tons of linseed cake and meal are produced annually. Previous to World War II nearly half the linseed cake produced in the United States was exported to Europe, but since the war the amount exported has been negligible.

All flaxseed except that needed for planting is sold to oil factories, where the oil is extracted. Almost none of the whole seed is used for feeding purposes.

TABLE 138

COMPARISON OF OLD PROCESS AND NEW
PROCESS LINSEED MEAL FOR FATTENING CATTLE

	Colorado Mimeo. Report, 1948–1949		Iowa AH Leaflet 158, 1939–1940		
	Expeller Linseed Meal	Solvent Linseed Meal	Hydraulic Linseed Meal	Expeller Linseed Meal	Solvent Linseed Meal
Av. initial weight, lb.	844	848	720	721	723
Av. daily gain	2.37	2.35	2.09	2.14	1.98
Av. daily ration					
Grain	17.7	17.7	12.2	12.8	11.9
Protein concentrate	0.9	0.9	1.5	1.4	1.5
Corn silage	....	....	12.6	12.6	12.6
Legume hay	4.9	4.9	1.7	1.7	1.7
Feed cost per cwt. gain	$22.81	$22.99	$8.65	$8.54	$8.93
Selling price per cwt.	24.25	24.25	10.10	10.30	10.15
Dressing percentage	61.8%	62.9%	....	....	....

Old and New Process Linseed Meal. Most of the linseed meal produced in the United States is made by first crushing and then heating the flaxseed, after which the oil is extracted by means of hydraulic or expeller presses. Such meal is called "old process" meal. In contrast with this is the so-called "new process" meal, in which the oil is removed from the crushed seeds by pouring over them a chemical, such as naphtha or benzol, which will dissolve the oil and carry it out in solution.   All traces of the dissolving agent are removed by applying heat, which causes the liquid to vaporize.

The new process removes a greater percentage of the oil than the old process, and the protein content of the new process meal is therefore approximately 3 per cent higher.   However, the protein of the old process meal is somewhat more digestible, so that there is but little difference in digestible protein between the two forms.   Most feeders prefer linseed meal made by the old process because of its higher percentage of oil.   This oil is believed to have a high feeding value and to produce a beneficial effect upon the general health of the animal through a proper regulation of the bowels.   However, feeding tests designed to compare old process and new process linseed meals have disclosed no significant advantage of one over the other for fattening cattle.

Physical Properties.   In appearance, linseed meal is of a grayish brown color and is somewhat coarser in texture than cottonseed meal. Like cottonseed products, it is made in various degrees of fineness, varying from finely ground meal to board-like slabs or cakes.   The "pea" size material has been increasingly popular and has largely displaced the finely ground product in many sections of the country.

Linseed meal, because of its marked adhesive qualities when under pressure, is especially easy to pellet.   Consequently, more of it is processed and sold in this form than is done with cottonseed meal. Practically all the linseed meal exported is in the form of "cake."

Linseed Meal and Cottonseed Meal Compared.   Theoretically, cottonseed meal is somewhat more valuable than linseed meal, since it is from 5 to 10 percent higher in protein.   Most practical feeders, however, prefer the linseed meal because of its beneficial effect on the general health of the cattle.   Cattle fed on linseed meal can frequently be distinguished by their glossy coats and their sleek, thrifty appearance.   As stated above, this is probably brought about by the tendency of the linseed meal to produce a slightly laxative effect.   Cottonseed meal, on the other hand, has a tendency to make cattle somewhat costive.   For this reason, it is often considered superior to linseed meal when used in connection with feeds that are themselves laxative, such as silage, alfalfa hay, or grass.   In general, however, feeding experiments do not bear out this contention.   Instead they show a distinct superiority for linseed over cottonseed meal under practically all conditions.   This superiority, according to some authorities, is due, at least in part, to "the presence of a slimy carbohydrate material called *mucin*, which has great capacity for absorbing water and plays a role in regulating digestion."[2]

[2] The Shorthorn World, Oct. 10, 1947, p. 71.

A summary of all available experimental results of the comparative feeding value of these two protein supplements discloses that linseed meal is approximately 40 per cent more valuable than cottonseed

TABLE 139

COMPARISON OF LINSEED MEAL AND COTTONSEED
MEAL FOR FATTENING CATTLE

| | Iowa Mimeo. Reports AH Leaflets D-86, 158, 159 | | | | Missouri Bull. 150 | | Ohio Bimonthly Bull. 140 | |
| | 2-Year-Old Steers | | Yearling Steers (Av. 2 trials) | | 2-Year-Old Steers (No Corn Ration) | | Calves | |
	Linseed Meal	Cotton-seed Meal	Linseed Meal	Cotton-seed Meal	Linseed Meal	Cotton-seed Meal	Linseed Meal	Cotton-seed Meal
Days fed............	120	120	225	225	132	132	119	119
Av. initial wt., lb.....	1080	1080	689	689	921	926	405	404
Av. final wt..........	1385	1318	1149	1109	1239	1212	652	633
Av. daily gain.......	2.56	2.05	2.06	1.85	2.42	2.18	2.07	1.92
Av. daily ration......								
Shelled corn.......	22.0	19.4	12.6	11.3	..	..	6.6	6.6
Protein concentrate	1.5	1.5	1.6	1.5	4.7	4.7	2.0	2.0
Corn silage........	..	..	12.1	12.1	43.5	42.1	9.1	8.7
Legume hay.......	7.1	8.1	1.6	1.6	4.9	4.3	1.9[a]	1.8[a]
Feed per cwt. gain								
Shelled corn.......	861	946	615	611	..	..	322	347
Prot. conc........	59	73	78	79	195	219	97	104
Corn silage........	..	..	586	649	1797	1921	441	453
Legume hay.......	278	396	79	87	203	195	91[a]	96[a]
Feed cost per cwt. gain	$13.44	$15.71	$9.14	$9.29	$10.08	$01.97	$9.60	$9.89
Selling price per cwt. .	$10.00	$9.75	$11.45	$11.20	$10.85	$10.75	$12.85	$12.85
Net return over feed costs..............	5.48	−0.97	11.47	7.03	19.07	14.63	7.53	6.23

[a] Mixed hay.

meal when fed in a dry lot, and 20 per cent more valuable when fed on bluegrass pasture.[3]   This wide difference in the money value per ton based upon profits actually returned is due largely to the difference in the price per hundredweight received for the finished cattle.   When linseed meal can be purchased at only $10 or $15 a ton more than cottonseed meal, its use is recommended; otherwise cottonseed meal is likely to be more profitable for feeding for the open market.

[3] Culbertson, C. C., et al., Proceedings of American Society of Animal Production, 1923, p. 24.

In three trials carried on with calves at the Wisconsin Station a mixture of equal parts of linseed and cottonseed meal proved equal in all respects to linseed meal alone.[4]

III. GLUTEN FEED

Gluten feed is a by-product of corn and is produced in considerable quantities by large starch factories. It consists of the outer layers of the corn kernel, which are separated from the starch particles in the wet milling processing of corn. Sometimes the outer hull is separated from the underlying gluten layer, which is then sold under the name "gluten meal."

TABLE 140

VALUE OF CORN GLUTEN FEED FOR FATTENING CATTLE.[*]

Two-year-old Steers Fed in Dry Lot

Supplement	None	Linseed Meal	Cottonseed Meal	Gluten Meal
	Lbs.	Lbs.	Lbs.	Lbs.
Daily Gain................	1.77	1.94	1.88	1.83
Feed per lb. Gain:				
Concentrates.............	10.47	9.56	10.03	10.49
Roughage................	6.63	5.29	5.89	5.95
Pork per Steer............	113.9	124.5	116.9	144.8
Selling Price per cwt........	$5.30	$5.35	$5.35	$5.25

* Iowa Bulletin No. 79, 1904.

Gluten feed contains about 25 per cent protein, whereas gluten meal has a protein content of approximately 40 per cent. Both these feeds are used more extensively for dairy cattle than for beef cattle. Inasmuch as the grain ration of beef cattle is likely to consist largely of corn, a concentrate from some other source is likely to be a more complete supplement through the supplying of certain amino acids and minerals in which corn is deficient or even lacking entirely. Equal parts of gluten meal and linseed meal gave results approximately equal to linseed meal alone in fattening calves at the Kansas Station. (See Table 149.) Since gluten feed contains less protein than cottonseed or linseed meal, it should be purchased at a correspondingly lower price per ton.

[4] Cf. p. 353.

IV. SOYBEANS AND SOYBEAN MEAL

Although soybeans were almost unknown in many sections of the United States before 1920, they now constitute one of the major crops, especially in the Corn Belt. Approximately 200 million bushels of soybeans are harvested annually in the United States, 85 per cent of which are sold to milling companies which extract the valuable oil and sell the residue to commercial feed companies and farmers as soybean oil meal. Since soybeans direct from the thresher or combine have a protein content of more than 35 per cent, they are sometimes fed in the form of whole or ground beans as a farm-grown protein concentrate, especially if they have a high moisture content or are discolored as a result of weather damage, and consequently have a low market value.

Soybeans contain not only a high percentage of protein, but also a high percentage of oil. The fat content varies from 15 to 20 per cent, depending somewhat on the variety of beans. When soybeans are fed in sufficient quantities to supply the protein needed to balance a full ration of corn, the amount of oil consumed is considerably above that which can be utilized by the animals. Scouring, or at least a marked looseness of the bowels, is very likely to result, particularly if the cattle are fed a rather liberal allowance of beans for a considerable length of time. Moreover, the presence of the oil apparently detracts from the palatability of the beans, since the cattle seem to tire of them after eating them a few months.

Soybean oil is a valuable commercial product, being used in the manufacture of paints and varnishes as well as in the preparation of various edible products. In the extraction of the oil, the beans are finely ground and heated, and the oil is either pressed out by mechanical presses or dissolved out with a chemical solution. If it is pressed out the residue is called "old process" soybean oil meal; if it is dissolved out the residue is termed "solvent" or "new process" meal. Two types of presses are used in making old process meal—hydraulic and expeller presses. Consequently, old process meal is often called "hydraulic meal" or "expeller meal," according to the type of press used in extracting the oil. The meal is subjected to very high temperatures in the screw-like expeller presses and as a result has a slightly burnt or "toasted" appearance and flavor not possessed by hydraulic or solvent meal unless it is given a special "toasting" treatment after the oil has been removed. Toasted soybean oil meal is more valuable than untoasted meal for both hogs and poultry but has little if any advantage for beef cattle. In fact, there is some evidence that the high tem-

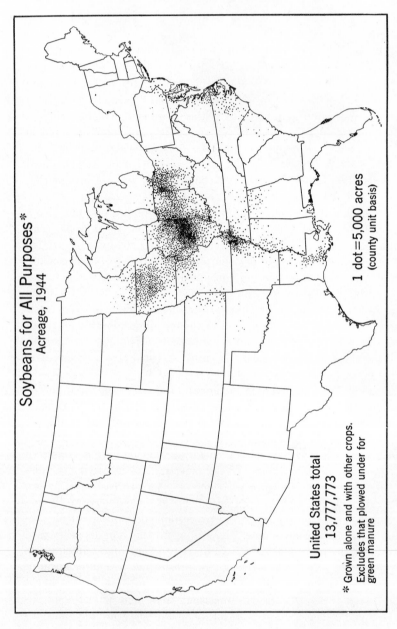

Soybeans for All Purposes*
Acreage, 1944

United States total
13,777,773

* Grown alone and with other crops.
Excludes that plowed under for
green manure

1 dot = 5,000 acres
(county unit basis)

FIG. 47. The principal soybean-producing area of the United States. Numerous large mills for processing soybeans are located in this area and produce large amounts of soybean oil meal for livestock feeding. (*Courtesy Bureau of the Census.*)

peratures to which the meal is subjected during toasting depress the digestibility of the protein slightly.

Soybean oil meal has the highest protein content of any feed that is available in quantity for beef cattle feeding, namely from 41 to 50 per

TABLE 141

COMPARATIVE VALUE OF SOYBEANS, SOYBEAN OIL MEAL,
AND COTTONSEED MEAL FOR FATTENING CATTLE

	Illinois Experiment Station Mimeo. Report, 1926–1927				Iowa AH Leaflets 158, 1940, and 159, 1941		Indiana Bull. 330, 1929	
	1 Trial with Calves				2 Trials with Yearlings		2 Trials with 2-Year-Old Steers	
	Ground Soy-beans	Whole Soy-beans	Soybean Oil Meal	Cotton-seed Meal	Soybean Oil Meal	Cotton-seed Meal	Whole Soy-beans	Cotton-seed Meal
Av. daily gains, lb.	2.11	2.26	2.36	2.35	1.78	1.85	2.51	2.29
Av. daily ration								
Shelled corn.	8.5	9.0	9.1	10.1	11.0	11.30	12.4	12.3
Protein concentrate .	1.3	1.3	1.4	1.5	1.3	1.5	2.3	2.3
Corn silage.	8.1	8.1	8.1	8.1	12.0	12.0	24.1	26.2
Legume hay.	2.0	2.0	2.0	2.0	1.6	1.6	3.5	3.7
Feed per cwt. gain								
Shelled corn.	401	395	387	428	594	611	492	538
Protein concentrate .	60	59	57	63	76	78	91	100
Corn silage.	385	358	344	343	677	649	961	1146
Legume hay.	95	88	85	85	92	87	139	162
Selling price per cwt. . .	$10.85	$11.15	$11.60	$11.85	$11.15	$11.15	$9.35	$8.95
Gain of hogs per steer, lb.	39	28	24	38	. .	. .	67	50

cent. Moreover, the quality or "biological value" of the protein is especially high, which means that it is digested and utilized by animals to a high degree. Because of these advantages and its ready availability, it is the most common protein concentrate purchased by Corn Belt cattle feeders to supply the protein needed by fattening cattle. In addition, it is the principal source of protein in many of the proprietary brands of beef cattle feeds manufactured by commercial feed companies. Soybean oil meal constituted 22.3 per cent of the total weight of ingredients used by the prepared feed industry in Illinois in 1947, not including bone meal and minerals.[5]

In chemical composition, soybean oil meal is very similar to choice cottonseed meal. Also, experiments indicate that it is practically equal to cottonseed meal in feeding value. For many years much complaint was made by some feeders that soybean oil meal was too laxative for cattle fed a full feed of shelled corn and legume hay, but, with the adoption by milling companies of better methods of removing the oil, such complaints have almost disappeared. Formerly much discussion was held regarding the relative merits of hydraulic, ex-peller, and solvent meals, and the superior value claimed for the toasted meals. Extensive experiments carried out at several of the Corn Belt stations have disclosed no important advantage of one over the others for fattening cattle. Apparently feeders should follow the practice of buying soybean oil meal on the basis of its guaranteed protein content, regardless of the method by which it was manu-factured. (See Table 142.)

Soybean oil meal, like linseed and cottonseed meal, is made and sold as cake, pellets, or finely ground meal. As a rule, the meal is cheaper and more available, because it is more easily made and is in great demand for feeding hogs, poultry, and dairy cattle. However, pea-size cake or pellets are much better for feeding with shelled corn, and pellets or cake 1 to 2 inches in size are recommended for use in the range area where the feed is frequently scattered on the ground.

Although whole soybeans are noticeably inferior to soybean meal, they make a fairly satisfactory supplement when carefully fed in moderate quantities. They appear to be more satisfactory for older cattle than for calves, probably because older cattle are fed for a shorter time and are given more roughage. There is some evidence that the feeding of corn silage with whole soybeans or with soybean oil meal tends to overcome the laxative effects sometimes caused by these feeds. For example, steer calves fed 2.5 pounds of soybean oil meal per head daily at the Iowa Station went off feed and scoured badly after the silage was reduced by half at the end of 210 days of feeding.[6] This theory may serve to explain the unusually good showing made by 2-year-old steers fed whole soybeans in the Indiana experiments, since the grain rations were to some extent restricted and relatively large amounts of silage were fed. (See Table 141.)

Some difference of opinion exists as to the advisability of grinding the beans for cattle. A few experiments indicate that grinding is not

[5] Illinois Farm Economics, University of Illinois, August, 1950.
[6] Iowa, AH Leaflet 140, 1932.

only unnecessary but even undesirable, at least for calves. Calves fed ground beans by the Illinois Station exhibited poorer appetites, made smaller gains, scoured more frequently, and showed a much more pronounced tendency to go off feed than calves fed whole beans. Pos-

TABLE 142

EFFECT OF THE METHOD OF PROCESSING UPON THE VALUE
OF SOYBEAN OIL MEAL FOR FATTENING CATTLE

Protein Concentrate Fed	Illinois Mimeo. Report, Oct. 20, 1933				Iowa AH Leaflets 158, 1940, and 159, 1941		Illinois Mimeo. Reports, 1935, 1936, 1938	
	Calves				Yearling Steers (Average 2 trials)		Steer Calves (Average 3 trials)	
	Hydraulic		Expeller					
	Max. Temp., F.		Max. Temp., F.		Expeller	Solvent	Old Process[a]	New Process
	180°	220°	200°	300°				
Av. daily gain, lb......	1.99	1.89	1.86	1.90	1.78	1.87	2.06	2.00
Av. daily ration								
Shelled corn........	9.2	8.8	8.4	8.6	10.5	10.6	10.2	10.1
Protein concentrate .	1.4	1.3	1.2	1.3	1.3	1.3	1.5	1.4
Corn silage........	8.1	8.1	8.1	8.1	12.0	12.0	4.9	4.9
Legume hay........	2.0	2.0	2.0	2.0	1.6	1.6	2.7	2.7
Feed per cwt. gain								
Shelled corn........	461	468	451	454	594	564	493	504
Protein concentrate .	68	69	67	67	76	68	72	73
Corn silage........	406	427	435	425	677	642	226[b]	231[b]
Legume hay........	100	106	108	105	91	86	134[b]	137[b]
Selling price per cwt...	....	....	....	....	$11.15	$11.30	$10.43	$10.42
Net return over feed costs.............	....	....	....	....	$ 7.11	$11.29	$15.38	$14.52

[a] The old process meal was made by the *hydraulic* method in 2 trials and by the *expeller* method in the third trial.

[b] Corn silage fed in 2 of the 3 trials. In the third trial alfalfa was the only roughage fed.

sibly grinding renders the oil content of the beans more available, so that its laxative action is more pronounced.

Considerable difficulty is sometimes encountered in grinding the beans. The large amount of oil present tends to make them gum up the buhrs of the grinder. Ground beans should not be stored for any length of time, as they tend to become rancid, particularly in hot weather.

V. WHEAT BRAN

Large quantities of wheat bran are produced annually by the flour mills of North America. Although comparatively little of this material is used in the fattening of beef cattle, it occasionally happens that feed prices are such as to make it the cheapest source of protein available. Because of its bulk and high percentage of fiber, bran is not an

TABLE 143

COMPARATIVE VALUE OF WHEAT BRAN AND COTTONSEED PRODUCTS FOR STEERS*

Supplement Fed	Full Corn Ration 140 Days		Two-thirds Full Corn Ration 112 Days	
	Wheat Bran	Cottonseed Meal	Wheat Bran	Cold Pressed Cottonseed Cake
Approx. Ratio of Corn to Supplement............	78 : 22	90 : 10	58 : 42	82 : 18
Initial Weight.........lbs..	973	988	778	743
Average Daily Gain........	1.76	2.11	1.55	1.59
Feed per lb. Gain:				
Concentrates............	14.19	10.83	7.19	6.93
Prairie Hay.............	....	....	5.14	4.94
Corn Stover.............	5.06	4.21	....	....
Value of Pork Produced per cwt. Gain on Steers.....	$2.30	$1.68	....	....

* Nebraska Bulletins Nos. 116 and 132, 1910 and 1912.

especially good feed for cattle that are being fattened for market. The rather pronounced laxative effect that it produces, when fed in large quantities, is also unfavorable to its extensive use by cattle feeders. On the other hand, these very qualities commend it as a feed for breeding animals and for young cattle that are intended for the breeding herd. When mixed with the common farm-grown grains, it adds bulk and lightness to the ration as well as generous quantities of phosphorus, an element greatly needed by pregnant cows and young, growing bulls and heifers.

Bran differs from most of the nitrogenous concentrates already dis-

cussed in that it has a much lower nutritive ratio. For this reason it
must be fed much more liberally than cottonseed or linseed meal to add
the same amount of protein to the ration. As a rule it is not advisable
to attempt to add as much protein through bran as would be possible
through cottonseed meal, since the amount of bran required would
render the ration too bulky and too laxative. Bran contains somewhat more carbohydrates than cottonseed or linseed meal, a fact that
should be considered in determining the relative economy of these
feeds. For practical purposes, 2 pounds of bran may be considered as
having the same feeding value as 1 pound of either of these narrower
concentrates.

The most extensive use of bran for fattening cattle is made in the
highly specialized cattle-feeding sections of the eastern states, where
not only protein concentrates but also carbonaceous feeds must be purchased in rather large quantities. Under such conditions, a feed like
bran, which carries both protein and carbohydrates, finds considerably
more favor than in the Corn Belt where an adequate supply of carbohydrates is available in farm-grown grain.

VI. TANKAGE

As a rule nearly all the tankage produced by meat-packing and rendering plants is utilized in the feeding of hogs and poultry. However,
it occasionally happens that its price per ton is sufficiently low to make
it a more economical source of protein for beef cattle than the protein

TABLE 144
VALUE OF TANKAGE FOR FATTENING CATTLE

| | Iowa Mimeo. Leaflets 149 and 151, 1935–1936 | | | Illinois Mimeo. Report, 1935 | | | Indiana Bulletin 428, 1938 | |
| | Calves (Av. of 2 tests) 240 Days | | | Calves—228 Days | | | 2-year-olds 140 Days | |
	Linseed Meal	Dry Rend. Tankage	Steam Rend. Tankage	Soybean Meal	Dry Rend. Tankage	Steam Rend. Tankage	Cottonseed Meal	Dry Rend. Tankage
Av. daily gain, lb.	2.30	2.09	2.22	2.27	2.18	2.09	2.62	2.65
Av. daily ration								
Shelled corn	11.3	10.2	11.1	11.7	11.5	11.5	12.5	12.5
Protein concentrate	1.4		.9	1.7	1.3	1.1	2.2	1.8
Corn silage	9.3	9.3	9.3	7.2	7.2	7.2	28.2	28.2
Legume hay	1.8	1.8	1.8	2.0	2.0	2.0	3.6	3.6
Feed per cwt. gain								
Shelled corn	493	492	503	513	525	549	478	473
Protein concentrate	81	40	41	74	58	53	83	69
Corn silage	405	416	423	315	328	341	1074	1061
Legume hay	59	83	80	88	92	96	138	138
Selling price per cwt.	$10.55	$9.90	$10.15	$11.90	$12.00	$11.60	$10.25	$10.40

concentrates ordinarily used in cattle feeding. Particularly was this so in the fall of 1934, when the heavy slaughter of drought cattle and sheep resulted in much larger stocks of tankage than could be used by the relatively small number of hogs being produced under the reduction program. Because of its low price, considerable tankage was fed to beef cattle during the winter of 1934–1935.

Although tankage is less palatable than other protein feeds, cattle will usually eat it in sufficient amounts to insure a properly balanced ration. Owing to its higher protein content, only about 75 per cent as much tankage as soybean oil meal is needed to supply a given amount of protein. Dry-rendered tankage or "meat scrap" is usually considered the best form of tankage for cattle. In some feeding tests, however, the ordinary steam-rendered product has given better results.

Tankage has given somewhat less favorable results with calves than with older cattle in feeding experiments where tankage and the standard protein concentrates have been compared. Calves may be more sensitive to its peculiar flavor and odor, or it may be that they tire of it because of the relatively long time that they are kept on feed.

VII. BREWERS' AND DISTILLERS' GRAINS

In the pre-Prohibition era, the expended grains of the liquor industry were commonly fed in the form of wet mashes and "slops" to cattle located near the distilleries. Now, however, they are usually dried, bagged, and sold as brewers' and distillers' dried grains. Brewers' grains, made principally from barley, contain about twice as much protein and fiber but only 90 per cent as much total digestible nutrients as the original grain. Because of their bulky nature, they are seldom fed to beef cattle but are used principally in the manufacture of mixed feeds for dairy cows. In a test made at the Illinois Station, brewers' dried grains proved to be a much less valuable source of protein for beef calves than soybean oil meal. (See Table 145.)

Distillers' dried grains are obtained from the use of corn, rye, wheat, or grain sorghum in the manufacture of beverage and industrial alcohol. Those resulting from corn and wheat are much higher in protein and total digestible nutrients than those made from rye or the grain sorghums. Consequently they are much more valuable per ton as a feed for livestock.

In the disposal of the distillery "slop" after the alcohol has been distilled off, the solid particles of grain are screened out and dried to make distillers' dried grains. The liquid portion, which contains the water-soluble nutrients and very fine particles of grain, is condensed by evaporation and dried to form distillers' dried solubles. This last-named product has received much publicity because it is an excellent source of the B vitamins, which are so important in the feeding of poultry and swine. Since cattle have little need for these vitamins, distillers' dried solubles are seldom fed to beef cattle except when mixed with distillers' dried grains. When so added the mixture is called distillers' dark grains or distillers' dried grains with solubles.

TABLE 145

THE VALUE OF BREWERS' AND DISTILLERS' DRIED GRAINS FOR FATTENING CATTLE

| | Brewers' Grains | | Distillers' Dried Grains and Solubles | | | | |
| | Calves, Illinois Mimeo. Report, 1936 | | 2-Year-Old Steers, Iowa AH Leaflet 153, 1937 | | Heavy Calves Nebraska Cattle Progress Report 194, 1949 | | |
	Soy-bean Oil Meal	Brewers' Grains (Barley)	Lin-seed Meal	Dis-tillers' Grains (Corn)	Lin-seed Pellets	Dis-tillers' Grains with Solubles	No Protein Con-centrate
Protein content of supplement	44.7%	31.5%	....	....	34.8%	25.9%	....
Wt. of supplement per bushel, lb.	31	18	....	....	....	....	....
Av. daily gain	2.06	1.88	2.36	2.21	1.88	1.68	1.35
Av. daily ration							
Shelled corn	9.2	7.2	10.5	9.2	12.7	10.4	11.3
Protein concentrate	1.3	3.0	1.5	2.0	1.7	2.6	....
Corn silage	7.4	7.4	35.5	32.1	....	....	....
Legume hay	2.0	2.0	1.2	1.4	5.7[a]	5.1[a]	6.0[a]
Selling price per cwt.	$8.65	$8.50	$14.00	$14.50	$26.50	$25.50	Not sold[b]
Hog gains per steer, lb.	25	18	66	57	....	....	....

[a] Prairie hay fed in Nebraska experiment.
[b] The steers in the lot fed no protein supplement were not fat enough to be sold for slaughter.

Distillers' dried grains may be regarded as a satisfactory substitute for soybean or cottonseed meal in the ration of fattening cattle if sufficiently large amounts are fed to furnish the proper amount of protein. Feeding tests indicate that 1 ton of distillers' dried grains will replace about 1500 pounds of soybean or cottonseed meal and 10 bushels of shelled corn if fed at the rate of 2 to 3 pounds per head daily. The feeding of larger amounts usually will not be economical unless the dried grains are no higher in price per pound than shelled corn.

VIII. UREA

For many years it was believed that animals were able to utilize nitrogen only when it was in the form of one of the amino acids, from which the body proteins are made. Later it was learned that the bacteria in the paunch of ruminants have the ability to synthesize many of the essential amino acids from non-protein nitrogenous compounds present in many feedstuffs, which are of no value to the animal until they are first elaborated by the bacteria. This discovery led to investigations to see whether perhaps the rumen bacteria might be able to utilize non-protein nitrogen that was fed as a substitute for part of the protein normally supplied to cattle and sheep in protein supplements like cottonseed and soybean meal. A non-protein nitrogenous compound that will furnish nitrogen to the rumen bacteria is urea, $CO(NH_2)_2$, a white crystalline substance much like table salt in appearance. It is readily soluble in water or molasses and can be made synthetically in large quantities at a relatively low cost.

Urea, as may be verified from its chemical formula, is 46.7 per cent nitrogen by weight. Since the crude protein content of a feed is determined by multiplying its nitrogen percentage by 6.25, the crude protein content of urea is found to be 292 per cent. Such an expression, of course, must be interpreted to mean that a given weight of urea contains as much nitrogen as a quantity of pure protein that is 2.92 times as heavy. Since cottonseed meal is only 43 per cent protein, it would require approximately 6.8 pounds of 43 per cent cottonseed meal to furnish as much nitrogen as is present in 1 pound of urea. Consequently, if the nitrogen of urea were utilized by cattle to the same extent as the nitrogen in cottonseed meal, 1 pound of urea would replace 6.8 pounds of cottonseed meal as far as the protein of the ration is concerned.

Urea, when administered to cattle in solution in the form of a drench, is highly toxic; even as little as ¼ pound of urea administered to an adult cow directly into the stomach will cause death in 40 to 90 minutes.[7] However, if urea is fed to cattle by mixing it with the grain ration or with silage, thereby insuring its going into the rumen where little or no absorption occurs, no ill effects are noted. In this case the bacteria of the rumen use the urea nitrogen in their own growth and development, building it into proteins and protein-like substances, which are digested and assimilated by the steer or cow. Thus the non-protein nitrogen of urea becomes available to the cattle through the action of the rumen bacteria.

Early studies of urea as a possible protein substitute indicated that it would be utilized to a higher degree if it were fed with some carbohydrate like molasses that would constitute a source of energy for the

---

[7] Journal of the American Veterinary Medical Association, February, 1949, pp. 90–92.

bacteria. However, feeding trials with dairy cows made at the Wisconsin Station,[8] as well as feeding experiments with beef steers conducted at the Iowa Station,[9] indicate that the addition of molasses is of no value, at least for cattle that are fed large quantities of carbohydrates in the form of farm grains. It is possible that molasses may favor the utilization of urea by stocker cattle fed principally low-grade roughages like ground corn stover and corn cobs, although here the principal value of molasses may be as an appetizer.

TABLE 146

VALUE OF UREA AS A PROTEIN SUBSTITUTE
FOR FATTENING CATTLE

	Oklahoma* Calves, 167 Days Average 2 Trials			Iowa† Yearlings, 175 Days Average 2 Trials			
	C.S.M.	$\frac{1}{4}$ Urea N $\frac{3}{4}$ C.S.M. N	$\frac{1}{2}$ Urea N $\frac{1}{2}$ C.S.M. N	Prot. Conc.	$\frac{1}{2}$ Urea N $\frac{1}{2}$ P.C. N	Urea	Urea Fed with 1 lb. Molasses
Av. daily gain, lb.....	2.14	2.11	2.17	2.26	2.32	2.24	2.22
Protein supplement...	1.5	1.5	1.5	1.25	0.75	0.20	0.20
Urea intake daily^a....	....	(.06)	(.12)	....	(.10)	(.20)	(.20)
Protein content of sup., %.........	41.8	46.7	47.3	....	....	....	....
Feed per cwt. gain...							
Shelled corn, lb.....	528	511	518	662	681	701	686
Protein sup.^{a}......	71	71	69	61	40	9	9
Molasses..........	....	....	....	....	....	....	45
Legume hay.......	47	49	46	214	213	226	217
Silage.............	445	457	436	....	....	....	45
Feed cost per cwt. gain	$25.92	$26.30	$25.53	$21.92	$21.06	$20.13	$21.39
Selling price per cwt...	26.75	26.125	26.75	33.00	33.125	33.00	33.00
Cost of prot. sup. per ton.............	92.50	98.05	98.05	....	....	....	....

* Oklahoma Misc. Pubs. 11 and 13, 1947 and 1948.
† Iowa Mimeo. AH Leaflets 176 and 179, 1950 and 1951.
^{a} Urea included in weight of protein supplement.

Authorities on animal nutrition differ somewhat in their recommendations as to how much urea may be safely fed to cattle. An early rule for feeding was that urea nitrogen should not constitute more than 16 per cent of the nitrogen in the entire ration, including that in the grain and roughage. This percentage has been raised

[8] Journal of Dairy Science, Vol. 26, pp. 647–663.
[9] Iowa, AH Leaflet 179, 1951.

gradually, and the maximum is now stated as 50 per cent by some investigators. In digestion trials at the Oklahoma Station steers fed prairie hay and urea received slightly over 70 per cent of their total nitrogen from urea. The apparent digestibility of the nitrogen of this ration was 57.5 per cent, compared with only 48.2 per cent for a ration of prairie hay and cottonseed meal.[10]

Urea is now recognized as a satisfactory ingredient of commercial protein supplements manufactured for cattle or sheep. However, its high nitrogen content makes it possible for mixed feed companies to put out a feed with a "crude protein" content of 20 to 30 per cent which would be of very low feeding value because of the very small amounts of total digestible nutrients present. Consequently, in buying a commercial protein supplement of which urea is one of the constituents, care should be taken to ascertain both the percentage which the urea nitrogen constitutes of the total nitrogen and the nature of the other ingredients of the mixture. If the other ingredients are high-grade materials like cottonseed meal, hominy feed, and alfalfa meal, urea nitrogen may well constitute 25 or even 50 per cent of the total nitrogen of the supplement. In feeding tests at the Oklahoma Station such supplements gave as good results as cottonseed meal. (See Table 146.) Pellets in which more than 50 per cent of the nitrogen is from urea are likely to be unpalatable, and not enough will be eaten to furnish the protein required. That pellets containing 4 per cent of urea by weight are not unpalatable is indicated by an average daily consumption of 10 pounds of such pellets by steer calves to which they were full-fed for 14 days at the Oklahoma Station. Beef cows fed 6 pounds of these pellets every other day during the winter calved normally and showed no toxic effects from the urea.[11]

IX. ALFALFA MEAL

Dehydrated alfalfa meal made from leafy alfalfa cut in the pre-bloom stage of maturity contains from 18 to 22 per cent protein, and may therefore be regarded as a protein concentrate. Because of the extreme fineness to which the meal is usually ground it cannot be mixed with other feeds easily and is much too fine and dusty to be fed alone. However, when it is formed into pellets about the size of corn kernels it is an excellent protein supplement to feed with shelled or ground corn. Since its protein content is only about half that of cottonseed or soybean oil meal, approximately twice as much must be fed to supply a given amount of protein.

[10] Journal of Animal Science, 1947, Vol. 6, No. 4, pp. 445–460.
[11] Oklahoma Miscel. Pub. 11, 1947.

The demand for dehydrated alfalfa meal for poultry and swine feeding is so great that its price is usually much too high to make it as economical a source of protein as linseed, cottonseed, or soybean oil meal for beef cattle. However, feeding tests conducted at the Nebraska Station suggest that dehydrated alfalfa may have a much

TABLE 147

VALUE OF DEHYDRATED ALFALFA PELLETS AS A
PROTEIN CONCENTRATE FOR BEEF CATTLE

| | For Fattening Yearling Steers | | | | | Fattening Steer Calves | | |
| | Nebraska Cattle Progress Report 190, 1947 | | | | | Nebraska Cattle Progress Report 194, 1949 | | |
	1.5 lb. S.B.O.M.	1 lb. S.B.O.M. 1 lb. Dehy. Alfalfa Meal	0.5 lb. S.B.O.M. 2 lb. Dehy. Alfalfa Meal	3 lb. Dehy. Alfalfa Meal	1.5 lb. Dehy. Alfalfa Meal	Linseed Pellets	Dehy. Alfalfa Pellets	No Prot. Conc.
Av. daily gain, lb.	2.32	2.52	2.62	2.71	2.47	1.88	1.98	1.35
Av. daily ration								
Ground ear corn	17.6	18.2	17.8	18.4	18.7	....	....	....
Shelled corn...	....	....	....	....	....	12.7	11.8	11.3
Protein conc...	1.5	2.0	2.5	3.0	1.5	1.7	3.3	....
Corn silage....	11.3	11.8	11.6	11.9	11.5	....	....	....
Prairie hay....	....	....	....	....	....	5.7	5.0	6.0
Feed per cwt. gain								
Corn.........	756	720	678	677	756	673	596	838
Protein conc...	64	79	95	110	61	91	166	....
Corn silage....	487	466	442	438	465	306	254	441
Prairie hay....	....	....	....	....	....	....	....	....
Dressing percentage........	61.6	63.7	60.8	62.5	59.8	59.6	59.4	a

[a] This lot was not fat enough to slaughter.

higher feeding value than its protein content would indicate. (See Table 147.) Alfalfa meal made from green, leafy alfalfa which was dehydrated immediately after it was cut contains an abundance of vitamin A. However, there is very little likelihood that the yearling steers in the Nebraska experiment did not receive an ample amount of this vitamin from the ground ear corn and corn silage. Attention should be called to the fact that dehydrated alfalfa pellets had a much lower feed replacement value in the second experiment with calves than in the first experiment with yearlings. The daily gains of all the yearling steers, except the check lot, were unusually large. Consequently, the results obtained from feeding the alfalfa pellets to the yearling cattle may have been somewhat better than would be obtained under normal conditions.

X. MISCELLANEOUS PROTEIN CONCENTRATES

In addition to the protein concentrates already discussed, a number of other nitrogenous materials are used to some extent in cattle feeding. However, they are produced in such small quantities as to make their use more or less local. Among the more important of these materials are peanut meal, cocoa cake, velvet beans, and dried blood. None of them is of any importance in Corn Belt cattle feeding at present, nor does it appear likely that any will be used extensively in the near future, with the possible exception of peanut meal.

Peanut meal is the residue of the kernels of peanuts, from which the greater part of the oil has been pressed out. It contains from 40 to 43 per cent crude protein, which is about the same as that present in cottonseed meal. In a trial conducted at the Texas Station,[12] peanut meal proved slightly superior to cottonseed meal in respect to both rate and economy of gains, when fed to yearling steers.

Although the steers fed peanut meal showed less avid appetites than those fed cottonseed meal, they had sleeker hair and a more attractive general appearance when marketed. In four of the six tests reported, the steers fed peanut meal had a slightly higher dressing percentage, and in five trials they returned a little more profit.[13]

Velvet beans are an important source of protein for cattle in the southern states. As their protein content is but 20 per cent, it is not likely that they will attain much commercial importance outside the region where they are grown. Also, their need for a long growing season and high temperatures will probably prevent their successful production in the Corn Belt.

Ammoniated molasses is a new form of non-protein nitrogen that may prove to be an even better protein substitute for cattle than urea. It is made by merely blowing anhydrous ammonia (NH_3) into black-strap molasses, the moisture of which combines with the ammonia to make ammonium hydroxide (NH_4OH). It is more stable than urea and is more easily fed under farm conditions. In a test conducted at the Iowa Station in 1949–1950, yearling steers fed 0.75 pound linseed meal and 1.35 pounds of molasses ammoniated to carry 20 per cent

[12] Texas Bulletin 263.
[13] Texas Bulletin 685.

protein equivalent gained approximately the same as similar steers fed the same amount of linseed meal and 0.10 pound of urea.[14]

XI. MIXED PROTEIN FEEDS

Most mixed cattle feeds are represented and sold as protein feeds and are often purchased and used as substitutes for cottonseed, linseed, and soybean oil meal. Although most brands contain some ingredients that are rich in protein, the percentage of protein in the total mixture often is not high enough to make it practical to rely entirely on such feeds for the protein needed to balance a corn, non-legume roughage fattening ration. Table 148 shows the composition of six widely used brands of commercial feeds made especially for beef cattle. The information about each feed was obtained from the bag tag.

The principal advantages claimed for mixed feeds are (1) the superior quality of their protein, and (2) the increased consumption of feed and the larger gains that result. Most mixed feeds derive their protein content not from a single nitrogenous concentrate such as linseed meal, but from a number of such feeds, as will be seen from a study of the last column of Table 148. Mixed-feed salesmen place much emphasis upon the fact that by thus combining feeding stuffs a much better quality of protein is obtained, inasmuch as the amino acid deficiencies of one feed are supplemented by the amino acids present in the others. Frequently the claim is made that the 12 or 18 per cent of protein present in a mixed feed is in reality more efficient than the much larger amount of protein in linseed or cottonseed meal fed alone, owing to the lack of certain essential amino acids in the ration when a single protein supplement is fed. This argument fails to recognize that the protein compounds eaten by cattle are broken down and resynthesized by the rumen bacteria before they are digested and assimilated by the cattle. Consequently, the quality of protein fed appears to be of relatively little importance in beef cattle rations. This viewpoint is supported by the results of experiments carried out at the Wisconsin and Kansas stations, in which none of the protein mixtures used proved significantly superior to linseed meal. (See Table 149.)

That the chief value of a mixture of proteins is to be found in its increased palatability instead of in its increased assimilation is indicated by the results obtained at the Ohio Station from feeding what is called an "all-purpose" protein supplement. This name has been

[14] Iowa AH Leaflet 176, 1950.

TABLE 148

COMPOSITION OF SOME OF THE BETTER-KNOWN BRANDS OF
COMMERCIAL SUPPLEMENTS USED IN FATTENING CATTLE

Name of Feed and Manufacturer	Guaranteed Analysis				Ingredients (obtained from printed bag tags)
	Protein (Min.), %	Fat (Min.), %	Fiber (Max.), %	N. F. E. (Min.), %	
1. Ful-O-Pep Steer Fattener, The Quaker Oats Co., Chicago, Ill.	12.0	2.0	12.5	48.0	Ground grain screenings (from wheat, barley, and oats), cane molasses, soybean oil meal, cottonseed meal, linseed oil meal, dicalcium phosphate 1%, iodized salt 1%
2. Kent Baby Beef Supplement, Mississippi Valley Grain & Feed Co., Muscatine, Iowa	34.0	1.5	8.5	....	Linseed oil meal, cottonseed oil meal, molasses, soybean oil meal, distillers' dried grains with solubles, vitamin A and D feeding oil, soybean lecithin, steamed bone meal, dicalcium phosphate, calcium carbonate (ground limestone) 2% iodized salt 1%, manganese sulfate iron oxide, copper carbonate, cobalt carbonate
3. Purina Blue Checker Steer Fatena, Ralston Purina Co., St. Louis, Mo.	12.0	2.0	14.0	48.0	Soybean oil meal, cottonseed meal, ground grain sorghums, wheat standard middlings, cottonseed feed, linseed oil meal, molasses, 2% calcium carbonate, 2% iodized salt, and traces of iron oxide, manganese sulfate, cobalt carbonate, copper carbonate
4. Tarkio Winner Pellets (¾ in.), Tarkio Molasses Feed Co., Kansas City, Mo.	12.0	1.5	9.5	53.0	Cane molasses (moisture reduced by cooking), flaxseed screenings oil feed, corn gluten feed, wheat gray shorts, ground and bolted grain screenings from flax and wheat, ½ of 1% calcium carbonate, ½ of 1% bicarbonate of soda
5. Tarkio Pro-Pellets (¼ in.), Tarkio Molasses Feed Co., Kansas City, Mo.	25.0	2.5	13.5	42.0	Linseed oil meal, expeller soybean oil meal, cottonseed meal, soybean mill feed, oat meal feed, hominy feed, corn gluten feed, cane molasses (moisture reduced by cooking), gray shorts
6. Wayne Sweet Mix, Allied Mills, Inc., Chicago, Ill.	27.0	3.0	10.0	38.0	Soybean oil meal, old process linseed oil meal, cottonseed meal, corn distillers' dried grains, corn gluten feed, wheat bran, cane molasses, irradiated yeast (source of vitamin D_2), 3.0% calcium carbonate, 0.6% steamed bone meal, 0.05% iron oxide, 1% iodized salt, 0.0005% cobalt carbonate

applied because it has been found to be a very satisfactory protein supplement for fattening calves, dairy cows, lambs, hogs, and laying hens. It consists of 30 parts by weight of dry-rendered tankage, 30 parts soybean oil meal, 20 parts cottonseed meal, 15 parts linseed meal, 2 parts finely ground limestone, 2 parts special steamed bone

TABLE 149

Protein Mixtures vs. Single Protein Feeds for Fattening Cattle

	Wisconsin* (Av. of 3 trials) 1925–1928		Kansas* (Average of 3 trials) Mimeo. Leaflet, 1933						
	Lin-seed Meal	Linseed Meal, ½ Cotton-seed Meal, ½	C. S. M.	L. S. M.	Corn Gluten Meal	C. S. M.½ L. S. M.½	C. S. M.½ C. G. M.½	L. S. M.½ C. G. M.½	⅓ Each C. S. M. L. S. M. C. G. M.
Av. daily gain, lb..	2.41	2.41	2.18	2.29	2.20	2.33	2.23	2.36	2.35
Feed per cwt. gain									
Shelled corn....	343	354	425	418	407	416	420	402	404
Protein conc....	83	73	45	43	45	42	44	42	42
Corn silage.....	504	505	368	350	344	338	352	354	356
Legume hay....	114	115	91	87	91	85	90	85	85
Selling price per cwt............	$11.30	$11.10	$10.60	$11.00	$10.55	$11.00	$10.75	$10.90	$10.85

* Mimeographed reports of cattle-feeding experiments.

TABLE 150

Comparative Value of a Simple and a Complex Mixture of Protein Concentrates for Fattening Calves

	1st Test—Ohio Bimonthly Bulletin 166, 1934				2nd Test—Ohio Bimonthly Bulletin 173, 1935			
	1st Series		2nd Series		1st Series		2nd Series	
	L. S. M.½ C. S. M.½	All-Purpose Sup.*	L. S. M.½ C. S. M.½	All-Purpose Sup.*	L. S. M.½ C. S. M.½	All-Purpose Sup.*	L. S. M.½ C. S. M.½	All-Purpose Sup.*
Av. daily gain, lb.....	1.91	2.10	2.12	2.19	1.96	1.99	1.94	2.14
Av. daily ration								
Shelled corn.......	8.8	9.6	9.8	10.2	11.1	11.4	10.0	11.4
Protein sup........	2.0	1.7	2.0	1.7	1.0	.8	2.0	1.6
Corn silage........	7.8	7.7	7.7	7.7	8.0	8.0	8.0	8.0
Hay..............	1.6	1.6	1.6	1.6	1.6	1.6	1.6	1.6
Molasses..........	....	....	.5	.5	....	....	....	....
Hog gains per steer, lb.	30	43	39	48	75	80	79	105
Selling price per cwt...	$6.90	$6.65	$6.80	$6.80	$8.65	$8.65	$8.50	$9.00

* Supplement: Dry-rendered tankage, 30%; soybean oil meal, 30%; cottonseed meal, 20%; linseed meal, 15%; powdered limestone, 2%; bone meal, 2%; salt, 1%.

meal, and 1 part salt. In three experiments with beef calves, in which this supplement was compared in double series with a mixture of equal parts of linseed and cottonseed meal, a larger consumption of feed and correspondingly larger daily gains were obtained from the all-purpose supplement in every comparison. (See Table 150.)

The other claim made for commercial mixed feeds, viz., that their use stimulates the cattle to eat more total feed than they otherwise would, also appears to lack support from impartial feeding investigations. Although the tests made with such feeds are few compared with the number of varieties and brands of mixed feeds sold, only a few of the trials that have been reported show a larger total feed intake where the commercial feed was used than was obtained with the check ration. Inasmuch as the daily gains, the cost of gains, and the prices received for the finished cattle have uniformly been in favor of the check rations, the particular brands of mixed feeds used in the experiments can hardly be recommended. (See Table 151.) It is freely admitted that brands of mixed feeds vary greatly in their feeding value. It is also a well-known fact that feed manufacturers vary their formulæ from year to year in an effort to improve the quality of their products. Hence, it is probable that the results secured in the experiments reported in the accompanying tables would not be duplicated, even though the same rations and brands of feeds were to be used at the present time.

Many of the mixed feeds contain 10 to 20 per cent molasses, partly to make them more palatable and partly to bind the finely ground ingredients together, so that the feed will not be dusty. That the small amount of molasses received by cattle fed a sweetened protein concentrate is of no significant value is indicated by the results obtained at the Iowa Station with two lots of yearling steers, one of which received linseed meal and the other a mixture of 50 pounds of linseed meal, 25 pounds of soybean oil meal, 10 pounds of cottonseed meal, and 15 pounds of cane molasses. In two trials of approximately 200 days each no significant differences were observed between the two lots in feed consumption, rate of gains, selling price, or net profits.[15]

Although the use of a high-grade mixed feed may result in more rapid daily gains, the cost of the gains is generally increased at the same time. Whether the use of such purchased materials is profitable depends largely upon the premium paid by the market for highly finished beeves. As a rule, such feeds have their greatest place in the fitting of cattle for show and sale, where cost of feed is secondary in importance to the condition and finish attained. Considerable use is

[15] Iowa AH Leaflets 160 and 161.

TABLE 151

VALUE OF COMMERCIAL MIXED FEEDS FOR FATTENING CATTLE

Supplement Fed	Nebraska Mimeo. Report, 1934-35 — Steer Calves, 150 Days		Nebraska Mimeo. Report, 1926-27 — Steer Calves, 110 Days			Nebraska Mimeo. Report, 1926-27 — Heifer Calves, 145 Days		Iowa Mimeo. Report, 1924-25 — 2-Year-Old Steers, 120 Days		Indiana Bulletins 183 and 191, 1915 and 1916 — 2-Year-Old Steers Av. of 2 Trials, 150 Days	
	C.S.M.	Commercial Feed	None	L.S.M.	Commercial Feed	C.S.M.	Commercial Feed and C.S.M.	L.S.M.	Commercial Feed	C.S.M.	Commercial Feed
Av. daily gain, lb.	1.46	1.34	2.38	2.58	2.29	2.40	2.38	3.27	2.48	2.15	1.99
Av. daily ration											
Shelled corn	....	....	15.7	14.6	14.5	10.9	10.1	21.3	13.7	11.7	9.7
Protein conc.	1.0	1.0	....	1.9	....	1.8	1.0	1.5	....	2.9	....
Comm. feed	....	....	....	....	2.0	....	2.0	....	6.4	....	5.3
Corn silage	33.5	33.1	7.7*	7.7*	7.7*	....	....	....	....	26.8	27.4
Legume hay	....	....	3.7	3.6	3.6	4.3	3.6	7.8	9.3	3.4	3.4
Feed per cwt. gain											
Shelled corn	....	....	662	564	634	455	425	650	553	542	486
Protein conc.	68	74	....	74	....	75	43	46	....	133	....
Comm. feed	....	....	....	....	88	....	87	....	257	....	269
Corn silage	2290	2472	325	300	338	....	....	....	....	1260	1387
Legume hay	....	....	157	140	156	180	152	239	375	156	167
Selling price per cwt.	$8.75	$8.50	$13.25	$13.60	$13.40	$10.20	$9.90	$11.60	$11.25	$8.45	$8.35
Profit per head	14.23	11.30	14.61	18.62	14.02	10.45	6.34	5.33	-2.06	3.08	-1.84

* Silage fed first 40 days only, during which time the average daily consumption was 21 pounds a head.

made of mixed feeds in preparing cattle for the carload-lot classes at the International Live Stock Exposition. Naturally, the feeder who aspires to win the coveted prize will spare no reasonable expense in fitting his cattle. The man who feeds for the open market, however, will do well to look upon most mixed feeds as a more or less doubtful investment. As a rule, he will find that the farm-grown grains, supplemented with such well-known and standard products as linseed and cottonseed meal, are much cheaper and more satisfactory in the end. This fact is brought out clearly by feeding trials, summaries of which are given in Table 151. Each of the commercial feeds used was fed according to the specific instructions furnished by the manufacturer. However, in no case was it found profitable to introduce such feeds into a ration that was already palatable and reasonably well balanced.

21 — Roughage and Its Use in the Fattening Ration

Roughages differ from concentrates principally in the amount of fiber or woody material that they contain. Most concentrates are very low in fiber, few of the common ingredients of the grain ration having more than 10 per cent of this material. Roughages, on the other hand, have a large amount of fiber, particularly when in the cured or dried state. Hay averages about 28 per cent and straw approximately 38 per cent of fiber when cut and harvested at the usual time.

Fiber consists largely of cellulose, a very complex, insoluble compound that forms the walls of plant cells. In young, immature plants the cell walls are comparatively thin; hence, the percentage of fiber is relatively small. With the approach of maturity, however, the cell walls become much thicker, which results in a great increase in the fiber content.

In its chemical composition fiber is a carbohydrate; i.e., it is essentially like starches and sugars. However, because of its insoluble nature, it is only partly utilized as a food nutrient by domestic animals. Obviously, the first important step in its digestion is its softening through the absorption of large quantities of water, after which it is partly converted to more simple, soluble compounds through fermentation brought about by the bacteria present in the alimentary tract. Because of the size and structure of the digestive organs, cattle are more efficient utilizers of roughage than other farm animals. The large rumen or paunch has a capacity of 3 to 5 bushels. All roughage material goes into this compartment, where it remains several hours, during which time it absorbs much water and is broken down into simpler compounds by the action of the billions of bacteria that live in the paunch. It is then regurgitated in small quantities back to the mouth, where it is thoroughly chewed before being reswallowed and passed into the true stomach. This ruminating feature of their digestive process, together with the large size of their alimentary tract, their strong jaws, and their broad molars, makes cattle ideal animals for the utilization of roughage.   Indeed, thousands of cattle through-out their entire lives get little or no other feed.

Classification of Roughages.   Roughages, like concentrates, may be classed as carbonaceous or nitrogenous, depending on the percentage of protein that they contain.   Carbonaceous roughages include hay and pasture from the grasses, the straws from cereal grains, and the stalks and leaves of corn and the grain sorghums.   Nitrogenous roughages include the hay and forage from legume crops.

Roughages may also be divided into dry roughages and green or succulent materials.   For dry roughages the plants are cut when almost mature and are allowed to cure before being fed.   For green roughages, green, immature crops are pastured by the animals, or the freshly cut green material is fed to cattle before it is withered by the sun and air. In silage, the freshness or succulence has been preserved by storage, immediately after cutting, in a specially designed, air-tight building that prevents the loss of moisture.

Function of Roughage in the Fattening Ration.   1.   *To Furnish Part of the Food Nutrients.*   Although most of the gain made by cattle in the feed lot is credited to the concentrate part of the ration, the part played by the roughage component should not be lost sight of.   On those farms where cattle feeding is carried on largely for the purpose of utilizing unmarketable roughages, the efficiency with which the roughage is used in the production of gains is the factor upon which the success of the feeding venture often depends.

In general, roughage is of most importance during the first part of the feeding period.   It is then that the appetite of the cattle for such material is greatest, and large quantities can be fed with little fear of the cattle's overeating or going off feed.   Except for short-fed cattle, which, of course, should be got on a full feed of grain in the shortest time possible, roughage should compose the bulk of the ration for the first month or 6 weeks.   Starting with a ration composed entirely of roughage, concentrates should be added gradually until the cattle are on a full feed of grain at approximately the end of the first fifth of the feeding period.   At this time the ratio of the weight of air-dry roughage to grain should be approximately 2 to 3 for steers that are to be fed until they attain a choice finish.   With a longer feeding period, the use of roughage alone for the first few weeks is often practiced, espe-cially with cattle that are thin and empty when they arrive at the feed lots.   With feeding stuffs at ordinary prices, such a plan tends to reduce the total cost of feed without materially affecting the total gains made.

Although the ratio maintained between the grain and roughage at

TABLE 152

The Relative Importance of Concentrates and Roughage at Different Stages of the Fattening Process*

Period	Average Daily Ration Concentrates (Sh. Corn) (C. S. Meal)	Average Daily Ration Roughage (Alfalfa or Clover Hay)	Ratio of Concentrates to Dry Roughage 1:	Total Digestible Nutrients† From Concentrates	Total Digestible Nutrients† From Roughage	Total Digestible Nutrients† Total	Total Digestible Nutrients† Per cent of Total Furnished by Roughage	Total Therms Net Energy† From Concentrates	Total Therms Net Energy† From Roughage	Total Therms Net Energy† Total	Total Therms Net Energy† Percent of Total Furnished by Roughage
1st month	11.80 lbs	16.08 lbs	1.36	9.44 lbs	8.04 lbs	17.48 lbs	46%	10.35	5.87	16.22	36%
2d month	17.62	13.43	.75	14.10	6.71	20.81	32%	15.46	4.90	20.36	24%
3d month	20.11	12.26	.61	16.09	6.13	22.22	27%	17.65	4.47	22.12	20%
4th month	22.22	10.90	.49	17.78	5.45	23.23	23%	19.50	3.98	23.48	17%
5th month	23.35	9.75	.42	18.68	4.85	23.53	20%	20.49	3.56	24.05	15%
Average, approximately 150 days	19.00	12.52	.66	15.20	6.26	21.46	29%	16.67	4.57	21.24	22%

* Average of 10 lots of two-year-old steers; Indiana Bulletins 153, 183, 191, 206.
† Computed from tables in Appendix of Henry and Morrison's Feeds and Feeding.

different stages of the fattening process varies considerably in practical feeding operations, the ratios given in Table 152 are fairly representative in this respect. Possibly more hay was fed than would be used if hay were scarce and had to be purchased, but no more than the farmer with his barns full of farm-grown hay would feed to mature steers fattened in a leisurely manner. That the rations fed were fairly good fattening rations is shown by the fact that the average daily gain of the ten lots was 2.32 pounds. The smallest gain made by any lot was 2.06 pounds, and the largest was 2.67 pounds.

2. *To Furnish Bulk to the Ration.* Owing to the great size and peculiar structure of their digestive systems, cattle are particularly well suited for consuming and utilizing a considerable amount of roughage. It has been demonstrated that mature cattle can exist, at least for several weeks, on an exclusive concentrate diet, but feeding experiments, as well as practical experience, go to show that they thrive much better if some roughage is supplied.

Roughage has formed the principal, if not the only, feed of cattle under natural conditions for countless generations. Evolution and the processes of natural selection have given them a digestive system that functions well only when moderately distended by coarse, bulky materials. Cattle, through habit, only partially masticate their food while eating. Upon being swallowed the food goes into the paunch, where it absorbs large quantities of water and undergoes fermentation through the action of rumen bacteria. It is then regurgitated into the mouth in small balls of about ¼ pound in size and is thoroughly chewed by the resting animal before it is again swallowed to pass into the true stomach. Roughage is very essential in the process of rumination. Cattle fed on an exclusive concentrate diet spend comparatively little time chewing their cuds. Hence, their imperfectly masticated grain is not so thoroughly digested as it would be if part of the ration consisted of roughage.

In furnishing bulk to the ration, roughage tends to lighten or dilute the contents of the alimentary tract, thus exposing the particles of concentrates to a complete envelopment by the digestive fluids. Also, the presence of roughage insures a normal fullness of the large intestines, a condition that makes for the proper regulation of the bowels. Dry, carbonaceous roughages, such as cereal straws and corn stover, which are capable of absorbing large quantities of water, are especially valuable for neutralizing the effects caused by a heavy consumption of feeds of a laxative nature.

3. *To Furnish Minerals and Vitamins.* A much larger concentration of minerals and vitamins occurs in the leaves and stems of plants

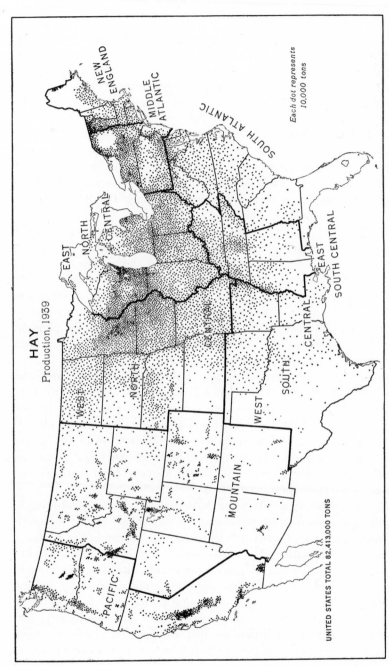

FIG. 48. Acreage of hay harvested in 1939. Hay constitutes the most important roughage fed to beef cattle. Base figures are from the Bureau of the Census. (*Courtesy U.S.D.A.*)

than in the seeds. Consequently, roughages are a better source of calcium, potassium, and vitamins A and D than the farm grains are. Cattle fed an abundance of high-quality roughage seldom show any symptoms of mineral or vitamin deficiency, whereas such symptoms are occasionally encountered among cattle that are fed heavy grain rations and limited amounts of low-grade roughage. The importance of roughages as a source of minerals and vitamins for cattle will be discussed in more detail in Chapter 26.

The Theory of Roughage Digestion. Although much information has been obtained about the method by which feeds, especially coarse roughages, are digested by cattle, some steps of the process are not yet well understood. Perhaps then an attempt to explain what goes on in the rumen should be called a theory of roughage digestion until more definite evidence is available.

It has long been known that the paunch of ruminants is essentially a huge tank, in which all coarse feeds consumed remain for several days. During this period they are attacked by the billions of bacteria which inhabit the paunch. This bacterial action is similar to the fermentation or decay that occurs in all moist organic materials exposed to the bacteria of the air and other sources of contamination. The principal difference is that there is little or no air in the paunch; consequently, the bacteria living there are special types that can thrive and multiply with little or no oxygen.

The bacteria of the paunch attack the feed soon after it enters the paunch and break down the complex organic compounds into more simple products that the cattle can digest. Materials like cellulose, which are only slightly digested by non-ruminants, become a valuable source of energy for cattle and sheep largely because of the action of the rumen bacteria. However, the bacteria can bring about the desired changes only if they are present in very large numbers and have the materials they need for growth and development. Consequently, in preparing a ration for cattle fed largely low-grade roughages, thought must be given to feeding the rumen bacteria the materials they require in order that they will release the energy in the roughage that is fed to the cattle. The needs of the bacteria are believed to be: (1) an adequate amount of protein or usable nitrogen; (2) a small amount of readily available carbohydrate, like molasses or ground corn, to serve as the initial food of the multiplying bacteria; and (3) an adequate amount of essential minerals, especially phosphorus and cobalt. If all these conditions are met, the bacteria will break down the complex compounds of the roughages into simpler organic products that the cattle can readily utilize. This theory helps explain why the feeding of a pound or two of a protein concentrate to cattle on winter range or low-grade hay produces an increase in their daily gain much larger than that due to the nutrients in the protein feed fed.

The Amount of Roughage to Feed. Great variation exists in the amount of roughage fed to fattening cattle. On the one hand, we have cattle that receive little else than silage and hay throughout the feeding period. In contrast with these are other cattle whose only roughage after they are on full feed is the cob particles in the ear corn fed. Neither of these conditions is often encountered in the Corn Belt. The common practice is to feed both roughage and concentrates, starting with a maximum of roughage and a minimum of concentrates and ending the feeding period with a minimum of roughage and a maximum of concentrates. However, because of variations in the supply of these two classes of feeding stuffs and variations in the length of time the cattle are to be on feed, considerable variation often exists between the ratio of concentrates to roughage at any given stage of the fattening process. When roughage is abundant and relatively cheap, the tendency is to feed it in unusually large quantities with considerably less grain than is fed when opposite price conditions prevail. Just as cheap money drives valuable money out of circulation and into hoarding places under the operation of Gresham's law, so does cheap feed drive expensive feed out of the feed lot and on to the market. This latter principle might well be called the law of "Feed Substitution." Any feeder who persistently violates this law is courting economic disaster.

The greater the length of the feeding period, the more roughage will ordinarily be utilized in proportion to the amount of grain fed. This condition results from the fact that in a long feed moderate daily gains will suffice to give the cattle the required finish by the end of the feeding period. Gains of such size can be secured from a ration containing considerable roughage. Short-fed cattle, on the other hand, must make maximum gains from the start. Hence, it is highly desirable that they be induced to eat as much grain as possible soon after they are placed on feed. The maximum consumption of grain can be secured only by rigidly limiting the roughage.

Ordinarily, at least one component of the ration should be fed according to the appetites of the cattle. In other words, the cattle should be given all they will eat of it. Only by supplying some feed in such amounts is the feeder sure that the cattle are satisfied. Roughage is ordinarily used for this purpose because of its low cost and the slight damage any uneaten portion will suffer from exposure to the weather.

The common practice is to feed only as much grain as is necessary to insure satisfactory gains and to allow the cattle to satisfy their remaining appetite by eating roughage. It occasionally happens, where the roughage is unusually palatable, that such large quantities are consumed that an insufficient amount of concentrates is eaten. It then will be necessary to limit the roughage allowance to an amount that will not interfere with the consumption of grain.

TABLE 153

APPROXIMATE RATIO OF GRAIN TO ROUGHAGE AT DIFFERENT STAGES
OF THE FEEDING PERIOD

Ratio of Grain to Roughage (Air-Dry Basis)

Division of Feeding Period	Large Amount of Roughage Available	Amount of Roughage Limited	Long Feeding Period (Over 200 days)	Short Feeding Period (Approx. 90 days)
1st third	1 : 4	1 : 1	2 : 3	2 : 1
2nd third	2 : 3	3 : 1	3 : 2	3 : 1
Last third	3 : 2	4 : 1	3 : 1	5 : 1
Average for Entire Period	2 : 3	5 : 2	3 : 2	3 : 1

Feeding tests at the Nebraska Station, in which five lots of cattle received shelled corn and alfalfa hay in ratios varying from 1:1 to 5:1 respectively after the first month of the feeding period, indicate that a ration of 2 or 3 parts of corn to 1 part of hay is probably the most satisfactory for both calves and yearlings, since it results in the maximum consumption of total digestible nutrients. The lots fed grain and hay at the ratios 4:1 and 5:1 ate no more corn and, therefore, less hay than the lots fed at the narrower ratios; consequently, their gains were smaller and more costly. Excellent results were secured in one test from calves that were started on a ration of 2 parts of corn and 1 part of alfalfa hay, which was changed each month, until at the end of the feeding period the corn and hay were fed at a 5:1 ratio. However, slightly larger and cheaper gains were made by another lot which was fed 2 parts of shelled corn and 1 part of hay throughout the test, except during the first month, when all lots were being brought up to a full feed.[1]

Fattening Cattle without Roughage. In times of roughage scarcity, large feeders, who perforce must buy both grain and roughage, occasionally omit roughage entirely from the ration because at such times roughages are always expensive relative to the total digestible nutrients that they contain. Seldom is this a profitable practice.

[1] Nebraska Cattle Progress Reports 195 and 198, 1950 and 1951.

Even though bulky grains like corn-and-cob meal or ground oats are fed, they do not completely fill the place of roughage in the ration. The feeding of a small amount of hay or silage to cattle that have been fed only grain will usually result in their consuming a larger amount of grain as well as the roughage. Immediately they will begin

TABLE 154

THE VALUE OF ROUGHAGE IN THE RATION OF FULL-FED CATTLE

	Ground Ear Corn*		Ground Ear Corn†		Ground Oats‡	
	Yearlings 62 days		Yearlings 65 days		Yearlings 112 days	
Roughage Fed	Alfalfa	None	Alfalfa	None	Silage and Alfalfa	None
Av. daily gain, lbs........	1.97	1.88	3.15	2.69	2.45	1.63
Av. daily ration						
Ground grain.........	16.3	16.9	19.5	19.2	11.3	12.0
Prot. conc...........	2.0	2.0	....	1.0	1.0	1.0
Corn silage..........	....	....	....	....	14.1	....
Alfalfa hay..........	2.7	....	3.2	....	2.0	....
Feed per cwt. gain						
Ground grain.........	827	897	620	711	459	738
Prot. conc...........	102	106	....	37	41	61
Corn silage..........	....	....	....	....	577	....
Alfalfa hay..........	137	....	101	....	81	....
Selling price per cwt......	$11.25	$11.25	$10.50	$10.25	$6.85	$5.85

* Nebraska Mimeo. Cattle Circular 126, 1928.
† Nebraska Mimeo. Cattle Circular 130, 1930.
‡ Illinois Mimeo. Cattle Circular, 1931.

to gain faster, partly because of a larger intake of food nutrients and partly because of better rumination and more thorough digestion of the feed eaten.

Roughage serves another important function in that it is an important source of vitamins, especially A and D. Cattle fed little or no legume hay or corn silage usually show signs of malnutrition, regardless of the amount of grain fed. Yearling steers fed a full feed of ground oats and cottonseed meal at the Illinois Station showed characteristic symptoms of vitamin A deficiency after about 90 days. After the cattle were changed to a ration containing moderate amounts of silage and alfalfa hay, the symptoms quickly disappeared.

Common Roughages

                                    Used in Fattening

Clover Hay. No other roughage is held in such high esteem by cattle feeders as red clover hay. So widely are its merits recognized that it is often regarded as a standard with which other, less-known feeds are compared. To be "just about as valuable as good clover hay" is a compliment that implies something like perfection in a roughage material.

Clover combines almost all the requisites of a good, dry roughage for cattle. It is of medium fine texture, is rich in both protein and total digestible nutrients, and is exceedingly palatable. It is but very mildly laxative, so that seldom does its use, even in large quantities, cause excessive scouring. Lastly, it is extensively grown throughout the Corn Belt. Its biennial growing period makes it especially well adapted for inclusion in nearly all Corn Belt rotations. A good crop of red clover hay has caused many a grain farmer to embark on the cattle feeding business.

Alfalfa Hay. Alfalfa is in reality a highly improved clover. It is more sensitive to acid soils than red clover; consequently, it is less frequently used in Corn Belt rotations. Only in the semi-arid and irrigated regions of the western states is alfalfa considered one of the major farm crops. Here its use as a cattle feed is well-nigh universal, and thousands of cattle are fattened annually with practically no other roughage. Large quantities are also shipped east to feeders who are compelled to buy a portion of their roughage material.

Often the market price of alfalfa hay is 20 to 30 per cent above that of clover, indicating that it is regarded by most feeders as being superior to clover. This superiority is due to its higher protein content and to its freedom from dust and mold. Western-grown alfalfa is seldom damaged by rain. Consequently, it usually retains its bright green color and does not spoil in the stack or bale. Hay made farther east, on the other hand, often encounters rain, which renders it discolored, dusty, and sometimes moldy. Obviously, such hay is less palatable than hay put up under ideal weather conditions.

Occasionally alfalfa hay is criticized because of its somewhat laxative nature when fed in large quantities. Also its use is sometimes attended by acute bloating. Both these effects are more pronounced in calves than in older cattle. They can usually be overcome by combining the alfalfa with a carbonaceous roughage, such as oat straw,

Fig. 49. A field of red clover in northwestern Iowa. A good crop of legume hay has caused many a grain farmer to embark on the cattle-feeding business. (*Courtesy U.S.D.A.*)

TABLE 155

COMPARISON OF CLOVER AND ALFALFA HAY FOR FATTENING CATTLE

	Illinois Experiment Station* (2-yr.-old Steers — 126 Days)		South Dakota Experiment Station† (Yearling Steers — 91 Days)	
	Ear Corn Corn Silage Alfalfa Hay	Ear Corn Corn Silage Clover Hay	Corn Silage Alfalfa Hay	Corn Silage Clover Hay
Average daily gain (lbs.)....	2.38	2.05	2.49	2.29
Average daily ration:				
Ear corn................	16.1	16.0	....	....
Corn silage..............	25.3	26.7	58.3	58.1
Legume hay..............	4.3	2.0	4.0	3.5
Feed per cwt. gain:				
Ear corn................	675	783	....	....
Corn silage..............	1065	1302	23	25
Legume hay..............	181	100	1.6	1.5

* Illinois Mimeo. Report, 1911.
† South Dakota Bulletin 160, 1915.

corn stover, or timothy, or by feeding corn-and-cob meal instead of shelled corn.

Much discussion has been raised concerning the relative value of clover and alfalfa hays as roughage for fattening cattle. Unfortunately, most of the comparisons that have been made have involved the feeding of sufficient nitrogenous supplements to make balanced rations without the additional protein furnished by the legume hays. Obviously under such conditions it would hardly be expected that the difference in the protein content of the hays would be apparent. Such a situation is encountered in the Indiana experiments summarized in Table 156. In all the lots involved in these comparisons 2.5 pounds of cottonseed meal were fed per thousand pounds live weight, an amount that fully met the protein requirements of the cattle even though no legume hay was included in the rations. It is only reason-

TABLE 156

COMPARISON OF CLOVER AND ALFALFA HAY WHEN A SURPLUS AMOUNT OF PROTEIN IS SUPPLIED

(2-Year-Old Steers)*

Average of 4 Trials	Corn Cottonseed Meal Clover	Corn Cottonseed Meal Alfalfa	Corn Cottonseed Meal Clover Silage	Corn Cottonseed Meal Alfalfa Silage
Av. daily gain, lb.	2.38	2.27	2.32	2.35
Av. daily feed				
Shelled corn	16.2	15.8	12.6	12.5
Cottonseed meal	2.9	2.9	2.9	2.9
Legume hay	12.1	12.7	2.9	2.6
Corn silage	....	....	27.6	28.9
Av. feed per cwt. gain				
Corn	679	700	542*	530
Cottonseed meal	122	128	126	125
Hay	509	558	126	111
Silage	....	....	11.90	12.28
Selling price per cwt.	$9.33	$9.29	$9.40	$9.375

* Indiana Experiment Bulletin 245, 1920.

able to believe that alfalfa would make a more favorable showing if no protein concentrate were fed, or if it were so limited as to make the protein contained in the legume roughages of real need to the animals. This method of feeding was followed by the Illinois, South Dakota, and Wisconsin stations in the feeding trials reported in Tables 155 and 157. In all these comparisons of red clover and alfalfa the superiority of alfalfa is well established. The results of the Wisconsin trials indicate that, where alfalfa is substituted for clover hay, a reduction of approximately ½ pound of nitrogenous concentrate may be made for each 5 pounds of legume hay fed without affecting appreciably the value of the ration.

One explanation of the good results usually obtained from alfalfa is found in its high "specific dynamic effect," by which is meant that its consumption has a marked tendency to promote a condition of thrift and well-being through raising the general level of metabolism of the animal. This property is possessed to a greater or lesser extent by all protein feed materials, but it seems to be more pronounced in alfalfa than in any of the other common legume roughages.

TABLE 157

COMPARISON OF CLOVER AND ALFALFA HAY WHEN A LIMITED AMOUNT OF PROTEIN SUPPLEMENT IS FED*

(Yearling and two-year-old Steers — Average of 4 trials)

Average Time Fed, 161 Days	Lot 1 Clover Hay	Lot 2 Alfalfa Hay
Average daily gain (lbs.)......................	2.19	2.22
Average daily ration:		
Corn...	8.5	8.9
Cottonseed meal............................	1.5	.9
Legume hay................................	5.3	5.3
Corn silage................................	28.0	28.0
Feed per cwt. gain:		
Corn...	394	407
Cottonseed meal............................	70	42
Legume hay................................	250	242
Corn silage................................	1292	1264
Pork credit per steer........................	$7.53	$6.92
Selling price per cwt........................	$10.00	$9.90

* Wisconsin Experiment Station; Mimeographed Reports of Calf Feeding Trials.

Soybean Hay. Soybean hay is frequently fed to beef cattle in many parts of the Corn Belt. Since soybeans are annuals, they are excellent to sow as an emergency hay crop to supplement light stands of clover and alfalfa which have resulted from unfavorable weather. Should it develop that the beans are not needed for hay, they may be allowed to mature for seed.

Soybean hay compares favorably with clover and alfalfa hay for fattening cattle when it is fed in limited amounts in combination with corn silage, mixed hay, oat straw, or some other non-laxative roughage. However, it is not so valuable as clover or alfalfa when no other roughage is fed, because it is likely to cause severe scouring. The laxative nature of soybean hay varies more or less directly with the maturity of the beans when cut, and consequently with the number of ripe beans present. Nevertheless, making the hay before the beans have formed will not always avoid this trouble.

Soybean hay varies greatly in its palatability and feeding value, depending upon the variety of beans, the stage of maturity at which the beans were cut, the amount and kinds of weeds present, and the weather conditions during the curing process. As a rule it is less palatable than alfalfa or clover, and a higher percentage of the weight of hay fed is left in the mangers uneaten in the form of coarse stems and weeds.

TABLE 158

VALUE OF SOYBEAN HAY AS THE SOLE ROUGHAGE FOR FATTENING CATTLE

Hays Compared	Iowa Mimeo. Report, 1923–24		Illinois Mimeo. Report, 1936		Kentucky Unpublished Data	
	2-year-olds 120 days		2-year-olds 84 days		Yearlings 142 days	
	Clover	Soybean	Alfalfa	Soybean	Alfalfa	Soybean
Av. daily gain, lbs.........	2.58	2.27	2.99	2.88	2.26	2.09
Av. daily ration						
Shelled corn..........	20.1	18.6	18.2	18.2	16.6[a]	16.6[a]
Prot. conc............	1.5	1.5	1.2	1.2	.6	.6
Legume hay..........	8.8	4.9	7.3	7.2	9.7	8.6
Feed per cwt. gain						
Shelled corn..........	778	818	609	630	734[a]	793[a]
Prot. conc............	58	66	39	41	27	29
Legume hay..........	339	214	244	248	427	413
Selling price per cwt......	$11.00	$10.35	....	....	$6.00	$5.75
Gain of hogs per steer, lbs.	51	44	34	23	55	53

[a] Broken-ear corn.

Soybeans that are grown for seed yield, upon being threshed, soybean hullings or *soybean straw*. As many of the best seed-yielding varieties of beans retain but few of their leaves at maturity, these hullings consist largely of the pods and stems of the plants. Although the base portion of the stems is too coarse and woody to be consumed in any quantity, cattle show a keen appetite for the finer portions of the stems and for the pods. Breeding cattle and stockers that are being maintained on cheap, coarse roughages will consume 70 per cent or more of the hullings fed. Soybean straw raked up after a combine consists almost entirely of the stems and branches and very few pods and leaves. Consequently, it is of value only for stocker and breeding cattle. (See Table 69.)

Miscellaneous Legume Hays. Red clover is but one of several different kinds of clover, all of which are used for hay to some extent. *Alsike clover* is usually considered more of a pasture than a hay crop because of its short growth and, consequently, low yield. However, when cut and harvested, it produces a hay of exceedingly fine texture which is greatly relished by cattle. In its chemical composition it has

TABLE 159

VALUE OF LESPEDEZA HAY FOR FATTENING CATTLE

Hays Compared	Illinois Mimeo. Report, 1934		Illinois Mimeo. Report, 1935		Missouri Mimeo. Report, 1934	
	2-year-old Steers 84 days		Yearling Steers 53 days		Calves 112 days	
	Alfalfa	Lespedeza	Soybean	Lespedeza	Alfalfa	Lespedeza
Av. daily gain, lbs.	2.99	3.02	2.52	2.54	1.92	1.69
Feed per cwt. gain						
Shelled corn.........	609	603	578	505	279	319
Prot. conc...........	39	39	40	38	23	27
Legume hay.........	244	241	208	203	494	443
Corn silage..........	....	....	....	....	113	129
Dressing percentage.....	60.2	61.5	57.6	56.3	....	....

slightly more protein than red clover but is somewhat lower in fat. *Mammoth clover* resembles red clover in general appearance but is taller, coarser, and somewhat later-maturing. Although its yield of hay is heavy, the hay is often rather coarse and unpalatable. It contains the lowest percentage of protein found in any of the more common legume crops used for hay.

Lespedeza or *Japan clover* is grown extensively as a hay and pasture crop in the southern part of the Corn Belt. An improved variety called Korean lespedeza grows to a foot or more in height and frequently yields as much as 2 tons of hay per acre. Lespedeza hay cut at the right stage of maturity and properly cured is an excellent roughage and compares favorably in feeding value with other legume hays, such as soybean and alfalfa. However, if it is allowed to become too ripe, the stems become very tough and wiry and are neither palatable nor easily digested. Such hay is sometimes deceptive, since it often has a good green color and contains an abundance of leaves.

Second-year sweet clover is not a satisfactory hay crop. It is too coarse and woody to make a high-grade, palatable hay. Its coarse, rank growth makes it exceedingly difficult to handle and adds to the labor of putting it into the stack or mow. Moreover, hay made from second-year sweet clover cannot be regarded as a safe feed for cattle, inasmuch as a number of serious death losses have resulted from its use. Especially should moldy sweet clover hay be fed in limited amounts and for continuous periods not to exceed 15 days. The most typical symptom of the disease is a decrease in the rate of coagulation of the blood.[1]

With favorable soil and weather conditions, a crop of hay may be secured in the fall from sweet clover sown in oats or wheat the previous spring. Such hay is very similar to alfalfa in color and texture. Cattle eat it readily as soon as they become accustomed to its characteristic flavor. Close clipping of the first-year growth in late September is not likely to result in any serious damage to the stand. Early mowing, however, cannot be recommended, because of the danger of losing a high percentage of plants from winter killing.

Timothy. Many years ago, timothy was the standard roughage for fattening cattle. At the present time most up-to-date feeders will apologize for its use. From the standpoint of production, timothy has several advantages. It thrives reasonably well on a wide variety of soils; it is a perennial, and hence does not require frequent reseeding; the hay is very easily cured and as a rule is quite free from dust and mold.

As a feed for cattle, however, it has few advantages. Practically the only favorable thing that can be said about it, apart from its brightness and quality, is its non-laxative properties. Steers or calves receiving this roughage are seldom troubled with scours. Also it should be said in defense of timothy that it has a high net energy value. In total digestible nutrients it is somewhat lower than the common legume hays, and its protein content is less than one-third and one-half that of alfalfa and clover, respectively.

Timothy hay cut at the usual time is somewhat stiff and woody. This fact, together with its low protein content, makes it less palatable for cattle than any of the roughages so far discussed. As a rule, cattle

[1] *Cf.* p. 620.

on full feed, if allowed roughage according to appetite, will eat from 20 to 35 per cent more legume hay than timothy. In former years, before the advent of the automobile and tractor, the market price of timothy was determined largely by its value as a horse feed. Now, however, its market is limited, so that it sells much lower than the legume hays. Under favorable price conditions it may well comprise 30 to 50 per cent of the roughage ration, especially for mature cattle.

Very poor results are secured from timothy hay when it is fed with no nitrogenous supplement. As it is low in protein, some high-protein feed is very necessary in order that the ration be reasonably well balanced. Two-year-old steers fed for 126 days at the Illinois Experiment Station on corn, timothy hay, and corn stover gained 1.86 pounds per day, while a second lot receiving 2.55 pounds of gluten meal in addition made daily gains of 2.27 pounds. The use of gluten meal resulted in a marked reduction in the feed required per pound of gain and an increase of 75 cents per hundred in the selling price of the finished cattle.[2]

TABLE 160

A COMPARISON OF RED CLOVER, TIMOTHY, AND
MIXED HAY FOR FATTENING CATTLE

(Iowa Bulletin 253, 1928)

2-Year-Old Steers	Red Clover Hay	Mixed Hay	Timothy Hay and Oat Straw
Protein content of hay, %	10.3	7.7	5.0 Timothy 3.5 Straw
Av. daily gain, lb.	2.47	2.28	1.99
Av. daily feed			
Shelled corn	20.3	21.0	20.0
Cottonseed meal	2.0	2.5	3.0
Hay	8.7	8.5	6.0
Oat straw	....	....	0.3
Feed cost per cwt. gain	$10.65	$12.47	$13.45
Selling price per cwt.	8.25	8.15	7.90

Prairie Hay. Prairie hay resembles timothy in chemical composition and general value as a cattle feed. It is usually much cheaper than timothy, however, especially on the farms where it is produced. In the western states great quantities of prairie hay are made with little cost other than the labor involved in cutting and stacking. In such areas, prairie hay may well be combined with alfalfa, especially in the feeding of mature steers. It should be remembered that prairie

[2] Illinois Bulletin 83, 1903.

hay varies greatly in the species of grasses and other plants that compose it. Occasionally such hay contains a large percentage of needle grass or other material that irritates the mucous lining of the cattle's mouths. Such hay, of course, should be avoided.

Prairie hay is non-laxative and has no tendency to produce bloat. This fact together with its freedom from mold makes it a popular roughage to feed cattle at stockyards and on the show circuit.

TABLE 161

VALUE OF PRAIRIE HAY FOR FATTENING CATTLE

	Nebraska Bulletin 93, 1906 84 Days			Nebraska Bulletin 100, 1907 Average of 3 Experiments	
	Snapped Corn Prairie Hay	Snapped Corn Prairie Hay 50% Alfalfa 50%	Snapped Corn Alfalfa Hay	Shelled Corn Prairie Hay	Shelled Corn 90%, Linseed Meal 10% Prairie Hay
Daily gain, lb.	1.20	2.01	2.06	1.51	2.18
Feed per cwt. gain					
Corn	787	470	460	1171	808
N conc.	....	....	....	....	90
Hay	1516	1047	1075	521	387

Mixed Hay. Mixed hay, as its name implies, is a mixture of clover and timothy. Clover and timothy are often seeded together under one or more of the following conditions:

1. When the soil is too acid to produce a good stand of clover.

2. When the soil is too wet to grow clover successfully.

3. When it is desired to use the meadow for more than one year. In this case the crop of hay removed the year following seeding is often largely clover. Thereafter it is largely timothy, since but little clover lives through the second winter.

4. When there is some prospect of pasturing the meadow instead of harvesting it for hay.

5. When the hay is to be fed to both horses and cattle.

6. When part or all the hay is to be sold.

The making of choice mixed hay is rather a hard task. Either the timothy is likely to be too green or the clover too ripe to give the best results. Mammoth clover is sometimes seeded with timothy instead of red clover because it matures later. Considered as a cattle feed, mixed hay depends for its value largely upon the percentage of clover it contains. Great variation exists in the amount of clover present—from a mere trace to 75 or 80 per cent.

Some feeders prefer mixed hay containing 50 to 75 per cent of clover to clover alone, believing that the presence of a small amount of timothy tends to counteract the laxative effect of the clover. The feeding of mixed hay to bulls and young calves is quite common with breeders of purebred cattle. Occasionally, bulls that get little exercise will bloat on clover or alfalfa, and calves sometimes show a tendency to scour. The substitution of a good grade of mixed hay for the legume often corrects these conditions.

Early Cut vs. Late Cut Hay. There is considerable disagreement as to when hay should be cut to obtain the most feeding value. Early cutting favors a higher protein content, finer texture, less fiber, and higher digestibility. Late cutting, on the other hand, results in a larger tonnage, more total digestible nutrients, and usually more favorable weather for field curing.

TABLE 162

EFFECT OF DATE AND FREQUENCY OF CUTTING ALFALFA
UPON THE YIELD AND QUALITY OF HAY*

Number of Cuttings	4	3	2
Approx. dates of cuttings	May 31 July 3 Aug. 7 Sept. 10	June 10–14 July 28 Sept. 10	June 20 Aug. 25
Total annual yield, lb.			
1926	8720	7800	6180
1927	6480	9840	6270
1928	5060	8660	6400
Average 1925–1932:			
Percentage of leaves in hay	51.8	44.5	38.1
Percentage of protein	19.4	16.8	15.2
Protein per acre, lb.	1633	1482	1022

* Ohio Bulletin 540

There is no question that hay cut while the plants are high in protein and low in fiber is a much better feed from the standpoint of the cattle than hay that is more mature. This is especially true of non-legume hays like prairie and timothy, which have a reasonably high protein content in the spring and early summer but are relatively low in protein upon becoming mature. Early-cut prairie hay (July 5–15) at the Nebraska Experiment Station[3] contained 7.2 per cent crude protein and 28.5 per cent fiber in comparison with 5.7 per cent protein and 30.9 per cent fiber for hay cut in August. Calves wintered on these hays and ½ pound of soybean oil meal per head made average daily gains of 1.01 and 0.52 pound, respectively, during a 106-day feeding period. Only 7.8 per cent of the July-cut hay was refused, whereas 10.8 per cent of the August-cut hay was refused by the calves. However, the yields of the early- and late-cut prairie hays were 1.12 and 1.43 tons per acre, respectively.

The feeding value and yield of alfalfa hay are affected not only by the date of the first cutting but by the frequency of cutting as well. Although four cuttings per season at the Ohio Experiment Station produced hay having more leaves and a higher protein content than hay obtained from three cuttings, the stand and, consequently, the yield deteriorated each year when four cuttings a year were made (see Table 162). Apparently, three cuttings made about June 10, August 1, and September 10 constitute the best practice for most of the Corn Belt region when nutritive value, yield per acre, and permanence of stand are considered.

Corn Stover. In the early days of cattle feeding, corn stover was one of the principal roughages used in fattening cattle. Large areas of corn were shocked in the fall to be fed to cattle during the winter months. Though considerable use is still made of this material in certain sections of the Corn Belt, it has been largely displaced by silage.

As a feed for fattening cattle, corn stover does not rank very high. It has a very low percentage of protein and is not high in total digestible nutrients. Because of the large amount of fiber present, it is rather unpalatable compared with most other farm roughages. The leaves, husks, and the tip of the stalk are eaten with more or less relish, but the main part of the stalk is too coarse and woody to be consumed. As this part constitutes approximately 40 per cent of the weight of the husked plant, the waste resulting from the feeding of stover is very high. The palatability is often lowered still further by delaying cutting until the corn is too ripe, at which time many of the bottom leaves are shriveled and dry. Also, great damage is often suffered by stover while it is standing shocked in the field. Heavy rains leach out a considerable amount of the food material, especially in poorly made shocks, while field mice and rabbits may damage the husks in their attempts to reach the unremoved ears.

[3] Nebraska Bulletin 385, 1947.

The amount of stover that cattle will eat is influenced largely by weather conditions. On bright, cold, crisp days it is eaten with considerable relish, whereas in warm, damp, rainy weather its consumption is very much lower. With the coming of the warm days of spring, cattle on full feed often cease to eat any appreciable amount of stover.

In proportion to its feeding value, the labor involved in cutting, shocking, and feeding corn stover is considerable. As a rule, it is left shocked in the field and is hauled in daily as it is needed. Deep snow or heavy rains often make the hauling very difficult. When storage space is available, the stover is sometimes shredded. However, stover that is even slightly damp at the time of shredding is very likely to mold, especially if stored in large amounts where heating will occur. Also, feeding trials show that shredded stover is but little, if any, better for cattle than whole stover.[4]

TABLE 163

COMPARISON OF CORN STOVER AND CORN FODDER WITH OTHER DRY ROUGHAGES FOR FATTENING CATTLE

*Indiana Bulletin 115, 1906

2-Year-Old Steers	Clover Hay	Corn Stover, Oat Straw	L. S. M. Conr Stover, Oat Straw	Iowa AH, Leaflet 21, 1927 120 Days		Iowa Bulletin 253, 1928 120 Days	
		180 Days		Alfalfa Hay	Corn Fodder	Alfalfa Hay	Corn Fodder
Av. daily gain, lb.	2.08	1.30	1.78	2.76	2.28	2.38	1.96
Av. daily ration							
Shelled or ear corn	19.7	17.6	18.9	18.0	15.0	20.3	16.3
Protein conc.	....	....	1.5	1.8	2.5	2.0	3.0
Stover or fodder	....	5.1	5.1	....	9.4	....	8.4
Hay or straw	8.3	2.5	1.9	7.4	.8	9.6	....
Feed per cwt. gain							
Shelled or ear corn	946	1345	1063	652	659	853	828
Protein conc.	....	....	85	63	110	84	153
Stover or fodder	....	392	285	....	410	....	929
Hay or straw	399	194	108	267	35	403	....
Selling price per cwt.	$5.35	$5.00	$5.35	$9.70	$9.35	$8.25	$7.75

The most common and perhaps the best way of feeding corn stover is to feed it as corn fodder or "shock corn," which is the term commonly used in referring to the stalk and unhusked ear taken together. This method of feeding requires a minimum amount of labor, inasmuch as the expense of husking is eliminated. Also, the ears of corn fodder possess a pleasing aroma and softness not found in corn that has been cribbed. Cattle apparently derive much satisfaction from searching out the ears and eating them before they are exposed to the air. When

4 *Cf.* p. 196.

feeding corn fodder to fattening cattle, it is a good plan to husk out a shock of average size every two or three weeks and weigh the corn secured, so as to know definitely the amount of grain the cattle are getting from this source.   Ordinarily, the husked ears constitute about 50 per cent of the weight of the shock, though there is considerable variation in this respect between different varieties of corn and from one year to another.   Since the weight of the material fed is seldom known, it is usually more satisfactory to determine the amount of grain in each shock.

TABLE 164

VALUE OF CORN STOVER WHEN FED WITH A
PROTEIN CONCENTRATE OR LEGUME HAY
Nebraska Bulletin 90, 1905

	2-Year-Old Steers 168 Days		Yearling Steers 183 Days	
	Alfalfa Hay	Alfalfa Hay 50%, Corn Stover 50%	Alfalfa Hay	Linseed Meal, Corn Stover
Average daily gain, lb.	2.30	2.39	1.97	1.96
Average daily ration				
Shelled corn	18.6	18.4	15.3	14.0
Linseed meal	....	....	....	1.6
Roughage[a]	9.2	9.9	9.2	11.2
Feed per cwt. gain				
Concentrates	814	789	770	800
Roughage	402	456	470	570

[a] Includes stover refused.

Corn stover may be fed to cattle in large racks or mangers, or it may be scattered on the ground.   With either method the refused portion has considerable value as bedding.   In some instances not only the sheds but also the lots used by the cattle are literally "paved" with corn stalks which serve to keep the cattle out of the mud during the late winter and spring months.   For bedding indoors, shredded stover is much to be preferred, since the manure that is secured is more easily hauled and spread on the fields.

In areas infested with corn borers corn stover should always be chopped or shredded to destroy the larvæ that live over the winter in the stalks.   The feeding of whole stover in racks or on the ground in areas where borers are present is not recommended because of the difficulty encountered in hauling the uneaten portions of the stalks to the field and plowing them under before the larvæ emerge in the spring.

Although corn stover alone or in combination with a dry carbonaceous roughage is an unsatisfactory feed even when fed with a nitrogenous supplement, it makes a more favorable showing when used with a legume hay or with silage. When combined with such feeds, well-cured corn stover may furnish from one-fourth to one-half of the total roughage when all roughage materials are figured on a dry-

Fig. 50. A field of forage-type grain sorghum. The grain sorghums are an important source of both grain and roughage throughout the semi-arid Southwest. (*Courtesy U.S.D.A.*)

matter basis. Any loss in rate of gains caused by the stover will probably be offset by the saving in total cost of feed that results from its use.

As a rule, cattle on full feed with silage as their principal roughage will eat scarcely enough stover to warrant its use. However, if hay or straw is not available to satisfy their appetite for dry material, stover may well be used for this purpose.

Milo and Kafir Stover. The stover of the grain sorghums is essentially like corn stover in chemical composition and feeding value. However, the stalks are of somewhat finer texture; hence, a greater percentage of the stalk is ordinarily eaten. When fed alone or with other dry carbonaceous roughage, milo or kafir stover will not prove very satisfactory for fattening cattle. When combined with legume hay or silage, much better results are secured. Although a legume hay constitutes half or more of the total roughage ration, some nitrogenous concentrate should usually be fed since all stovers are low in protein.

Cereal Straws. Of the straws of the common cereal grains, oat straw is the most valuable as a cattle feed. When cut with a binder at the proper time and stored before it is damaged by the weather, oat straw has a feeding value not greatly inferior to that of timothy hay. When raked up after a combine it has little chaff or leaves and often has been damaged by sun and rains. In such condition it is not very palatable, and comparatively small quantities will be eaten. It is, of course, a carbonaceous roughage and should be fed to fattening cattle only when other constituents of the ration furnish the necessary protein. As stated elsewhere, the feeding of a small quantity of oat straw will tend to reduce the tendency to bloat and scour occasionally noticed in cattle receiving a heavy feed of alfalfa hay. Also, its addition to a heavy silage ration will supply, at a very low cost, the desire of the cattle for a dry roughage material.

Barley straw is somewhat inferior to oat straw for feeding purposes, principally because most varieties of barley are bearded, and the beards sometimes cause the mouths of the cattle to become sore.

Wheat straw has the lowest feeding value of any of the common cereal straws and should be regarded as an emergency feed for fattening cattle, to be fed only when ordinary roughages are scarce and high priced. Very satisfactory gains were obtained at the Nebraska Station from yearling steers that were fed a full feed of shelled corn, cottonseed cake, and equal parts of wheat straw and alfalfa hay.[5]

When straw is fed to fattening cattle, it is usually fed according to appetite. When cereal grains were cut with a binder and threshed, cattle frequently were permitted to run around the straw stack, which afforded shelter as well as feed. Now that the grain is combined the straw usually is fed in the form of baled straw in mangers and racks. Since it is a low-grade, inexpensive feed, it is usually fed in much larger amounts than the cattle will eat, and the refused portion is removed every few days for bedding.

Corn Cobs. Corn cobs have long been regarded as an important roughage for grain-fed cattle, when fed in the form of corn-and-cob meal. However, their value was believed to lie chiefly in the volume and bulk that they gave the ration rather than in the digestible nutrients that they supplied. The fact that cobs are hard and woody in appearance and will not be eaten alone even by starving cattle

[5] Nebraska Bulletin **355**, 1944.

has caused farmers to consider them almost worthless as a source of feed nutrients. Nevertheless, digestion trials have shown that cobs contain 45 pounds of digestible nutrients per hundredweight, or about the same as oat straw. The fact that cobs have usually saved both grain and roughage in producing 100 pounds of gain in experiments

TABLE 165

THE VALUE OF CORN COBS AS A FEED FOR FATTENING CATTLE

	Ohio Mimeo. Series 52, 1947			Iowa Mimeo. AH Leaflet 165, 1947			Nebraska Bulletin 396, 1949		
	Calves and Yearlings (Average 3 Trials)			Yearlings (Average 2 Lots Each)			Yearlings (Average 3 Trials)		
	Shelled Corn	Ground Ear Corn	Ground Ear Corn +Cobs	Shelled Corn	Ground Ear Corn	Ground Ear Corn +Cobs	Shelled Corn	Ground Ear Corn	Ground Ear Corn +Cobs
Av. daily gain, lb....	1.92	1.92	1.85	2.38	2.43	2.23	2.42	2.35	2.13
Av. daily ration									
Shelled corn......	12.4	11.1	9.4	15.2	14.3	13.0	13.5	13.5	13.1
Corn cobs........	....	2.5	4.2	....	2.7	5.4	....	3.1	6.2
Protein conc......	2.0	2.0	2.0	1.5	1.5	1.5	1.5	1.5	1.5
Hay.............	4.3	4.3	4.2	5.1	3.6	3.6	....	....	....
Sorgo silage.......	....	....	....	....	....	....	27.3	16.7	6.1
Total daily consumption of air-dry roughage (including cobs).	4.3	5.8	8.4	5.1	6.3	9.0	8.2[a]	8.1[a]	8.0[a]
Rates of corn to roughage (including cobs).	2.9:1	1.6:1	1.1:1	3.4:1	2.6:1	1.4:1	1.6:1	1.7:1	1.6:1
Feed eaten per cwt. gain									
Shelled corn......	631	552	478	657	651	576	559	574	613
Corn cobs........	....	129	220	....	123	240	....	131	291
Prot. conc........	103	103	108	64	66	67	62	63	70
Hay.............	221	223	226	219	163	158	....	....	....
Sorgo silage.......	....	....	....	....	....	....	1126	712	286

[a] Sorgo silage reduced to 15 per cent moisture basis.

where corn-and-cob meal has been compared with shelled corn is evidence either that cobs possess a definite feeding value or that their presence in the ration favors the utilization of the other components.[6]

Experiments carried on at the Ohio, Iowa, and Nebraska Stations, in which ground cobs in addition to those present in corn-and-cob

[6] Cf. Table 215.

meal were fed, show clearly that corn cobs are a valuable roughage material for fattening cattle. (See Table 165.) In the Ohio and Iowa tests, where both corn and hay were fed according to appetite, the added cobs replaced grain rather than roughage in both the daily ration and in feed consumed per hundred pounds of gain. But in the Nebraska experiments, where the roughage fed was sorgo silage, the addition of cobs had little effect upon the consumption of corn on a shelled basis but greatly reduced the consumption of silage. These results indicate that corn cobs are a better companion roughage for low-grade hay, which is eaten in small amounts, than for highly palatable hay and silage. It is possible that the additional bulk imparted to the Ohio and Iowa rations by the ground cobs resulted in a more complete digestion of the corn and protein concentrate.

Studies made of rumen digestion indicate that the feed nutrients of roughages which are high in fiber like corn cobs are rendered available to the cattle through the action of the rumen bacteria which attack the cellulose and other nutrients of the cobs and convert them to more digestible compounds. Some scientists believe that an abundance of nitrogen favors the growth and action of the bacteria and for that reason recommend the feeding of more protein with corn cobs than would be needed with ordinary roughages. However, steers fed 1 pound of linseed meal at the Iowa Station did fully as well on a full feed of ground ear corn with added cobs as another lot fed the same feeds and 2 pounds of linseed meal.[7] Likewise, some authorities recommend the feeding of a small amount of molasses with a heavy corn cob ration on the theory that the bacteria require a source of readily available carbohydrates for their growth and development. Yet in another Iowa test a heavy ration of corn cobs reinforced with 2.5 pounds of cane molasses was not so well utilized as one reinforced with the same weight of shelled corn.[8] This lack of agreement between theory and results indicates that much study must be made of rumen digestion before we shall know what takes place in this important organ of cattle. However, a study of Tables 165 and 166 indicates that the addition of 14 pounds of ground corn cobs to each 70 pounds of corn-and-cob meal will materially reduce the cost of gains if roughage is high in price and must be conserved. But if roughage may be fed liberally because it is cheap, the feeding of cobs is not economical, since the value of the roughage saved by their use will usually be less than the expense of grinding and handling

[7] Iowa AH Leaflet 165, May, 1947.
[8] Iowa AH Leaflet 173, May, 1949.

TABLE 166

FEEDS REPLACED BY 1 TON OF CORN COBS

(ON BASIS OF FEED EATEN PER 100 POUNDS GAIN)

I. Nebraska experiments Lots compared	1 Ton of Cobs plus		Replaced Sorgo Silage
	Shelled Corn	S. B. O. M.	
1. Shelled corn and ground ear corn.........	4.1 bu.	15 lb.	3.14 tons
2. Shelled corn and ground ear corn plus added cobs...............................	6.6	55	2.89
3. Ground ear corn and ground ear corn plus added cobs...........................	8.7	87.5	2.66

II. Ohio experiments Lots compared	1 Ton of Cobs plus		Replaced Shelled Corn
	Prot. Conc.	Hay	
1. Shelled corn and ground ear corn.........	No lb.	31 lb.	22 bu.
2. Shelled corn and ground ear corn plus added cobs...............................	46	46	25
3. Ground ear corn and ground ear corn plus added cobs...........................	110	66	29

III. Iowa experiments Lots compared	1 Ton of Cobs plus L. S. M.	Replaced	
		Shelled Corn	Hay
1. Shelled corn and ground ear corn.........	33 lb.	1.7 bu.	913 lb.
2. Shelled corn and ground ear corn plus added cobs...............................	25	12.0	506
3. Ground ear corn and ground ear corn plus added cobs...........................	17	22.9	85

the cobs plus the cost of the additional protein concentrate required and the molasses, minerals, and vitamin supplements needed.

Cottonseed Hulls. In the South, huge quantities of cottonseed hulls accumulate at the cottonseed oil pressing mills. These are extensively used throughout the cotton-growing states in livestock feeding. As they are low in protein and very high in fiber, their feeding value is very low compared with most other roughage materials. According to chemical analyses,[9] they have the remarkably wide nutritive ratio of 1:436. In total digestible nutrients and in net energy value, they are approximately equal to oat straw.

TABLE 167

VALUE OF COTTONSEED HULLS FOR FATTENING CATTLE

Roughages Compared	2-year-old Steers 112 Days		Mature Steers 111 Days (Av. 3 Trials)		Steer Calves 185 Days		
	Cotton- seed Hulls	Corn Silage	Cottonseed Hulls, Johnson Grass Hay	Corn Silage, Johnson Grass Hay	Cotton- seed Hulls	Cotton- seed Hulls, Kafir Silage	Alfalfa Hay
Av. daily gain, lb.........	1.28	1.69	1.88	1.99	1.90	1.99	1.94
Av. daily feed							
Shelled corn....	....	....	....	....	6.3	6.8	6.7
Cottonseed meal........	7.5	7.5	6.4	6.4	2.8	2.5	1.0
Cottonseed hulls........	26.0	....	23.5	....	5.6	2.9	....
Hay..................	....	....	3.0	3.0	....	....	5.6
Silage.................	....	30.6	....	48.4	....	6.6	....
Mineral supplement.....	....	....	....	....	.2	.2	.2
Cost of roughages, per ton.							
Cottonseed hulls........	$6.00	....	$7.00	....	$5.00	$5.00	....
Hay..................	....	....	$12.00	$12.00	....	....	$7.00
Silage.................	....	$3.00	....	$5.00	....	$2.50	....
Cost of gain per cwt.......	$13.74	$9.87	$11.35	$12.80	$4.88	$4.77	$4.36
Source of data...........	North Carolina Bulletin 222, 1912		Mississippi Bulletin 278, 1930		Oklahoma Mimeographed Report, 1933–34		

The wide use of cottonseed hulls in the South in past years has been due to the fact that they were relatively cheap and to a scarcity of more valuable roughage materials. Many farmers devoted almost their entire time to their cotton crop and in return expected their cotton to support not only themselves but their livestock as well. Consequently, not only beef cattle but also work horses and dairy cattle were fed largely on cottonseed meal and cottonseed hulls.

The limitations of a ration composed of 4 to 8 pounds of cottonseed meal and a full feed of cottonseed hulls has been demonstrated repeatedly by southern experiment stations. Cattle fed on these

[9] Morrison, Feeds and Feeding.

feeds apparently do fairly well for 2 or 3 months, after which time they gradually lose their appetites and become unthrifty. Formerly this condition was believed to be due to poisonous qualities of the cottonseed meal, but it is now known that it is due to nutritive deficiencies in both cotton seed meal and cottonseed hulls, especially deficiencies of vitamin A and calcium. If cottonseed hulls are fed with some other roughage, such as legume hay, which contains adequate amounts of both these nutrients, or with a calcium supplement and sufficient yellow corn or corn silage to supply the necessary amount of vitamin A, the trouble will be avoided. Results secured from feeding cottonseed hulls in properly balanced rations have compared favorably with those secured from other roughages, such as sorghum silage and prairie, peanut, and Johnson grass hays.

As greater diversification of crops has been practiced by southern farmers, the use of cottonseed products as the whole ration for fattening cattle has rapidly declined. Cottonseed meal is being combined with corn, and cottonseed hulls are being fed with other roughages, particularly silage and legume hay. The long growing season makes it possible to grow a great variety of valuable forage crops, so that farmers in the Cotton Belt have a choice of several good roughages that are more satisfactory for fattening cattle than cottonseed hulls.

23 ——————— Corn Silage as a Feed for Fattening Cattle

Considerable reference has already been made to the use of corn silage for fattening cattle, particularly in the discussion of limited grain ration in Chapter 17. When fed to cattle getting little or no grain, corn silage fills the rôle of a concentrate and also that of a roughage. Or it may be considered as a diluted concentrate, such as the beet pulp fed in the sugar-producing regions of the West, or as the turnips and mangels used so extensively in fattening cattle in the British Isles. However, in most places where silage is used, it is fed in connection with a full feed of grain. Hence, it is regarded by most feeders as a roughage rather than a concentrate, and it will be so considered in this chapter.

The Increased Use of Silage. Extensive use of corn silage in beef cattle feeding began about 1910. Before that time it was generally believed that silage was a feed mainly for dairy cows. It was thought that its succulent nature would produce a marked looseness of the bowels, a very undesirable condition for steers on full feed. However, the results obtained by its use both at agricultural experiment stations and in feed lots of progressive cattlemen were so favorable that the feeding of silage to fattening cattle soon became a common practice throughout the Corn Belt.

By no means has the use of silage been confined to the Corn Belt. Although it is true that corn was the first and is still the principal crop used in the making of silage, many other crops are ensilaged in those regions of the country where corn cannot be grown successfully. In the arid West and Southwest, the grain sorghums furnish an enormous tonnage of silage, while in the high altitudes of the northwestern states sunflowers are grown to make silage on which beef cattle can be maintained and fattened. Also a large amount of silage is now made from alfalfa, oats, field peas, clover, cowpeas, soybeans, rye, Sudan grass, and other farm crops. Indeed, it appears that the time will soon be at hand, if, in fact, it is not already here, when silage will be the principal roughage used in beef production both in the Corn Belt and throughout the United States.

Chemical Changes That Take Place in the Silo. Contrary to general belief, comparatively few chemical changes occur in the silo. Immediately after the silo is filled, extensive bacterial and enzymic actions are set up, which result in the breaking down of some of the proteins into amino acids and other nitrogen compounds. Also, the simple carbohydrates are acted upon by the lactic acid-forming bacteria, which change the sugars of the plant into lactic and other organic acids. In reasonably mature, well-packed, carbonaceous material, however, this bacterial action does not continue long, for it is soon arrested by a lack of oxygen and by the accumulation of acids that result from the breaking down of the sugars. In ensilaged legumes the formation of organic acids proceeds more slowly. Hence, bacterial action continues for a longer time and results in a greater destruction of material before it is finally arrested and the silo is automatically "sealed." Because of this fact, more difficulty is usually experienced in ensilaging such crops as cowpeas and soybeans than is had with corn and the grain sorghums. Also, more spoiled material is encountered when the silo is opened preparatory to feeding. The particularly offensive odor usually encountered in connection with spoiled silage made from legumes is due to the advanced stage of decomposition brought about by the putrefying bacteria before their work was stopped by the accumulation of acids.

Losses Due to Ensilaging. The effect of these chemical changes upon the feeding value of the ensilaged material is detrimental rather than beneficial. Without question, the most serious result is the action of the bacteria on the simple carbohydrates to produce alcohol, carbon dioxide, organic acids, and water. The percentage of the carbohydrates (nitrogen-free extract) that may be so converted varies greatly with the maturity of the material but may be as high as 20 to 25 per cent in immature corn, which contains much sugar. With reasonably mature corn the loss probably does not exceed 5 to 10 per cent.

The splitting of the protein compounds into amino acids, amides, and other non-albuminous nitrogen products does not, in the light of careful investigations, appear to be serious, inasmuch as the proteins themselves are broken down into these products in the digestive tract. Should seepage occur through the floor or walls, however, such changes may result in much loss, since these compounds are soluble, whereas most proteins are not. Owing to the loss of carbohydrates, the percentage of crude protein in silage frequently is higher than it was in the freshly cut corn. The total amount of nitrogen in the silo can, of course, be no greater than that put in. Frequently a slight loss occurs, due to the escape of small quantities of ammonia.

As a result of the chemical changes whereby certain nutrients are broken down, a noticeable decrease in dry matter content occurs. The loss of dry matter due to ensilaging varies directly with the amount of bacterial action taking place. Hence, the greater losses are suffered in ensilaging immature corn and in silos where the material is not well packed. In such cases the loss in dry matter may be as high as 20 per cent, though the normal loss is but approximately half this figure.

Fig. 51. A badly damaged shock of corn. The losses of food nutrients taking place in the silo are small compared with those commonly occurring in corn shocked in the field.

These losses taking place in the silo, great as they may seem, are by no means as serious as those occurring in corn cut and shocked in the field in the usual manner. Investigation carried on by Ragsdale and Turner[1] at the Missouri Station indicate that the storage losses of the combined corn and stover can be reduced fully half by ensilaging.

Loss in Weight of Ensilaged Corn. The weight of material fed from a silo is always somewhat less than that put in. The difference represents the losses due to the escape of gases and moisture resulting from the fermentation process, any seepage that may occur through the walls or floor, and the weight of the layer of spoiled material that must be removed from the top in opening the silo preparatory to feeding. The sum total of these losses in weight is termed "shrinkage." The percentage of shrinkages varies greatly with the depth of the

[1] Missouri Research Bulletin 65, 1924.

silage and with the thoroughness with which it is packed. With well-packed silage stored to a depth of 30 to 40 feet and covered with a reasonably effective seal the shrinkage should not exceed 5 to 10 per cent.

TABLE 168

LOSS OF NUTRIENTS OCCURRING IN SILAGE AND IN SHOCK CORN*

Method of Storage	Percentage Gain or Loss					
	Dry Matter	Protein‡	Fat	Ash	Crude Fiber	N. F. E.
1. In Silo............	−4.01	+4.06	+24.96	+11.44	+6.66	−10.01
2. Shocked in Field†.	−15.12	−.84	+7.36	−9.30	+3.82	−22.51

* Missouri Research Bulletin 65, 1924.

Physical Changes That Occur in the Silo. If the process of ensilaging results in a loss of some 10 per cent of the weight of material ensilaged, and if the feeding value of the silage removed is somewhat lower per unit of dry matter than that of the green roughage put in, wherein, it may reasonably be asked, does the value of silage lie? The answer to this very pertinent question is revealed by a study of the physical changes that occur in the silo.

Outside the silo, green forage soon undergoes marked changes in its physical nature. Whether cut or uncut, it quickly loses its green color and tender freshness and becomes dry, hard, and more or less woody. In other words, if cut down it becomes "cured" through the rapid evaporation of a large part of the water in the severed stem and leaves; if left standing it "ripens," which is the term given to the slow, natural curing process whereby nature transfers a great part of the soluble food material from the stem and leaves to the grain and roots. In either condition the forage is dry and hard and much less palatable than it was in the green state. Also, when consumed, this dry material must absorb great quantities of water while undergoing the processes of digestion. Hence, it tends to slow down or clog the movement of the food through the alimentary tract.

When put into the silo, however, green forage retains much of its original freshness. Indeed, there is a marked tendency for those harder portions of the stem to become softer and more succulent from the breaking down of the cellulose through the processes of fermentation and by the absorption of the surplus water contained in the greener portions of the plant, or of the water that may be added if the forage is rather dry. Hence, properly made silage possesses many of the physical properties of green forage. It is much more palatable than cured or field-ripened fodder. Because of this fact, the entire plant, when put into the silo, is eaten, while in the case of corn fodder 15 to 25 per cent of the weight of material fed is refused.

Fig. 52. Harvesting corn with a field cutter. (*Courtesy Illinois Experiment Station.*)

Retaining, as it does, its succulent nature, silage has a wholesome effect upon the digestive process, being similar to pasture grass in this respect. The large mass of soft, moist material acts as a mild laxative in keeping the digestive tract in good order, while the moderate amounts of weak acids present tend to retard too rapid fermentation in the paunch and intestines. Everything considered, well-preserved silage serves as a mild conditioner or tonic when fed in moderate quantities.

The Place of Silage in the Fattening Ration. In all cases where cattle are given a liberal amount of grain, any silage fed should be considered a part of the roughage ration. Hence, its use should be in accordance with the well-recognized rules for the feeding of roughage discussed in Chapter 21. Because silage contains some corn, men inexperienced in its use often make the mistake of treating it as a concentrate. Beginning with a small amount of silage, they gradually increase the allowance per day throughout the feeding period, when, as a matter of fact, the reverse of this procedure usually should be followed. In view of the fact that silage contains little corn in proportion to its weight and bulk, it is manifestly impossible for steers to consume any great amount of grain and silage at the same time. The logical procedure to follow is to feed the maximum amount of silage during the first part of the feeding period, decreasing the amount from month to month, so as to permit a larger consumption of concentrates.

Corn Silage as the Principal Feed for Fattening Cattle. That a full feed of corn silage supplemented with an appropriate amount of protein concentrate will cause cattle to lay on fat was discussed under the subject of limited grain rations in Chapter 17. If the silage has been made from high-yielding corn and was harvested at the proper stage of maturity, thin cattle will make a noticeable improvement in condition during the first half of the feeding period, on silage alone, with no additional corn. Usually it is important to feed only 2 or 3 pounds of hay per day, or no hay at all, in order to obtain the consumption of as much silage as possible. This, of course, means that 2 to 3 pounds of protein concentrate must be fed daily, as well as a mineral supplement.

Cattle with sufficient quality to sell near the top of the market, if they had the necessary finish, usually will return more profit if they are fed a full feed of corn during at least the last half of the feeding period, but cattle of medium grade sometimes show the greatest net return if they are continued on a heavy silage ration until they are marketed. Two-year-old or long yearling steers are more satisfactory for such a plan of feeding than younger cattle, since they will attain a satisfactory finish for their grade in a shorter time. Gains made by cattle on limited grain rations are relatively low after 120–130 days.

Calves, because of their rapid growth, cannot attain a satisfactory finish on silage alone. However, corn silage may constitute the principal item or their ration for the first one-third or two-fifths of a feeding period that is to extend over 9 or 10 months. Daily gains of $1\frac{3}{4}$ or even 2 pounds a day may be obtained if 2 to $2\frac{1}{2}$ pounds of protein concentrate are fed and the silage is of excellent quality. Attention is called to the excellent gains made by calves at the Indiana Experiment Station, which were fed a full feed of corn silage and $3\frac{1}{2}$ pounds of a supplement composed of soybean oil meal, molasses, various minerals, and a vitamin A concentrate. (See Table 169.)

TABLE 169

THE VALUE OF CORN SILAGE AS THE PRINCIPAL
FEED FOR FATTENING CATTLE

	Indiana[a] 2-Year-Old Steers		Ohio[b] Yearling Steers		Indiana[c] Calves	
	1918–1919	1919–1920	1928–1929	1929–1930	1949–1950	1950–1951
Yield of corn, bu..........	25	25	48	.....	70	70
Yield of silage, tons........	.....	.....	.....	.....	15	14
Days fed the following ration:.	90	60	174	177	112	147
Corn silage..............	49.4	45.4	47.4	49.4	31.0	37.0
Supplement.............	2.4	2.6	2.0	2.0	3.5	3.5
Legume hay.............	4.7	6.6	1.2	2.8	.....	.....
Av. initial wt., lb...........	885	1008	622	662	478	481
Av. final wt., lb............	1105	1139	971	1036	721	806
Av. daily gain.............	2.45	2.18	2.01	2.11	2.18	2.21
Supplement fed	C. S. M.	C. S. M.	C. S. M.	C. S. M.	Soybean oil meal 2.25 lb. Molasses feed 1.0 Bone meal 0.18 Iodized salt 0.06 Vitamin conc. 0.01	3.50

[a] Purdue (Indiana) Bulletin 240, 249.
[b] Ohio Bimonthly Bulletin 151.
[c] Indiana Mimeo. Reports AH 47 and 59.

Effect of Silage on Consumption of Grain. Except when fed in very small quantities, the use of silage lessens slightly the consumption of grain. This is probably due both to the fact that well-preserved silage is more palatable than most dry roughages and hence competes more actively for the appetite of the steer, and to the fact that the corn present in the silage naturally tends to replace part of that in the grain ration. The use of silage in moderate amounts will decrease the consumption of corn by approximately 10 per cent of the weight of the silage fed, whereas the shelled corn equivalent of the silage usually is 15 to 17 per cent of the weight of silage eaten. Consequently, the feeding of silage in moderate amounts usually results in a somewhat larger total consumption of corn than would be realized from a non-silage ration.

The Amount of Silage to Feed. Silage varies so much in its moisture content that it is impossible to lay down definite rules as to the amount that should be fed. Some men put the corn into the silo when it is comparatively green, whereas others wait until it is fairly mature. Naturally the greener silage contains more water. Also, it frequently happens that silage in a given silo varies greatly in moisture content from top to bottom. This is particularly likely to happen in a large silo which requires several days to be filled, or in a silo containing silage made from rather dry corn to which considerable water has been added. Unless the flow of water is carefully regulated, some of it will filter down through the silage, leaving the material

TABLE 170

EFFECT OF SILAGE UPON THE CONSUMPTION OF GRAIN
(Two-year-old Steers)

Indiana Experiment Station	Number of Trials Averaged	Average Daily Consumption		Corn Present in Silage, pounds*	Total Corn Consumed, pounds
		Shelled Corn, pounds	Corn Silage, pounds		
I. {Shelled Corn, C. S. M. Clover Hay, Corn Silage....	10	14.2	25.1	3.8	18.0
{Shelled Corn, C. S. M. Clover Hay...............	10	17.1	....	....	17.1
II {Shelled Corn, C. S. M. Corn Silage...............	5	14.5	29.9	4.5	19.0
{Shelled Corn, C. S. M....... Clover Hay...............	5	17.5	....	....	17.5

*Assuming that 15% of weight of silage is corn.

at the top only moderately moist while that near the bottom is saturated. Consequently, any recommendation that may be made as to the amount of silage to feed should be regarded as only a rough estimate.

The best index to follow in determining the amount of silage to feed is the appetites of the cattle. Knowing the approximate amount of grain that should be consumed at a given stage of the feeding period, one may feed as much silage as will not decrease appreciably the consumption of grain. Less than this amount may, of course, be fed if some form of dry roughage or pasture is supplied, but the use of greater amounts is almost certain to result in smaller daily gains and lower finish.

Although from the standpoint of the cattle there is no minimum amount of silage to feed, there are certain practical objections to using

this material in small quantities. The principal items in the cost of
silage are the labor, machinery, and storage charges. These items
decrease rapidly per ton as the amount of silage made increases.
Hence, silage is a much cheaper feed when put up in large quantities.
Also considerable labor is involved in the feeding of silage compared
with most other roughages; but this labor decreases per ton with the
amount of silage fed. Consequently, if silage is to prove a cheap and
economical feed it must be fed in relatively large quantities. Except
in special situations, silage, if used, should furnish 60 to 80 per cent
of the roughage ration on an air-dry basis.

TABLE 171

APPROXIMATE AMOUNTS OF CORN SILAGE TO FEED
AT DIFFERENT STAGES OF THE FEEDING PERIOD

	Approx. Initial Weight, pounds	First Month of Feeding Period (Little or No Grain)			First Month of Middle Third of Feeding Period (Full Feed of Grain)			First Month of Last Third of Feeding Period (Roughage Limited)		
		Shelled Corn, pounds	Corn Silage, pounds	Legume Hay, pounds	Shelled Corn, pounds	Corn Silage, pounds	Legume Hay, pounds	Shelled Corn, pounds	Corn Silage, pounds	Legume Hay, pounds
1. Calves.....	400	..	15	4	9	8	2	12	6	2
2. Yearlings..	700	3	25	5	12	15	3	15	12	2
3. 2-year-olds.	900	5	35	6	14	20	4	17	18	3

Owing to the high water content of silage, inexperienced feeders
find it somewhat difficult to determine its dry roughage equivalent.
Because of the great variation in moisture, this can only be approximated, but for practical feeding purposes it may be roughly estimated
by dividing the weight of fresh silage by four. By this is meant that
cattle fed 30 pounds of silage are consuming approximately the same
amount of roughage as cattle eating 7½ pounds of hay.

Table 171, based upon this ratio, has been compiled in an effort to
give the inexperienced feeder an idea of the approximate amounts of
silage to feed at different stages of the feeding period. With a longer
feeding period the decrease in the amount of roughage fed would, of
course, be made more slowly.

Silage vs. Dry Roughage. When silage is supplemented with the
proper amount of nitrogenous concentrate to balance the ration, it
compares very favorably as a roughage with clover or alfalfa hay.

The principal advantages it has over these dry roughages are its certainty of supply—the total failure of corn or sorghum to make a silage crop being extremely rare—and the opportunity it affords to utilize a large amount of roughage that has no market value. The chief disadvantages of silage compared with legume hay are the comparatively large amount of labor and equipment required for its manufacture and storage and the necessity of making a cash outlay for commercial feeding stuffs to furnish the protein needed to balance the ration.[2] Comparatively little additional protein is needed with clover hay as the roughage, and still less with alfalfa. Silage, however, requires a daily allowance of 1 to 2 pounds of cottonseed or linseed meal per steer if satisfactory results are to be obtained from its use.

TABLE 172

COMPARISON OF CORN SILAGE AND LEGUME HAY AS ROUGHAGES FOR STEERS ON FULL FEED

	Number of Trials Averaged	Daily Gain, pounds	Corn, pounds	Feed per Cwt. Gain		Hay, pounds
				C. S. M. pounds	Silage, pounds	
I. Indiana: 2-year-olds						
Corn, C. S. M., Corn Silage	5	2.42	600	115	1240	. . . .
Corn, C. S. M., Clover Hay	5	2.35	742	118	. . . .	456
II. Illinois: Calves						
Corn, C. S. M., Corn Silage	5	2.08	476	70	377	96
Corn, Alfalfa Hay	5	1.97	525	73	. . . .	254

Whether silage or legume hay will prove most satisfactory for a particular feeder depends both upon his method of feeding and handling his cattle and upon the amount of legume hay and other dry roughages that is available. As stated elsewhere, silage is unsurpassed as a roughage for common or medium steers that are to be fed only a short time before being sent to market. It is also well suited for cattle of any grade that are to be fattened in a leisurely manner over a long period. Legume hay, on the other hand, is preferred by many feeders for putting a high finish on well-bred steers within 120 to 140 days and for fattening calves within a period of 6 to 8 months. Legume hay is much more satisfactory than silage

[2] *Cf.* p. 318.

where the cattle are fed their grain in self-feeders. By using large racks or mangers, hay need be fed but two or three times a week. Silage, on the other hand, must be fed daily.

The cost of constructing a silo and the outlay for corn binders, silage cutters, etc., amount to a considerable expense, which is justified only when the tonnage of silage made and used is reasonably large. Otherwise, the machinery and storage charge per ton of silage will be so high that silage will cease to an economical feed. Silage is a more satisfactory feed for the man who feeds 2 or more carloads of cattle per year than for the farmer who feeds only 15 to 25 head, unless the feeding of relatively large amounts of silage is made possible by limiting the grain ration to considerably less than a full feed.

Corn Silage vs. Shock Corn. The comparative value of corn silage and shock corn for wintering stocker calves and for fattening mature steers with no grain other than that contained in these feeds has already been discussed.[3] They will now be compared as roughages for cattle that are fed approximately a full feed of grain. Such comparison will be limited to relatively mature steers, since shock corn is not a satisfactory feed for calves or light yearling cattle on account of its coarse texture.

Corn silage has given much better results than shock corn when each of these roughages has been feed according to appetite with approximately a full feed of grain, enough protein supplement to make a fairly well-balanced ration, and a limited amount of legume hay. A study of the relative amounts of dry matter actually consumed in the form of silage and fodder emphasizes the higher palatability of silage and the almost complete elimination of waste when the corn plant is fed in this form. That shock corn possesses much merit as a cattle roughage when fed in such amounts as to allow the cattle to eat only the more palatable portions of the stalk is shown by the results of a Missouri experiment in which both silage and fodder were fed in such amounts as would furnish the cattle with equal quantities of dry matter. When fed in this manner both lots gained at the same rate. (See Table 173.)

Feeding Silage to Calves. Some feeders who have found corn silage a satisfactory feed for mature steers consider it to be too bulky for fattening calves. However, in some respects it is more useful in feeding animals of this age than older cattle for the reason that calves are fed for a much longer time and, hence, have greater need for variety and succulence in their rations. By starting calves on nearly a full feed of silage, 12 to 15 pounds a head, and adding grain and

[3] *Cf.* pp. 155 and 274.

protein concentrate as the calves grow and attain capacity for more feed, the calves are gradually got up to a full feed with almost no risk of their going off feed or becoming foundered. On most farms the silo will be empty by April or May, and the change to dry roughage will result in an increased consumption of grain at the time of year when the appetite of full-fed cattle is usually slowed down by the advent of

TABLE 173

COMPARISON OF CORN SILAGE AND SHOCK CORN FOR FATTENING CATTLE

| | Iowa Bulletin 253, 1928 | | Iowa A. H. Leaflet 21, 1927 | | Missouri Bulletin 112, 1913 | |
| | 2-year-olds 120 Days | | 2-year-olds 120 Days | | 2-year-olds 130 Days | |
	Corn Silage	Shock Corn	Corn Silage	Shock Corn	Corn Silage	Shock Corn
Av. daily gain, lbs.	2.64	1.96	2.69	2.28	3.16	3.15
Av. daily ration						
Shelled or ear corn	18.0	16.3	14.1	15.0	16.3	17.1
Protein conc.	3.0	3.0	2.5	2.5	2.7	2.8
Silage or fodder	23.6	8.4	25.7	9.4	20.8*	10.4*
Legume hay	3.0	....	.8	.8	3.9	5.8
Feed per cwt. gain						
Shelled or ear corn	682	828	525	659	517	543
Protein conc.	114	153	93	110	86	90
Silage or fodder	896	429	957	410	659	330
Legume hay	114	....	29	35	123	185
Selling price per cwt.	$8.50	$7.75	$9.35	$9.35	$6.45	$6.35
Gain of hogs per steer, lb.	63	44	59	66	61	87

* Fed in such amounts as would furnish equal quantities of dry matter.

hot weather. Should the supply of silage last until the calves are finished, the amount should be reduced to 4 or 5 pounds a day upon the arrival of summer, or on approximately June 1.

The proper amount of silage for calves is a somewhat disputed question. Obviously the amount to feed will depend largely upon the size and age of the calves and the length of the feeding period. The Illinois Station had excellent success feeding 8 pounds of silage and 2 pounds of legume hay per head daily for the first 6 or 7 months, and 6 pounds of silage and 2 pounds of hay thereafter. However, in experiments in which different amounts of silage were compared, equally good gains were secured by feeding 16 pounds of silage and 3 pounds of hay during the first 140 days and approximately half these amounts thereafter. The calves fed in this manner maintained their feed consumption and rate of gain much better during the summer than the other lots. Consequently, this plan of feeding appears to be satisfactory for calves that are to be carried into the late summer and fall.

Calves fed medium or large amounts of silage in the Illinois experiment exhibited much steadier appetites than those fed little or no silage. No signs of scouring were observed in the two lots receiving the larger amounts of silage, whereas the calves in the other lots scoured intermittently during the first half of the experiment but very little thereafter.[4]

Replacement Value of Silage. The introduction of corn silage into a ration will affect the consumption of grain and dry roughage in respect to both the amounts eaten per head daily and the amounts consumed per 100 pounds of gain. Experiment station bulletins, mimeographed circulars, and other reports of feeding experiments that have been made to determine the value of corn silage for fattening cattle contain a large amount of data on these points, a few of which have been summarized in Table 174.

TABLE 174

REPLACEMENT VALUE OF CORN SILAGE

| | Feeds Replaced by 1 Ton of Silage | |
	Shelled Corn	Air-Dry Roughage
Indiana Bulletin 235, 1920	4.61 bu.	613 lb.
Ohio Bulletin 193, 1908	4.43 bu.	588 lb.
Author's average of 61 paired lots of steers	4.30 bu.	645 lb.
Average	4.45 bu.	615 lb.
	250 lb.	
Correction factor for hybrid corn	+20%	−20%
Adjusted value	300 lb.	494 lb.
Percentage of silage (2000 lb.)	15%	25%

Corn silage, because of the wide differences encountered in grain and moisture content, varies in its replacement value in terms of shelled corn and hay. Its replacement value is also affected by the amount of silage fed, large amounts displacing somewhat more grain and hay from the daily ration per pound of silage fed than small amounts but replacing less grain and hay per pound of silage than small amounts in respect to feed required per 100 pounds gain. However, these variations are not so great as to make it impossible to assign corn silage a replacement value that will be highly useful for

[4] Illinois Mimeo. Report, 1938.

the practical feeder. By comparing the daily feed consumption and
the feed consumption per 100 pounds of gain of more than 60 paired
lots of cattle, when only one of each pair was fed silage or when both
were fed silage but in different amounts, the author has determined
the average replacement value of a ton of corn silage to be 4.3 bushels
of shelled corn and 645 pounds of air-dry roughage. These figures
agree closely with 4.6 bushels of corn and 613 pounds of hay reported
in Indiana Bulletin 235, and 4.4 bushels of corn and 588 pounds of
corn stover and mixed hay given in Ohio Bulletin 193. Inasmuch as
most of the feeding experiments from which these results were derived
were carried out many years ago with silage made from open-pollinated corn, which had more stover but fewer ears than our present-
day hybrid varieties, it seems wise to increase the corn and decrease
the dry roughage replaced by silage by about 20 per cent. When this
is done the average replacement value of corn silage in terms of shelled
corn and air-dry roughage is 15 and 25 per cent, respectively. (See
Table 174.)   This means that a drove of cattle that is fed 400 pounds
of shelled corn, 100 pounds of hay, and 600 pounds of corn silage is
receiving the equivalent of 490 pounds of corn and 250 pounds of air-
dry roughage, since 15 per cent of the weight of the silage is its shelled-
corn equivalent and 25 per cent of its weight is its approximate air-dry
roughage value. If the feeding of silage is discontinued, the corn and
hay should be immediately increased by 90 and 150 pounds, respectively, to keep the cattle on the same level of feeding.

Value of a Dry Roughage with Silage. Although very satisfactory
results may be expected from a ration consisting of shelled corn, a protein concentrate, and corn silage, feeding experiments indicate that the
ration is improved by the addition of a small amount of dry material,
such as hay, straw, or stover. The amount of such roughage eaten is
usually only 2 or 3 pounds a day, but it appears to have a noticeable
effect upon the rate of gains, especially if the roughage fed is clover or
alfalfa hay. These legumes are rich in minerals and vitamins, both of
which are likely to be deficient in a ration in which silage is the only
roughage. Inasmuch as calves have more need for minerals and vitamins than older animals, their response to the addition of a legume
hay is usually greater. If no legume hay is available, calcium should
be supplied in the form of ground limestone.[5]

If the dry roughage fed is straw or stover, it may be kept before the
cattle with little danger of their eating enough to interfere with their
consumption of grain or silage. However, if it is legume hay of good
quality, it should be fed at the rate of 2 or 3 pounds a head, preferably

[5] *Cf.* p. 463.

about noon after the morning's feed of grain and silage has been eaten.

At What Stage Should Corn Be Ensilaged? The best quality of silage is produced by cutting the corn when the kernels have hardened to the point where their interior is of a stiff dough-like consistency but a large portion of the stalk and most of the leaves are still green. Silage made from immature corn is likely to be sour and "sloppy." Moreover, the cutting of very green corn entails a waste, since the total

TABLE 175

THE VALUE OF A DRY ROUGHAGE WITH A HEAVY SILAGE RATION

Number of Trials Averaged	Rations Compared	Daily Gain	Feed per Pound Gain				
			Shelled Corn	C.S.M.	Legume Hay	Oat Straw	Corn Silage
		lbs.	lbs.	lbs.	lbs.	lbs.	lbs.
4 (Two-year-olds)	Shelled Corn, Cottonseed Meal, Corn Silage	2.37	5.97	1.14	....	....	12.66
	and						
(Indiana Experiment Station)	Shelled Corn, Cottonseed Meal, Clover Hay, Corn Silage	2.45	5.74	1.12	1.41	....	11.16
3 (Two-year-olds)	Shelled Corn, Cottonseed Meal, Clover Hay, Corn Silage	2.41	5.67	1.16	1.09	....	10.37
	and						
(Indiana Experiment Station)	Shelled Corn, Cottonseed Meal, Oat Straw, Corn Silage	2.45	5.67	1.15	....	.56	10.59
2 (Calves)	Shelled Corn, Cottonseed Meal, Corn Silage	2.03	5.09	1.02	....	....	7.49
	and						
(Illinois Experiment Station)	Shelled Corn, Cottonseed Meal, Alfalfa Hay, Corn Silage	2.20	4.79	.96	1.53	....	4.64

amount of food nutrients in the corn plant continues to increase until the ears are fully mature. On the other hand, corn that is almost ripe is made into silage with considerable difficulty. Unless sufficient water is added to soften the dry stalks and leaves to permit their being packed so firmly that all air is excluded, silage made from over-ripe corn is very likely to mold.

A measured area of corn ensiloed in the roasting-ear stage from August 12 to 14 at the Ohio Station proved to be of much lower feeding value than an equal acreage ensiloed September 5 to 8, when the corn was well dented. Samples taken of the corn at the time of harvest showed that 17 per cent less dry matter per acre was obtained from the early-harvested corn. Moreover, considerable juice leached out of the silo after this corn was stored. As a result only 755 pounds of gain per acre were obtained from the immature silage compared with 940 pounds per acre from the well-dented corn. The cattle fed the immature silage were not so well finished and were valued 25 cents a hundred less than the steers fed the riper silage.[6]

Obviously, weather conditions will often determine the time of making silage. During periods of severe drought it may happen that the corn must go into the silo with the base of the stalk and the lower leaves brown and dry and the ear and upper portion of the stalk still green. Whereas first-class silage cannot be made under such conditions, to delay longer would permit the drying up of the entire plant.

Effect of Corn Yields upon Value of Silage. It would seem that silage made from hybrid corn yielding from 80 to 100 bushels per acre would have a much higher feeding value per ton than the silage made from open-pollinated corn that yielded considerably less. Also, it would seem that silage made during a dry year, such as 1934 or 1936, would have a low feeding value because of the low yield of grain. However, corn yields have a much greater effect upon the production of silage per acre than upon the feeding value per ton. (See Table 176.) Although the yields of both dry corn and silage at the Illinois Station have varied widely from year to year, the corn content per ton of silage has remained rather constant, especially for the hybrid varieties of corn.

Silage made and fed at the Nebraska Station during the extremely dry years 1934 and 1936, produced gains on stocker calves and yearlings as large as those secured in previous tests with normal corn silage. "The silage was made from corn which grew stalks 5 to 7 feet high but made little or no grain. The few ears that filled were immature and watery. Part of the corn was relatively immature when cut and part of it needed to be watered as it went into the silo."[7] Obviously the yield of silage per acre was very low, but apparently many of the food nutrients that would have gone into the ears were still present in the stalks and leaves and so were available to the cattle.

Varieties of Corn for Silage. Although certain varieties of corn yield an enormous tonnage of silage owing to their rank growing tendencies, such silage is not especially valuable for fattening cattle because of the low percentage of grain present. Silage made from such corn

[6] Ohio Bimonthly Bulletin 223, 1943.
[7] Nebraska Mimeo. Cattle Circulars 155 and 161, 1935 and 1936.

may be very well suited for dairy cattle that need a highly succulent ration, but the ordinary varieties of corn, which produce a large yield of sound grain, will make a much more satisfactory silage to feed beef cattle. Not only will it require the addition of less concentrates when

TABLE 176

EFFECT OF YIELD OF CORN UPON CORN CONTENT OF SILAGE*

	Yield of Corn per Acre, bushels (14% Moisture)	Yield of Silage Corn per Acre, tons	Corn per Ton of Silage, bushels
1. Open-pollinated corn			
1925	72.9	8.84	8.24
1926	44.7	8.71	5.13
1927	68.5	14.73	4.65
1928	78.9	12.62	6.25
1929	48.3	9.70	4.98
Average	62.7	10.92	5.85
2. Hybrid corn			
1946	92.2	13.29	6.64
1947	66.9	10.51	6.37
1948	106.5	16.68	6.39
1949	91.0	12.63	7.20
1950	52.0	9.35	5.38
Average	81.7	12.49	6.40
Percentage of increase	30.3	14.4	9.4
3. Dry years			
1934 (dry year)	35.0	6.38	5.49
1935 (normal rainfall)	57.1	10.25	5.57
1936 (dry year)	33.9	7.51	4.50

* Illinois Station, unpublished data.

fed to animals that are being fattened, but it will also produce more growth and development when fed to heifers and stockers that are being carried through the winter.

Value of Frosted Corn for Silage. The silo offers the best possible way to utilize corn that has been frosted before the ears are mature. If put into the silo immediately after the frost, the silage will have practically the same feeding value as though the corn had been ensilaged just before the frost occurred. If, however, the corn is allowed to stand until the leaves are withered and dry, many of the leaves will be blown away and the quality of the silage greatly damaged. A heavy rain on frosted corn will also cause much damage by leaching out a considerable amount of the soluble food nutrients. It will usually be necessary to add some water to frosted corn to make it pack well in the silo.

The Feeding of Moldy and Frozen Silage. Seldom does any trouble result from feeding small quantities of moldy silage to beef cattle. All roughage consumed by cattle goes first to the paunch, where it remains several hours before going into the true stomach. Apparently the process of fermentation that occurs in the paunch destroys or renders harmless the ordinary molds.

Spoiled silage has very little feeding value, since the fermentation process has resulted in the breaking down of a large amount of the food nutrients. Also, it should be realized that spoiled feed of any sort may harbor not only the harmless molds but deadly toxin-forming organisms as well. Hence, the careful feeder will take all reasonable precautions to see that no great amount of moldy silage is fed.

During extremely cold weather a considerable amount of frozen silage will be encountered, especially in silos where but little feed is removed each day. This frozen material should be removed from the walls of the silo as soon as it is possible to knock or pry it loose. If the pieces are small and not too numerous they may be piled in the center of the silo after the morning's feed, where they will often thaw out before night. With a large quantity of frozen silage, however, or with the temperature much lower than freezing, this method will not prove practical. Instead, the frozen silage should be piled just outside the silo where it can be carefully watched and fed as soon as it is reasonably well thawed out. To leave it longer will result in its becoming moldy and unfit for use.

The presence of small quantities of frozen silage in the ration need occasion no alarm, as no trouble is usually encountered from them. To feed a considerable amount of frozen silage, however, is highly inadvisable. Not only is such material very unpalatable and difficult for the cattle to eat, but it is likely to cause serious derangements of the digestive tract. Excessive scouring is one of the common aftereffects of feeding frozen silage.

Effect of Silage upon Hog Gains. Since the use of silage results in a decrease in the consumption of grain, hog gains are naturally smaller after silage-fed cattle than after cattle fed dry roughage. Apparently the corn present in the silage is so thoroughly digested that little of it is available for hogs. Tests conducted with mature dairy cows show that less than 10 per cent of the grain in silage is voided in the manure whereas from 22 to 35 per cent of the shelled corn fed may be excreted by such cattle.

TABLE 177

EFFECT OF SILAGE UPON PRODUCTION OF PORK*

(Total of 3 Lots)†	Silage-Fed Cattle (20 Steers)	Dry-Fed Cattle (21 Steers)
Total gains of hogs	1445 lb.	1670 lb.
Average daily gain per pig	1.027	1.187
Pork produced per steer	72.25	79.52
Total corn fed cattle (including corn in silage)	929 bu.	934 bu.
Pork produced per bushel corn fed cattle	1.55 lb.	1.79 lb.

* Ohio Bulletin 193, 1908.

† A small amount of tankage was fed to the hogs in both silage and non-silage lots.

Effect of Silage upon Shipping and Sale. Some feeders hold the opinion that silage-fed cattle suffer much larger shrinkage between feed lot and market than cattle fed dry roughage. Hence, they sometimes will remove the silage from the ration a few days before shipping and supply a dry roughage in its place. However, records kept of the actual shrinkage suffered by silage-fed and non-silage-fed cattle, respectively, show that this practice is unwise, as the cattle fed silage had in reality a smaller shrinkage than cattle fed hay. Whereas it was true that cattle fed silage in some cases lost more weight while in transit, they were more inclined to take on a better "fill" after they were unloaded. Silage cattle have a reputation at the market for being unusually good "drinkers." Whereas this kind of fame probably does not work to their advantage as regards their selling price, it does indicate that their owners get good weights.[8]

In former years, when dry roughage was the orthodox feed for fattening cattle, the few silage-fed steers received at the market were regarded with considerable suspicion. It was feared that they would resemble grass-fattened cattle in having a low dressing percentage and dark-colored flesh of rather poor quality. Comparisons of the carcasses of such cattle with those of animals finished on dry roughage disclosed no important differences in thickness or quality of flesh that could be traced to silage. As the number of silage-fattened cattle increased, packers and shippers bought them as a matter of course and frequently found them superior to any dry-roughage-fed cattle included in their purchases. Naturally the tendency to discriminate against such cattle soon disappeared, and they were bought on the basis of their actual worth.

At the present time, a large percentage of grain-fed steers received at Chicago and other large livestock markets have been fed silage. Seldom does a buyer stop to inquire whether a given drove has had

[8] *Cf.* Table 244.

silage or not. If the cattle show unusual size of paunch and an indication of a rather large "fill," he may suspect that they have been fed silage; but whether this fact or something else is the cause of their condition makes very little difference to him. He estimates their dressing

TABLE 178

Comparison of Selling Prices of Silage and Non-silage Cattle*

| Year | Selling Price per cwt. of Finished Cattle | | | | | | Lot Bringing Highest Price |
| | Silage Cattle | | | Non-silage Cattle | | | |
	Number of Lots	Range	Average	Number of Lots	Range	Average	
1906–07	1	....	$5.30	1	....	$5.45	Non-silage
1907–08	2	$6.00–6.70	6.35	2	$5.95–6.70	6.33	Equal
1908–09	2	6.80–6.90	6.85	2	6.55–6.75	6.65	Silage
1909–10	3	7.20–7.60	7.35	1	....	7.30	Silage
1910–11	3	5.75–5.95	5.85	1	....	5.85	Silage
1911–12	3	8.10–8.35	8.23	1	....	8.25	Silage.
1912–13	2	7.75–7.85	7.80	1	....	7.90	Non-silage
1913–14	2	8.40–8.70	8.55	2	8.50–8.60	8.55	Silage
1914–15	2	8.20–8.35	8.28	2	8.25–8.30	8.28	Silage
1915–16	2	8.70–8.75	8.73	2	8.65–8.65	8.65	Silage
1916–17	2	12.00–12.00	12.00	2	11.75–11.75	11.75	Silage
11 years	24	....	$7.75	17	....	$7.72	8 Silage 2 Non-silage 1 Equal

* Indiana Experiment Station, Bulletins on Steer Feeding.

percentage, judges their thickness and quality of flesh, and forthwith states the price he will pay for them.

Effect of Silage upon Profits. No one ration or plan of cattle feeding is more profitable than another under all conditions. However, if an attempt were made to classify rations on the basis of the net profit realized from their methodical use over a period of years, those containing moderate and fairly liberal amounts of silage probably would be at the top. This probably is due partly to the fact that cattle fed silage have a smaller feed bill than those fed only dry roughage and, as a rule, develop more uniformly with a smaller percentage affected by founder and bloat. Because of their attractive appearance when marketed, they frequently sell higher than cattle of similar quality, fed for the same length of time, but not fed rations containing corn silage.

It is not without significance that nearly all Corn Belt experiment stations have for many years used a ration containing corn silage as a check or standard with which new and little-tried feed combinations are compared. This practice is the result of repeatedly obtaining better

TABLE 179

Effect of Silage Upon Profits Realized from Feeding Cattle*

Year	Age of Cattle	Selling Price per Cwt.		Return per Head Over Feed Costs		Return per Bushel of Corn Fed	
		Fed Silage	No Silage	Fed Silage	No Silage	Fed Silage	No Silage
1912–13	Calves	$8.70	$8.50	$10.33	$6.84	$0.73	$0.61
1913–14	Calves	10.00	10.00	12.13	8.86	0.86	0.78
1928–29	Calves	15.90	15.65	18.73	8.17	1.15	0.94
1929–30	Calves	10.30	10.60	−20.85	−22.35	0.26	0.28
1931–32	Calves	8.35	8.15	22.03	19.96	0.71	0.68
1937–38	Calves	11.15	10.75	20.88	13.08	0.93	0.82
1938–39	Calves	9.60	9.15	11.85	6.61	0.65	0.59
Average		10.59	10.40	10.73	5.88	0.76	0.67
1910–11	2-year-olds	5.95	6.10	4.24	3.85	0.53	0.49
1911–12	2-year-olds	7.45	7.55	11.63	7.66	0.91	0.77
1941–42	2-year-olds	12.60	12.25	21.21	16.42	1.14	1.11
Average		8.67	8.63	12.36	9.31	0.86	0.79

* Illinois Experiment Station Mimeo. Reports of Cattle-Feeding Experiments.

returns from cattle fed corn silage than from those fed dry roughages in literally scores of experiments made over a period of more than 40 years. Typical of such returns are those of the Illinois Station given in Table 179. In all ten of the Illinois tests better returns per head were obtained from cattle fed corn silage than from those fed the same feeds but with the silage omitted.

24

A Comparison of Various Silages for Cattle

To the man who lives in the Corn Belt, the term "silage" means, without further qualification, ensilaged Indian corn. However, outside the region where corn can be successfully grown, various other crops are used for silage purposes. Since the tonnage of corn silage greatly exceeds that made from all other materials, it will be convenient to compare these other kinds of silage with that made from corn as a standard.

Sorghum Silage. The various grain sorghums, such as milo, kafir, and darso, are very satisfactory silage crops and are grown extensively for this purpose in the semi-arid regions of the Southwest. On account of the close spacing of their heavily leaved stalks, their yield of silage per acre is usually larger than that of corn, especially when the rainfall is deficient during the growing season. Also, the grain sorghums mature more quickly than corn and, hence, are better suited to high altitudes and latitudes where corn ordinarily will not ripen before frost. Should early frosts occur, less damage is suffered by the sorghums than by corn.

However, silage made from the grain sorghums is somewhat lower than corn silage in both protein and fat, and is higher in crude fiber. Feeding experiments in which both corn and grain sorghum silages have been used point, with but few exceptions, to the superiority of corn silage.   Although the difference is not large, it is sufficient to indicate that corn is the more valuable silage crop for the Corn Belt except during unusually dry weather.

Several varieties of grain sorghum are grown for silage in the arid Southwest, but the variety most popular in the Corn Belt is called Atlas sorgo. This forage crop has yielded twice the tonnage of corn silage in Kansas and Nebraska during very dry years and 50 per cent more in Illinois during years of average rainfall. The silage is of finer texture and slightly more palatable than corn silage, but it possesses less feeding value per ton, probably because many of its small, hard seeds are swallowed whole and are not digested. Apparently Atlas sorgo silage compares less favorably with corn silage for wintering stocker calves[1] than it does as a roughage for cattle that are given a full feed of grain. However, for either of these classes of cattle it usually surpasses corn silage when the returns are expressed on an acre basis.

TABLE 180

COMPARISON OF CORN AND SORGHUM SILAGES FOR FATTENING CATTLE

	Kentucky Bulletin 233, 1921 Average of 3 Trials with 2-Year-Old Steers		Oklahoma Bulletin 139, 1921 Calves, 185 Days				Illinois Exp. Sta. Unpublished Data, 1938–1939 Calves, 150 Days	
	Corn Silage, pounds	Sorghum Silage (Red Top), pounds	Corn Silage, pounds	Cane Silage, pounds	Kafir Silage, pounds	Darso Silage, pounds	Corn Silage, pounds	Atlas Sorgo Silage, pounds
Average daily gain	2.05	1.81	2.08	1.99	1.98	2.05	2.18	2.08
Feed per cwt. gain								
Shelled corn...	226*	240*	541	565	569	549	358	390
Silage.........	2158	2469	630	658	662	639	380	393
Protein conc...	182	210	50	52	52	50	54	59
Dry roughage..	132	168	50	52	52	50	92	96
Relative amount of pork per head..	....	....	100	62	102	37	100	80
Average yield per acre, tons.....	10.4	16.2	....	....	....	....	10.6	17.8

* Corn fed during only last part of trials.

Sunflower Silage. Sunflowers have long been grown in certain European countries, notably Russia, for their oil-bearing seeds. Except at high elevations, they are now grown in the United States only as an emergency crop. As is often true of a plant that is grown on a limited scale under special conditions, spectacular claims have been made for sunflowers, especially as a silage crop. It has been stated that the tonnage obtained from sunflowers is much greater than that from an equal area of corn, and that, ton for ton, sunflower silage is equal to corn silage, if not more valuable. While the former statement

[1] Cf. Fig. 35.

is, in the main, true, the latter has been thoroughly disproved by numerous feeding experiments. The improved varieties of sunflowers do make a valuable silage crop for those sections of the country that have too short a growing season for the successful production of corn or the grain sorghums. On this account, they are especially well adapted to the higher altitudes of such states as Idaho, Wyoming, and Montana. They are also valuable as an emergency crop to be planted after floods, poor seed, or insects have ruined a field of corn or small grain too late in the season for the field to be replanted in corn. Sunflowers planted as late as the tenth of July, south of an east-and-west line through Chicago, will ordinarily mature sufficiently for silage before frost.

TABLE 181

COMPARATIVE VALUE OF SUNFLOWER AND CORN SILAGE FOR BEEF CATTLE

	South Dakota Bull. 199 Silage and Oil Meal to 2-Year-Old Steers		South Dakota Bulletin 199, 1922 Silage Only to Yearling Steers				Oklahoma Bulletin 139, 1921 (Calves receiving full feed of corn, etc.)	
	Sunflower Silage	Corn Silage	Sunflower Silage	Sunflower Silage 75% Corn Silage 25%	Sunflower Silage 50% Corn Silage 50%	Corn Silage	Sunflower Silage	Corn Silage
Daily gain (lb.) .	0.87	1.88	−0.71 (loss)	0.17	0.78	1.26	2.13	2.08
Value of hog gains per steer.....	....	....	....	....	....	....	$4.90	$9.52

The making of a good grade of sunflower silage is attended with considerable difficulty. So far, no variety of sunflowers has been discovered that has the desired degree of uniformity in the maturity of the heads. Some heads will be too ripe and dry for making the best grade of silage while others are still in scarcely more than full bloom. Sunflowers also show a tendency to drop their lower leaves many days before the heads of the plants are mature. Frequently, one-half or more of the leaves will have fallen by the time the plant as a whole is ready to be cut for silage. The large, heavy heads in which the stalks terminate make sunflowers top-heavy and somewhat harder to handle than Indian corn.

In chemical composition, sunflower silage is not very different from corn silage. It is somewhat higher in moisture and fiber and slightly lower in nitrogen-free extract and fat. Feeding trials have been conducted by several experiment stations in which both silages have been used, but the results of the several stations by no means agree. It has, however, been pretty generally demonstrated that sunflower silage is less palatable than corn silage and that cattle usually have to be accustomed to eating it by withholding, for a few days, all other feeds. In few cases have cattle receiving sunflower silage made larger or more economical gains than cattle fed corn silage. However, in several trials, exactly the opposite results have occurred. (See Table 181.)

During the winter of 1921–1922, Dowell and Bowstead of the Alberta Experiment Station[2] compared sunflower silage with oat and pea silage and oat silage for 2-year-old steers receiving a full feed of grain and a small amount of prairie hay. The daily gains made by the three lots of cattle concerned during a 140-day feeding period were 2.06, 2.48, and 2.52 pounds, respectively.

Soybean Silage. Soybeans grown either alone or with corn or Sudan grass are regarded as a good silage crop for the Corn Belt. This legume crop is exceedingly valuable from the standpoint of the cattle feeder, since it furnishes either a high grade of palatable hay or dry beans that are sufficiently high in protein to make them a possible substitute for cottonseed or linseed meal. It frequently happens, especially in the northern part of the Central States, that heavy fall rains or early frosts interfere greatly with the successful harvesting of both hay and beans. If, however, the crop is made into silage, it will be damaged but slightly by rains and will usually be harvested safely before the first killing frost.

Soybeans contain a relatively high percentage of protein and, hence, when ensilaged alone, make a silage that is likely to be rank and strong at the time it is fed.[3] When combined with corn, however, the amount of sugars and starches present is sufficient to prevent more than a slight decomposition of the protein compounds of the soybeans. Corn silage is very low in protein, whereas soybeans are relatively high. If the mixing of these materials in the silo should result in a well-balanced, nutritious feed, one of the most difficult problems of the cattle feeder would be solved.

Soybeans intended for the silo are sometimes grown with the corn,

[2] Alberta Experiment Station, Mimeo. Report of Cattle-Feeding Trials, 1922.
[3] *Cf.* p. 387.

two to four beans being planted in each hill. This method of planting
cannot be recommended, since the weight of bean forage harvested is
insufficient to compensate for the lower yield of corn obtained. A
much better plan is to grow the corn and beans separately and to mix
them at the time of filling the silo. With either method, some care
should be taken to select a variety of beans that reaches the desired
stage of maturity at the proper time. Soybeans, when put into the
silo, should be a little riper than when cut for hay. The beans themselves should be fully formed but still soft and green. Whereas the
upper leaves and pods should be still green, near the base of the stalk

TABLE 182

COMPARISON OF CORN AND CORN-SOYBEAN SILAGE FOR FATTENING STEERS
(Average of 4 trials, Indiana Experiment Station)

Two-year-old Steers Time Fed: 120 @ 140 Days	With Cottonseed Meal		Without Cottonseed Meal	
	Corn Silage	Corn-Soy-bean Silage	Corn Silage	Corn-Soy-bean Silage
Average Daily Gain, lbs.	2.37	2.43	2.15	2.18
Feed per lb. Gain				
Shelled Corn, lbs.............	5.07	4.91	6.02	5.87
Cottonseed Meal..........	1.14	1.12	......	......
Clover Hay..............	1.49	1.44	1.68	1.65
Silage...................	13.95	13.47	15.83	15.01
Selling Price per cwt.........	$12.52	$12.59	$12.30	$12.25
Net Pork per bu. of Corn Fed				
Cattle..................	1.95	1.81	2.01	1.65

they should be turning yellow. Naturally, ideal conditions will not
always be realized. Oftentimes the corn must be cut while the beans
are still green. Since the corn will usually be the most valuable component of the silage, it, rather than the beans, will determine the time
when the silage should be made.

Theoretically, silage made of a mixture of corn and soybeans should
be decidedly superior to that made from corn alone. Even though but
20 per cent of the silage is composed of soybeans, the nutritive ratio
is increased from 1:13 to approximately 1:9.5 by their presence.
When the silage is composed of 2 parts of corn to 1 part of beans, the
nutritive ratio is 1:7.8, which is sufficiently narrow to indicate that
the mixture is a well-balanced feed without the addition of a protein

concentrate.[4] Theoretically, when such silage is fed to steers getting a full feed of corn, only enough protein concentrate need be used to balance the grain component of the ration.

Feeding experiments, however, indicate that corn and soybean silage is but little superior, when fed with a full feed of corn, to silage made from corn alone. This condition probably results from the fact that the amount of protein furnished by the beans is, after all, relatively small compared with that needed to balance both the shelled corn and the corn silage. The benefit resulting from the presence of this protein is apparently largely neutralized by certain objectionable features of the corn-soybean silage. Such silage does not keep fresh as long as ordinary silage when exposed to the air; also, it tends to have a rather undesirable laxative effect on the cattle to which it is fed. However, it is important to note that silage composed of 2 parts of corn and 1 part of beans has been fully as efficient in producing gains as silage made from corn alone. Although soybeans will usually be too valuable to replace merely their weight of green corn in the silo, they can be so used should unfavorable weather conditions make it necessary to harvest them in this way.

Hay-Crop Silage. This term refers to silage made from alfalfa, clover, brome grass, timothy, and other crops that are ordinarily grown, either in pure stands or in mixtures, for hay. Other designations for this kind of silage are legume silage, grass silage, or merely alfalfa, red clover, or brome-grass silage, if one of these species comprises most or all of the freshly cut forage. Whether it is better to ensilo these crops than to cut them for hay depends upon a number of factors. In general, the advantages of ensiloing over harvesting for hay are as follows:

(*a*) The crop is less seriously damaged by rains encountered during the harvest period.

(*b*) A much smaller percentage of the leaves is lost, which are the most valuable portion of the forage.

(*c*) Considerably more protein is obtained per acre. This results largely from the saving of more leaves but is partly due to the fact that some crops, principally the grasses, are cut for silage earlier than for hay; consequently the protein content is higher.

(*d*) The vitamin A present at the time of cutting is preserved much better in silage than in hay.

(*e*) Silage is somewhat more palatable and digestible than hay; consequently it may constitute a larger percentage of the ration of fattening cattle without seriously reducing the rate of gain.

[4] Ratios computed from figures from Morrison, Feeds and Feeding.

The principal disadvantage of using legumes and grasses for silage rather than for hay is the higher cost of harvesting.[5] This added cost is represented chiefly by the expensive field harvesters, the blowers required to blow the cut forage into the silo, and the silos required for storage. Should the regular haying equipment be used for loading and hauling the uncut forage to a stationary cutter at the silo, a great deal more labor is required to load and unload the heavy green forage than is needed to handle dry hay. If, by chance, silage-making equip-

FIG. 53. Making hay-crop silage with a mower-cutter type of machine. This same machine can be used to pick up partly wilted forage from the windrow by replacing the cutter head with a pick-up head. (*Courtesy Illinois Experiment Station.*)

ment is already available for making corn silage, it can, of course, be used for making hay silage with little additional expense.

Making Hay-Crop Silage. Much more care and judgment must be exercised in making hay-crop silage than in making corn silage if silage of high quality is to be produced. Cutting the forage when it is either too ripe or too green, allowing it to lie in the swath or windrow too long before it is ensiloed, or failing to add the proper amount of preservative to the cut forage will be likely to result in unpalatable silage of low feeding value.

Two types of field cutters are available, one of which both mows and chops the forage in a single operation and the other type picks up the forage from the windrow after it has been cut with a mower and windrowed with a side-delivery rake. If the former type of harvester is used, the forage should be cut somewhat riper than is advisable for

[5] *Cf.* Table 223.

the latter type, since no moisture is lost by the forage during handling. Cutting the forage too green with this type of harvester will result in a wet, "sloppy" silage, which is unpalatable and of low feeding value because of its high moisture content. If the moisture is too high, a considerable percentage of the feed value is lost in the juices that seep

TABLE 183

EFFECT OF DIFFERENT PRESERVATIVES UPON THE VALUE
OF ALFALFA SILAGE FOR BEEF CATTLE*
(Average of 3 Trials)

	No Preservative	Beet Molasses	75% Phosphoric Acid
Preservative per ton of forage	....	60 lb.	5 qt.
Av. initial weight, lb.	693	717	692
Av. daily gain	2.01	2.09	2.02
Av. daily ration			
Grain	15.5	15.8	15.5
Protein concentrate	1.0	1.0	1.0
Silage	10.1	9.1	10.2
Hay	0.2	0.4	0.2
Feed per cwt. gain			
Grain	784	777	782
Protein concentrate	49	47	49
Silage	501	433	503
Hay	9	20	9

* Colorado Mimeo. Report, February, 1951.

through the doors of the silo, and perhaps through the walls as well, if the silo is not well constructed. Free water in a silo, whether or not seepage occurs, is to be avoided, since its presence is highly destructive to the silo, first through the enormous hydrostatic pressure exerted on the walls, and second through the constant corroding action of the silage acids on the walls of concrete and metal silos.

Most authorities agree that the best quality of hay-crop silage is made from forage that contains from 65 to 70 per cent moisture at the time it is put into the silo. If it is desired to fill the silo when the moisture content is higher, the forage should be allowed to lie in the swath or windrow to permit the evaporation of the excess water. Normally on a warm, sunny day the moisture content will drop 3 or 4 per cent between the time the forage is cut and the time it is stored in the silo, when the forage is mown, raked, and chopped with a field cutter from the windrow without waiting for it to dry.

Use of Preservatives. Because grasses and legumes contain small amounts of simple carbohydrates which are easily and quickly converted into organic acids by the bacteria of fermentation, a preservative of some kind is usually added to such crops when they are ensiloed. Theoretically, the best preservative would be a highly diluted acid which would prevent fermentation before it began. This is the basis

TABLE 184

Amounts of Preservatives Usually Recommended
for Hay-Crop Silages*

	Molasses, pounds (12 lb. = 1 gal.)	75% Phosphoric Acid, pounds (13.2 lb. = 1 gal.)	Ground Corn or Corn-and-Cob Meal, pounds
1. Corn, sorghums, sunflowers, etc.	None	None	None
2. Sudan grass, reed canary grass (well matured)	0–40	0–10	0–75
3. Sudan grass, reed canary (immature)	40–60	10–15	75–150
4. Small grains (milk stage)	40–60	10–15	75–150
5. Meadow or pasture grasses	40–60	10–15	75–150
6. Mixed legumes and grasses	60–75	12–15	100–200
7. Alfalfa, sweet clover, red clover, etc.	75–100	15–25	150–200
8. Soybeans (beans well matured)	75–100	15–25	150–200
9. Soybeans (beans very immature)	100	15–30	150–250

* Minnesota Bulletin 360, 1942.

of the A. I. V. method of making corn silage, described later in this chapter. Since acids are relatively expensive and corrode the metal parts of silo-filling equipment, they are not used extensively by the practical farmer. Molasses or finely ground shelled corn or corn-and-cob meal are the preservatives most commonly used. Molasses diluted with appropriate amounts of water is recommended in siloing forage that is a little dry; finely ground corn-and-cob meal is more satisfactory if the moisture content of the forage is somewhat too high. The amounts of preservatives commonly used are given in Table 184.

Wilted Grass Silage. There is much evidence that a preservative is not needed if the moisture content of the forage is such as to favor the action of the acid-forming bacteria and retard the development of those which give rise to disagreeable flavors and odors. This method of making hay-crop silage is called the "wilted grass" method. It was first developed and described by Professor J. B. Shepherd of the Bureau of Dairy Industry, U. S. D. A., who lists the following steps as highly important in making grass silage of good quality.[6]

[6] Mimeo. Circular BDIM-Inf-38, Bureau of Dairy Industry, June, 1946.

1. Silos should be airtight and have smooth walls.

2. Wilt the crop slightly. When it is put in the silo the average moisture content should not be higher than 68 per cent or lower than 60 per cent. Scattered loads can have as much as 70 per cent moisture without producing undesirable fermentation and odors, or they can have as little as 55 per cent moisture if such loads are not close to the top of the silo. If a trench silo is used, none of the crop should contain less than 60 per cent moisture.

Fig. 54. Adding molasses to hay crop silage. Here the molasses is drawn from the barrel by a pump geared to the blower. A simpler arrangement is to support the barrel above the blower and allow the molasses to flow through a hose onto the cut forage under the force of gravity. (*Courtesy Illinois Experiment Station.*)

The time required to wilt the crop to the desired moisture level may be only 1 or 2 hours on good drying days, or it may be 2 or 3 days during rainy weather.

3. Set the cutter for ¼-inch cut. This is a *must* requirement to insure close packing to exclude the air.

4. Distribute the silage evenly during fillings and tramp the top third of the silage thoroughly.

5. Put 4 to 6 feet of heavy unwilted silage on top of the wilted silage to insure rapid settling and to keep out the air.

6. Level off the top layer of silage and keep it well tramped near the wall while the silage is settling.

Feeding Value of Hay-Crop Silage. Several experiments have been carried out to compare the feeding value of silage made from grasses and legumes with that of hay made from the same field and also with corn silage grown and harvested the same year. The most extensive tests thus far reported are those made at the Michigan and Pennsylvania Stations. At each station three lots of cattle were fed to compare corn silage, alfalfa silage, and alfalfa hay, respectively. At the Pennsylvania Station all lots of cattle were fed the same amounts of corn-

TABLE 185

COMPARISON OF CORN SILAGE, LEGUME SILAGE
AND LEGUME HAY FOR FATTENING CATTLE

	Pennsylvania Bulletin 410, 1941 (Average 3 Trials)			Illinois Mimeo. Report, May, 1942 (1 Trial)			Michigan Quarterly Bulletin, 1939–1942, Vols. 22–25 (Average 4 Trials)		
	Corn Silage	Alfalfa Silage	Alfalfa Hay	Corn Silage	Alfalfa Silage	Alfalfa Hay	Corn Silage	Alfalfa[a] Silage	Alfalfa[a] Hay
Av initial wt.. lb..........	627	627	630	852	854	852	491	493	488
Av. daily gain..............	2.18	2.15	2.06	2.87	2.55	2.45	1.81	1.93	1.81
Av. daily ration									
Corn...........	12.6[b]	12.6[b]	12.6[b]	16.3	15.5	16.5	2.0[c]	9.2	9.2
Protein conc......... ..	1.5	..	..	2.3	1.0	1.0	1.6	1.0[d]	1.0[d]
Silage.....	15.1	20.1	.	22.0	21.7	..	28.0	25.0	..
Legume hay............	..	.	8.3	2.0	2.0	6.8	2.0	..	9.5
Feed eaten per cwt. gain									
Shelled corn............	581[b]	586[b]	609[b]	568	610	671	111	473	506
Protein conc......	68	..	..	80	39	41	87	9	10
Silage......	688	938	..	766	853	..	1532	1293	.
Alfalfa hay...	..	..	399	70	79	279	136	..	504
Feed cost per cwt. gain......	$8.76	$8.62	$9.02	$11.35	$11.23	$11.39	$7.82	$9.17	$9.63
Selling price per cwt........	$8.95	$8.92	$8.95	$12.50	$12.00	$12.25	$9.90	$10.07	$9.91
Dressing percentage.........	60.3	60.0	59.8	59.3	59.5	59.4	..	..	.

[a] A mixture of alfalfa and red clover fed in two trials.
[b] Corn-and-cob meal fed in Pennsylvania trials.
[c] Average for entire period but fed during only last half.
[d] Average for last 30 to 60 days, during which time it was fed.

and-cob meal, while the silages and hay were fed according to appetite. In the Michigan tests no grain was fed to the corn-silage lots during the first half of the test, and about one-third of a full feed during the last half. Grain was fed to the legume-hay and silage lots in such amounts as would make these cattle gain as much as those fed corn silage. The results of these two series of experiments are given in Table 185.

The relative value of silage made from alfalfa or other legume crop and corn silage is well stated by Professor G. A. Branaman of Michigan State College, who in discussing the results of the Michigan feeding experiments said:

> More than one pound of grain per day per hundred pounds of steer weight must be added to a legume hay or a legume silage ration in order to produce gain and finish equivalent to that obtained when steers are full-fed well-eared corn silage and hay, balanced for protein with a protein concentrate.[7]

Miscellaneous Silage Materials. Almost any green material can be ensilaged successfully if it is packed so tightly in a well-built silo that no air pockets remain to furnish oxygen for the processes of fermentation, which begin as soon as the material is cut. Naturally, some crops are better suited for silage purposes than others. In addition to having a sufficiently high carbohydate content to produce enough organic acids to arrest the action of putrefying bacteria before they have caused much decomposition, a good silage material must be of such physical texture as to produce an abundance of fine particles, which will insure close packing. All plants that have an abundance of leaves in proportion to the amount of coarse, woody stems are good silage materials in this respect. A silage crop should also produce a heavy yield per acre; otherwise the expense of cutting, the time consumed in hauling, and the land rental will be so great that the cost of making the silage will be abnormally high.

Few of the silages discussed below have been used extensively in either practical or experimental beef-cattle feeding. However, their yield and physical and chemical properties are such as to make them suitable silage crops for those regions where they can be successfully grown.

1. *Sudan Grass.* Sudan grass belongs to the same group of plants as the grain sorghums. It differs from the sorghums principally in being of finer texture and in having a comparatively light yield of seed. When seeded in rows or broadcast in fertile soil, it grows to a height of 6 to 8 feet and yields an enormous tonnage of green forage per acre. Sudan grass intended for silage should be planted in rows, since this method of planting encourages a better development of heads and leaves and a greater production of seed. Cutting should be done when the seeds are in the dough stage, though very good silage can be made in almost any stage of maturity. In the southern states, where the growing season is long, both the first and second growths of Sudan grass are available for silage. Next to Indian corn and the grain

[7] Michigan Quarterly Bulletin, November, 1940, Vol. 23, No. 2.

sorghums, Sudan grass is probably the most satisfactory silage crop so far developed.

One-half of a small field sown to sweet Sudan grass at the Illinois Station produced 14.2 tons of silage forage per acre while the other half produced 11.8 tons of corn silage. In a feeding test made with these feeds, yearling steers being roughed through the winter gained at the rate of 1.07 pounds daily during the 69 days when Sudan grass was fed, and at the rate of 1.16 pounds during the following 75 days when they were fed corn silage.[8] No significant difference was observed in the palatability of the two silages.

2. *Oat and Pea Silage.* A mixture of oats and field peas is often grown for forage purposes in the northern part of the United States and in Canada. Should the supply of such forage prove to be greater than is needed, its successful harvest is often a perplexing problem, since oats and peas do not usually mature at exactly the same time. The silo offers a very satisfactory way of harvesting such a crop. The carbohydrates of the oats insure the successful preservation of the pea vines which, if ensilaged alone, would be likely to spoil because of their high protein content. That silage made from oats and peas is both a palatable and nutritious feed for beef cattle is shown by Table 186.

TABLE 186

OAT AND PEA SILAGE FOR FATTENING CATTLE*

Full Feed of Grain plus:	Prairie Hay	Oat and Pea Silage Prairie Hay	Sunflower Silage Prairie Hay
Daily gain....................	1.79 lbs.	2.48 lbs.	2.06 lbs.
Feed per lb. gain			
Grain mixture...............	5.87	4.06	5.49
Hay........................	9.24	.96	1.15
Silage.....................	....	13.24	15.00
Linseed meal...............	.55	.40	.48

* University of Alberta, Canada. Mimeograph Report of Cattle Feeding Trials, 1922.

3. *Millet Silage.* Formerly several varieties of millet were frequently grown by Corn Belt farmers as emergency hay crops. Millet is still occasionally sown in corn fields where the stand of corn has been ruined by floods or insects too late in the season to warrant replanting. It is a very rank-growing crop and produces a large yield of hay per acre. The quality of hay, however, is very poor, because

[8] Illinois Mimeo. Report, 1949.

of the coarse texture of the plants and the presence of the numerous hard seeds found in the heavy heads.

Experiments show that the ensilaging of millet greatly improves its value as a feed. While in the silo, the seeds absorb sufficient water to render them soft, so that they are much less objectionable. Because of the small amount of labor involved in growing and harvesting millet, the high yields obtained, and the fact that it matures in sufficient time to allow it to be seeded after a crop of wheat or early oats is removed, millet silage can be produced at a very low cost per ton. In feeding value, however, it is distinctly inferior to corn silage.

TABLE 187

MILLET SILAGE FOR FATTENING CATTLE*

Two-year-old Steers Fed 120 Days	Corn Silage	Millet Silage
Daily gain..............................	2.33 lbs.	1.82 lbs.
Feed per lb. gain		
Silage...............................	27.82	40.76
Linseed meal........................	1.22	1.56
Oat straw...........................	.76	.77

* South Dakota Bulletin 189, 1920.

4. *Oat Silage.* Oats are very generally grown throughout the Corn Belt. They seldom, however, return a satisfactory profit to the farmer because of their low yield and low market price. Their yield is often greatly reduced by the sudden advent of hot, dry weather a few days before they are ripe enough to cut. This hazard can be avoided, in part at least, by cutting the oats while they are still green and making them into silage. Oats that are to be ensilaged should be cut when the kernels are in the soft dough stage.

In the northern and northwestern states, where oats are grown much more successfully than corn, oat silage may well take the place of corn silage in beef-cattle rations. Two factors that tend to lower the cost of oat silage per ton are the comparatively small amount of labor required in handling the bundles and the saving in machinery costs resulting from using an ordinary grain binder in cutting.

5. *Canning Refuse.* The pea vines, cobs and husks from sweet corn, and beet leaves that accumulate around large canning factories are quite generally used for fattening beef cattle. Frequently these

materials are allowed to accumulate in huge stacks which in time become "natural silos" through the exclusion of air from the interior by the decomposition of the material at the surface. Not only the top but also the sides of the pile may be spoiled for a distance of 2 to 3 feet, depending on the nature of the material and the care with which it has been stacked.

TABLE 188

OAT SILAGE FOR FATTENING CATTLE

Two-year-old Steers	University of Alberta, Canada* (Av. of 3 Trials)		Illinois Experiment Station†	
	Oat Silage	Sunflower Silage	Oat Silage	Corn Silage
Daily gain.................	2.48 lbs.	2.28 lbs.	2.88 lbs.	3.08 lbs.
Feed per cwt. gain:				
Grain....................	403	525	568	507
N. conc..................	37	41	81	72
Hay.....................	129	161	70	65
Silage...................	1300	1562	608	622

* University of Alberta, Bul. No. 8, 1924.
† Mimeographed Report of Cattle Feeding Trials, 1928.

Some farmers who live in the vicinity of canning factories realize the feeding value of this factory refuse and are willing to buy it and store it in modern silos. Very often it is returned to the owners of the land on which the crops were grown in partial payment for the use of the land leased by the canning factory, or it is returned in partial payment for the canning crop purchased.

The feeding of cattle in the vicinity of canning factories is quite generally practiced, both because of the large amount of cheap feed available and because a supply of manure must be had to keep the soil at its maximum productivity. Owing to the wide variation in such silages, resulting from different kinds of crops, different stages of cutting, and different methods of storing, no definite rules for feeding can be given. As a rule, much better returns will be secured from feeding them in combination with small amounts of grain and hay than from feeding them alone.

6. *Wet Beet Pulp.* In the sugar-beet-growing areas of Michigan, Colorado, and other beet-producing states, large quantities of wet beet pulp are used in fattening cattle for market. Whether it is fed directly from the mill, from a trench silo, or from a wire silo lined with

straw, its feeding value compares favorably with that of corn silage. In feeding trials at the Colorado Station 1 ton of corn silage replaced 3980 pounds of wet beet pulp but required 43 pounds more beet molasses, 33 pounds more cottonseed cake, and 74 pounds more alfalfa hay.[9]

7. *Potato Silage.* Silage made from surplus or cull potatoes compared favorably with corn silage as a feed for beef calves in tests of these feeds made at the Colorado Station. Each ton of potato silage replaced 2642 pounds of corn silage, 42 pounds of barley, and 7 pounds of linseed cake but required 476 pounds more alfalfa hay.[9]

A.I.V. Silage. In an attempt to preserve green forage in as nearly its freshly cut state as possible, A. I. Virtanen, an agricultural chemist of Finland, added acids to the green material as it was ensilaged to arrest fermentation with its consequent loss of food nutrients. Lactic, hydrochloric, and sulfuric acids were found to be about equally effective for this purpose, provided enough was used to produce a pH of 3.5 to 4.0 in the silage after treatment. Not only does this method prevent the loss of food nutrients, but it also preserves the vitamin A present in the freshly cut forage. This method of ensilaging grasses and legumes is called the A.I.V. method and has been patented by its inventor in both Europe and the United States. American rights are controlled by the Chapman Dairy Farms of Kansas City, Missouri, to whom a royalty must be paid before permission to use the process is granted. Because of the royalty charge and the cost of the acid, the method has been used so far only by dairymen who specialize in the production of milk with a high vitamin A content.

The discovery that phosphoric acid, which is not covered by the patent, may be used successfully has resulted in some use of the acid method in preserving legume crops which are difficult to ensilage alone. Sixteen pounds, or approximately 5 quarts, of phosphoric acid are recommended per ton of green forage. The acid should be diluted with 8 to 10 times its volume of water and the mixture run into the blower drum of the silage cutter. Theoretically, somewhat less acid is necessary in ensilaging non-legume forages than legume crops, but in practice the same amount is usually applied. Since the addition of the acid adds about a dollar a ton to the cost of the silage, its use is recommended only for high-grade legume roughages, like alfalfa, which often spoil badly when siloed alone.

Kinds and Types of Silos. The most common type of silo found in the Corn Belt is the upright silo, 12 to 16 feet in diameter and from 30 to 50 feet high. Bricks, vitrified or glazed tiles, and concrete

[9] Colorado Bulletin 422, 1936.

staves are the most popular building materials, although many mono-lithic concrete silos and a few wooden stave silos erected many years ago are still serviceable and are being used. Metal silos are increasing in number, especially the glass-coated steel silo called the "Harvestore," which has the unique feature of being airtight. Consequently, the ensiloed forage undergoes little loss of nutrients and vitamins as the result of fermentation. The chopped forage is blown into the silo through a hole in the roof and is removed at the bottom of the silo by a special machine designed for that purpose. A valve in the top attached to an inflatable "breather bag" under the roof serves to main-tain the same pressure within the silo as that on the outside. It is the claim of the manufacturer that small quantities of green forage may be put in the "Harvestore" from time to time during the summer with little or no spoilage between the different layers.

Inasmuch as the cost of a silo made of brick, concrete, or similar material is high, various attempts have been made to provide less expensive structures for the storage of silage. Perhaps the most com-mon form used is the trench silo, which consists of a long straight-sided ditch from 8 to 20 feet wide, constructed on a 5- to 10-degree slope in order that surface water that seeps into the trench will drain out at the lower end. An important advantage of the trench silo, besides its inexpensive construction, is its low cost of filling. No special equip-ment is required at the silo, since the trucks that are used to haul the corn from the field harvester are driven into the silo, where they dump and spread the corn with little or no hand labor. The driving of the truck over the silage during filling insures thorough packing of the material. The principal disadvantages of the trench silo are the tend-ency of the trench to become wider each year through the crumbling of the walls and the difficulty of maintaining roads to the silo over which the silage may be hauled to the cattle during bad weather. Except in areas of light rainfall, the walls and floors of trench silos should be made of concrete to prevent serious erosion damage by heavy rains during the spring and summer when the silos are empty.

Another kind of inexpensive silo is the picket or snow-fence silo, which is usually laid out 16 to 20 feet in diameter and carried up to a height of 4 or 5 tiers of fencing or to about 16 feet after the silage has settled. Building or roofing paper is placed against the inner side of the fencing to keep out as much air as possible. Considerable shrinkage is usually encountered with this type of silo because of the large top surface relative to the height and because the paper lining frequently is torn while the silage is settling.

Some farmers claim fairly good results from storing hay-crop silage in large, carefully made stacks in the open without protection to either the tops or sides of the piles. The losses encountered from spoilage are claimed to be less than the annual interest and depreciation charges on a conventional type of silo. This method of storage is, of course, com-

Fig. 55. A trench silo. (*Courtesy Dixon Springs Branch, Illinois Experiment Station.*)

monly used for the preservation of pea vines, cannery refuse, beet tops, and other silage materials of low feeding value. It may prove to be the best method of preserving grasses and legumes, which have little sale value, but it cannot be recommended for corn silage, which contains the equivalent of 4 to 7 bushels of shelled corn per ton.

Sealing the Silo. Many farmers make no attempt to seal their silos but allow a natural seal of rotted and moldy silage to form at the top, through which little air gains access to the silage below. This is a very wasteful practice, as the amount of spoiled silage, which must be discarded when the silo is opened, may represent the decomposition of 5 to 10 per cent of the total weight of green forage stored. This loss of feed may be greatly reduced by leveling the surface of the silage, tramping the silage thoroughly to exclude the air from the top layer, and covering the silage with roofing or building paper weighted down with 4 or 5 inches of earth, limestone, or sand. Ordinary agricultural limestone makes an especially good seal on uncovered silos because of the tight, impervious crust that it forms after it is wetted by a heavy rain. Well-packed silage stored to a depth of 40 to 50 feet and covered with a felt roofing-limestone seal should not shrink in weight more than 3 to 5 per cent.

TABLE 189

EFFECT OF VARIOUS TYPES OF SILO SEALS
ON SHRINKAGE OF CORN SILAGE*

| | | Heavy Felt Roofing Paper Covered with Approximately 6 Inches of | | |
	Not Sealed	Loam Soil	Sand	Agricultural Limestone
1. Number of silos averaged	12	4	1	8
2. Av. days between filling and opening	206	365	280	202
3. Av. tons green corn stored	79.3	80.6	84.4	80.2
4. Av. tons silage fed	65.4	74.5	80.6	77.1
5. Av. shrinkage, percentage	17.5	7.6	4.6	3.8

* Illinois Station Mimeo. Report, April 25, 1941.

Several companies have attempted to manufacture large canvas or rubber cups of the same diameter as the silo, which are placed on top of the leveled silage and then filled with water to a depth of 6 to 8 inches. Although such seals are highly efficient from the standpoint of preventing spoilage, they usually are so badly damaged by the acids of the silage that they are serviceable for only a year or two. Thus far their cost has been too high to justify their purchase for so short a time, but this method of preventing spoilage should have wide use when more acid-resistant materials are made.

Trench silos usually are sealed by covering the silage with 6 or 8 inches of earth. The practice of placing a layer of straw between the silage and earth cover is not recommended, as the air trapped in the straw will prolong fermentation of the silage below. Usually enough spoiled silage will be encountered when the silo is opened to prevent any contamination of the good silage with the earth used as a cover. Often the earth together with the spoiled silage is removed with a blade on the front of a tractor and is left near the edge of the silo to be used as a cover the following year.

25 ——————— Grass as a Feed for Fattening Cattle

Before 1900 most of the beef cattle sent to market from the Corn Belt had made a considerable percentage of their gains from grass. Summer feeding on pasture rather than winter feeding in dry lot was the rule, and the carrying of stockers through the summer on grass alone was a common practice. The widespread preference for summer feeding at this date is shown by the answers to a questionnaire mailed to several hundred experienced cattle feeders by the Missouri Experiment Station.[1] Their replies in regard to the best season of the year to feed were as follows:

Per cent preferring spring	6.60
Per cent preferring spring and summer	12.83
Per cent preferring summer	50.61
Per cent preferring summer and fall	7.94
Per cent preferring fall	11.01
Per cent preferring winter	8.68
Per cent expressing no preference	2.32

Over 70 per cent expressed a preference for those months of the year that furnish the best grazing; less than 20 per cent preferred to feed during the winter and fall when pastures are usually bare.

With the steady rise in Corn Belt land values that began soon after the opening of the twentieth century, many of the large bluegrass pastures were plowed up. Thus, many farmers were forced into winter feeding, particularly in the prairie sections where all the land was tillable. For the small farmer who perforce must keep most of his land in cultivated crops, winter feeding has certain advantages, as will presently be pointed out; but to that man who, because of the large size of his farm or the presence of rolling or timbered land, has a considerable area of pasture, summer feeding will always have an appeal, and for the following reasons:

Advantages of Summer Feeding on Grass.

1. Summer gains on pasture are usually cheaper than winter gains.
   a. Less grain is eaten per pound of gain.

[1] Missouri Bulletin 76, 1907.

b. Grass is a cheaper form of roughage than harvested hay.

c. Less labor is required in feeding and caring for the cattle.

(1) The labor incident to the feeding of roughage is eliminated.

(2) Frequently but one feed of grain per day is given to cattle on grass, while two feeds are customary in a dry lot.

(3) Owing to favorable weather conditions and to the fact that the roughage, grass, is highly palatable, supplying the grain through a self-feeder is likely to be more satisfactory in summer than in winter feeding.

2. As a rule, larger daily gains are secured in the summer than in the winter over feeding periods of equal length. Cattle are likely to be more comfortable in summer than in winter, because weather conditions are more uniform and feed lots are not muddy. In addition, summer rations are on the whole superior to winter rations, as explained in the following paragraph.

3. Cattle fed on pasture during the summer usually get a better-balanced diet than cattle fed during the winter in dry lot. Fresh pasture forage is an excellent source of protein, minerals, and vitamins. Hence, cattle fed on pasture are not often handicapped by a shortage of one of these important food nutrients.

4. No investment in buildings to afford shelter is required.

5. Hogs following cattle on grass make larger gains and show a lower death loss than when following cattle in a dry lot.

6. The manure produced is spread on the fields by the cattle themselves, thus avoiding much loss of fertility through leaching and heating, as well as saving much labor.

7. Summer-fed cattle are commonly marketed during the late summer and fall when well-finished cattle are usually higher than at any other season of the year. Winter-fed cattle, on the other hand, are marketed in the late winter and spring when the prices paid for fat cattle are relatively low.

Disadvantages of Summer Feeding on Grass. Summer feeding of cattle on grass, however, has certain disadvantages. As mentioned above, these disadvantages are more likely to apply to the small farmer who has a quarter-section or less of land than to the man who owns several hundred acres.

1. The land needed for pasture may return a larger gross cash income if planted in crops.

2. An adequate supply of feed in the form of grass is uncertain, owing to the possibility of unfavorable weather. Winter killing

or a late freeze after germination may result in the complete failure of rotation pasture.

3. Grain, especially corn, is relatively scarce and high in price during the summer and early fall.

4. The farmer has less time to devote to cattle in summer than in winter.

5. Flies and extremely hot weather may cause cattle much discomfort.

6. If permanent pastures are used, the manure is dropped on the same fields year after year.

7. Shade and water are hard to provide in temporary and rotated pastures.

TABLE 190

COMPARISON OF DRY LOT AND NON-LEGUME PASTURE FOR SUMMER-FED STEERS

	Full-Fed in Dry Lot *					Full-Fed on Pasture				
	Daily Gain	Shelled Corn per Day	Feed per Cwt. Gain		Selling Price per Cwt.	Daily Gain	Shelled Corn per Day	Feed per Cwt. Gain		Selling Price per Cwt.
			Conc.*	Hay				Conc.*	Hay	
2-year-olds:										
Illinois Bull. 328.........	2.12	19.7	927	411	$10.40	2.00	19.9	992	..	$10.50
Kentucky Mimeo. Report, 1934-1936 (3-year-average)[a]...............	1.81	10.1	608	908	8.47	2.07	10.1	531	..	8.55
St. Joseph stockyards, 1916	3.08	18.2	671	288	11.10	2.76	18.6	763	112	10.25
Average 5 trials.........	2.13	13.6	684	685	10.98	2.19	13.8	670	20	10.70
Yearlings:										
Kansas Circ. 117........	1.76	11.5	706	242[b]	10.75	2.10	13.0	667	55[b]	11.25
Ohio Bimonthly Bull. 138.	1.88	12.8	787	401[b]	16.50	2.36	12.7	625	..	16.25
Ohio Bimonthly Bull. 144.	1.92	15.0	840	331[b]	13.55	2.13	15.0	758	..	12.91
Missouri Mimeo. Report, 1933................	1.85	13.4	804	121	6.25	2.18	15.5	780	..	6.40
Missouri Mimeo. Report, 1934................	2.32	12.9	611	229	8.00	2.20	12.3	613	..	7.75
Missouri Mimeo. Report, 1935................	2.46	15.4	680	135	11.50	2.13	12.7	653	..	10.60
Nebraska Bull. 354 (Average of 3 trials)........	2.19	16.1	743	187	6.48	2.31	15.7	686	112	6.37
Illinois Mimeo. Report, 1935................	2.45	14.1	618	204	11.00	2.34	12.3	483	58	10.00
Average of 10 trials......	2.12	14.3	728	222	9.70	2.24	14.1	665	45	9.43

* Grain plus protein concentrate.
[a] Mixed pasture used in this experiment.
[b] Includes some silage reduced to dry roughage equivalent.

8. Feeder cattle are scarce and high in price in the spring, and the grade and weight desired are hard to obtain.

9. Beef steers lacking somewhat in condition or quality sell rather poorly in the fall because of the competition which they encounter from western grass cattle at this season of the year.

Dry Lot vs. Pasture for Summer Feeding. A considerable number of cattle are fed in dry lot for the late summer and fall markets. However, a majority of these cattle are purchased in the fall and have been fed considerable grain by the arrival of spring. Consequently, they usually carry too much flesh to be fed on pasture during the summer;[2] therefore, they are kept in the dry lot until they are ready for market. Only steers of strictly choice grade justify such a long feeding period, but, if they possess sufficient quality and finish to sell near the top of the market, they usually are more profitable than they would be if marketed earlier, because of the high prices paid for choice and prime fat steers during the late summer and fall.

Although it is generally agreed that cattle in good, thrifty feeder condition in the spring will make faster and more economical gains when fed on pasture than they will in the dry lot, it is often claimed that these advantages are more than offset by the lower prices received for pasture-fed cattle when they are marketed. This opinion is well supported by numerous feeding experiments in which the prices paid for the lots fed on pasture have usually been 25 cents to $1.00 a hundred less than for those fed in the dry lot. Buyers defend these prices by stating that cattle fed on pasture yield less beef in proportion to their live weight, that their carcasses have a higher shrinkage, and that the beef is of poor color, the lean being too dark and the fat yellow instead of white, as it is in cattle fed in the dry lot. Although none of these claims, except that pertaining to the fat color, has been supported by slaughter and carcass studies made by impartial investigators, the fact remains that market buyers look with disfavor upon pasture-fed cattle, even though they show good quality and finish. Such cattle can be distinguished while alive from dry-lot cattle by their rough, dry, sunburned hair and by the green color of their feces. Removing the cattle from pasture about 2 weeks before marketing will correct the color of the feces, but even a month of dry-lot feeding will not as a rule improve their hair sufficiently to escape some price discrimination. Obviously no improvement in the appearance of the hair will be obtained unless the dry lot contains a barn or shed which will afford protection from the sun and flies.

[2] *Cf.* p. 434.

Despite the fact that the financial statements on comparable droves of cattle frequently show a larger net return over feed costs for dry-lot than for pasture feeding, it should not be assumed that this system of feeding is necessarily better under all conditions. Such financial statements seldom take into account the relative farm costs of harvested roughages and pasture, the relative amounts of labor expended in feeding, or the comparative quantities of manure recovered and returned to the land. All these items are very much in favor of the pasture-fed cattle. Hence, all things considered, the net difference between pasture and dry-lot feeding is not great.

FIG. 56. Prime steers, self-fed on bluegrass pasture. The self-feeder is frequently used for summer feeding on grass.

In the final analysis, the factor that usually determines whether cattle purchased in the spring or carried through the winter in feeder condition are fed on pasture or in the dry lot is the amount of available pasture. If the topography of the farm or the crop rotation results in a larger acreage of pasture than is needed by the ordinary stock, the cattle, in all likelihood, will have been purchased mainly for the purpose of utilizing the otherwise surplus grass. Thus, in the Corn Belt at least, feeding on pasture is likely to be the result of a system of farming, rather than a separate project undertaken because of advantages peculiar to the enterprise itself.

Selecting Cattle for Summer Feeding. Cattle to be fattened during the summer may be purchased any time between September or October of the preceding year and the date on which it is desired to turn them on grass. Purchases made in the fall consist largely of calves and yearlings, which will make considerable growth during the winter before the period of heavy feeding begins. Spring purchases, on the other hand, are often mature steers or yearlings with sufficient flesh to insure their being in choice slaughter condition after a feeding period of 4 or 5 months.

Regardless of their age and time of purchase, cattle that are to be fed during the summer should be selected with considerable care. Because of the expense of wintering, or their high cost per hundred-weight if bought in the spring, cattle when turned on grass represent a large investment. This high initial cost, plus the relatively high value of corn during the summer months, makes a high selling price imperative if a profit is to be realized. With heavy receipts of grass-fattened steers at all central and western markets during the late summer and fall, a satisfactory selling price can be expected only for cattle of strictly good, choice, and prime grades. Hence, cattle intended for summer feeding should possess such breeding and quality as will insure their being graded "good" or better when they are marketed.

Steers are usually better than heifers for summer feeding. The large fall runs of grass-fattened steers, together with the thousands of cows and heifers that are culled from breeding herds at the end of the grazing season, make for a rather inactive butcher stock market during the fall months. Although cows and heifers fattened on corn will command a premium over those accustomed to an exclusive grass diet, the advance in selling price may not be sufficient to leave a profit after feed bills, labor charges, and marketing expenses have been paid.

Steers bought in the spring for summer feeding should possess a fair amount of flesh; otherwise it will be difficult to make them ready for market by the end of the grazing season. In selecting steers with plenty of flesh, one should be careful to avoid cattle that have been "warmed up" on corn, or, what is still worse, poor-doing steers cut from droves that have been fed corn all winter. Most experienced feeders prefer cattle that have never had any corn. Two-year-old western hay-fed steers or yearlings wintered in the Corn Belt principally on corn silage make ideal cattle for summer feeding. While each spring thousands of half-fat, corn-fed steers are sent back to the country for further feeding, the gains made by such animals are, as a rule, more expensive than those made by cattle unaccustomed to a heavy grain diet.

Varieties of Pasture. Bluegrass is the pasture most commonly used in the summer fattening of steers. This valuable forage crop occupies fully 80 per cent of the total area in permanent pastures in the Corn

Belt, where practically all the summer feeding of cattle on pasture is done. Bluegrass is considered an especially valuable forage for grain-fed cattle because of its freedom from any tendency to cause scouring or bloat. It is ready to graze much earlier in the spring than most of the legume forages, and its firm sod withstands trampling much better than most other pasture crops. During the spring and early summer it is very palatable and nutritious, but after ripening its seed in mid-summer it becomes more or less dormant, especially during a dry season. At this stage it is not very palatable, and cattle getting a full feed of grain will eat comparatively little of it. However, with the coming of fall rains and cooler weather, it starts growing again and often furnishes considerable grazing during September and October. The common practice is to remove the cattle to the dry lot before this growth begins, lest the new, green grass interfere with the consumption of grain.

Along the western and northern borders of the Corn Belt bluestem, brome-grass, and orchard-grass pastures are used extensively for summer-fed steers. All these pasture forages are similar to bluegrass in composition, and similar gains may be expected from their use. Recently brome grass has been grown extensively in the Corn Belt proper, where it has given considerably better results than bluegrass, particularly when it is mixed with alfalfa.

Many cattle feeders of the old school look with disfavor upon legume forages for grain-fed cattle, believing that they produce both scouring and bloat. However, comparisons of these forages with bluegrass have shown legume pastures capable of producing so much more gain per head and per acre that they must be rated as valuable pasture crops for cattle despite these objections. Both red clover and alfalfa, either alone or in mixtures, have given much larger and more economical gains than bluegrass in experiments carried on at the Illinois Station. (See Table 191.) Fairly good results have been obtained with sweet clover, but the short grazing season of the second year's growth makes it necessary to transfer the cattle to other pasture or to the dry lot about the middle of August.

One important fact disclosed by the Illinois experiments is that the feeding of ground ear corn to steers on legume pastures will eliminate both scouring and bloating to a great extent. Apparently the cobs serve as a substitute for the dry roughage that is frequently fed to cattle on legume pastures to prevent these maladies.[3]

Another legume forage in which there is a great deal of interest at present is lespedeza clover. A low-growing type of this legume, known

[3] *Cf.* p. 600.

as Japan clover, has been common in the South for many years, but only recently have attempts been made to grow lespedeza in the Corn Belt states. An improved variety, known as Korean lespedeza, is much more vigorous than the common form and can be grown success-

TABLE 191

VALUE OF LEGUME FORAGES FOR STEERS FULL-FED ON PASTURE

Yearling Steers Initial Weight 550 @ 650 lbs.	Nebraska Bulletin No. 315			Illinois Mimeo. Rpt. 1930			Illinois Mimeo. Rpt. 1935		
	May 5–Nov. 3, 1936 182 days			May 4–Oct. 23, 1929 172 days			May 6–Nov. 15, 1935 193 days		
	Dry Lot	Alfalfa Pasture	Native Pasture	Blue-grass Pasture	Red Clover Pasture	Sweet Clover Pasture	Brome Grass Pasture	Alfalfa Pasture	Mixed Clover Pasture[c]
Date turned on pasture............	......	May 5	May 5	May 5	May 5	May 5[b]	May 6	May 6	May 13
Date turned off pasture............	......	Sept. 22	July 28	Oct. 23	Oct. 23	Oct. 23	Sept. 23	Sept. 23	Sept. 23
Days on pasture.....	......	140	84	172	172	172	140	140	133
Steers per acre......	......	3	2	2	2	2[b]	2.4	2.4	2.4
Days in dry lot......	182	42	98	None	None	None	53	53	53
Av. daily gain on pasture............	2.67[a]	2.70	2.49	2.16	2.47	2.27	2.25	2.44	2.28
Av. daily gain in dry lot............	2.19[a]	2.60	2.51	......	......	......	2.57	2.36	2.27
Av. daily gain total period.........	2.41	2.68	2.50	......	......	......	2.34	2.42	2.28
Feed per cwt. gain									
Shelled corn......	659	605	661	658	663	648	574[d]	553[d]	609[d]
Prot. conc........	......	65	141	45	44	44	25	24	27
Alfalfa hay......	289	29	18	......	......	......	58	57	62
Selling price per cwt..	$11.15	$11.35	$11.40	$15.10	$15.50	$15.25	$10.00	$10.25	$10.25
Hog gains per steer, lbs...............	......	......	......	67	67	58	......	......	......

[a] Average daily gain in dry lot before and after July 28.
[b] Spring seeding of sweet clover used after August 7, one steer per acre.
[c] Clover mixture: approximately 80% sweet clover and 20% red clover.
[d] Weight of ground ear corn.

fully at least as far north as the 40th parallel. Since lespedeza is a self-seeding annual, it does not, as a rule, attain sufficient growth to be grazed heavily until about July 15. From this date until frost, it produces a wealth of palatable, nutritious forage. The Missouri Station reports 106 pounds of cattle gains per acre from lespedeza during a 6½ week grazing period in comparison with only 25 pounds per acre from bluegrass.

Widespread use of sweet clover as a legume crop in the Corn Belt has naturally raised the question of its value as a forage crop for fattening cattle. Practical cattlemen are somewhat divided as to its merits. Some men make great claims for it, both from the standpoint of its carrying capacity per acre and its flesh-forming properties. Concerning the first claim there can be no question; the second, however, has not been fully sustained. Indeed, it appears from the small amount of data available that sweet clover is too laxative a feed for full-fed cattle during the fore part of the grazing season; also, that upon ripening its seed in midsummer (usually about August 1 to 10), its value for pasture is practically over. Hence, it would seem that sweet clover, when seeded alone, should be regarded as a supplementary forage crop in summer steer feeding. Some other kind of pasture or dry-lot feeding should be relied upon for the gains made in early spring and in late summer and fall. The months of June and July usually find sweet clover at its best, and few forages are its equal at this time of year.

Turning Steers on Pasture. Better results will be secured if the forage is allowed to make a fairly good start before the cattle are turned on it in the spring. The first growth that appears is high in moisture and possesses little fattening properties. April 20 to May 1 will usually see bluegrass sufficiently mature to be used in the central part of the Corn Belt. In the famous bluegrass sections of Kentucky and Iowa the grazing season opens about 10 days earlier and later, respectively.

Steers that have received a heavy feed of grain during the winter months are an exception to the above statements regarding the proper time to turn on grass. Better results will usually be obtained if such cattle are turned onto the pasture in late March or early April as soon as the grass begins to grow. In this way they will become accustomed to the grass so gradually that they will not tend to lose their appetites for corn. When full-fed cattle are turned on to a heavy growth of grass their consumption of grain temporarily falls off, sometimes to but half of what it was in the dry lot. Although their appetite for grain usually will return by the end of the third or fourth week, it is obvious that the gains made during such a transition period are far from satisfactory.

Cattle which are to be turned onto pastures containing an abundance of legumes, especially red clover or alfalfa, should be allowed to graze their fill of some non-legume forage, such as bluegrass or brome grass, before being turned into the field. Once in the field they should not be removed unless severe bloating occurs, in which case, of course, they

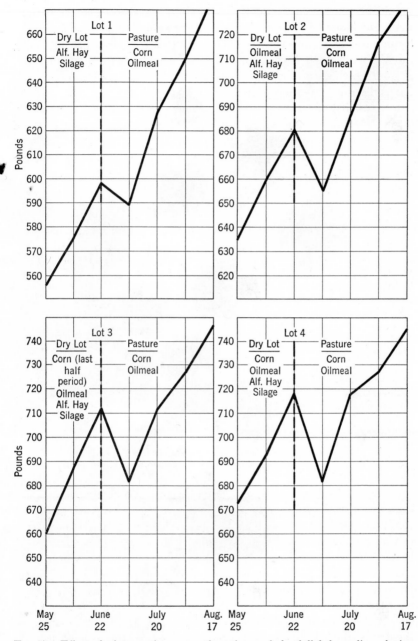

FIG. 57. Effect of winter rations upon the gains made by full-fed yearlings during the first few weeks on pasture. (*Courtesy Ohio Experiment Station.*)

should be removed as quickly as possible. At least two inspections should be made daily until the cattle are thoroughly accustomed to the legume forage. However, the fact that no case of bloat occurs during the first week or 10 days is not proof that it may not give trouble later. A close watch should be kept of the cattle throughout the summer, but especially during periods of high humidity.

Day vs. Night Grazing. Many farmers who full-feed their cattle during the summer confine them in the dry lot overnight and turn them onto the pasture during the day. The object of this procedure is to induce the cattle to eat as much grain as possible by holding them in the feed yard.

TABLE 192

A COMPARISON OF NIGHT- AND DAY-GRAZING FOR FULL-FED CATTLE*

	Confined in Dry Lot	On Pasture at Night	On Pasture during Day	On Pasture Continually
Av. daily gain, lb.	1.74	2.20	1.99	2.00
Av. daily ration				
Shelled corn	12.3	13.6	12.4	13.7
Soybean oil meal	1.0	1.0	1.0	1.0
Clover hay	4.7	1.9	1.8	0.2^a
Pasture, acres per steer	....	0.25	0.25	0.50
Feed per cwt. gain				
Shelled corn	706	617	625	686
Soybean oil meal	55	45	49	49
Clover hay	272	86	93	11
Pasture days	....	11	12	24
Selling price per cwt.	$11.75	$12.25	$12.00	$12.00
Return per head above feed costs	14.00	25.72	20.58	16.89

* Illinois Mimeo. Report, Nov. 14, 1941.
[a] Hay fed in dry lot 6 days before marketing.

Since cattle continually on pasture spend more time grazing at night than during the day, especially in hot weather, it would appear that confining them in the lot during the day, where they would have access to water and shade, and turning them onto the pasture at night might be a better procedure. These two methods of using pastures were compared at the Illinois Station. A third and fourth lot, fed in dry lot and on pasture, respectively, were also included in the test. Grazing at night proved to be much the best plan of utilizing the pasture. Observations made of the cattle disclosed that the cattle confined in the dry lot during the day and turned onto the pasture at night usually grazed steadily for about 3 to 4 hours after they were turned onto the pasture, whereas the cattle pastured during the day usually sought the protection of an artificial shade soon after they were put into the field. The principal difference observed between the cattle pastured at night and those left on pasture continually was that the night-pastured cattle spent much time during the day lying in their well-bedded shed, while the cattle continually in the pasture stood most of the time under their sun shade. (See Table 192.)

TABLE 193

SHELLED VS. GROUND EAR CORN FOR CATTLE FULL-FED ON PASTURE

	Mixed Pasture*			Bluegrass†		Alfalfa†	
	Shelled Corn	Ground Shelled Corn	Ground Ear Corn	Shelled Corn	Ground Ear Corn	Shelled Corn	Ground Ear Corn
Av. weight, lb........	660	667	667	703	709	705	708
Days fed............	190	190	190	133	133	133	133
Av. daily gain, lb.....	2.47	2.40	2.19	2.38	2.08	2.31	2.32
Av. daily ration							
Shelled corn........	16.6	15.9	15.3^a	15.0	13.2^a	12.8	11.4^a
Protein conc........	....	....	....	1.0	1.0	1.0	1.0
Alfalfa hay........	2.2	2.4	2.3	....	....	....	....
Feed per cwt. gain							
Shelled corn........	673	663	654^a	599	635^a	554	491^a
Alfalfa hay........	90	98	105	....	....	....	....
Selling price per cwt...	$5.50	$5.50	$5.50	....	....	....	....
Gain of hogs per steer.	....	....	....	63	23	66	38

* Nebraska Mimeo. Circular 140, 1934.
† Illinois Mimeo. Report, 1934.
^{a} Shelled basis.

Grain Rations for Pasture-Fed Steers. Corn is the usual grain fed to cattle on pasture. Its small bulk makes it combine well with a bulky roughage like pasture, whereas its hard kernels insure rapid drying should it be exposed to rain before being consumed. For this reason whole shelled corn is much better than ground shelled corn for pasture cattle. Ground ear corn is too bulky and unpalatable for cattle fed on non-legume pastures but is better than shelled corn for cattle on sweet clover or alfalfa, as the cob particles tend to reduce the prevalence of scours and bloat.

Owing to the relatively high percentage of protein in young grass, the need for a nitrogenous concentrate is by no means as urgent with pasture- as with dry-lot fed cattle. Except for slightly higher daily gains, resulting from a larger consumption of the more palatable ration, no important advantage is to be secured from feeding protein supplements to full-fed steers that have access to an abundance of fresh, green grass. However, bluegrass, brome grass, as well as all legume forages contain a much lower percentage of protein in midsummer than they do in the spring. Moreover, they are less palatable and

TABLE 194

VALUE OF A PROTEIN SUPPLEMENT AT DIFFERENT STAGES OF THE GRAZING PERIOD FOR STEERS FED ON BLUEGRASS PASTURE

	First Period		Second Period		Total Period	
	May 5 to June 30		July 1 to October 20		May 5 to October 20	
	Av. Daily Gain	Feed Per Cwt. Gain	Av. Daily Gain	Feed Per Cwt. Gain	Av. Daily Gain	Feed Per Cwt. Gain
Missouri Bulletin No. 90* (Av. 4 trials)...................						
Corn alone.....................	2.26	613	1.76	1581	1.97	940
Corn and C. S. M...............	2.27	612	2.05	1332	2.12	833
Missouri Mimeo. Rpts. (Av. 3 trials)						
Corn only 1st 56 days........... } Corn 8 : C. S. M. 1, last 112 days.. }	2.46	330	2.33	771	2.37	637
Corn 8 : C. S. M. 1, 168 days	2.44	354	2.30	806	2.36	671
Corn only 1st 56 days........... } Corn 12 : C. S. M. 1, last 112 days. }	2.47	330	2.23	826	2.31	667
Corn 12 : C. S. M. 1, 168 days......	2.64	324	2.38	776	2.47	600

* First period, May 1–July 31; second period, August 1–December 1.

consequently are consumed in smaller amounts. For these reasons, the feeding of a protein concentrate should be begun on grass pastures about July 1 and on legume pastures about August 1, unless unusually favorable weather conditions delay the maturing of the forage beyond the usual time. The need for a protein concentrate during the summer and fall by cattle fed on bluegrass pasture is well shown by Table 194.

Thus, it appears that during the first 2 months of the feeding period, while the supply of green grass was abundant, no material advantage resulted from the use of the supplementary protein feeds.   The need for additional protein beyond that furnished by the late fall pasture is well shown by Table 195, which reports a trial in which linseed meal was introduced into the ration of one lot at the end of the fifth month.

TABLE 195

VALUE OF PROTEIN SUPPLEMENT DURING THE LATTER PART OF THE GRAZING SEASON*

1906	Daily Gains			Total Feed per lb. Gain		
	Corn Alone	Corn and Linseed Meal	Corn 5 mo. Corn and Linseed Meal 2 months	Corn Alone	Corn and Linseed Meal	Corn 5 mo. Corn and Linseed Meal 2 months
	lbs.	lbs.	lbs.	lbs.	lbs.	lbs.
Yearling Steers						
First 5 months................	1.93	2.23	2.01			
Last 2 months.................	1.69	2.12	2.48			
Total — 7 months............	1.86	2.20	2.14	7.40	6.95	7.09
Two-year-old Steers						
First 5 months................	2.94	2.92	2.95			
Last 2 months.................	1.85	2.12	2.27			
Total — 7 months,............	2.63	2.70	2.78	7.73	6.96	7.28

* Missouri Bulletin 90, 1911.

In summing up these Missouri grazing experiments, which constitute the outstanding investigations of their kind carried on in the United States, one cannot do better than to quote a few items from the Summary and Conclusions of Bulletin 90:

1. *Rate of Gain.*   In general, where nitrogenous supplements were fed the rate of gain was greater than where corn alone constituted the grain ration.

2. *Palatability.*   One explanation of the larger gains is that the supplemented rations seemed to be more palatable and were eaten in larger quantities.

3. *Grain for 1 Pound Gain.*   There is little difference between the various rations in respect to the number of pounds of grain required to make 1 pound of gain.

4. *Cost of Gains.*   The relative cost for each hundred pounds of gain was less for the lots receiving shelled corn than for the lots receiving supplemented rations.

5. *When to Feed Supplements.*   Our results clearly indicate the value of supplements in maintaining the appetite and in securing satisfactory gains during the last stages of the feeding period.   The use of supplements during

the first part of the feeding period has in many experiments been of doubtful economic value.

6. *Supplement for Half-Fat Cattle.* The fatter the animals, the more efficient relatively are the supplemented rations.

7. *Proportion of Supplement to Feed.* A grain ration composed of 6 or 7 parts of corn to 1 of linseed or cottonseed meal has been more efficient than rations containing larger proportions of supplement.

With the high cost of protein concentrates compared with the price of corn, the consumption of these relatively expensive materials should be kept as low as possible consistent with the actual needs of the cattle. Although the ratio named above should probably be considered satisfactory for yearling steers during the last 2 months of the feeding period, a still wider ratio is recommended for older cattle that are being

TABLE 196

DRY LOT *vs.* PASTURE FOR FINISHING HALF–FAT CATTLE*

Place Finished	1st Trial		2d Trial		3d Trial		Average 3 Trials	
	Dry Lot	Pasture	Dry Lot	Pasture	Dry Lot	Pasture	Dry Lot	Pasture
	lbs.	lbs.	lbs.	lbs.	lbs.	lbs.	lbs.	lbs.
Weight in Spring	880	880	870	875	827	809	859	855
Average daily gain:								
1st month	2.06	0.66	2.16	1.61	2 37	1.34	2.20	1.20
2d month	1 90	2.05	1.58	1 41	1 35	1 66	1.61	1.71
3d month	1.01	1.00	1.38	1 56	1.35	1.38	1 25	1.31
Total — 90 days	1.65	1.24	1.71	1.53	1 69	1.46	1.68	1.41
Grain eaten per day:								
1st 10 days	14.90	8.22	14.55	10.27	16.00	14.50	15.15	11.00
Total — 90 days	17.04	11 84	16 17	14.46	16.74	15.92	16.65	14.07
Grain per lb. gain:								
1st month	7.60	13 94	7 06	6.62	6.96	11.02	7.21	10.53
Total — 90 days	10.28	9.55	9.46	.9.45	9 89	10.88	9.88	9.96

* Indiana Bulletin 142, 1910.

fed on grass. One to 7 for yearlings, 1 to 8 for 2-year-olds, and 1 to 10 for 3-year-olds may be taken as approximately correct. Somewhat wider ratios probably would meet the nutritional requirements of the animals, but the larger amounts of protein will tend to improve the hair coats and general appearance of the cattle, thereby enhancing their market value.

Turning Half-Fat Cattle on Grass. Cattle that have received a fairly liberal ration during the winter, so that they are half-fat or better at the opening of the grazing season, should be finished in a dry lot rather than on grass. To turn such animals on pasture will in all probability result in a marked decrease in grain consumption for the first 3 or 4 weeks while they are becoming accustomed to grass. This decreased consumption of grain, together with the "washy" character of the spring grass, will result in very moderate gains for the first month or 6 weeks. In fact, it is not unusual for cattle under such conditions to show an actual loss in weight when weighed 2 or 3 weeks after leaving the dry lot.[4]

Should it be necessary to put half-fat cattle on pasture because of a scarcity of dry roughage, they should be turned on grass early in the spring when the grass first starts to grow, and their dry roughage should be continued until the grass is fairly mature. In this way the cattle will become accustomed to the change in their ration very gradually and will not be likely to go off feed.

Fattening Cattle on Grass Alone. Comparatively few cattle are grazed without grain in the Corn Belt with the expectation of selling them for slaughter in the fall. In only a few sections of the central states is the grass sufficiently nutritious and abundant to put feeder steers in satisfactory killing condition without the aid of grain. The common practice where no grain is fed is to buy light steers in the spring, graze them until September or October, and finish them on corn during the fall and early winter. In other words, the cattle are handled as "stockers" during the summer, growth and development, rather than a marked improvement in condition, being the results sought for. Good, thrifty steers weighing from 500 to 700 pounds are the kind desired for this purpose. Thin animals, rather than those showing some flesh, are preferred, as they can be bought with fewer dollars and will make larger gains when turned on grass.[5] With good grazing conditions such steers will improve greatly in appearance and will usually grade at least one grade higher in the fall than they did the previous spring. If marketed when removed from pasture they will not, as a rule, be fat enough to be sold for slaughter but will be returned to the country for further feeding.

Advantages of Grazing Without Grain. The grazing of stockers during the summer affords a means of utilizing permanent or temporary pasture crops during years when corn is scarce or high in price. Instead of being fattened on high-priced old corn, the cattle are held until the new crop, which is usually much cheaper, is ready to feed. Other advantages of this method of management are that a minimum

[4] *Cf.* Fig. 57.
[5] *Cf.* p. 191.

of labor is required during the summer and that the cattle may run on the same pasture area as other kinds of livestock.

Notwithstanding these advantages in favor of grazing cattle without grain, comparatively few steers are so handled in the Corn Belt, because of the unfavorable market conditions that commonly prevail for stockers and feeders in the spring and fall. Such cattle are bought in the spring when prices for stockers are at the highest point of the year, and are ready for the market or the feed lot in the fall when feeders are relatively cheap, owing to the large receipts of western range cattle at this season. Consequently, it not infrequently happens, if indeed it

FIG. 58. Yearling steers on brome-grass pasture. Brome grass, if sown on fertile soil, produces an abundance of nutritious, palatable forage in the spring and early summer. Frequently two yearling steers per acre can be carried from about May 1 to the middle of July, and one per acre thereafter. (*Courtesy C. B. & Q. Railway.*)

is not the rule, that stocker cattle will cost more per pound in the spring than they will be worth the following fall when they are considerably heavier and in much better flesh.

It should not be inferred that profits are impossible from cattle that are grazed without grain. Gains from grass alone are very cheap and may be well below the market price of good or choice feeder steers. However, this method of management brings the Corn Belt farm into direct competition with the large ranches of the West, where land values and other grazing costs are much lower than they are in the Corn Belt. If this system of handling cattle is to be successfully followed on high-priced land, the carrying capacity of each acre grazed must be kept high by the use of heavy-yielding, temporary pasture crops that are grown as a part of the regular farm rotation.

Limited Grain Rations for Pasture-Fed Cattle. The feeding of a limited grain ration to cattle on pasture is not a common practice. Unless they are removed from the pasture to the dry lot for feeding, some of the animals may not be at the bunks when the grain is fed and, hence, will not get any. The more common practice is to feed no grain at all during the first 2 or 3 months, while the pasture is palatable and nutritious, and to supply a full feed during the late summer and fall, when grazing conditions are less favorable. This plan has the advantage of utilizing the pasture when it is at its best and of supplying an abundance of digestible nutrients during the period when cattle on even a limited feed of grain will eat relatively little of the dry, unpalatable pasture. Another advantage of deferring the feeding of grain to the last half of the summer is that considerable labor is saved.

Yearling steers fed a half feed of shelled corn during the entire grazing period at the Nebraska Station gained about as fast as a second lot full fed on pasture.[6] This indicates that they ate considerably more pasture than the full-fed cattle. It will be recalled that in the Indiana limited corn experiments, which were carried on in dry lot, the steers fed no corn during the first half of the period but a full feed during the last half ate less grain and more roughage and made larger gains than the lot that received a half feed of grain throughout the test.[7] It seems reasonable to believe that these two methods of feeding corn would give similar results with cattle fed on good pasture.

Supplementing Pastures with Small Amounts of Concentrates. In the range states the most commonly used feed in times of grass shortage is a protein concentrate, usually in the form of "cake" or "cubes." These feeds are usually scattered on clean ground at the rate of 1 to 3 pounds per head daily. Often they are fed every other day at double the daily allowance in order to save labor and to insure that every animal will get at least a mouthful.

Since range pastures frequently mature early as the result of dry weather and are therefore low in protein, many ranchers feed cottonseed or soybean cake during the late summer and autumn to those cattle which they plan to sell in the fall. This practice results in heavier weights and higher selling prices per hundred because the cattle are more attractive to both packer buyers and Corn Belt feeders. In three trials made at the Oklahoma Station $3\frac{1}{2}$ pounds of either cottonseed cake or shelled corn per head daily proved to be valuable supplements to bluestem pasture. Also, a supplement fed after July 1 was almost as effective as one fed during the entire grazing season. All

---

[6] Nebraska Cattle Progress Report 51, 1951.

[7] *Cf.* p. 272.

three lots fed the supplements were much more profitable than the check lot which was fed none. (See Table 197.) It is not likely that small amounts of concentrates would give as favorable returns on Corn Belt pastures as were secured at Oklahoma except during a severe drought when very little green forage was available. If a supplement is to be fed while pastures are still green, shelled corn would be preferred to a protein concentrate on the basis of the Oklahoma experiments.

TABLE 197

THE VALUE OF PROTEIN CONCENTRATES AS SUPPLEMENTS TO BLUESTEM
PASTURE IN PRODUCING GRASS-FATTENED STEERS*

(3-Year-Old Steers; Average of 3 Trials)

Average, Grazing Period: Apr. 25–Aug. 12 (109 Days)	None	C. S. M.	Ground Shelled Corn	C. S. M. After July 3
Av. daily ration, lb.	. .	3.4	3.4	3.3
Av. daily gain	2.19	2.62	2.54	2.47
Av. selling price	$23.15	$25.15	$25.50	$24.15
Av. net return over feed costs	45.23	61.22	65.28	58.25
Av. dressing percentage	57.4	58.3	58.6	58.1

* Oklahoma Misc. Publs. 11, 13, and 15, 1947, 1948, and 1949.

Self-Feeding Protein Concentrates on Pasture. The self-feeding of a mixture of cottonseed meal and rock salt to range cattle has been practiced with apparent success for several years, especially in the state of Texas. By varying the amount of salt in the mixture the desired consumption of protein concentrate is obtained. A mixture of 20 per cent salt and 80 per cent cottonseed meal will usually result in the consumption of about 2 pounds of cottonseed meal daily by yearling steers on good range pasture. As the range grasses dry up and become less palatable it is necessary to increase the salt in the mixture to about 30 per cent of the total weight. This method of feeding a protein concentrate results in the consumption of far more salt than is needed by the cattle, and it may have harmful results if continued over several months. More information is needed about the effect of a heavy consumption of salt upon the bacteria of the rumen and upon the general health of the cattle before the practice can be recommended.[8]

Gains Made from Grass. Gains made wholly from grass are, as a rule, from 60 to 75 per cent of the gains made by cattle on full feed. On good pastures that furnish an abundance of forage, yearling steers

[8] Cf. p. 462.

will average 1.25 to 1.5 pounds per day for the entire grazing season. Two-year-olds should gain 1.5 to 2 pounds per day. Steers that have been poorly wintered and are very thin when turned on grass will make larger gains, owing to the "fill" taken on during the first month.

The largest gains are usually obtained during June and July, when conditions for grazing are most favorable. Earlier in the year the grass is too soft and "washy" to be highly nutritious, and later in the

TABLE 198

THE EFFECT OF AGE AND CONDITION UPON THE GAINS MADE ON
PASTURE ALONE*

Class of Cattle	Kansas Flint Hills Section (U. S. D. A. Dept. Bull. 1454), 1926				Southwestern Virginia (Virginia Bulletin 258), 1927			
	Days on Pasture	Acreage per Steer	Total Gain (lb.)	Aver. Daily Gain (lb.)	Days on Pasture	Acreage per Steer	Total Gain (lb.)	Aver. Daily Gain (lb.)
Thin aged steers......	133	4.5	293	2.20	199	4	235	1.18
Half-fat aged steers....	128	4.2	233	1.82	..	..	..	..
Fat aged steers........	115	4.5	167	1.45	..	..	..	..
Thin 2-year-old steers..	132	3.7	232	1.76	189	3.25	297	1.57
Half-fat 2-year-old steers	155	5.2	233	1.50	..	..	..	...
Thin yearling steers...	168	3.9	206	1.23	168	2.5	234	1.39
Half-fat yearling steers.	187	4.0	193	1.03	..	..	..	..

season it becomes dry and unpalatable so that the cattle tend to eat little more than is required to maintain their weight. Flies and extremely hot weather also are responsible for the smaller gains made during the late summer and early fall.

These statements are more or less opposed to the belief commonly held by stockmen that the largest gains are made during the late summer and early fall when the grass is hard and dry. Such a belief, although erroneous, arises from the fact that the flesh of grass-fattened cattle seems to undergo a change with the curing of the grass toward the end of the grazing season. Apparently the flesh loses some of its high water content, so characteristic of grass-fed cattle in midsummer, and becomes drier and firmer to the touch. During years of copious fall rains that keep the pastures fresh and green, this change in quality of the flesh is barely discernible.

Green grass is also conducive to heavy "fills" at the time of shipment. Such fills mean a large shrinkage during transit, as well as low dressing percentages at the time of slaughter. Hence, cattle that are soon to be marketed should be kept away from green, tender grass for 4 or 5 days before loading. This may be done by either feeding them hay in a dry lot or turning them on a pasture that consists of relatively ripe, mature forage.

TABLE 199

SEASONAL VARIATIONS IN GAINS MADE ON PASTURE ALONE

	Missouri Bluegrass*		Illinois Bluegrass		Illinois Alfalfa		Illinois Brome Grass		Kansas Blue Stem		Virginia Bluegrass	
Source of Information	Mimeo. Rpt.		Mimeo. Rpt.		Mimeo. Rpt.		Mimeo. Rpt.		Kansas Circ. No. 97		Virginia Bull. No. 164	
	Days	Total Gain per Acre	Days	Av. Daily Gain	Days	Av. Daily Gain	Days	Av. Daily Gain	Days	Av. Daily Gain	Days	Av. Daily Gain
1st period	28	42.0	25	2.26	18	2.94	28	2.14	28	1.92	31	2.09
2nd period	28	22.7	28	1.90	28	2.96	28	2.37	30	2.33	30	3.53
3rd period	28	14.4	28	1.49	28	2.09	28	1.56	31	1.25	31	1.90
4th period	28	14.6	28	.89	14	1.63	28	.71	31	1.40	31	.53
5th period	28	9.0	28	2.23	28	2.36	28	.36	32	1.46	15	1.43
6th period	28	3.7	20	.75	24	1.33	28	.71	31	.20	..	....
7th period	..	.....	..	....	..	....	17	.29	28	−.55	..	....
Total	168	106.4	157	1.80	140	2.16	185	1.32	209	1.15	138	1.94

* Average of 3 years.

Area of Pasture per Steer. Pastures vary so much in productiveness that no definite statement can be made as to their carrying capacities. Two acres of average Corn Belt bluegrass are commonly regarded as the area necessary to pasture a 1000-pound steer during a normal grazing season. Lighter cattle require a smaller area in proportion to their weight.

When cattle receive a full feed of grain, only one-third to one-half as much pasture is required as when the cattle are fattened on grass alone. Some feeders use a minimum of grass, feeding as many as 80 mature steers and as many or more hogs on 20 acres. A pasture so heavily stocked, however, becomes so thickly covered with manure as to render the grass unpalatable. This is particularly likely to be true of permanent bluegrass pastures adjoining feeding yards that are used year after year. The presence of a heavy growth of grass under such conditions is not always proof that the cattle have an adequate amount of pasture. The same cattle turned on an equal area, similar as far as growth of forage is concerned but free from objectionable odors, might eat the grass down to the roots in the course of 2 or 3 weeks.

That the pasture should be no larger than is necessary to insure an adequate amount of forage is shown by the work of the North Dakota Experiment Station in coöperation with the United States Department of Agriculture.[9] In these trials, covering a period of 6 years, it was found that 7 acres of range pasture per steer produced larger daily gains than either 5 or 10 acres. By observing the steers carefully throughout the day, it was noticed that the cattle in the larger fields tended to spend more of their time in walking about and less time in grazing than those in the smaller tracts. Steers in a 30-acre pasture walked $1\frac{5}{8}$ miles per day; those in a 100-acre pasture, $3\frac{1}{16}$ miles; and a herd of dairy cows in a 640-acre field of similar grazing land walked $5\frac{1}{2}$ miles.[10]

Although these figures have little direct application to Corn Belt conditions where the pastures are relatively small, they do serve to emphasize the fact that cattle in large pastures spend a considerable amount of time and energy moving about on more or less aimless excursions. Anything that can be done to lessen this tendency, such as the providing of water and shade in various parts of the fields, will result in larger and more economical gains.

A proper balance between cattle and available forage is indeed difficult to maintain. Heavy stocking will insure the utilization of all available forage and a maximum gain per acre. However, under such conditions the cattle will get somewhat less than what they want to eat and, hence, will make less than maximum gains per head. On the other hand, if the rate of stocking is low enough to insure each animal his fill of choice forage each day, some forage, especially the less desirable plants and parts of plants, will not be eaten. The result will be maximum gains per head but low gains per acre. (See Table 200.) A happy medium, represented by moderate grazing, is the desired goal, but it is often difficult to attain, especially during abnormal weather conditions which greatly affect the growth of pastures.

Since legumes and mixtures of grasses and legumes grown in a 3- to 5-year crop rotation are valued largely for the nitrogen and organic

[9] U. S. D. A. Dept. Bulletin 1170, 1923.
[10] North Dakota Bulletin 154, 1921.

matter they will add to the soil, they should not, if pastured, be grazed too closely, else they will be of little benefit to the grain crops that follow. It is much better that they be stocked with only enough cattle to eat 50 to 70 per cent of the forage, leaving the remainder to

TABLE 200

EFFECT OF RATE OF STOCKING UPON GAIN
PER ACRE AND GAIN PER HEAD*

	Overgrazed			Moderately Grazed			Undergrazed		
	Area per Head, acres	Gain per Acre, lb.	Gain per Steer, lb.	Area per Head, acres	Gain per Acre, lb.	Gain per Steer, lb.	Area per Head, acres	Gain per Acre, lb.	Gain per Steer, lb.
1946	1.87	36	67	3.2	49	156	5.4	33	180
1947	2.03	68	138	3.4	39	134	5.2	28	146
1948	2.03	95	193	3.4	69	234	5.2	48	248
1949	2.03	52	105	3.4	49	165	5.2	38	194
Average	1.99	63	126	3.4	52	172	5.2	37	192

* Kansas, Ft. Hays Station Reports, 1947–1950.

TABLE 201

RECOMMENDED RATE OF STOCKING BEEF CATTLE PASTURES*
(Acres per Head)

	Permanent Grasses Unfertilized		Legumes or Mixed Grasses and Legumes in Rotation with Grain Crops	
	Yearlings	2-Year-Olds	Yearlings	2-Year-Olds
1. Pasture only				
a. Entire season	1.5	2.25	1.0	1.5
b. Until Aug. 1, then				
removed to dry lot	1.0	1.50	0.66	1.0
2. Full fed on pasture				
a. Entire season	0.5	0.75	0.33	0.5
b. After July 1	1.0	1.50	0.66	1.0

* For soils of average fertility which will produce 40 to 50 bushels of corn or 1½ tons of hay in an average season.

be returned to the soil. Even permanent pastures, like bluegrass and brome grass, will not remain productive if they are grazed closely year after year. Under such unfavorable conditions the stand becomes thin, and the bare spots are gradually taken over by weeds. A weedy permanent pasture is almost unmistakable evidence of overgrazing. It is believed that the rates of stocking recommended in Table 201 will prevent overgrazing except during extremely dry years and will result in permanent pastures becoming better with the passing of each year and rotation pastures adding large amounts of both nitrogen and humus to the soil.

Cattle Gains per Acre. Gains secured from improved pastures during recent years have been so high as to disprove the statement that the level lands of the Corn Belt are too valuable to be seeded to pastures

TABLE 202

GAINS SECURED PER ACRE OF IMPROVED PASTURE
WHEN NO CONCENTRATES ARE FED*

(No Nitrogen Fertilizer Applied after Seeding)

Location	Kind of Forage	Period Grazed	Days Grazed	Gains per Acre, pounds
Central Missouri	Bluegrass	May 6–Sept. 27	144	216
(Columbia)	Bluegrass-lespedeza	May 6–Sept. 27	144	279
Northwest Missouri	Wheat-lespedeza	Apr. 21–June 26		
(Lathrop)		July 27–Aug. 31	91	313
	Bluegrass-sweet clover	Apr. 27–Oct. 4	160	315
	Bluegrass-ladino	Apr. 27–Oct. 4	160	359
Northwest Indiana	Alfalfa-timothy	May 5–Oct. 14	162	264
(Upland)	Bluegrass	May 5–Oct. 14	162	198
Central Illinois	Bluegrass			160
(Urbana)	Bluegrass-ladino	Apr. 15–Sept. 20	158	329
	Brome grass-ladino	Apr. 15–Sept. 20	158	304
	Brome grass-alfalfa	Apr. 13–Nov. 1	202	342
	Alfalfa	May 6–Sept. 23	140	383
	Sweet clover, 2nd year	May 6–Aug. 2	88	220
	Haas mixture, 2nd year	Apr. 30–Nov. 1	185	416
Southern Illinois	Basic mixture[a]	Apr. 20–Nov. 25	219	277
(Dixon Springs)	Basic mixture + alta fescue	Apr. 20–Nov. 24	218	325
	Basic mixture + brome grass	Apr. 20–Nov. 24	218	364
	Basic mixture + orchard grass	Apr. 20–Nov. 24	218	337
	Basic mixture + bluegrass	Apr. 20–Nov. 24	218	296
	Ladino, timothy, red clover, alta fescue	....	...	564[b]

* Source of data: mimeographed reports of state experiment stations.
[a] Basic mixture (pounds per acre): ladino 1, timothy 4, red top 3, alfalfa 4, lespedeza 5.
[b] Three-year average; combined gains of cattle and sheep.

for beef cattle. (See Table 202.) With yearling and 2-year-old feeder cattle costing from 20 to 30 cents a pound as they did during the period 1946–1950, it is not difficult to show that an acre of pasture, which puts 300 pounds of gain on a yearling or 2-year-old steer each summer, will return as much net profit per year as an acre of 80-bushel corn.

The most surprising fact disclosed by the pasture experiments listed in the preceding table is that the productiveness of pastures seems to bear little relation to the natural fertility of the soil. For example, pastures established on thin, eroded land at the Dixon Springs, Illinois, Station have been somewhat more productive than those at Urbana on level, brown silt loam. Part of the difference may be explained by the

FIG. 59. A bluegrass-ladino clover pasture 2 years after it was seeded. This 10-acre pasture carried fifteen 2-year-old steers from April 22 to June 24, and seven steers from June 24 to Sept. 20. Total gain per acre, 329 pounds. Photograph taken July 19. (*Courtesy Illinois Experiment Station.*)

longer grazing season, but the principal difference appears to be that the legumes encounter less competition from the grasses on the poor soil and, hence, constitute a larger percentage of the available forage. Obviously, much heavier applications of fertilizers, principally limestone and phosphate, are required on the poor soil in preparing it for seeding. Also more labor is usually required to clear the land of brush, to fill in gullies, and to construct brush dams to control erosion.

Better Methods of Utilizing Pasture. Many different methods of utilizing pastures in the fattening of cattle are in use throughout the Corn Belt, each of which probably has more or less merit for a given situation. Farmers who have a considerable area of pasture land will do well to study their present use of pastures critically, since pastures can easily be more of a liability than an asset in beef production. In fact, a cattleman of much experience and a close observer of other feeders' methods once made the statement that "inexperienced feeders have lost more money trying to use pastures to save a little feed than pastures have ever made for those few feeders who know how to use them wisely." This is an excellent statement of the situation and emphasizes the fact that summer-feeding cattle on pasture is in many respects a more difficult task than winter-feeding in the dry lot in so far as profits are concerned.

Apparently one common error in the management of pastures is an attempt to use the available pasture in a cattle-feeding enterprise that would succeed as well or even better without it, instead of adopting a plan of feeding that seems to offer the best opportunity to use the pasture efficiently. This is merely another instance of the necessity of fitting the cattle-feeding program to the available feed supply.

Cattle full-fed grain on pasture throughout the spring and summer use too small an amount of grass to make this plan of feeding satisfactory from the standpoint of utilizing comparatively large areas of pasture. If the pasture is stocked sufficiently heavily to consume most of the grass, 2 to 3 head an acre, the number of cattle required may be greater than the supply of corn available on the farm will finish satisfactorily.

A study of the monthly gains of cattle on pastures, given in Table 199, will disclose that pasture is at its best in spring and early summer. Consequently it should be utilized at this time if the greatest returns are to be realized from a given area. To stock a pasture in the spring with only the number of cattle that it will carry through the entire season with average weather conditions is to permit a great waste of forage through failure to harvest the grass when it is most valuable. Too heavy stocking at any time during the grazing season will result in little or no gain, since all the available grass will be used for maintenance and none for production. Consequently, the logical thing to do is to stock the pasture with the number of cattle that will insure the consumption of the forage at about the rate it grows at that time of year. This will mean stocking the field fairly heavily at the beginning, perhaps 2 or more head to the acre, and removing animals from time to time to supplementary pastures or to the dry lot where they are got onto a full feed of grain. This system of grazing has been used at the Illinois Station with very satisfactory results, as is shown by the fact that the gains from pasture alone have averaged 295 pounds an acre over a 5-year period.

Rotation Grazing. The dividing of a pasture into two or more small fields each of which is to be grazed in turn is frequently recommended.

TABLE 203

EXAMPLES OF ADJUSTING THE RATE OF STOCKING PASTURES
TO CORRESPOND WITH THE FEED SUPPLY*

Yearling Heifers, 1938				Yearling Steers and Heifers, 1939			
	5 Acres Timothy	10 Acres Mixed Forage	10 Acres Orchard Grass		10 Acres Bluegrass	5 Acres Mixed Forage	10 Acres Orchard Grass
Heifers on fields				Cattle on fields			
Apr. 30–June 25				Apr. 28–June 26			
(56 days).........	8	18	16	(59 days).......	10	8	14
June 25–Sept. 3				June 26–July 24			
(70 days).........	4	17	8	(28 days)........	10	12	8
Sept. 3–Sept. 17				July 24–Aug. 28			
(14 days)........	4	8	8	(35 days)........	8	6	6
Sept. 17–Oct. 21				Aug. 28–Sept. 18			
(34 days).........	4	5	15	(21 days)........	8	6	11
Oct. 21–Nov. 1				Sept. 18–Oct. 3			
(11 days)........ .	None	5	11	(15 days)........	6	4	11
				Oct. 3–Oct. 25			
				(22 days)........	6	2	4
Cattle days per acre....	184	253.5	220	Cattle days per acre..	152.8	247.2	172.6
Total gain per acre, lb...	262	416	245	Total gain per acre, lb.	137	286	169

* Illinois Mimeo. Reports, Aug. 25, 1939, and Nov. 8, 1940.

Such a plan of grazing has given good success on dairy farms where the cows normally are driven to and from the pasture twice daily. However, it has several disadvantages from the standpoint of the beef producer. Among them are (1) the expense of constructing extra fencing and providing water and shade, (2) the tendency of the pastures that are deferred in the spring to be coarse and unpalatable by the time they are needed, and (3) the slowness with which closely grazed pastures recover if the weather is unfavorable for the growth of forage. Experiments carried on at the Indiana Station indicate that rotation grazing of permanent pastures on which only mineral fertilizers have been applied results in less than 5 per cent increase in production and, hence, is unprofitable.[11] If the rotation grazing of permanent pastures is to be practiced, a carefully worked-out plan of fertilization with nitrogen should be followed, which will insure their quick recovery after the cattle are removed. Rotation grazing may also be used successfully with rye, alfalfa, ladino clover, Sudan grass,

[11] Purdue University Agronomy Mimeo. AY-11A, 1948.

and other crops that normally produce a heavy second growth after they have been closely grazed.

TABLE 204

EFFECT OF ROTATION GRAZING UPON CATTLE GAINS PER ACRE*

| Forage Grazed | Number of Years Averaged | Fertilizer Applied | Total Gains per Acre, pounds | |
			Continuous Grazing	Rotation Grazing
Permanent bluegrass	6	Lime, P, and K	215	224
Alfalfa-timothy	5	Lime, P, and K	180	216

* Purdue University Agronomy Mimeo. AY-35A, 1950.

Deferred Grazing. Many Corn Belt pastures are grazed so early in the spring that the grass has no opportunity to build up root reserves before the leaves, where the food nutrients are elaborated, are eaten off by the cattle in their search for a bite of green forage. The food value of early spring pasturage is very low because of the very high moisture content. This is especially true of legume forages like alfalfa and sweet clover. Cattle turned onto such pastures when the forage is only a few inches high usually scour badly and make little if any gain. Indeed, they may even lose weight unless they have been wintered on very poor rations. Much better results usually are secured if grazing is deferred until the plants have made a good growth of both roots and tops and have had time to store an appreciable amount of dry matter in the stems and leaves. (See Table 205.)

The deferring of grazing in midsummer by removing the cattle from a closely grazed pasture and returning them, perhaps in smaller numbers, after the forage has made a good growth is an important phase of good cattle and pasture management. A fertilized bluegrass pasture at the Indiana Station which was heavily grazed from May 20 to July 15 and then rested until September 9 when grazing was resumed produced 346 pounds of gain per acre in comparison with only 237 pounds of gain for a similar pasture on which rotation grazing was practiced the entire season. Thus, grazing the bluegrass during spring and early summer and again in the fall, during the seasons when bluegrass pasture is most productive, resulted in an increase of 46 per cent in total gains per acre.[12]

The Kansas Plan of Utilizing Pasture. The Kansas Experiment Station has conducted extensive experiments on the utilization of pasture in fattening yearling cattle for market with particular reference

[12] Purdue University Agronomy Mimeo. AY-11A, 1948.

to the bluestem pastures of that state. Although this grass differs somewhat from pasture forages grown in the Corn Belt proper, results obtained at the Missouri, Nebraska, and Illinois stations, where the same methods of grazing have been used, are so similar to those obtained in Kansas as to leave little doubt that the plan of grazing

TABLE 205

COMPARISON OF EARLY AND DEFERRED GRAZING OF BLUEGRASS PASTURES*
(Yearling Steers)

Period	Days	Early Grazing (5 Acres)			Deferred Grazing (10 Acres)		
		Number of Cattle	Area per Head	A. D. G.	Number of Cattle	Area per Head	A. D. G.
Apr. 23–May 11.	18	10	0.5	1.28	..	..	..
May 11–May 28	17	10	0.5	0.12	..	..	..
May 28–June 22	25	3	1.7	1.13	14	0.7	2.26
June 22–July 20.	28	3	1.7	1.19	16	0.6	1.90
July 20–Aug. 17.	28	3	1.7	1.07	16(4)[a]	0.6(2.5)	1.49
Aug. 17–Sept. 14	28	3	1.7	0.48	4	2.5	0.89
Sept. 14–Oct. 12.	28	3	1.7	2.62	4	2.5	2.23
Oct. 12–Nov. 1..	20	3	1.7	0	4	2.5	0.75

Total time grazed......		172 days	157 days
Total cattle days.......		821	1310
Cattle days per acre....		164	131
Total gain............		800 lb.	2360 lb.
Av. daily gain........		0.97	1.80
Gain per acre.........		160	236

* Illinois Mimeo. Report, Aug. 25, 1939.
[a] Sixteen steers until July 28, and 4 steers thereafter.

recommended by the Kansas Station is well suited for all pasture forages that produce their heaviest growth in the spring and early summer.

The object of the Kansas experiments was to determine the best method of using pasture in the fattening of beef calves purchased in the fall and marketed approximately a year later as fat yearlings. Some of the different methods of feeding and grazing used are shown in Table 206. The plan which almost always was most profitable was as follows:

1. Steer calves wintered sufficiently well to gain from 1.3 to 1.5 pounds a day. A ration consisting of 16 to 20 pounds of Atlas sorgo silage, 2 pounds of legume hay, 1 pound of protein concentrate, and 4 to 5 pounds of shelled corn was found to be excellent for this purpose. Omitting the shelled corn from the winter ration was found to be

TABLE 206

THE KANSAS METHOD OF UTILIZING PASTURE IN FATTENING YEARLING CATTLE*
Standard Plan: Winter well; graze 90 days; full-feed 100 days in dry lot

Comparison of Standard Plan with Variation Therefrom (3-yr. averages)	Winter Gain 136 days	Pasture Gain 90 days	Gain While Full-fed Grain	Total Gain	Selling Price per Cwt.	Margin a Head	Corn-Fed per Head (bu.)
(1926–1929)							
Standard Plan	258	98	256	612	$14.92	$43.54	37
No corn fed in winter	183	123	263	569	14.58	40.54	26
(1929–1932)							
Standard Plan	270	91	285	646	9.00	11.76	39
Full-fed on pasture after May 1	268	...	283	551	8.83	.69	43
Full-fed on pasture after August 1	269	93	271	633	8.08	4.17	39
(1932–1936)							
Standard Plan	240	93	259	592	7.75	4.66	37
Fed 60 days on pasture after Aug. 1; last 40 days in dry lot	236	93	250	579	7.42	3.01	37
(1933–1937)							
Standard Plan	231	90	265	586	10.35	10.17	38
Winter grain ration discontinued gradually during first 4 weeks on pasture	229	104	256	589	9.73	5.87	39
Winter grain ration continued on pasture	219	131	247	597	10.20	3.64	46

* Kansas Experiment Station: Mimeographed Report.

advisable with heifer calves but not with steer calves, as steers wintered only on cane silage and hay lacked sufficient finish to sell satisfactorily the next fall.

2. Graze on pasture without grain for approximately 90 days, or from May 1 to August 1. Although these were the limiting dates in all the Kansas experiments, results obtained at other stations indicate that the condition of the pasture should be taken into consideration in deciding when to begin and end the grazing period. Obviously nothing is to be

gained by leaving cattle on a pasture that does not furnish enough feed to insure reasonably good gains.

3. Full-feed in dry lot for 100 days, or from approximately August 1 to November 15. Various other plans of feeding were tried, but none was found to be as satisfactory as this. Steers fed on pasture during the last 100 days did not gain as fast as those removed to the dry lot and sold for a much lower price. Other plans involving various combinations of pasture and dry-lot feeding were also inferior to the standard method. (See Table 206.)

As stated above, the Kansas plan of using pastures has been successfully used at the Nebraska, Missouri, and Illinois stations. Its chief points are: (1) the cattle are wintered in such a way as to make them able to use pasture efficiently; (2) the grass is grazed at the stage of growth when it is most palatable and nutritious; (3) when the productive season of the pasture is over the cattle are removed to the dry lot and full-fed for the late fall market, which usually is a good season to market grain-fed yearling steers of good quality.

The Missouri Plan. Many valuable grazing experiments have been carried out at the Missouri Station to compare different methods of utilizing the pastures of that state. The plan found to be most satisfactory differs from the Kansas plan principally in the kind of pastures used and in the length of the finishing period in dry lot. Fall-sown wheat, bluegrass, and Korean lespedeza pastures, usually grazed in that order, have provided good grazing from about April 15 until October 1, or for 5½ months. As a result of the long grazing season, the period of dry-lot feeding has often been reduced to 60 or 70 days. Usually from 550 to 600 pounds of gain are made by each steer, which is fed from 20 to 30 bushels of corn, excluding the corn in the silage. About 30 per cent of the total gain is made during the winter on silage and legume hay, 45 per cent in the summer on pasture, and 25 per cent during the fattening period in dry lot. The cost of gains has been remarkably low.

Some of the cattle in the Missouri experiments have been carried over the second winter, grazed the following summer, and sold in the fall as 2-year-olds after a feeding period of only 6 or 8 weeks. Approximately 85 per cent of the 825–850 pounds of total gain has been made from roughages and pasture, and only 15 per cent from the corn and hay fed in the dry lot. (See Table 207.)

The Dixon Springs Plan. The University of Illinois, at the Dixon Springs Station on the badly eroded hilly area in the southern part of the state, has compared several methods of utilizing pastures with home-bred calves. One plan, which has given excellent results, differs from the Kansas plan only in respect to the finishing period during the late summer and fall. At the Dixon Springs Station both yearling and 2-year-old steers are full fed on pasture, whereas at the Kansas Station they are fed in dry lot. Lespedeza and ladino clover, either

TABLE 207

THE MISSOURI PLAN OF UTILIZING PASTURE IN PRODUCING
FAT YEARLING AND 2–YEAR–OLD STEERS*

	Fat Yearlings[a]			Fat 2-Year-Olds[b]		
	Length of Period, days	Gains, pounds	Percentage of Total	Length of Period, days	Gains, pounds	Percentage of Total Gains
Initial weight..........	..	(577)	..		(430)	
Gain: 1st winter.......	140	167	29	127	130	15.6
1st summer......	170	225	39	221	282	33.8
2nd winter.......	..	..	..	125	110	13.2
2nd summer.....	..	..	..	169	201	24.1
Full fed in dry lot	84	185	32	51	111	13.3
Total................	394	577	100	693	834	100.0
Final weight, pounds...		1154			1264	
Av. corn fed, bushels...		25.3			17.2	
Wt. of live cattle produced per bushel of corn fed, pounds[c]....		45			73	

* Missouri Livestock Feeder's Day Progress Reports 7 and 10, 1949 and 1950.
[a] Average of 2 years.
[b] Average of six lots, December, 1946–November, 1948.
[c] Not including corn in silage.

alone or in mixed feedings, are excellent forages during August, September, and October, and their value would not be utilized if they were not grazed heavily during these months.

Yearling and 2-year-old steers which were marketed directly from pasture in October without being fed any grain have also been included in the Dixon Springs tests. The younger cattle have usually been sold for return to the country for feeding, but the 2-year-olds have almost always been sold for slaughter. The fact that these grass-fat 2-year-old steers have sold for $32 per hundred when the top of the market was $35.50 and have dressed as high as 59.8 per cent is evidence of the high nutritive value of the improved pastures at the Dixon Springs Station.

TABLE 208

METHODS OF UTILIZING PASTURES AT THE DIXON SPRINGS
EXPERIMENT STATION IN SOUTHERN ILLINOIS*

	Sold as Yearlings				Sold as 2-Year-Olds			
	Full Fed 100 Days on Pasture		Sold Directly Off Pasture		Full Fed 94 Days on Pasture		Sold Directly Off Pasture	
	Total	Per-centage	Total	Per-centage	Total	Per-centage	Total	Per-centage
Winter period, dry lot, days....	138	39	140	44	292[a]	40	292[a]	42
Pasture, without grain........	119	33	181	56	336[a]	47	405[a]	58
Full fed on pasture...........	100	28	...	...	94	13	...	...
Total..................	357	100	321	100	722	100	697	100
Gain during winter, lb........	127	28	141	46	303[a]	38	299[a]	42
Gain on pasture, no grain.....	145	32	164	54	285[a]	36	418[a]	58
Gain while full fed on pasture..	184	40	...	...	206	26	...	...
Total gain...............	456	100	305	100	794	100	717	100
Initial wt................	407		399		396		394	
Final wt..................	863		704		1190		1111	
Shrinkage................	40		40		42		83	
Sale wt..................	823		664		1148		1028	
Feed per head								
Corn, bu..................	23.6		......		26.9		......	
Protein conc., lb...........	267		141		394		276	
Corn silage..............	3327		3466		9047		9047	
Hay.....................	397		350		1285		1285	
Pasture, acres............	1.7		1.7		3.3		3.3	

* Illinois Extension Service Mimeo. Circular, February, 1950.
[a] The 2-year-old steers were carried through two winters and sold at the end of the second summer.

Miscellaneous
Feeding Stuffs

Water. Water, because of its abundance and universal use, is seldom regarded as a feed, and yet it is one of the most essential nutrients for all animal life. No farmer would consider letting his cattle go without water for a single day, but many farmers do not see that the water provided is clean, pure, and uncontaminated by objectionable odors.

TABLE 209

WATER CONSUMED BY CATTLE FULL–FED IN DRY LOT

Station	Reference	Period	Daily Water Consumption, pounds	Consumption per 100 lb. Live Weight, pounds
Calves:				
Iowa	Bulletin 271	Feb. 4–14	26	4.8
		Mar. 5–15	27	4.4
		May 4–14	51	6.7
		July 3–13	65	7.1
Ohio	Bimonthly Bulletin 154	Apr. 15–Aug. 18	57	6.5
Yearlings:				
Iowa	Bulletin 271	Feb. 4–14	29	3.4
		Mar. 5–15	25	2.7
Illinois	Mimeo. Report, 1937	Aug. 5–19	92	8.8
		Aug. 22–Sept. 6	86	7.7
2-year-olds:				
Iowa	Bulletin 271	Feb. 4–14	36	3.4
		Mar. 5–15	33	3.0

The amount of water required by cattle varies with the character of the feed and with the air temperature. Data on the water consumed on different rations and by cattle of different ages are extremely meager, but enough are available to permit the making of a rough estimate of the daily water requirements of cattle full-fed in dry lot. Apparently no data have been gathered in respect to the water consumption of cattle on pasture.

Water should be kept slightly above freezing temperature during the winter by the use of insulated tanks, and by tank heaters during extremely cold weather. Electric, oil, or gas heaters are preferred, since they can be equipped with a control device which will keep the water at an even temperature of 40 to 50 degrees. The principal advantage of heaters is the labor saved in keeping the tanks free of ice, since cattle appear to thrive as well on ice-cold water as on water at moderate temperatures.[1]

Salt. Salt is essential to the growth and health of all kinds of livestock. Cattle exhibit an especial eagerness for it and will soon show signs of restlessness and malnutrition if it is long withheld. The amount of salt that should be supplied depends upon the character of the ration and the kind of salt used. Cattle that are on pasture will require somewhat more salt than those kept in a dry lot and fed only harvested feeds. More salt is consumed during the early spring months when the grass is green and fresh than later in the summer when the grass is more mature. Records kept at the Kansas Station showed a monthly consumption of 2.83 pounds per head during the early part of the grazing season, and only 1.42 pounds during the late summer and fall.[2] On the other hand, Iowa Station steers that were full-fed in dry lots during the winter and early spring consumed but 0.64 pound per head per month as a 5-year average.[3]

The form in which the salt is fed has an effect upon the amount consumed. Cattle that have free access to granulated or loose salt will consume approximately twice as much as they would get from salt furnished in the form of 50-pound blocks. Whether or not enough is obtained from licking blocks kept in the feed bunk or in the pasture near the water supply is a disputed subject among cattlemen. The flake form is not to be recommended for use in the open, because of the large amount lost through weathering. At the Kansas Station the flake form weathered 24 per cent per month, while the blocks weathered but 11 per cent. In those states having a heavier rainfall, greater losses may be expected. Cattle accounted for the disappearance of 604 pounds and weathering for 141 pounds of block salt exposed in pastures at the Illinois Station from April 30 until October 21, or 175 days. The blocks were supported on stakes and were replaced when they became so small and lopsided from licking that they tumbled to the ground. The total disappearance of salt per 2-year-old steer was approximately 3 pounds per month. Little difference was observed at the Illinois Station between the consumption of

[1] *Cf.* Oregon Bulletin 183, 1921.

[2] Hensel, R. L., Breeders' Gazette, Aug. 11, 1921, p. 181.

[3] Glatfelter, G. V., Breeders' Gazette, Dec. 16, 1920, p. 1315.

salt by yearling cattle wintered on good roughages in the dry lot and by the same cattle on good pasture the following summer.

The amount of salt consumed is greatly affected by the amount and character of the ration. Apparently the more nearly the ration satisfies both the appetite and the nutritional requirements of the animal, the less salt will be consumed. For example, calves on a full feed of

TABLE 210

SALT CONSUMED BY BEEF CATTLE UNDER DIFFERENT FEEDING CONDITIONS

| | | | Daily Consumption per Head, pounds | |
| | | | Barrel Salt | Block Salt |
Station	Reference	Feeding Conditions		
Calves:				
Iowa	Leaflet 127	Full fed in dry lot	0.015	0.007
Kansas	Circular 265	Wintered on bluestem pasture	0.04	
		Wintered on sorgo silage	0.05	
	Circular 250	Wintered on sorgo silage and hay	0.06	
		Sorgo silage plus ⅓ feed of corn	0.05	
		Sorgo silage plus full feed of corn	0.013	
Montana	Bulletin 401	Wintered well on hay and straw	0.063	
		Limited amounts of hay and straw	0.183	
Yearlings:				
Illinois	Unpubl. data	Wintered on hay and silage	0.18	0.096
Iowa	Leaflet 127	Full fed in dry lot		0.013[a]
	Leaflet 131	Full fed in dry lot		0.03[b]
Kansas	Circular 265	Full fed in dry lot	0.07	
Montana	Bulletin 401	Wintered well on hay and straw	0.08	
		Limited amounts of hay and straw	0.26	
2-year-olds:				
Illinois	Unpubl. data	Bluegrass-ladino pasture		0.09
Iowa	Leaflet 110	Full fed in dry lot	0.042	0.018
Iowa	Mimeo. Report 1923	Full feed of corn with corn silage		
		No protein concentrate		0.04
		1.5 lb. protein concentrate		0.026
		3.0 lb. protein concentrate		0.013
		Full feed of corn with legume hay		
		No protein concentrate		0.07
		1.5 lb. protein concentrate		0.024
		3.0 lb. protein concentrate		0.025

[a] Average of 2 lots.
[b] Average of 11 lots.

grain at the Kansas Station ate only 1.8 pounds of salt per month, whereas calves wintered on a full feed of roughage ate 4.5 pounds. Apparently the low plane of nutrition on which the latter animals were carried induced a "hunger" which they tried to satisfy by eating more salt.[4] Likewise heifer calves and yearling and 2-year-old replacement heifers that were fed limited amounts of alfalfa hay and straw during the winter at the Montana Station ate approximately three

[4] Kansas, 38th Livestock Feeders' Day Report, 1951.

times as much salt as heifers that were full-fed these roughages.[5] That the consumption of salt is greatly influenced by the nutritional level of the cattle is strikingly shown by the salt consumption of 2-year-old steers fed different amounts of protein concentrate, with and without corn silage, at the Iowa Station.[6] In the silage series the consumption of salt varied inversely with the consumption of linseed meal, but in the legume-hay series increasing the linseed meal above 1.5 pounds per day resulted in no decrease in the amount of salt eaten. Apparently the protein requirements of the steers fed legume hay were completely met with the addition of 1.5 pounds of linseed meal. (See Table 210.)

The Forced Feeding of Salt. In view of the lack of information about the salt requirements of cattle, the forced feeding of salt by mixing it in the feed is of doubtful merit. For example, yearling steers fed 25.5 pounds of salt mixed with their grain ration during a 150-day feeding period at the Illinois Station still consumed 2 pounds of block salt per head. On the other hand, another lot in the same experiment fed no salt in the feed consumed only 7 pounds of block salt during the test. The only difference between the two lots was that the former steers received 50 per cent of their concentrates in the form of cane molasses whereas the latter lot was fed straight shelled corn. Since molasses contains much more potassium than corn and since potassium is an element that probably can replace sodium to some extent in the body, one would logically predict that cattle fed molasses would require less salt than cattle fed shelled corn as the only carbonaceous concentrate.

The mixing of salt with cottonseed meal in order to limit the consumption of the meal to about 2 pounds per head daily when the mixture was self-fed resulted in the consumption of over 1 pound of salt per day by cows and 2-year-old steers at the Kansas and Oklahoma stations.[7] This amount of salt was far above the ability of cattle to handle it, as was indicated by their heavy water consumption and their abnormal output of urine. Studies made in Germany indicate that the administration of approximately ½ pound of salt daily to a mature cow over a period of 30 days greatly reduced the protozoa in the rumen. In one instance the number of fauna was reduced by 50 per cent, and the number of species by 25 per cent. The treatment with heavy doses of salt had a detrimental effect on

[5] Montana Bulletin 401, 1942.
[6] Iowa Mimeographed Report, 1923.
[7] Kansas Circular 250, 1949, and Oklahoma Miscel. Publ. 22, 1951.

the health of the cows, which lost weight until the administration of salt was discontinued.[8]

Minerals. Salt supplies two of the chemical elements needed by cattle, viz., sodium and chlorine. In addition, there are two other essential minerals in which farm rations may be deficient, calcium and phosphorus. Farm grains and protein concentrates, with the exception of linseed meal, are relatively low in calcium but are good to excellent sources of phosphorus. Legume roughages, on the other hand, are excellent sources of calcium but are likely to be low in phosphorus unless they have been grown on phosphorus-rich soils. Thus, concentrates and legume roughages are natural supplements to each other in respect to these two elements. Non-legume hays and pasture are better sources of calcium than of phosphorus but are not sufficiently high in either to make them of value in correcting a mineral deficiency.

A phosphorus deficiency is most likely to be encountered in stocker cattle that are being wintered principally on roughage grown on low-phosphorus soils whereas calcium deficiencies are likely to occur among grain-fed cattle that are fed little or no legume hay. For the roughage-fed stockers the feeding of a protein concentrate, especially wheat bran or cottonseed or linseed meal, will correct the phosphorus deficiency if it has not developed too far, but in serious cases a mineral supplement rich in phosphorus should be fed. Steamed bonemeal (13–15 per cent phosphorus), dicalcium phosphate (18–20 per cent phosphorus), and tricalcium phosphate (18 per cent phosphorus) are the usual forms fed. Rock phosphate should not be fed, because it usually contains fluorine, which is toxic to cattle. To correct a serious phosphorus deficiency which is known to exist, 2 to 3 ounces of one of the phosphorus supplements mentioned above should be mixed with the grain ration or spread over the silage. Mild or doubtful cases are usually treated by feeding a mixture of 2 parts bonemeal and 1 part salt free-choice.

A calcium deficiency in cattle is best corrected by feeding 0.1 pound daily of limestone flour, mixed with the grain ration or scattered over the silage. Cattle that are fed rations suspected of being low in calcium should have free access to a mixture of 2 parts of limestone and 1 part iodized salt or equal parts of salt, limestone, and bonemeal.

Experiments carried on at the Indiana[9] and Iowa[10] Stations have shown practically no advantage in feeding minerals to mature steers

[8] Nutrition Abstracts and Reviews, 8, 1938, p. 249.

[9] Indiana Bulletins 281, 1924; 291, 1925; and 314, 1927.

[10] Iowa Mimeo. Reports 116, 1926; and 117, 1927.

that are fattened on well-balanced rations. However, the Kansas Station[11] has shown that calves fed a non-leguminous, low-calcium roughage, such as prairie hay, should be supplied with finely ground limestone or some other mineral rich in calcium. Finely ground lime-

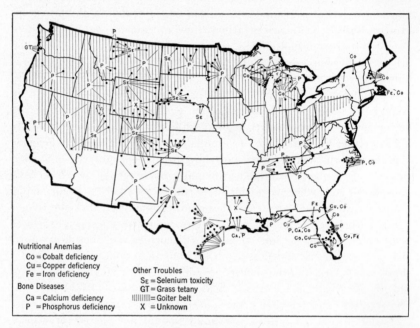

Fig. 60. Areas deficient in important minerals needed for the adequate nutrition of livestock. (*Courtesy U.S.D.A.*)

stone fed at the rate of $\frac{1}{10}$ pound daily to calves gave much better results when fed with prairie hay than did either acid phosphate or bonemeal. As will be seen by a study of Table 211, no benefit was derived from the addition of ground limestone to the ration of calves receiving 6 pounds of alfalfa hay. When only 2 pounds of alfalfa were fed, the feeding of the limestone was profitable.

Trace Minerals. Considerable discussion has been held on a possible deficiency of some of the rare or "trace" elements in present-day animal rations, including those of beef cattle. It is claimed that such elements as iron, manganese, copper, sulfur, iodine, and cobalt, which are present only in minute amounts in virgin soil, have been so depleted through leaching and cropping that not more than a "trace" of them remains. Consequently, feeds grown on such soils do not supply the

[11] Kansas Circular 151, 1929.

TABLE 211

VALUE OF ADDING GROUND LIMESTONE TO A LOW–CALCIUM RATION*

(375 lb. Calves, Fed 180 Days)

Kind of Hay Fed......	Alfalfa Hay				Prairie Hay			
Other Roughage	None		Cane Silage		None		Cane Silage	
Mineral Fed............	None	Ground Lime-stone	None	Ground Lime-stone	None	Ground Lime-stone	None	Ground Lime-stone
Daily gain, lbs....	2.46	2.44	2.32	2.49	2.15	2.25	2.07	2.43
Av. daily ration:								
Shelled corn.....	9.74	9.60	9.77	9.51	9.83	10.09	9.65	9.85
Cottonseed meal.	1.12	1.11	1.00	1.00	1.36	1.40	1.16	1.16
Hay.............	6.03	5.84	2.01	2.00	4.43	5.03	1.36	1.41
Cane silage......	....	....	9.71	10.05	....	...	8.91	10.14
Ground limestone	...	.11	....	.10	....	.12	....	.10
Feed per cwt. gain:								
Shelled corn.. ..	396	394	422	382	457	448	466	406
Cottonseed meal.	46	45	43	40	63	62	56	48
Hay.............	245	239	87	80	206	223	65	58
Cane silage......	....	....	419	404	....	....	430	418
Ground limestone	....	5	...	4	...	5	....	4
Selling price per cwt............	$13.25	$13.00	$12.75	$13.00	$12.50	$12.75	$12.50	$13.00

* Kansas Circular 151, 1929.

animals' requirements for these elements, infinitesimal though they be. Therefore, the elements should be added to the ration.

Some of the trace minerals may be needed not so much by the cattle themselves as by the rumen bacteria. For example, there is considerable evidence that cobalt is essential for the production of the important vitamin B_{12} by the microorganisms of the rumen.

It has been definitely shown that in local areas of the world the feeding of certain trace elements is necessary to prevent symptoms of malnutrition. A few such areas have been identified in the United States. (See Fig. 60.) If one has any reason to believe he lives in such an area he should guard against a possible deficiency by feeding a mineralized salt which is fortified by the trace element in questionable supply in the soil. Such salt, which bears a tag stating the percentage of the different ingredients present, is a much safer, as well as a much cheaper, source of trace elements than the so-called complete mineral supplements. Mineralized salt should be fed in the same way as ordinary salt, i.e., in the block, or as barrel salt, with the cattle having free access to it at all times.

Drugs. The feeding of medicines or drugs to beef cattle to stimulate their appetites and improve their finish is occasionally practiced by professional herdsmen and fitters in conditioning cattle for the show ring. The drugs most commonly used for this purpose are Fowler's solution and nux vomica. Fowler's solution is an aqueous solution of potassium arsenite (K_3AsO_3); nux vomica is a drug made from the poisonous seed of an Asiatic tree which contains several alkaloids, chiefly strychnine. Since both these drugs are highly poisonous, their stimulating effect is achieved by their powerful reactions on the organs of the digestive and circulatory systems. Obviously the dosage must be gauged very carefully, or an acute toxemia will be produced which may result in death.

Yearling heifers fed nux vomica and arsenic trioxide at the Washington Station showed no more avid appetites than the control heifers but made somewhat larger daily gains. Consequently, the drugs apparently improved the animals' ability to digest and assimilate the feed. However, when the feeding of arsenic trioxide was discontinued, the rate of gain dropped from 2.24 to 1.41 pounds per day, despite the fact that the daily feed consumption did not change significantly during this period.[12] Such behavior in cattle after stopping the feeding of these highly stimulating drugs has been noted frequently by practical cattlemen.

It is commonly believed that the feeding of Fowler's solution, and perhaps nux vomica as well, to cattle in appreciable amounts or over long periods will affect their fertility adversely. Consequently, the use of such drugs is regarded as a dishonest and unethical practice and is strongly condemned.

Hormones. The name hormones is applied to substances secreted within the animal which bring about a harmonious functioning of the different organs. Thus, progesterone, a hormone secreted by the corpus luteum of pregnancy, inhibits the further development of Graafian follicles and also conditions the lining of the uterus for the fœtal attachments by which the fœtus will be nourished.

Physiologists have identified nearly a score of hormones, not so much by their isolation as by the results they produce or by the abnormal development or behavior that is observed if the gland or organ that secretes the hormone is removed. The hormones about

[12] Journal of Animal Science, August, 1949, pp. 411–424.

which most is known at present are those secreted by the pituitary, thyroid, and sex glands. Some of these hormones apparently play an important role in nutrition; consequently they are of interest to the livestock feeder.

Chemists have succeeded in producing synthetically organic compounds which when administered to an animal will produce much the same reaction or behavior as the hormones secreted by the body itself. Thus, it is now possible to give an animal an unusually large "dose" of a hormone or to administer a synthetic hormone that will cancel out the effect of a body hormone and thus bring about essentially the same effect that would occur if the gland or organ that secretes the hormone were removed by a surgical operation. Several tests have been carried out to ascertain what value, if any, these hormones have for growing beef cattle. None of the tests have progressed far enough to warrant the use of hormones by the practical feeder. However, some of the results obtained appear to warrant the prediction that in a few years their use will be widespread.

TABLE 212

The Effect of Stilbestrol upon the Gains of Full–Fed Cattle*

	Trial I Heifers		Trial II Heifers		Trial III Steers		Trial IV Steers	
	Control	Treated	Control	Treated	Control	Treated	Control	Treated
Av. daily gains, lb.....	2.07	2.32	1.72	2.00	2.26	2.55	2.56	2.90
Feed per cwt. gain....								
Concentrates.........	463	442	688	623	820	760	782	698
Roughage.........	312	301	424	369	373	334	269	264

* Indiana Mimeo. AH Reports 37, 1948; 46, 1950; and 60, 1951.

The most promising of the hormones administered to beef cattle to date is *stilbestrol*, a synthetic substance which has much the same effect as the hormone estrogen, which is secreted by the ovary.[13] Both open heifers and steers treated with stilbestrol by Andrews and Beeson at the Indiana Station made significantly larger and cheaper gains than the control animals. (See Table 212.) On the face of these results it would appear that stilbestrol should be hailed as an outstanding discovery. However, there are some serious objections

[13] *Cf.* p. 86.

to its use which must be corrected before it can be recommended. Heifers treated with stilbestrol had abnormally frequent and long heat periods and spent much time riding one another. Both steers and heifers that were treated developed high prominent tail heads, low loins, and unusually full, paunchy middles. All heifers receiving the stilbestrol showed a noticeable development of the mammary glands comparable to that of pregnant heifers in late gestation. These characteristics would no doubt have detracted from the apparent slaughter merit of the cattle had they been sold on the open market. The carcass grades reported for one of the tests were somewhat lower for the treated cattle than for the controls, which would warrant a lower price for the live cattle.

Other hormones that have been administered to cattle at the Indiana Station are (1) testosterone, a male hormone secreted by the testes; (2) thiouracil, which inhibits the secretion of thyroxine by the thyroid gland; (3) thyroprotein, which stimulates the thyroid gland to greater activity. In four trials none of these hormones gave results significantly different from those obtained from the control cattle.[14]

Antibiotics. Antibiotics is the name given to certain bacterial products that, when administered to animals orally, weaken or destroy certain types of bacteria and protozoa that are in the alimentary tract. The feeding of small amounts of antibiotics to hogs and poultry has given highly favorable results in many instances, and most commercial feed companies are now incorporating antibiotics in many of their different brands of hog and poultry feeds. The more commonly used antibiotics are aureomycin, streptomycin, terramycin, and penicillin, but no doubt additional and more effective materials will be discovered.

Only a few tests to study the value of antibiotics for beef cattle have been conducted. Those that have been reported show a detrimental rather than a favorable effect from the antibiotics used. For example, Bell at the Oklahoma Station reported that feeding 0.2 gram of aureomycin daily to yearling steers resulted in a reduction in the digestibility of the total dry matter, crude fiber, and nitrogen-free extract. He explained the decrease by the detrimental effect of the aureomycin upon the microorganisms in the gastrointestinal tract which break down the cellulose and render it digestible.[15] Neumann, feeding aureomycin at the Illinois Station to yearling heifers, noted a marked depression of the appetite about 24 hours after the first

[14] Journal of Animal Science, August, 1950, pp. 321–330.

[15] Proceedings of the Society for Experimental Biology and Medicine, 1951, Vol. 76, pp. 284–286.

feeding. This effect continued for about 10 days, after which the consumption of feed by the test cattle gradually increased until it regained the level of the control lot.[16]

In view of the important role played by bacteria in the digestion of feed by cattle especially the bacteria and protozoa of the paunch, it is doubtful that the feeding of antibiotics to cattle will be a profitable practice.

Bacterial Cultures. Whereas antibiotics are administered to cattle to weaken or destroy harmful bacteria that may be present in the digestive tract, bacterial cultures are given to introduce desirable bacteria or enzymes that are suspected of being in short supply. Thus far, yeast is the only such culture that has been tested sufficiently to justify a statement in regard to its value for cattle.

The principal value of yeast as a feed for cattle lies in its high protein content, which is approximately 50 per cent. Consequently, it may replace soybean oil meal, cottonseed meal, or other high-protein supplements on a pound-for-pound basis. However, it is usually sold to be fed in very small quantities of only $\frac{1}{4}$ or $\frac{1}{10}$ pound per day for the purpose of seeding a small quantity of the yeast germs in the paunch, where they will multiply rapidly and aid in the fermentation and digestion of the feed. The feeding of a small quantity of yeast for this purpose from time to time would no doubt be of value were it not that cattle in normal health which are fed a well-balanced ration already have literally billions of the yeast type of organisms in their digestive tracts; consequently, the addition of a few more produces no noticeable results.

Working on the same theory, some concerns now prepare and offer for sale bacterial cultures which consist, in part at least, of the rumen material obtained from slaughtered cattle. If the cattle were fed individually for several months before slaughter and the rumen content processed only from those that had made unusually economical gains, the product might have some value. However, bacterial cultures must be subjected to extensive tests, including digestion trials, before they can be recommended for use by the practical farmer.

Stock Foods. Some years ago, agricultural papers were full of advertisements of various brands of stock foods and tonics for which extravagant claims were often made by their manufacturers. As these claims were seldom realized, most farmers have come to look upon such materials as of little or no account in practical feeding operations. Even now, however, one occasionally encounters a feeder who honestly believes, chemical analysis notwithstanding, that a spoonful

[16] Journal of Animal Science, November, 1951, pp. 1058–1059.

or two of a medicated powder sprinkled over a bushel of corn will achieve wonderful results.

Any value possessed by stock foods and tonics lies in their medicinal rather than their nutritive qualities. Their high cost precludes their use in large enough quantities to affect the ration's nutritive value. They may, however, act as seasoners or appetizers and thus affect the rate of gain indirectly. Also, most of them contain ingredients that are mildly laxative, which may be of some benefit to the cattle. The price asked for such feeds is usually entirely out of line with their real value. Preparations that are just as good can often be made up by the local veterinarian at a very much lower cost.

Vitamins. Vitamins are substances that are highly necessary to normal development and good health of the body, in both man and beast. They are produced principally in plants and occur in such small amounts that thus far no one has been able to isolate them. That they are actually present in foods is evident from the various maladies that result when they are lacking in the ration.

So far there is good evidence that there are some twelve or fifteen different vitamins, each of which is beneficial, if not essential, for the health and well-being of at least certain species of animals. Fortunately for the beef cattleman, only two or three of the vitamins are of importance in the feeding of beef cattle. In fact, only under unusual conditions is a vitamin deficiency in beef cattle likely to be encountered in the Corn Belt or in the better grazing areas of the Western Range states.

Vitamin A is required by all farm animals, but a deficiency is seldom encountered because the vitamin may be formed in the body from carotene, a yellow, fat-soluble substance which is abundant in all forms of green plant material. Animals that receive an abundance of carotene while on green pasture store it in the body tissues, where it is available for conversion into vitamin A if a shortage occurs in the ration at a later date. That weanling calves, despite their sensitivity to a deficiency of vitamin A, usually have enough carotene stored in their bodies to last them through the winter was shown in a Nebraska test in which range calves fed ground grain sorghum and carotene-free alfalfa and prairie hays maintained as good health and made as much gain as similar calves that were supplied a vitamin A supplement in the form of dehydrated alfalfa hay.[17]

Usually the first observed symptom of vitamin A deficiency is night blindness, or an inability of the animal to see clearly in dim or subdued light. If this condition is suspected, the cattle should be driven

[17] Nebraska Progress Report 51, 1951.

about at twilight or in moonlight to see whether they have difficulty avoiding large objects that lie in their path. Subsequent symptoms are muscular incoordination, staggering gait, and excessive running of the eyes and nose caused by the inflammation of the epithelial membranes of these organs. In fattening cattle a pronounced swelling of the legs and abdominal regions may occur.

TABLE 213

ESTIMATED CAROTENE CONTENT OF FEEDS IN RELATION
TO APPEARANCE AND METHODS OF CONSERVATION*

Feedstuff	Carotene, milligrams per pound
Fresh green legumes and grasses, immature	15 to 40
Dehydrated alfalfa meal, fresh, dehydrated without field curing, very bright green color	110 to 135
Dehydrated alfalfa meal after considerable time in storage, bright green color	50 to 70
Alfalfa leaf meal, bright green color	60 to 80
Legume hays, including alfalfa, very quickly cured with minimum sun exposure, bright green color, leafy	35 to 40
Legume hays, including alfalfa, good green color, leafy	18 to 27
Legume hays, including alfalfa, partly bleached, moderate amount of green color	9 to 14
Legume hays, including alfalfa, badly bleached or discolored, traces of green color	4 to 8
Non-legume hays, including timothy, cereal, and prairie hays, well cured, good green color	9 to 14
Non-legume hays, average quality, bleached, some green color	4 to 8
Legume silage	5 to 20
Corn and sorghum silages, medium to good green color	2 to 10
Grains, mill feeds, protein concentrates, and by-product concentrates, except yellow corn and its by-products	0.01 to 0.2
Yellow shelled corn[a]	1.1 to 2.2

* National Research Council, Recommended Nutrient Allowances for Beef Cattle, 1945.
[a] Morrison, Feeds and Feeding, 21st edition, 1948.

Since the vitamin A value of a feed has a very close relation to its carotene content, the vitamin A value of feeds, as well as the vitamin A requirements of farm animals, is frequently given in terms of milligrams of carotene instead of international units of the vitamin itself. Roughly, 0.6 milligram of carotene corresponds to 1000 I. U. of vitamin A.

Since carotene is a constituent of green pasture forage, silage, and hays that have been cured without too much exposure to the sun, beef cattle receive an abundance of this vitamin through their feed.

Yellow corn also is fairly high in this vitamin, but most of the other farm grains and commercial concentrates are low. In view of the fact that all beef cattle store an abundance of carotene in their bodies while on pasture during the summer, there is little likelihood of their suffering from a deficiency of vitamin A even though they are on a relatively low ration during the winter. Symptoms have been observed most frequently among cattle fed white corn or grain sorghums and sunburned hay in dry lot after an unusually dry summer.

The best source of vitamin A for cattle suffering from a deficiency is a commercial vitamin A supplement, made from fortified cod-liver oil, such as "NOPCO XX," which contains 3000 I. U. of vitamin A per gram.[18] One-fourth to ½ ounce of such supplement per day, depending upon the age and size of the animal, should correct the deficiency over a period of about 10 days. Two or three feedings a week thereafter or smaller amounts daily should be sufficient to prevent a recurrence of the trouble.

Another excellent source of vitamin A is dehydrated alfalfa hay made from freshly cut green alfalfa that was not exposed to the sun before drying. Its carotene content is approximately 45 milligrams per pound, compared with 20 milligrams for ordinary alfalfa hay, 11 milligrams for red clover hay, 4 milligrams for corn silage made from well-matured yellow corn, and 2 milligrams for No. 2 yellow shelled corn. The vitamin A requirements of beef cattle for growth and for building up some reserve will be adequately met by supplying from 4 to 6 milligrams of carotene daily per 100 pounds live weight.[19]

Vitamin D is essential for the utilization of calcium by the animal body. In the absence of vitamin D, particularly if the mineral content of the diet is low, or if the proportion of phosphorus to calcium is very high, growing animals will develop rickets. Rickets is a disease characterized by faulty calcification of the bones. Although vitamin D is required by all the higher animals, its occurrence in nature is quite restricted. Cod-liver oil is by far the richest known source of vitamin D. All grains and grain products are deficient in this vitamin, and fresh or dried forages are neither good nor reliable vitamin D foods. Fortunately animals do not need to rely upon their food for a supply of this very important vitamin. Through the action of the sun's rays, especially the ultraviolet rays, upon *ergosterol*, a substance widely distributed in nature, vitamin D potency is acquired by a large variety of foodstuffs. Thus, grains, hays, and other feeds

[18] Manufactured by the National Oil Products Company, Harrison, New Jersey.
[19] National Research Council, Recommended Nutrient Allowances for Beef Cattle, 1945.

may acquire mild antirachitic properties by exposure to intense sunlight. However, the most important source of vitamin D is the ergosterol present in the subcutaneous tissues of the animal. Under the action of strong sunlight this substance, in some way as yet not understood, is converted into vitamin D, which is absorbed by the blood and acts in the same way as vitamin D obtained from the food. Inasmuch as cattle are almost constantly out of doors where they are subject to the full power of the sun, they have little likelihood of suffering from a vitamin D deficiency.

Vitamin E is a vitamin that appears to be specifically concerned with fertility. Thus far, its need has been demonstrated only with rats, but it is quite possible that it is necessary to the normal functioning of the reproductive organs of ordinary farm animals. Since, however, it is reported to be present in effective concentration in most natural foods, it seems improbable that farm animals on their ordinary rations ever suffer from a lack of this vitamin. Wheat-germ meal, lettuce leaves, and sprouted oats are rich in vitamin E, and these feeds are coming into use in the treatment of valuable breeding animals that have become impotent or sterile. Insufficient data are available to warrant drawing conclusions regarding the value of these feeds in correcting temporary sterility. However, in view of the abundance of this vitamin in farm feeds, fertility regained after the feeding of vitamin E concentrates probably should be credited to some other factor.

The Vitamin B complex, which includes biotin, niacin, pantothenic acid, riboflavin, and thiamine, as well as the much-discussed APF (animal protein factor), B_{12}, and vitamin K, are synthesized by the microorganisms in the rumen of cattle and, consequently, need not be furnished in the ration. The excellent results that have been obtained from supplying these vitamins to hogs and poultry have led some manufacturers of mixed feeds to include them in cattle supplements. However, there is no evidence that they are essential for cattle, except possibly very young calves, the rumen of which is not yet functioning.

Vitamin C is required only by animals that are susceptible to scurvy. Since cattle, as well as all other domesticated animals, are free from this disease, this vitamin has no importance in beef-cattle feeding. Essentially the same may be said of the other vitamins, such as F, which prevents scaly tail in rats, and G, which is essential for the hatchability of eggs in poultry and which prevents black tongue in dogs.

Probably no question connected with the fattening of cattle is more seriously regarded by the inexperienced feeder than that of the proper preparation of feeds. So much propaganda has been put forth by manufacturers and distributors of feed grinders, crushers, cooking apparatus, etc., that it is not surprising that this phase of cattle feeding has received much attention.

Under normal conditions, the particular way in which feeding stuffs are given to cattle is of minor importance. Generally speaking, they should be fed in the form that involves the least labor. However, there occasionally arise situations in which a more or less elaborate preparation of the materials entering into the ration is justified.

Preparation of Corn. Corn is fed to beef cattle in the following well-recognized forms:

1. Standing in the field.
2. Shock corn.
3. Snapped corn.
4. Ear-corn silage.
5. Broken ears.
6. Chopped corn.
7. Crushed corn and cob.
8. Corn-and-cob meal.
9. Shelled corn.
10. Ground corn or corn meal.

In addition, corn is sometimes fed after having been soaked or cooked. Neither of these methods of preparation, however, is extensively practiced.

"Cattling" down Corn. The use of cattle to harvest corn from the standing stalks is seldom practiced. In the few instances where this method of feeding has been followed the wastage of corn has been very high. Cattle in eating the corn knock many of the ears to the ground and show little inclination to eat these ears as long as they can get a full supply from the standing stalks. The fallen ears become dirty and unpalatable with the first rain and must be salvaged by hogs. In a test conducted at the Illinois Station, 10.5 acres of standing "soft" corn furnished a full feed for ten 2-year-old steers for only 58 days, in comparison with 80 days for an equal acreage fed as shock corn to similar steers in dry lot. The combined cattle and hog gains per acre for the two areas were 175 and 240 pounds, respectively.

One of the problems of running cattle in a field of standing corn is the difficulty of supplying the protein required to balance the ration. Since the cattle consume considerable roughage in the form of husks and cobs, they will eat relatively little legume hay. The feeding of a protein concentrate presents the problem of insuring that each steer gets his share of the small amount fed. This may be done by mixing the protein supplement with about its own weight of chaffed hay, in order to prevent the forward steers from consuming all of it before the more timid animals reach the feed trough.

Cattling down corn should be attempted only with cattle accustomed to a full feed. A sufficient number of hogs should be put into the field to utilize both the corn that the cattle knock to the ground and the undigested corn voided by the cattle in their feces. Three times as many hogs are needed with a drove of cattle running in a corn field as are needed in a dry lot. From two to four 80- to 120-pound shotes per steer will usually be required.

Shock Corn. Shock corn, the most common form in which corn was fed in the early days of cattle feeding, cannot be recommended for feeding in areas where heavy infestations of corn borers occur. The importance of destroying the borer larvæ by burning or plowing under all corn stalks makes the feeding of whole corn fodder infested with borers impractical. However, in areas free from the corn borer well-preserved shock corn has considerable merit, especially during the first few weeks of the feeding period when the cattle are getting less than a full feed of corn and, consequently, have keen appetites for coarse, bulky roughages.

The ears of shock corn do not dry out as fast as ears that have been husked; hence, they are softer and more easily chewed. In addition they possess a fragrance or aroma which adds to their palatability. Inasmuch as the ears are eaten entire, 2-year-old steers are better suited for a heavy ration of shock corn than light yearlings or calves. When a considerable part of a full feed of grain is supplied in the form of shock corn, a great surplus of roughage results, the disposal of which presents a serious problem in a small feed lot. On account of the accumulation of stalks and husks in the feed racks, some ears may not be discovered by the cattle. They will, however, be eaten by the hogs when the racks are cleaned out before the next feeding. Shock corn is used to better advantage if it is fed but once a day, preferably for the morning feed, shelled or broken-ear corn being given in the evening. In this way a better balance is maintained between grain and roughage. The feeding of additional corn also provides a convenient way for feeding the protein supplement that cattle fed shock corn should have, because of their heavy consumption of carbonaceous roughage.

No doubt the most serious objection to shock corn is the amount of labor involved in cutting and shocking the corn, and hauling it from the field in the bad weather that often prevails during the winter

FIG. 61. Shock corn constitutes a "three-in-one" feed for fattening cattle. It furnishes grain, roughage, and bedding, a fact too often overlooked by present-day feeders. (*Courtesy Illinois Experiment Station.*)

months. Fields are greatly damaged by hauling when the ground is soft, while ice and snow often make the handling of fodder an extremely hard and unpleasant task. Nevertheless, a few well-set-up shocks of fodder will be relished by cattle during crisp winter weather and, when both harvest and storage charges are considered, will usually supply grain, roughage, and bedding material at a very low cost.

Snapped Corn. The term "snapped corn" is applied to corn that has been gathered with the inner layers of the husks remaining on the ears. These husks are of fine texture and are of considerable value as a roughage material. They also tend to preserve the freshness of the ears and prevent the grain and cobs from becoming dry and hard. Snapped corn is, therefore, somewhat more palatable than ordinary ear corn and is consumed, as a rule, in somewhat greater quantities. However, a greater wastage of feed occurs, as the cattle tend to pick the ears up by the husks and will drop some beyond the edges of the troughs before getting them firmly between their jaws. Such ears will, to a large extent, be recovered by the hogs.

With the exceptions noted above, snapped corn is comparable to ear corn in feeding value. In practice, snapped corn is fed mainly during the fall and early winter months when it can be fed directly from the field.

Ear Corn. During the first two decades of the twentieth century, when the feeding of 2- and 3-year-old steers was a common practice, large amounts of whole and broken ear corn were fed to beef cattle. For small droves numbering less than 50 head the ears were usually broken by hand into two to four pieces over the edge of the feed trough, but for large droves they were broken into smaller pieces by means of a power-driven mechanical breaker or slicer. Often yearling cattle and calves would be brought up to a full feed on ear corn chopped into pieces about an inch long with an ordinary hand corn-knife. The present scarcity of labor and the availability of tractor and electric power for grinding on nearly every farm have resulted in the almost complete disappearance of broken ear corn from Corn Belt feed lots. Nevertheless, it is an unusually good form of corn for starting cattle on feed, especially in the fall and early winter, when the corn often contains too much moisture to be ground easily or to be stored in the form of ground ear corn for more than 2 or 3 days without spoiling.

Ear corn is more satisfactory for feeding during the fall and winter while the cobs are soft and spongy. In the spring, with the arrival of warm weather, much of the moisture in the cobs evaporates, rendering the ears more difficult to masticate. For this reason ground ears and shelled corn are more satisfactory for summer feeding.

Shelled Corn. Shelled corn is a more concentrated feed than ear corn since the cobs are not present. Corn cobs have a low feeding value[1] and serve largely as a filler to dilute the grain ration. In this respect they are comparable to the roughage component, and their presence will usually permit some saving in this item. The value of cobs as a source of roughage normally is of little importance to the general farmer, who has an abundance of hay, silage, stover, and straw; but it is often considered by feeders in drought years when roughages are in short supply. By feeding ear corn, either whole or ground, rather than shelled, the roughage requirements of yearling and 2-year-old steers may be reduced as much as one-half.

Given a fairly liberal roughage ration, cattle will make more rapid gains on shelled than on ear corn. This is due principally to the fact that a larger weight of corn kernels is consumed. This larger consumption results both from the fact that shelled corn is more

[1] Cf. p. 380.

palatable and from the fact that none of the digestive capacity is taken up by cobs. It may appear from the results of some feeding experiments that shelled corn is more thoroughly digested, since the hog gains per bushel of corn fed were larger with ear corn. However, some of this pork probably was due to ears that were "nosed" from the trough or were dropped to the ground and, hence, were not consumed by the cattle.

The superiority of shelled corn over ear corn is at no time large but is more pronounced during the summer and fall, when the ears are likely to be hard and dry and difficult to masticate. The claim is often made that shelled corn has a decided advantage for cattle getting silage or for cattle on grass, as the succulent feeds tend to make their mouths tender, rendering them less able to masticate ear corn. A more plausible explanation is that cattle fed silage or running on grass tend to consume large quantities of these palatable roughages and have too little capacity for a bulky feed like ear corn to eat enough of it to make large gains.

Ear corn is a somewhat safer feed than shelled corn, as cattle getting it are not so likely to overeat and go off feed. Many practical feeders prefer ear corn for this reason. It is often used for the first 5 or 6 weeks while the cattle are learning to eat, a change being made to shelled corn as soon as all the cattle are eating well and are on nearly a full feed.

One of the chief advantages possessed by shelled corn is the comparative ease with which it may be fed. It can be hauled or carried from the bin to the feed bunk without expending any labor in its preparation, or enough of it can be put into a self-feeder to last the cattle 2 or 3 weeks. Ear corn, on the other hand, should be broken before or at the time of feeding. Although the cost of breaking is no greater than the cost of shelling, the breaking job is, as a rule, performed by hand, a feed at a time, whereas shelling is usually done by machinery, which may turn out a month's supply of shelled corn in but little more than an hour.

Ground Corn. The term "ground corn" may be used to refer either to the ground ears or ground shelled corn. Strictly speaking, ground ears go by the name "crushed ear corn" or "corn-and-cob meal," according as it is ground coarse or fine, and ground shelled corn is called merely "ground corn," or "corn meal" if the grinding has been especially thorough. As a rule, crushed ear corn is the form more commonly used by feeders who are preparing cattle for the open market, and corn meal is extensively used in fitting cattle for the show-yard and sale ring.

The grinding of corn, either ear or shelled, is performed primarily to promote faster daily gains. This increase in gain results partly from a larger consumption of grain and partly from a better utilization of the grain on the part of the cattle. More ground than whole

TABLE 214

THE VALUE OF GRINDING SHELLED CORN FOR YEARLING STEERS

	Nebraska Experiment Station[a]				Iowa Experiment Station[b]	
	1932–1933		1933–1934		1940–1941	
	Shelled Corn	Coarsely Ground Shelled Corn	Shelled Corn	Coarsely Ground Shelled Corn	Shelled Corn	Coarsely Ground Shelled Corn
Initial weight, lb	638	642	671	670	657	656
Final weight, lb	1067	1075	1063	1076	1121	1105
Average daily gain	2.38	2.40	2.17	2.26	1.94	1.87
Average daily ration						
Corn (shelled basis)	16.5	17.8	14.9	15.2	12.1	11.2
Corn (cobs)	..	..	..	..	..	..
Alfalfa hay	5.3	5.9	5.4	5.3	1.5	1.5
Corn silage	..	..	..	..	11.5	11.5
Feed per cwt. gain						
Corn (shelled)	692	742	686	673	625	600
Corn (cobs)	..	..	..	..	..	..
Alfalfa hay	222	247	250	235	79	82
Corn silage	..	..	..	..	593	612
Hog gains per steer	29	15	51	25	57[c]	18[c]
Dressing percentage	60.4	61.2	59.7	59.5	..	..

[a] Nebraska Mimeo. Cattle Circular 143.
[b] Iowa Animal Husbandry Mimeo. Leaflet 159.
[c] Feed saved by hogs per 100 pounds of cattle gains.

grain is eaten, largely because less effort is required. Also, the breaking up of the kernels into many minute particles probably renders the corn more palatable or "tasty." This division of the grains into many small particles is responsible for its more thorough digestion. The finer the corn is ground, the greater the surface that is exposed to the action of the digestive fluids. These fluids easily penetrate each small piece of the ground grains, transforming their proteins and starches into simpler products that are easily absorbed, whereas a by no means negligible percentage of corn that is fed whole passes through the entire digestive tract without having even its outer covering broken. In addition, there are other kernels that have been but partly chewed and are imperfectly digested. That grinding aids the process of digestion is indicated both by the smaller amount of ground than of whole corn required per pound of gain and by the smaller gains made by hogs which are in the lot with cattle fed ground corn. However, the results of the Nebraska and Iowa experiments reported in Table 214 indicate that coarsely cracked shelled corn is utilized little, if any, better by yearling cattle than shelled corn. The difference observed in hog gains in these experiments, as in most comparisons between whole and ground corn, must therefore, be attributed principally to the inability of the hogs to recover the small particles of undigested grain voided by the steers fed ground corn.

Corn-and-cob meal has practically the same relation to ground corn that broken ears have to the shelled grain. The cob particles that are in the former result in a slightly smaller daily grain consumption than may be secured from feeding the latter. In the absence of sufficient roughage, these cob particles may be of considerable benefit in lightening the ration and giving it bulk. For this reason ground ear corn is a very desirable feed for cows and heifers in the breeding herd. The presence of the cob particles also makes corn-and-cob meal a somewhat safer feed than ground shelled corn, as cattle getting it are not as likely to overeat and go off feed.

Great variation exists in the degree of fineness attained in grinding corn. In some cases, the ears are merely crushed, leaving many of the grains unbroken and slivers of cob ½ inch or more in length. In others, the grinding is so thorough that the ground cobs have much the appearance of coarse middlings or bran. Shelled corn may be merely cracked or it may be reduced to a genuine meal.

As a rule, coarsely ground shelled corn is preferred to that finely ground. When reduced to the consistency of a fine meal it tends, when eaten, to make a sticky, pasty mass which is more or less unpalatable to full-fed cattle. Ear corn, on the other hand, should be ground rather fine. Cattle that are full-fed on coarsely crushed ear corn spend considerable time separating the grain from the larger pieces of cob. Unless the cob is eaten, the time and labor spent in grinding would be employed to better advantage in shelling the corn for the cattle.

Shelled Corn vs. Corn-and-Cob Meal. Although more than a score of comparisons have been made between shelled corn and corn-and-cob meal, it appears impossible to rate one above the other without making a number of qualifications. Most of the early experiments showed that shelled corn was somewhat superior in respect to palatability, rate of gain, and degree of finish produced, but several tests made more recently have raised serious doubts in regard to these points. For example, in the experiments reported in Table 215 calves

TABLE 215

THE COMPARATIVE VALUE OF SHELLED AND GROUND
EAR CORN FOR FATTENING CATTLE

	Calves				Yearlings		Yearlings	
	Ohio Bi-monthly Bull. 179, 1936 (Av. 3 trials)		Nebraska Mimeo. Cattle Circ. 115, 1923		Nebraska Mimeo. Cattle Circ. 127, 130, 143 (Av. 4 trials)		Iowa Mimeo. AH Leaflet 159, 1941	
	Sh. Corn	Gr. Ear Corn	Sh. Corn	Gr. Ear Corn	Sh. Corn	Gr. Ear Corn	Sh. Corn, 240 Days	Gr. Ear Corn, 120 Days; 25% Gr. Ear Corn, 75% Gr. Sh. Corn, 120 Days
Av. daily gain, lb	2.00	2.10	2.52	2.48	2.59	2.53	1.94	1.98
Av. daily ration								
Corn	9.7	11.2	10.9	12.8	18.3	22.3	12.1	12.0*
Protein conc.	1.8	1.8	1.1	1.3	......	......	1.7	1.7
Corn silage	7.1	7.1	......	......	......	......	11.5	11.5
Hay	2.7	2.8	3.9	3.9	5.2	4.0	1.5	1.5
Feed per cwt. gain								
Corn, bu	8.7	7.6	7.7	7.4	13.5	13.2	11.2	10.9
Protein conc., lb	88	83	43	51	......	......	88	86
Corn silage	267	260	......	......	......	......	593	581
Hay	280	274	155	158	212	164	79	77
Feed cost per cwt. gain	......	......	$7.63	$8.43	$8.17	$8.74	$9.58	$10.00
Selling price per cwt.	......	......	$9.70	$9.35	$9.35	$9.40	$12.40	$12.65
Hog gains per steer, lb	82	38	17	13	36	10	57	11
Net return over feed costs (including pork)	......	......	$8.37	$1.48	$8.52	$7.17	$17.98	$16.81

and yearling cattle gained at practically the same rate on shelled corn as on corn-and-cob meal. However, the steers in the Missouri experiments reported in Table 216 gained somewhat faster on shelled corn than on ground ear corn. In all the Ohio tests reported in Table 215, fewer bushels of corn were eaten per hundredweight gain by the steers fed ground ear corn, but in the Missouri experiments approximately the same amounts of corn were consumed per hundredweight of gain made. Such disagreement in the results obtained from these two forms of corn are frequently encountered in tests made at different stations or at the same station in different years or under different conditions. The fact that ground ear corn produced significantly less gain than

TABLE 216

A COMPARISON OF VARIOUS FORMS OF CORN FOR FATTENING CATTLE*
(Average of Three Tests. Two-year-old Steers. Average Time Fed, 130 Days.)

Preparation of Corn	Broken Ears, pounds	Shelled Corn, pounds	Crushed Ear Corn, pounds	Corn-and-Cob Meal, pounds	Ground Shelled Corn, pounds
Average initial weight	971	983	973	981	980
Average daily gain	2.52	2.71	2.59	2.61	3.08
Average daily ration					
Corn (shelled basis)	17.42	17.87	17.24	17.10	18.33
Nitrogenous conc.	2.78	2.96	2.75	2.71	3.05
Corn silage	17.58	17.75	16.00	16.61	18.22
Legume hay	2.49	2.69	2.53	2.38	3.08
Feed per pound gain					
Corn (shelled basis)	6.80	6.57	6.58	6.48	5.95
Nitrogenous conc.	1.10	1.09	1.06	1.05	0.99
Corn silage	6.93	6.55	6.17	6.35	5.91
Legume hay	0.99	1.00	0.98	0.91	1.01
Beef per bushel corn fed cattle	8.24	8.52	8.51	8.64	9.40
Pork produced per steer	91.76	68.09	40.62	17.94	19.29
Pork per bushel corn fed cattle	2.27	1.63	1.01	0.46	0.45
Gain on cattle and hogs per bushel of corn fed cattle	10.51	10.15	9.52	9.10	9.85
Pounds of dry matter fed per pound gain on cattle and hogs	7.62	8.42	8.78	9.36	8.73
Per cent of total gain on cattle and hogs made by hogs	21.63	16.02	10.63	4.98	4.56
Per cent of corn fed recovered by hogs (based on estimate of 5 pounds corn per pound pork)	20.3	14.5	9.0	4.0	4.0

* Missouri Bulletin 149, 1917.

shelled corn at the Iowa Station in 1946–1947 with only 1 pound of linseed meal but slightly larger gain with 2 pounds of protein supplement suggests that some of the corn-and-cob meal rations may have contained insufficient protein to sustain the optimum bacterial action on the corn cobs during rumen digestion.[2]

[2] Iowa Experiment Station, AII Leaflet 165, 1947.

When Is the Grinding of Corn Justified? A careful study of Tables 215 and 216 brings out the fact that whole corn produces more meat, both beef and pork combined, than ground corn. This, without doubt, results from the inability of the hogs to recover the small particles of ground corn that pass through the cattle undigested. Unless the price of fat cattle is considerably higher than the price of hogs, the grinding of corn is not ordinarily justified where hogs are available to follow the cattle. In the absence of hogs, medium or finely ground shelled corn should be fed, as the larger gains made by the cattle are more than enough to pay for the expense of grinding. In this connection, attention is called to Table 217.

Obviously the cost of shelling, breaking, crushing, or grinding will vary greatly with the kind and size of machinery used. A large amount of corn can be ground or shelled at a much lower cost per bushel than a single wagonload. The greater the amount of man labor required to get the corn to and from the machine, the greater the cost.

TABLE 217

ADVANTAGES RESULTING FROM PREPARATION OF CORN*

	Increase in Cattle Gains per Bushel of Corn Fed	Value of Cattle Gains at 20 cents per Pound	Increased Cost of Preparation per Bushel†	Shortening of Time to Put on 350 lb. Gain
1. Shelling ear corn.........	0.28 lb.	5.6¢	3–4¢	10 days
2. Crushing ear corn........	0.27	5.4	5–6	4 days
3. Grinding ear corn........	0.40	8.0	6–8	5 days
4. Shelling and grinding corn meal.................	1.16	23.6	8–10	27 days
5. Grinding shelled corn.....	0.88	17.6	5–7	17 days

* Computed from Table 216.

† Cost of breaking ear corn per bushel estimated at 4 cents.

The effect of the preparation of corn on the length of the feeding period, or on the finish attained by the cattle during a stated number of days, is, perhaps, of more practical importance than the actual saving of feed by shelling or grinding. Ground corn is habitually used in the fitting of cattle for show and sale for the reason that it produces more rapid gains than whole corn. For the same reason, men who are feeding for the open market will use ground feed when they wish to "crowd" their cattle as much as possible in order to finish them on a short feed or to put them in market condition before an expected decline in prices occurs.

One advantage possessed by ground corn over whole corn, especially over ear corn, is the ease with which it may be mixed with other feeds such as bran, linseed or cottonseed meal. Particularly is this true where self-feeders are used and a considerable quantity of feed is mixed up at one time. The self-feeding of cottonseed meal along with broken ear corn is rather unsatisfactory, as two materials varying so much in texture do not mix together well. With shelled or ground corn, however, no such difficulty is experienced. In the feeding of young, purebred breeding cattle and in the fitting of animals for the show ring, the use of ground corn is well-nigh universal, largely because it is more easily mixed with the other components of the ration.

Ground ear corn is superior to shelled corn for cattle which are full-fed on legume pastures, such as sweet clover and alfalfa, as the dry particles of cob tend to overcome the tendency of these forages to cause scours and bloat.[3] However, shelled corn appears to be much better on bluegrass and other non-legume pastures, as larger quantities are eaten and therefore greater gains secured. Shelled corn is less badly damaged by rain than ground corn. It is therefore better suited for feeding out of doors and for using in self-feeders, into which some moisture may enter during a bad storm.

One very serious disadvantage of ground ear and ground shelled corn is the impossibility of storing it in quantity without its becoming unpalatable through the action of mold-forming bacteria. These bacteria develop rapidly in ground corn with a moisture content above 15 or 16 per cent at winter temperatures, or above 13 or 14 per cent at temperatures above 70° Fahrenheit. Since these limits are seldom obtained until late spring, it is usually necessary to grind corn every 3 or 4 days in order to prevent its becoming musty and rancid before it is fed. Shelled corn, on the other hand, can be stored safely if its moisture content does not exceed 18 per cent. Consequently, shelled corn is preferred to either ground corn or ground ear corn by feeders who find it convenient to store large quantities of corn in the same form in which it will be fed.

Preparation of Oats, Barley, and Wheat. The advisability of grinding oats, barley, and wheat for cattle has already been discussed.[4] Inasmuch as the saving effected by grinding oats for calves usually does not exceed 5 to 10 per cent, grinding oats for animals of this age is not likely to be profitable unless oats are high in price.

[3] Cf. p. 437.
[4] Cf. pp. 287–292.

It is doubtful, however, that barley or wheat should ever be fed whole, as so many of the small, hard grains are swallowed whole and are imperfectly digested.

TABLE 218

VALUE OF GRINDING OATS, BARLEY, AND WHEAT FOR CATTLE

	Indiana Bulletin 371, 1933				Minnesota Bulletin 300, 1933		Missouri Bulletin 325, 1933		
Grain Ration	Oats, ⅓; Shelled Corn, ⅔				Barley (alone)		Wheat Alone and Mixed with Corn		
	Whole Oats	Coarsely Ground	Medium Ground	Finely Ground	Whole	Ground	Whole Wheat	Ground Wheat	Ground Wheat ½ Shelled Corn ½
Initial weight, lb......	997	997	993	995	693	687	562	554	557
Av. daily gain, lb.....	1.93	2.06	2.11	1.95	2.12	2.25	2.16	1.84	2.57
Grain consumed daily.	14.5	14.6	14.6	14.6	14.8	12.5	14.4	9.6	13.2
Grain per cwt. gain...	756	710	695	749	700	554	668	523	513
Hog gains per steer...	25	23	28	22	34	8	46	5	14
Feed cost per cwt. gain	$14.72	$14.00	$14.17	$16.06	$16.37	$13.89	$13.96	$12.16	$11.34

Preparation of Milo and Kafir Grain. Threshed milo, kafir, and other sorghum grains are so small and hard that they should be ground for cattle of all ages. Experiments carried on at the Texas Station with calves showed that grinding threshed milo increased its value 41 per cent, and grinding unthreshed milo heads increased their value 62 per cent.[5] That the unground grain was poorly utilized was indicated by the fact that the hog gains per steer were approximately four times as great as those of the calves fed ground milo grain.

The results of digestion trials and feeding experiments carried out at the Kansas Station with whole and ground milo are given in Table 219. In these trials no significant difference was observed between coarsely and finely ground milo grain. In a test at the Kansas Station 42 per cent of whole milo grain fed to dairy cows was screened out of the feces, whereas the recovery of coarsely and finely ground milo grain were only 4.8 and 1.5 per cent, respectively, of the amount fed.[6]

[5] Texas Bulletin 547, 1937.
[6] Kansas Mimeo. Report, May 1, 1948.

TABLE 219

Effect of Grinding upon the Digestibility
and Feeding Value of Milo Grain*

Lot Number	1	2	3
Ration	Whole Milo, Atlas Silage, Cottonseed Meal	Coarsely Ground Milo, Atlas Silage, Cottonseed Meal	Finely Ground Milo, Atlas Silage, Cottonseed Meal
Average percentage of nutrients digested:			
Dry matter	48.0	52.3	60.2
Crude protein	42.7	46.8	54.9
Ether extract	50.1	64.7	72.5
Crude fiber	56.4	50.3	51.0
Nitrogen-free extract	51.4	57.3	65.1
Feeding trial, 122 days			
Average initial wt., lb.		540	540
Average gain per steer		295	303
Average daily gain		2.42	2.48
Feed eaten per cwt. gain			
Ground milo		539	524
Cottonseed meal		62	60
Alfalfa hay		295	298
Prairie hay		282	256
Appraised value per cwt.		$29.00	$30.00

* Kansas Experiment Station Circular 230, 1949.

The low digestibility of the grain of the sorghums lowers the feeding value of sorghum silage to a marked extent. An examination of the feces of cattle fed sorghum silage will disclose that a high proportion of the seeds are voided with little evidence of their having been masticated. This waste may be prevented by removing the heads at the time of siloing, running them through a grinder, and returning the ground material to the stover on the feed table of the ensilage cutter. Atlas sorgo silage processed in this way at the Kansas Station produced 19 per cent more gain per ton than silage made in the usual way.[7] However, if normal sorgo silage is valued at $7.50 a ton, the saving effected by grinding would hardly cover the expense involved.

Rolled vs. Ground Grain. Crushed oats, barley, and wheat are usually preferred to ground grains by professional herdsmen and feeders of show cattle. Crushing is preferred to grinding, as the hulls are pressed into the kernels rather than split into fine slivers. However, 2-year-old steers fed a grain mixture of equal parts of crushed wheat and oats at the Illinois Station consumed less feed and made less rapid

[7] Mimeographed Report, 1938.

gains than steers fed ground oats and wheat. The reason for these differences probably lay in the greater bulkiness of the crushed grains, which occupied 40 per cent more volume per unit of weight than the ground grains. In rations where bulk is desired, rolled grains are excellent feeds; however, their advantage over ground grains would hardly justify the purchase of a crusher except in the case of a very large herd.

TABLE 220

THE COMPARATIVE VALUE OF GROUND AND
ROLLED GRAIN FOR FATTENING CATTLE

	Oklahoma Bulletin 270, 1943			Illinois Mimeo. Report, 1930	
	Whole Oats	Ground Oats	Rolled Oats	Ground Grain 1:1	Rolled Grain, 1:1
Weight per bushel, lb.					
Oats	32.5	26	16	23.5	16.5
Wheat	..	..	..	52.5	39.5
Average initial weight	360	360	359	910	913
Average daily gain	2.11	2.14	1.82	2.36	2.15
Average daily ration					
Grain	7.2	6.9	6.1	15.0	14.0
Protein conc.	2.0	2.0	2.0	2.1	2.0
Altas sorgo silage	9.6	9.6	9.6	..	..
Clover hay	..	..	..	5.2	5.2
Feed eaten per cwt. gain					
Grain	341	321	336	634	652
Protein conc.	93	92	108	88	91
Altas sorgo silage	452	447	525	..	..
Clover hay	..	..	..	219	240
Selling price per cwt.	..	..	..	$9.70	$9.25

Soaking Feed. The soaking of corn for beef cattle is seldom practiced. Such a method of feed preparation has little merit except during the summer when the corn is dry and hard. However, at this time of year it is very difficult to keep soaked corn from fermenting and becoming sour. Soaking corn resulted in larger daily gains and brought about a better utilization of the corn eaten in a Kansas experiment summarized in Table 221. These results were obtained from two lots of 2-year-old steers fed during the winter months. During very cold weather the cattle were fed five times a day to prevent the corn's freezing in the troughs.

It was found that the corn recovered from the droppings of Lot I did not increase in weight from further soaking, whereas that from Lot II increased perceptibly, showing that the kernels fed dry had not been fully saturated during their passage through the alimentary tract. By feeding a small amount of red corn for a single day it was possible to measure the time required for shelled corn to pass through a steer. The red kernels first began to appear in the feces 21 hours after they were fed and increased in number until about the 48th hour, at which time the maximum was apparently reached. On the fourth day after they were fed, only a few red kernels were observed.

TABLE 221

SOAKED VS. DRY SHELLED CORN FOR FATTENING STEERS*

(Two-year-old Steers — 150 days)

	Lot I (Soaked Corn) (Dry Roughage)	Lot II (Dry Corn) (Dry Roughage)
	lbs.	lbs.
Average Daily Gain.....................	2.18	1.96
Average Corn Ration per Day (dry)......	21.0	22.0
Corn Consumed per lb. Gain (dry).......	9.67	11.07
Total Food Eaten per lb. Gain (dry)......	14.78	16.60
Pork Secured per Steer.................	76.2	92.5
Weight of Corn Recovered from Droppings per Day†..........................	5.92	7.73
Estimated Dry Weight of Corn in Droppings per Day†.....................	2.42	3.47
Per cent of Corn Eaten Voided in Droppings per Day†.....................	11.1	15.9

* Kansas Bulletin 47.
† Based on samples taken during a 28-day period.

Cooking Feed.   Seldom is the cooking of feed for beef cattle justified.   Cooking apparently increases the palatability of certain feeds, especially during cold weather; hence, it is sometimes practiced in fitting cattle for the late fall and winter shows.   Barley is the feed most commonly cooked.   Its hard, flinty kernel is rendered soft and palatable by soaking it overnight and then steaming it over a low fire for 2 or 3 hours.   Special cookers using coal, oil, or electricity as the source of heat may be purchased from dealers and manufacturers, but most experienced herdsmen who use cooked feed devise their own.   Carefully conducted experiments show conclusively that cooking decreases the digestibility of most of the common feeding stuffs.   This fact, together with the labor and fuel charges incident to cooking, makes this method of preparation wholly devoid of merit for the practical cattleman.

Preparation of Roughage.   During the last few years much interest has been shown in the possibility of increasing the feeding value of dry roughages by grinding or chaffing them.   The presence of tractors and electric motors on most Corn Belt farms affords a source of power to drive feed grinders and hay chaffers, and manufacturers of this kind of equipment have sought to increase their sales by making profuse claims for the benefits to be obtained by feeding ground hay

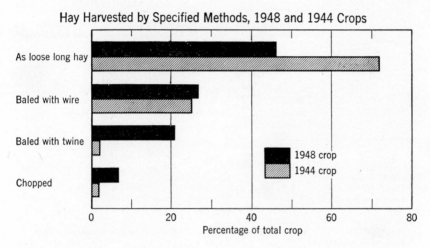

Hay Harvested by Specified Methods, 1948 and 1944 Crops

Fɪɢ. 62. Changes in methods of harvesting hay during the 5-year period 1944–1948. Baling and field chopping are practiced more widely each year, largely because less man labor is required in storing and feeding. (*Courtesy U.S.D.A.*)

and fodder.   Fortunately for the farmer who takes the pains to learn the facts before spending his money, a great deal of information is available which indicates that the grinding of roughage is seldom a profitable practice in the feeding of beef cattle.   It is true that hay and stover ground or chaffed are fed with less waste than they are in their natural forms and that ground roughage may be stored more easily under cover; but, unless roughage is very scarce and expensive the cost of grinding is usually much greater than the saving made. As a rule, the money and labor expended in grinding roughages could be much better spent in harvesting sufficient amounts of hay and fodder to permit the cattle to eat only the more palatable and digestible portions and not the woody stems and butts, as they must do if these roughages are cut or ground.

Grinding and Chaffing Hay. The claim that the feeding value of hay is improved by grinding is not supported by most of the tests which have been made with long and ground hay. Instead these

TABLE 222

VALUE OF GRINDING OR CHAFFING HAY FOR FATTENING CATTLE

	Nebraska Mimeo. Cattle Circular 157, 1935[a]		Iowa Mimeo. AH Leaflet 162, 1944			Minnesota Bulletin 300, 1933	
	Shelled Corn and Alfalfa Hay		Shelled Corn and Alfalfa Hay			Ground Shelled Corn and Alfalfa Hay	
	Long Hay Fed Separately	Ground Hay Mixed with Corn	Long Hay Fed Separately	Coarsely Chopped Hay Mixed with Corn	Finely Chopped Hay Mixed with Corn	Whole Hay Fed Separately	Ground Hay Mixed with Corn
Av. initial wt.	611	610	692	690	690	688	689
Av. daily gain	2.20	2.15	2.35	2.40	2.35	2.49	2.52
Av. daily ration							
Corn	13.5	13.8	15.7	15.3	14.8	17.0	17.2
Protein supplement	.....	.....	1.0	1.0	1.0	.....	.....
Hay[b]	5.5	3.5	4.6	4.6	4.5	7.0	6.4
Feed per cwt. gain							
Corn	616	642	667	636	629	682	684
Protein supplement	.....	.....	42	41	42	.....	.....
Hay	250	162	196	192	194	279	256
Feed cost per cwt. gain	$11.29	$11.01	$15.02	$14.41[c]	$14.34[c]	$10.52	$10.48
Selling price per cwt.	9.80	9.80	17.15	17.00	16.85	12.00	12.00
Net return per steer	.....	.....	30.50	32.93[c]	29.96[c]	30.10	30.37

[a] Average of 2 trials.
[b] Including hay that was wasted.
[c] Cost of chaffing hay not included.

tests have shown that cattle often do not like ground hay; that the feeding of ground hay decreases the time spent in rumination; and that, as a result of the smaller consumption and less thorough digestion of the ground roughage, the gains are smaller and more costly.

The practice of grinding the hay and feeding it mixed with the grain has in some tests resulted in larger gains than when whole feeds were fed, but in a number of experiments opposite results have been obtained. In few, if any, of the tests have the advantages been sufficient to pay for the expense of grinding and mixing the feeds, especially if the gains made by the hogs kept with the cattle are taken into account.

Apparently the principal advantage possessed by ground hay over long hay is that it is fed with less waste. Cattle fed long hay often pull some of it out of the manger and trample it under foot. Also, they usually leave some of the stems uneaten, particularly if the hay is full-fed. Obviously, both these losses are greater if the hay is coarse and poor in quality. Since it is only hay of poor quality that is fed with appreciable waste, it is this kind of hay that is most frequently ground. Even though the waste of the long hay were as much as 25 per cent, it is doubtful if grinding would be profitable, since the coarser portions which constitute most of the waste usually are worth much less than the cost of grinding the whole supply of hay fed.

If hay is so scarce and valuable that its waste must be prevented more than is possible through the use of properly built racks and mangers, it should be cut or chaffed by running it through a silage cutter, or similar machine, which will cut it into 2- to 4-inch lengths. Chaffed hay is better digested by ruminants than ground hay and is prepared with much less labor and power.

One of the advantages of chaffed or chopped hay is the low cost of harvesting and storage. If it is chopped from the windrow with a field cutter and blown into the barn where it can be "pushed down" to the cattle with little or no handling, less labor is required than in harvesting and feeding long or baled hay. (See Fig. 63.) Also, approximately twice as many tons of chopped as of long hay can be stored in a given shed or mow. However, hay that is to be chopped in the field must be much drier when stored than ordinary hay or hay that is stored in the bale. Consequently, a rather high percentage of the leaves and fine stems are reduced to such fine particles by the chopper and blower that they are lost in harvesting and feeding. The storage of chopped hay with a moisture content much above 15 per cent will usually result in the loss of valuable food nutrients from extensive "mow burning." There is also the risk of the loss of both hay and barn from spontaneous combustion. Consequently, the field chopping of hay can be recommended only when it is to be stored in a barn or bin equipped with forced ventilation. When so stored it may be chopped while it is still sufficiently "tough" to prevent the loss of valuable leaves and stems, since the excess moisture will be driven off by the forced ventilation before serious heating occurs.

Grinding Shock Corn. The practice of feeding ground rather than whole shock corn to fattening cattle has increased greatly during the past few years, especially in those sections of the Corn Belt where shock corn is a major item of the ration during the winter months.

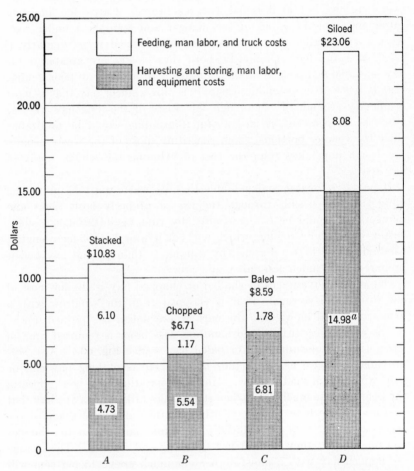

FIG. 63. Effect of the method of harvesting and storing upon the cost per acre of harvesting and feeding the first crop of alfalfa. (A) Stacked in field with bull rakes and overshot stackers; hauled to cattle about once a week; usually hay was the only feed fed. (B) Chopped from windrow; hauled from field in trucks and stacked near feed lot; fed mixed with grain in grain bunks. (C) Baled from windrow with pick-up balers; bales picked up with tractor and sled and piled in the field or near the feed lot; fed by breaking bales and scattering hay in grain bunks. (D) Ensiled alfalfa was either mowed and chopped in one operation or mowed and windrowed and chopped from windrow; hauled in trucks to upright or trench silos; usually a preservative was added as the silo was filled; alfalfa silage fed mixed with grain to beef cattle; fed alone to dairy cows after milking. (Constructed from data in Colorado Bulletin 417-A, 1951.)

Fodder (ears and stover) is ground for the purpose of compelling the cattle to eat the entire stalk, the lower half of which is seldom consumed when large amounts of long fodder are fed. Apparently many farmers do not realize that this portion is refused because it has little

TABLE 223

THE EFFECT OF METHOD OF HARVEST AND STORAGE OF ALFALFA
HAY UPON ITS VALUE FOR FATTENING CATTLE*

(Average of 3 Trials)

	Stacked Alfalfa Hay	Baled from Wind-row	Chopped from Wind-row	Dehydrated Alfalfa Hay	Molas-ses-Alfalfa Silage
Av. initial wt., lb.	696	692	689	694	717
Av. daily gain	2.04	2.11	2.13	2.19	2.09
Av. daily ration					
Grain	15.5	15.6	15.4	15.5	15.8
Soybean oil meal	1.0	1.0	1.0	1.0	1.0
Hay or silage	3.6	3.9	3.9	3.5^a	9.5^a
Feed per cwt. gain					
Grain	773	756	738	724	777
Soybean oil meal	48	47	46	45	47
Hay or silage	177	187	183	155^b	453^b
Av. TDN per cwt. gain	712	705	689	669	702

* Colorado Experiment Station Progress Report, February, 1951.
[a] Includes approximately 0.5 lb. of long stacked hay.
[b] Includes approximately 20 lb. of long stacked hay.

feeding value and that to force cattle to eat it will result in their consuming a smaller amount of the palatable portions, which they would eat if they were given a full feed of whole fodder. In feeding tests steers fed whole fodder have gained practically as fast as steers fed ground fodder and at a much lower cost, if the labor and machinery used in grinding are taken into account. In some experiments, considerably more gain per acre has been obtained from ground fodder; in others but little difference in this respect has been observed.[8] If the fodder is coarse and woody, there will be less advantage in grinding it than if it were of finer texture, since the hard shell and the pith of heavy corn stalks are detrimental to cattle. Digestion trials conducted at the South Dakota Station with mature dairy cows fed the refused portion of whole corn stover obtained from another experiment gave a negative balance in all nutrients. "These results would seem to indicate that cows cannot utilize the nutrients in the refused

[8] See results of Iowa experiment in Table 224 and Michigan experiment in Table 225.

corn stover even though the chemical analysis shows that nutrients are there in appreciable amounts."[9]

One very serious objection to ground corn fodder is its tendency to mold if stored for more than a few days. Since cut fodder contains

TABLE 224

VALUE OF GRINDING OR CUTTING CORN FODDER FOR FATTENING CATTLE

	Iowa* 2-Year-Old Steers (2-Year Average)			Ohio† Steer Calves			Minnesota‡ Yearling Steers	
	Corn Fodder and Whole Alfalfa Hay			Whole Stover and Alfalfa vs. Proc. Stover and Alfalfa			Whole Shelled Corn, Whole Fodder, Long Alfalfa vs. These Feeds Ground and Mixed§	
	Whole Fodder	Cut Fodder	Ground Fodder	Whole Rough- age	Chopped Rough- age	Ground Rough- age	Whole Feeds	Feeds Ground and Mixed
Av. daily gain, lb.....	2.08	2.24	2.20	1.82	1.93	1.86	2.27	2.30
Av. daily ration								
Grain and prot. conc.	7.3[a]	7.7[a]	7.5[a]	7.8	7.7	7.8	Same amounts	
Corn fodder (fed) ...	17.9	17.8	18.2	3.0	3.3	3.3	of feed fed	
Hay..............	1.5	1.0	1.0	3.7	3.3	3.3	to each lot	
Fodder refused, %....	18.7	9.7	3.1	......	......	......	......	......
Feed cost per cwt. gain	$7.92	$7.78	$8.46	$10.26[b]	$9.45[b]	$9.83[b]	$12.68	$13.44
Hog gains per steer, lb.	87	70	37	......	......	......	27	17
Cost of processing fodder per ton....	......	$1.10	$2.30	Cost disregarded			......	$2.00
Net return per steer (includes hogs)....	$18.93	$16.68	$13.01	$12.34[b]	$17.18[b]	$12.27[b]	$14.50	$10.02

* Iowa Mimeo. AH Leaflets 156 and 157, 1938 and 1939.
† Ohio AH Circular 10, 1928.
‡ Minnesota Bulletin 300, 1933.
§ Corn fodder fed first 56 days, alfalfa hay last 119 days.
[a] Approximately 54 per cent of weight of fodder fed was ears.
[b] No charge made for processing roughage.

relatively little fine material, it can be stored in quantity much more safely than ground fodder. This fact, together with the lower labor and power costs, makes cutting a much more satisfactory method of preparing fodder or stover than grinding, when an acute shortage of roughage requires the utilization of all available supplies.

[9] South Dakota Bulletin 252, 1930.

Ground Shock Corn vs. Corn Silage. Numerous comparisons have been made between ground shock corn and corn silage as roughages for beef cattle, in almost all of which corn silage has proved to be much superior. Several of these comparisons have been made on an acre basis by siloing and shocking equal areas of corn and feeding them with equal amounts of other feeds to different lots of steers. In

TABLE 225

COMPARATIVE VALUE OF GROUND SHOCK CORN AND CORN SILAGE

	Ohio Bimonthly Bulletin 157, 1932		Iowa Mimeo. Circular 156, 1938		Michigan Special Bulletin 293, 1938		
	Yearling Steers		2-Yr.-Old Steers		Yearling Steers (av. of 3 trials)		
	Ground Shock Corn	Corn Silage	Ground Shock Corn	Corn Silage	Ground Shock Corn	Corn Silage	Whole Shock Corn
Av. daily gain, lb.	1.81	2.03	2.20	2.41	1.73	1.87	1.63
Av. daily ration							
Grain and prot. conc.	1.9	1.9	7.7	7.7	......	......	......
Shock corn or silage	24.8	48.2	19.5	43.9	......	......	......
Legume hay	3.8	2.7	1.0	1.0	......	......	......
Steer days per acre of corn	350	374	325	301	201	259	162
Cattle gain per acre of corn, lb.	633	759	715	725	355	484	264
Hog gains per acre of corn, lb.	17	17	......	......	11	10	54
Cost of preparing 1 acre of corn for cattle feed	$19.09	$9.24	......	......	$13.37	$10.77	$4.91
Net return per acre of corn	−1.79	21.95	8.92[a]	11.14[a]	14.37	31.63	19.97
Labor required to prepare 1 acre of corn							
Man, hr.	53.6	28.3	......	......	21.3	17.1	13.8
Horse, hr.	18.7	26.9	......	......	11.8	18.3	11.6
Tractor, hr.	9.3	2.1	......	......	5.1	1.5	.... .

[a] Net return per steer.

all these tests the total cattle and hog gains per acre have greatly favored silage, whereas at the same time the cost of harvesting and processing has been less for silage than for ground fodder. In view of these results, it appears that the feeder who depends largely upon the corn crop to fatten his cattle should supply most of the roughage in the form of silage.

Effect of Grinding and Chopping Roughage upon its Palatability. It might seem that ground or chopped roughage would be more palatable than whole roughage, since it can be eaten more easily. Also, all the ground roughage fed is usually eaten, whereas a noticeable percentage of whole hay or stover is refused. With coarse, stemmy hay and corn stover the refused portion may amount to 20 to 40 per cent of the total amount fed.

However, feeding experiments show that cattle usually will eat more whole hay than ground or chopped hay if both kinds of hay are fed according to appetite. For example, in the Nebraska experiments reported in Table 222 it was necessary in both trials to limit the feeding of whole hay in order to obtain the desired consumption of corn, whereas some difficulty was experienced in getting the lots fed ground alfalfa to eat their hay. Likewise in palatability tests conducted at the Wisconsin Station with purebred beef cows and heifers a marked preference for whole hay and coarsely chopped hay (1.8 inch) and a dislike for hay chopped to ½ inch and ¼ inch were noted. In one of the Wisconsin tests, where all four kinds of hay were available in adjacent mangers, whole hay constituted 71.5 per cent of all the hay consumed.[10]

"Predigested" Feeds. Some manufacturing concerns, a few years ago, advocated the predigesting of coarse feeds before feeding by subjecting them to bacterial action which presumably would break down the fiber and cellulose into soluble, easily digestible starches and sugars. Such changes were to be brought about by treating the chopped or ground roughage with a special "converter" or "digester compound" possessing powerful enzymic properties, steaming the mixture in a special container, and letting it stand for 24 hours before feeding it to the cattle. By adding fresh material at the top of the chamber as the "converted" roughage was withdrawn at the bottom, a continuous supply of feed would be made available. Fortunately for those feeders who appear to be continually looking for some magic way to prosperity, experiment stations quickly investigated the new process and found it to be without merit. "There was no advantage to this method of preparation as compared with feeding dry roughage. Salt was fully as efficient as the digestor compound. Steaming the roughage did not help in this test."[11] Following the publication of the findings of these investigations, interest in this method of preparing feeds rapidly subsided.

[10] Shorthorn World, Sept. 25, 1947, p. 46.
[11] Ohio Agricultural Experiment Station Circular 10, 1928.

Self-Feeding vs. Hand Feeding. The use of self-feeders in fattening cattle is very common, especially for cattle that are given a short feed before being marketed. Such animals are on a full grain ration during practically the entire feeding period; hence, the self-fed method of feeding is in many ways advantageous. On the other hand, self-feeders are manifestly impractical for an extended feeding period during most of which something less than a full feed of grain is used.

The principal *advantages* derived from the use of self-feeders are as follows:

1. There is a saving in the time and labor expended in feeding.
2. Larger daily gains are secured.
3. The cattle are less likely to go off feed.

Of these advantages, the saving of labor is by far the most important. By using self-feeders with large bins or hoppers, it is necessary to feed the cattle but once every week or 10 days. Large quantities of feed can be prepared by the use of machinery, hauled, and shoveled directly into the feeders with a minimum of time and labor. Hand feeding, on the other hand, requires the preparation of each feed at the time it is fed, or the rehandling of the material if it is prepared in quantity and stored. This saving of labor is of most consequence to the farmer during the summer months when he is busy in the field and, hence, begrudges the time spent in doing morning and evening chores. For this reason, self-feeders are more extensively used in summer than in winter feeding.[1]

Carefully conducted feeding experiments indicate that self-feeding usually results in larger gains than hand feeding. This is usually true even where the hand feeding is carefully done at regular intervals by experienced feeders. Under ordinary farm conditions, where more or less irregularity often occurs as regards time of feeding, quantity and character of rations, etc., the difference in favor of self-feeding will as a rule be greater than the results obtained in experimental trials in which these two methods have been compared.

[1] *Cf.* p. 427.

Next in importance to the saving of labor is the value of the self-feeder in lessening the tendency of the cattle to go off feed. "Going off feed" is due principally to overeating. The appetites of animals are affected greatly by weather conditions, and cattle that are hand-fed frequently come to the feed trough with much keener appetites than they ordinarily possess. The result is that some of the larger and stronger steers eat more than their share, bolting the greater part of it

FIG. 64. A good type of self-feeder. It is filled through a window in the other end. (*Courtesy Illinois Experiment Station.*)

without much chewing. On the following day these cattle are likely to be "off feed." The usual symptoms are partial loss of appetite and pronounced scouring. The customary method of treatment is to cut down the feed to about one-half the usual amount, to favor the correction of the digestive disturbance. Although this treatment is perhaps as good as any practical means that can be devised, it is likely to cause a recurrence of the trouble unless great care is exercised in bringing the cattle back to their normal ration. They should be brought back as rapidly as their recovery of appetite will permit. However, the ration should be increased gradually to guard against overeating by steers that are ravenously hungry.

Cattle that are self-fed exhibit comparatively little tendency to go off feed. They soon learn that the feed is accessible at all times; hence, they eat in a leisurely manner and only enough to satisfy the appetite that they feel at the moment. There is no inclination to gorge themselves with enough feed to last until the next feeding time, or to eat as rapidly as possible in order to get their share before all the feed is gone.

Care must, of course, be exercised in putting cattle on a self-feeder.

As a rule, hand feeding is practiced until the cattle are accustomed to a full feed of grain. This period may vary from a week to 60 or even 90 days, depending on the length of the feeding period.

The principal *disadvantages* of using self-feeders are the following:

1. It is impossible to utilize large amounts of farm-grown roughages.
2. Considerable labor is required in preparing feeds for the self-feeder—shelling, grinding, mixing, etc.
3. A larger investment in equipment is required.
4. There is a slight increase in cost of gains.

None of these items require any extended discussion. As regards the first, it is freely admitted that self-feeders have no place on those farms where the grain ration is more or less limited with a view to utilizing large quantities of roughage.

The second disadvantage, however, is not so easily passed by. Ear corn is not suited for use in self-feeders. The ears, even if broken, do not run down into the troughs easily but tend to accumulate at the opening, clogging the feeder. Daily inspection should be made to see that the corn is accessible to the cattle. Much wastage of ear corn results from the cattle's "nosing" it out of the troughs and letting it fall to the ground before the ears are entirely eaten. The cattle often get into the habit of but partially eating the ears and spitting out the cob and the grains that have not been shelled off, knowing that another ear is always within reach. No such wastage of feed occurs with ground or shelled corn.

If a nitrogenous concentrate is to be fed in a self-feeder along with the corn, the corn should be either shelled or ground, as the common protein feeding stuffs cannot be mixed with ear corn satisfactorily. A somewhat better mixture results with ground corn than with shelled.

Self-feeders are somewhat more expensive to build than ordinary troughs and bunks. Moreover, the former do not wholly replace the latter, as wide-open bunks are more satisfactory than the troughs along the sides of the feeders for getting the cattle on full feed. Such bunks are also necessary for the feeding of silage. However, the cost of both bunks and self-feeders is relatively small, so that the increased investment due to duplicate equipment is not a serious matter.

It is rather generally believed that hand feeding results in more economical gains than can be obtained from self-feeding. Granting that such may be true where the hand feeding is carefully done, this advantage is not likely to exist where the ordinary methods of hand feeding are practiced. Inasmuch as nearly half the experiments involving hand-fed and self-fed lots show a slightly lower feed requirement per pound of gain for the latter, we may draw the conclusion that no material difference exists between these methods of feeding in so far as the cost of the gains is concerned.

TABLE 226

COMPARISON OF SELF–FEEDING AND HAND FEEDING STEERS

| | Wisconsin, Mimeograph Report, 1929 168 Days | | | Iowa Bulletin 182, 1918 Average of 2 Trials | | | |
| | | | | 1st 120 Days | | Total Period First Trial 160 Days Second Trial 150 Days | |
	Fed Twice-a-Day	Fed Once-a-Day	Self-fed Corn; Other Feeds Fed Once-a-Day	Self-Fed	Hand-Fed	Self-Fed	Hand-Fed
Av. daily gain...	2.51 lb.	2.56 lb.	2.55 lb.	3.24 lb.	3.06 lb.	2.94 lb.	2.68 lb.
Av. daily ration:							
Corn.........	12.4	12.4	12.8	15.15	14.47	16.14	15.00
N conc.......	1.50	1.50	1.50	2.25	2.25	2.25	2.25
Legume hay..	2.0	2.0	2.0	1.44	1.44	1.28	1.28
Corn silage...	17.1	17.1	17.1	32.47	31.43	29.24	28.74
Feed per lb. gain							
Corn.........	4.95	4.86	5.00	4.71	4.76	5.55	5.64
N conc.......	0.60	0.58	0.59	0.69	0.73	0.77	0.84
Legume hay..	0.80	0.79	0.79	0.45	0.47	0.44	0.48
Corn silage...	6.79	6.66	6.68	10.04	10.27	10.00	10.78

The Free-Choice Method of Feeding. The placing of several different kinds of feed in separate feeders, from which the animals may eat as much or as little of each as their appetites prompt, is termed "the free-choice" method of feeding. Although this method is used extensively in the fattening of hogs, it is practiced but rarely in the feeding of cattle. The theory underlying the free-choice plan is that the appetite of the animal is the best possible guide as to the kind and quantity of feeds that it needs. That this theory is in the main sound is suggested by the data in Table 227, obtained from a number of feeding trials carried on at the Oklahoma Experiment Station with calves after they were weaned. Although the calves had free access to cottonseed meal, no more of this feed was eaten than was needed to balance the ration.   In this respect the Oklahoma results differ from those obtained at the Iowa[2] station, where in a similar test calves ate approximately as much protein concentrates as grain when all components of the ration were fed "free-choice."

TABLE 227

SELECTION OF FEEDS MADE BY BEEF CALVES FED
"FREE–CHOICE" IN DRY LOT AFTER WEANING*

	Lot 1: Not Creep Fed	Lot 2: Creep Fed before Weaning	Average of 7 Lots, 3 Creep Fed, 4 Not Creep Fed
Hand fed after weaning, days	4	None	3 hand fed 56 days 1 hand fed 4 days 3 not hand fed
Av. initial weight, lb.	398	418	398
Time fed, days	173	173	167
Av. daily gain, lb.	2.10	1.99	2.11
Av. daily ration			
Shelled corn	7.3	8.0	5.4
Oats (whole)	4.9	4.7	4.4
Cottonseed cake (43%)	1.2	.6	1.3
Prairie hay	1.3	1.2	1.1
Alfalfa hay	0.8	0.8	1.2
Nutritive ratio	1:6.4	1:7.5	1.6
Feed consumed per cwt. gain			
Concentrates	641	668	523
Hay	100	97	106

* Oklahoma Bulletin 262, 1942.

Further experimental data are needed before any statement can be made as to the wisdom of using this method in practical feeding operations.   It would seem that at best its use would be limited to young animals that were being fattened as rapidly as possible.

Group vs. Stall Feeding.   Occasionally one hears lavish claims made for the stall method of feeding practiced in some European countries. However, the reports of attempts made to use this method in America do not lend encouragement to its adoption here.   Apparently cattle are influenced by "crowd psychology" in much the same way as human beings; each is interested in what its companions are doing; each has a strong desire to enter into the activity engaged in by the rest.   In no way is this tendency more clearly shown than in the activity of eating.   No sooner does one steer get up from his comfortable bed and walk to the feed trough than others lying nearby begin to do likewise.

[2] Iowa Mimeo. Report of Calf Feeding Tests.

As a result, animals with sluggish appetites are stimulated to eat through observing the behavior of their greedy mates. At any rate it is a well-known fact that cattle fed together out of a common trough will eat considerably more than if they are fed separately. Many calf club members who have been unsuccessful in imparting the desired finish to a single calf fed by itself have adopted the plan of feeding two or three animals together in a large box stall.

TABLE 228

GROUP *vs.* STALL-FEEDING OF BEEF CALVES*

Calves and Yearlings Fed 203 Days	Stanchion Fed	Group Fed
Initial weight.................(lbs.)	518.7	526.6
Final weight....................	886.0	982.0
Average daily gain..............	1.81	2.24
Average daily ration:		
Ground corn.................	8.81	9.62
Linseed meal.................	.94	1.03
Alfalfa hay....................	2.63	2.90
Corn silage...................	13.68	16.53
Cost of gain per cwt............	$10.64	$9.56

* Ohio Bimonthly Bulletin Vol. XI, No. 6, 1926.

Details of Hand Feeding: *a. Combining Feeds.* As a rule, grain and other concentrates should be fed separately from the roughage. An exception occurs in the case of cattle that are fed silage. Here the silage should be put in the trough first and the grain and protein concentrate poured over it. If the grain is self-fed, the protein concentrate should be spread over the silage instead of fed with the corn. Where silage is not fed, all concentrates used, including corn, should be fed mixed together.

Roughages, on the other hand, should be fed separately. In the first place, it is almost impossible to make an even mixture of such bulky materials. Secondly, mixing is likely to decrease the total consumption of roughage through the enforced consumption of the less palatable or more bulky feeding stuff. For example, the mixing of cut straw and silage at the Illinois Experiment Station resulted in a lower consumption of roughage than was obtained by feeding the two separately.

b. Number of Feeds per Day. Considerable variation exists among practical cattle feeders as to the number of times the different constituents of the ration are fed each day. In some cases the cattle are fed but once a day, enough of every item being given to supply them for the next 24 hours. (Should the practice be to offer a surplus of feed

Fig. 65. Hand feeding is still the most common method of supplying grain to cattle fed in the dry lot.

so that feed will be before the cattle at all times, hand feeding no longer exists, even though the usual self-feeding equipment is not used.) Although feeding but once a day results in the saving of considerable time and labor, it is not likely to bring about as good results as the feeding of smaller quantities at shorter intervals. This statement applies to the grain rather than the roughage, particularly if more than one kind of roughage is used.

Two feedings per day are the usual number, though the most careful feeders, such as the men who fit cattle for exhibition purposes or who let pass no opportunity to "top the market," give three or even four feeds of grain. The advantage of the larger number is that frequent feedings stimulate the appetites of the cattle by supplying fresh, clean feed that has not been "mussed over." Also, at each feeding time the curiosity of the animals is aroused, and they come up to the troughs to see what they have been given.

Where two feedings per day are made, they should be given fairly early in the morning and late in the evening. The exact time of day will depend upon the season of the year. Cattle should not be disturbed before daylight, at which time they usually begin to stir about; nor should they be fed so late in the evening that they will not finish eating a little before dark. With three feedings, the second one should be made at noon; with four, the last one should be given about 9 o'clock at night. Four feedings are impractical except in the case of show animals. Such cattle are usually fed in barns where each one can be fed separately. Hence, it is comparatively easy to judge the exact amount of feed that each animal should have. A typical four-feed schedule that would apply to July and August, the months when cattle are undergoing preparation for the coming show season, would call for feedings at 5.00 A.M., 11.00 A.M., 4.00 P.M., and 9.00 P.M.

Seldom are more than two feeds of roughage given per day. If more than one roughage material is used, it is a common practice to feed one in the morning and the other in the evening. The less palatable material should be fed in the morning, so as to afford a longer time for its consumption. Where silage and a legume hay are fed, the former may be fed in the morning and the latter at evening, since, as a rule, more silage than hay will be used; or both silage and hay may be fed in the morning and only silage at evening.

No hard and fast rules can be laid down concerning either the best time or the best method of feeding. They necessarily must be determined largely by the location of the feed supply in reference to the cattle and the amounts of the different feeding stuffs used. It is obvious that the more labor involved in feeding a given material, the greater is the likelihood that a single feeding per day will give the best results.

The following feeding schedules are given to illustrate the many ways in which the daily "menu" may be varied to suit local conditions:

I. All feeds accessible; no hauling required.
  No. 1. Grain and silage, at sunrise.
      Hay, at noon.
      Grain, ½ hour before sunset.
  No. 2. Grain, at sunrise.
      Hay, 1 to 2 hours later.
      Grain, at noon.
      Grain and hay, ½ hour before sunset.
  No. 3. Grain and silage, at sunrise.
      Hay, at noon.
      Grain and silage, 1 hour before sunset.
II. Grain accessible; roughage hauled.
  No. 1. Grain, at sunrise.
      Hay and silage, 2 hours later.
      Grain, at sunset.
  No. 2. Grain, at sunrise.
      Hay, 2 hours later.
      Grain, at noon.
      Grain, at sunset.
  No. 3. Grain, at sunrise.
      Hay and straw, 2 hours later.
      Grain and silage, 1 hour before sunset.
III. Both grain and roughage hauled.
  No. 1. Grain and silage, 1 hour after sunrise.
      Grain and hay, 1 hour before sunset.
  No. 2. Grain, silage and straw, morning.
      Grain and silage, evening.
  No. 3. Grain and stover, morning.
      Grain and hay, evening.
  No. 4. Shock corn, morning.
      Ear or shelled corn, linseed meal, and hay, evening.

PART · 4

General Problems in
Beef Production

29 ——————————— Baby-Beef Production

The marketing of cattle at 9 to 18 months of age has achieved much importance during the past years. The demand of the consumer for small retail cuts of beef, the need for the Corn Belt feeder to keep down production costs, and the necessity for a quick "turnover" on the part of the western rancher to meet urgent financial obligations have together brought about a steady increase in the number of calves consigned directly to feed lots upon their being weaned.

The fattening of calves rather than older cattle has brought about many changes in the established practices of beef production. However, it would seem that the more important of these changes affect the western rancher more than the Corn Belt feeder. Nevertheless, the feeding of calves differs sufficiently from the feeding of older cattle to justify some consideration of the problems faced by the man who is feeding calves perhaps for the first time. Moreover, the production of baby beef *par excellence* involves the rearing and fattening of calves upon the same farm as a single, continuous process. Obviously, the Corn Belt is the area best suited for such an enterprise.

The Economics of Baby-Beef Production. Many articles have been written hailing the fattening of calves as the most progressive step taken by beef producers since the introduction of purebred bulls onto the ranges of the far West. With this view of baby-beef production the author does not fully agree. In his judgment the marketing and slaughter of fat cattle under 18 to 20 months of age is an economically sound business only when carried on with small breeding herds maintained on relatively high-priced land where intensive methods of production prevail. The small area of land in pasture, the large amounts of concentrates available for fattening, and the importance of balancing high overhead charges with the most economical use of expensive feeds frequently require that breeding herds maintained in the Corn Belt be operated according to the baby-beef plan of production.

In the case of western-bred cattle a different situation prevails. These cattle are kept principally because of their ability to make good use of roughage, especially grass. Hence it would seem that the animal which is best able to convert grass into flesh is the one best suited

509

for this region. A comparison of the average increases in live weight obtained from a given area of grass and hay when consumed by cattle of various ages indicates that yearling cattle have an advantage over both cows and 2-year-olds in the better grazing regions of the range states. Not only do yearlings excel cows in the increase in live weight produced per unit of feed consumed, but also they show a much smaller death loss, lower labor charges, and much less depreciation than cows. If these things are true, and several economic studies made of western cattle ranches indicate that they are, it appears that many western cattlemen might be making a mistake by proceeding to adjust their ranching operations to a straight cow and calf basis.

TABLE 229

A COMPARISON OF THE PRODUCTION OF YEARLING STEERS
AND RANGE BREEDING COWS*

Weight Groups of Yearling Steers	Gain per Head 12 Months after Weaning, pounds	Per Cent of Feed for 1 Cow Consumed by 1 Steer	Number of Steers Grazed on Feed for 1 Cow	Gain Produced by Steers from Feed for 1 Cow, pounds	Per Cent of Production of 1 Cow Made by Steers from Same Feed[a]
Light	366.5	59.2	1.69	619.4	154.7
Medium light	350.6	62.3	1.61	564.5	141.0
Medium heavy	351.0	66.6	1.50	526.5	131.5
Heavy	325.8	68.0	1.47	478.9	119.6
All yearling steers	343.5	65.4	1.53	525.6	131.3

* New Mexico Mimeo. Report, Ranch Day, Oct. 31, 1941.
[a] The average production for each breeding cow for the period covered was 400.4 pounds, with an average calf crop of 91 per cent and average calf weaning weights of 440 pounds.

Production records kept on the breeding herd of the New Mexico Station over a 10-year period show that a yearling gained 85.6 pounds for each 100 pounds of weanling calf produced by a cow.[1] The average weaning weight of the calves during this period was 423 pounds, and the average calf crop 90 per cent. Hence, the average weight of weaned calf per cow was 380 pounds, and the gain in weight of each yearling was 325 pounds per cow. However, it was calculated that each calf-yearling ate only 65 per cent as much feed during the 12 months following weaning as the average breeding cow; or 3 yearlings ate about as much feed as 2 cows. Consequently, the feed required by 200 cows producing 76,000 pounds of weanling calves annually would produce 97,500 pounds of gain if consumed by yearlings. Hence, it would seem that the retention of calves by ranchers until they are 18–20 months of age would be highly profitable, unless perchance Corn

[1] New Mexico Station, Mimeo. Report, Ranch Day, 1947.

Belt feeders were willing to pay a sufficiently high premium for calves to offset this difference in weight. In addition, the marketing of year- lings would permit important savings in the items of interest, depreci- ation, and losses from death. These arguments are meant to apply only to those areas of the range region which furnish sufficiently good forage to permit the wintering of young cattle without stunting and to insure a good rate of gain during the grazing season. On the semi- desert ranges of the Southwest, where from 30 to 40 acres are required for the sustenance of a single animal, the marketing of yearlings instead of calves would in most cases be inadvisable.

Another factor that is often lost sight of by those who advocate the selling of young stuff is the fact that we have, every now and then, years of very light rainfall, which results in poor grazing conditions and scant feed. This means a reduction in the herd. . . . On those ranches where only calves are sold it means a cutting into the breeding herd, which is much more serious than the cutting back of older steers. It requires years to replace breeding animals, while in the case where the surplus steers and heifers are sold, it means no cutting into the breeding herd and the number can be readily replaced.[2]

From the standpoint of the Corn Belt feeder, western calves have important advantages over yearlings and 2-year-old steers in that (1) they cost less per head, (2) they are better suited than older cattle for a long program which involves the use of pasture and roughage before they are put in the feed lot, and (3) they make much cheaper gains than older cattle if they are put on a fattening ration soon after they arrive on the farm. However, calves are not as satisfactory as older cattle for utilizing roughage during the fattening period. For this reason they are not popular with farmers who wish to market their hay, straw, and silage by fattening cattle in the dry lot. Yearling steers and heifers weighing from 600 to 750 pounds as feeders and from 950 to 1150 pounds when marketed are the ideal type of cattle from the standpoint of all persons concerned with their production and use. They are the kind which can be produced most economically by the western ranchers. They are able to utilize to advantage all feed avail- able in the Corn Belt for beef cattle feeding; and they furnish trim, handy-weight carcasses that fulfill the demands of the majority of consumers.

Nevertheless there will continue to be a considerable number of feeders who will prefer calves to older cattle. Corn Belt farmers with more grain than roughage to dispose of will find calves best suited for their feed lots and will pay a sufficient premium for them to justify their sale by the western rancher. Also, they will be bought to advan-

[2] Wyoming Bulletin 147.

tage by those farmers who have hay, silage, and good pastures on which to carry their cattle for 9 to 12 months before putting them into the feed lot.

Development of Home-Bred Calves. Corn Belt farmers who maintain herds of breeding cows have the choice of three recognized methods of developing their calves. In the first place the calves may be allowed

FIG. 66. Home-bred calves ready for market in early summer at about 15 months of age. (*Courtesy N. E. Franklin, Lexington, Illinois.*)

to run with their mothers without grain until about November 1, when they are weaned, removed to the dry lot, and started on feed. When handled in this way home-raised calves are comparable to western-bred calves as far as their weight, condition, and so forth are concerned.

The second method of handling home-bred calves is to start them on a good grain mixture when they are from 3 to 5 weeks old and to continue their feeding throughout the time they are nursing their mothers. This feeding may be done by the use of creeps in the case of calves which are allowed to run with their dams, or the calves may be kept in a separate lot or pasture and fed mornings and evenings before the cows are turned in for the calves to nurse. By thus feeding the calves during the suckling period, they are considerably heavier and fatter at weaning time than western-bred calves and, consequently, may be marketed after a much shorter feeding period. Usually such animals are in good slaughter condition at 12 to 15 months of age, when they weigh from 800 to 900 pounds. These are the kind of calves which the butcher has in mind when he speaks of the superior quality of "native baby beef."

The third and last method of developing home-bred calves to be mentioned is one representing ultra-baby-beef production. As yet it is carried on on a rather limited scale, but with the growing demand for younger and lighter carcasses this method eventually may come into rather general use throughout the Corn Belt. This plan calls for the birth of calves preferably in January and February, or at least by the middle of March, so that they will be sufficiently mature and well finished to be marketed directly off the cows from October to December of the same year. If backed up with the right kind of early-maturing ancestry and if fed to the limit of their capacity to utilize feed, such calves will weigh from 600 to 750 pounds at 9 to 11 months of age. Though the beef from such animals lacks the color and flavor usually associated with choice beef, butchers seem to have no trouble disposing of it to the increasing number of customers whose chief considerations in their meat purchases are tenderness and freedom from waste.

Each of the three methods of developing calves mentioned above has its advantages and disadvantages. Which method is best on a particular farm will depend largely upon the type of the individuals composing the cow herd, the feeds available for the cows after freshening, the equipment for taking care of young calves in cold weather, the milking qualities of the cows, the intended date for marketing the finished calves, and so forth.

Advantages of Feeding Nursing Calves. Experiments carried on at Sni-a-Bar Farms, Grain Valley, Missouri, under the supervision of the United States Department of Agriculture and the University of Missouri, show conclusively that calves fed grain while suckling their dams return much more profit when sold at weaning time than those which are not so fed. (See Table 231.) As a result of feeding from 3 to 6 pounds of grain daily, or an average of approximately 700 pounds per head, the calves were 100 pounds heavier at weaning time and were valued at approximately $2 more per hundred. Thus, by feeding from $7 to $22 worth of grain per head, depending upon current feed prices and the length of the suckling period, the average value of the calves when weaned was increased from $14.33 to $18.84 per head above the market value of the grain consumed. These figures apply to the calves which were fed while running with their mothers during the whole summer period. Smaller increases were obtained where the feeding was done during only the 4 to 8 weeks immediately preceding weaning.

Early calves that have been fed grain throughout the summer are sufficiently fat and mature by late fall to be sold directly from the cows without further feeding. Profits from calves so handled have been very satisfactory in recent years, judging from the results of the records made in the Kansas Beef Production Contest for 1946–1950. (See Table 230.) When calves can be sold at around 11 months of age for $165 to $250 per head after eating from 15 to 25 bushels of grain

TABLE 230

RESULTS OBTAINED BY KANSAS FARMERS IN CREEP–FED
DIVISION OF BEEF PRODUCTION CONTEST*

	1946	1947	1948	1949	1950	5-Year Average[a]
Number of herds.............	4	9	12	5	15	9
Number of cows.............	166	300	503	177	497	329
Per cent calf crop...........	95	95	92	95.5	98	95
Feed cost per cow...........	$30.53	$37.64	$43.57	$35.36	$50.55	$39.53
Other costs[b]................	$9.90	$7.74	$14.19	$12.26	$17.18	$12.25
Total costs per cow..........	$40.43	$45.38	$57.76	$47.62	$67.73	$51.78
Age of calves when sold, days .	347	310	351	347	334	338
Av. selling weight, lb.........	778	710	717	690	760	731
Av. sale price per cwt........	$22.80	$27.65	$25.85	$23.95	$33.15	$26.70
Gross value per calf.........	$177.38	$196.31	$185.34	$165.25	$251.94	$195.22
Feed fed per calf............	$29.80	$53.26	$37.01	$28.99	$48.32	$39.53
Other expenses per calf[c]......	$3.12	$2.93	$3.11	$4.69	$6.28	$4.03
Cow cost per calf............	$42.56	$47.77	$62.78	$49.86	$67.73	$54.14
Net return per calf..........	$101.90	$93.35	$82.43	$81.71	$129.61	$97.80

* Computed from Kansas Extension Service, Mimeo. Reports, Beef Production Contests, 1946–1950.
[a] All averages are simple averages, not weighted.
[b] Bull costs, taxes, and other cash costs, but not labor, interest, depreciation, etc.
[c] Principally marketing costs.

there is little incentive for their being kept over the winter months and sold in May or June on what is likely to prove a less satisfactory market than that which prevailed the previous fall. While it may be argued that the selling of calves at so young an age is economically unsound as far as the meat supply of the nation is concerned, the individual producer can hardly be critized for disposing of his cattle at such time as they will return him the most profit. However, in order to acquire satisfactory market condition by late fall or early winter, spring calves must be born early in the year. Also, they must have as mothers heavy milking cows that will give them a good start and keep them growing at their maximum ability throughout the summer and fall. Indeed, should the cow continue to suckle her calf until it is ready for market, so much the better under this system of baby-beef production.

Fig. 67. A well-located feeder for creep-feeding calves. (*Courtesy American Shorthorn Association.*)

Although it is highly important to feed grain to calves that are to be sold for slaughter when or soon after they are weaned, grain feeding during the suckling period does not appear to be especially advanta-

Fig. 68. Some Sni-a-Bar creep-fed calves as they appeared at weaning time. These calves had gained an average of 2.5 lb. daily while nursing and were ready for market at about 10½ months of age. (*Courtesy University of Missouri and U.S.D.A.*)

geous if the calves are to be fed throughout the winter and spring and marketed sometime the following summer. Here again data furnished by the Sni-a-Bar experiments are of considerable value. Reference to Table **231** will disclose that while the calves fed grain during the nursing period were worth about $20 more per head at weaning time than the calves that were not so fed, this difference in value had de-

TABLE 231

EFFECT OF FEEDING NURSING CALVES UPON RETURN REALIZED WHEN CALVES ARE SOLD AT VARIOUS AGES*

	Not Fed	Creep-fed While Running with Cows	Kept from Cows and Fed Separately	Creep-fed During Last 4–8 Weeks
Sold at weaning time:				
Av. weight (without shrink)	490	593	588	522
Value per cwt.............	$9.30	$11.30	$10.90	$9.75
Value per head.............	$45.60	$67.00	$64.10	$50.90
Amount of grain fed to date.	....	720 lbs.	720 lbs.	180 lbs.
Value of grain fed to date[a]..	....	$10.80	$10.80	$2.70
Gross return per head above cost of feed.............	$45.60	$56.20	$53.30	$48.20
Sold after 84 days of dry-lot feeding:				
Av. weight (without shrink)	665	770	760	695
Value per cwt....	$10.30	$11.70	$11.25	$10.05
Value per head.............	$68.50	$90.10	$85.50	$69.85
Amount of grain fed to date..	760 lbs.	1760 lbs.	1700 lbs.	1050 lbs.
Amount of hay fed to date..	335 lbs.	265 lbs.	245 lbs.	290 lbs.
Amount of silage fed to date	220 lbs.	135 lbs.	120 lbs.	200 lbs.
Value of feed fed to date[a]...	$14.60	$28.80	$27.70	$18.50
Gross return per head above cost of feed.............	$53.90	$61.30	$57.80	$51.35
Sold after 196 days of dry-lot feeding:				
Av. weight (without shrink)	927	1007	976	947
Value per cwt.............	$12.75	$12.95	$12.60	$12.60
Value per head.............	$118.20	$130.40	$123.00	$119.30
Amount of feed fed to date:				
Grain....................	2535 lbs.	3610 lbs.	3445 lbs.	2840 lbs.
Hay.....................	720 lbs.	580 lbs.	550 lbs.	655 lbs.
Silage...................	500 lbs.	365 lbs.	295 lbs.	470 lbs.
Value of feed fed to date[a]....	$44.90	$59.60	$56.70	$48.90
Gross return per head above feed cost...`..............	$73.30	$70.80	$66.30	$70.40

* Calculated from data in Table 165. Feed quantities given to nearest 5 lbs.; financial data to nearest dime.

[a] Feed prices used: Grain — $30 per ton; Hay — $15 per ton; Silage — $6 per ton.

creased to only about $10 per head at the end of 196 days of dry-lot feeding. Meanwhile feed costs had mounted much more rapidly, both on the basis of cost per head and cost per hundredweight of gain made, where grain had beed fed previously to weaning, so that when marketed after 6½ months of feeding the calves that had had only mother's milk during the summer were the more profitable. These data indicate that with good feeding well-bred calves may be brought to satisfactory market condition in about 200 days and that when fed so long a time the extra flesh possessed by the creep-fed calf at the start of the period is in reality a handicap as it interferes with making the most rapid and economical gains. The practical application of this discussion is simply this: If calves are to be sold at weaning time or after a comparatively short feed in dry lot, grain feeding during the suckling period is highly essential in producing a satisfactory market finish. However, if the calves are to be marketed in late spring or summer, creep feeding is not to be recommended, as the extra flesh so acquired will result in slower and costlier gains during the long feeding period.

Methods of Feeding Western-Bred Calves. Three recognized and widely practiced methods of handling and feeding western calves also prevail. In the first place the calves may be started at once upon a fattening ration, got up to a full feed of grain by the end of the sixth or eighth week, and marketed in the early summer after having been on feed from 200 to 250 days. In the second place only from one-half to two-thirds of a full grain ration is fed until about March 1, after which date the calves are full-fed, often in self-feeders, until they are marketed in August, September, or October. Formerly many feeders who followed this method of feeding turned their cattle onto pasture about May 15, but at present the inadvisability of putting half-fat, grain-fed cattle on grass is rather generally recognized.[3] The third method of handling western calves which is practiced by Corn Belt feeders is to carry the calves through the winter on a good growing ration, such as silage and legume hay, that will produce gains of 1 to 1½ pounds per day, but which will not cause the cattle to be too fat in the spring to make rapid and economical gains from pasture. With this method grain feeding may be begun 2 or 3 weeks before the opening of the grazing season, so that the cattle will be accustomed to eating corn before they leave the dry lot, or feeding may be delayed for 2 or 3 months, or until such time as the gains from pasture alone are slackened by flies, hot weather, and the drying up of the grass. Calves which are carried through the winter largely on roughage must, of course, be fed until late in the fall if they are to attain a satisfactory market finish. As a rule such animals are sold in November and early December after the majority of the calves which were full-fed during

[3] *Cf.* p. 434.

the winter have been marketed. Owing to the poor condition of pastures in the late summer and fall and the importance of forcing the cattle as much as possible during the last few weeks of feeding, the animals usually are removed from pasture about September 1 and finished in the dry lot.

Calves handled according to this third method obviously are not as highly finished when marketed as those that have been full-fed during both winter and summer and, consequently, sell at somewhat lower prices. However, considering that a large part of the feed consumed is unmarketable roughage and pasture and that the cattle are sold at the time of year when prices for fat cattle are usually most favorable, profits realized from this system of feeding often exceed those made from either of the other two methods. (See Table 232.) However, it should be clearly understood that if this plan of handling calves is to be successful they must be fed a sufficiently good ration during the winter to enable them to make maximum growth without fattening.

SPECIAL PROBLEMS OF FATTENING CALVES

Among some persons the opinion prevails that the fattening of calves differs materially in theory and in practice from the fattening of older cattle. Particularly is it believed that the feeding of calves requires a peculiar judgment and skill such as is not possessed by the ordinary rank and file of successful cattle feeders. Nothing is farther from the truth. As a matter of fact, the same principles of feeding and management apply to cattle of all ages, though, of course, some of these principles may be violated with less serious results in the case of mature cattle than in the case of calves. The principal purport of the paragraphs that follow is to cite experimental data supporting this point of view of calf feeding. However, in connection with each topic discussed those matters which are of especial importance to calf feeders will be pointed out.

Protein Requirements of Calves. As is explained in Chapter 19, calves, because of their rapid rate of growth, require more protein in proportion to their live weight than older cattle. Although this fact is usually taken into consideration in preparing the ration of calves, the tendency of practical feeders is to underestimate the amount of protein concentrate needed by calves to make maximum gains. Particularly is it likely that too little protein will be fed during the first few weeks of the feeding period while the calves are being accustomed to eating grain. The ½ to 1 pound of linseed or cottonseed meal which is commonly fed at this time is altogether too small, in the light of certain investigations, to meet the needs of the young animals during the period

TABLE 232

COMPARISON OF METHODS OF FEEDING WESTERN CALVES

Method of feeding	Missouri Experiment Station[1] (Av. of 3 trials 1925-26; 1926-27; 1927-28)					Kansas Experiment Station[2]							
	Full fed during winter and marketed in late spring	One half a grain ration during winter		No grain during winter		Av. of 2 trials 1924-25; 1925-26. One half a grain ration during winter. Grazed without grain until Aug. 1		Av. of 2 trials 1926-27; 1927-28		1 trial 1923-24. One half a grain ration during winter		1 trial 1922-23. No grain during winter	
		Full fed on grass 168 days	Pasture only 1st 56 days. Full fed on grass last 112 days	Full fed on grass 168 days	Pasture only 1st 56 days. Full fed on grass last 112 days	Full fed after Aug. 1 on pasture	Full fed after Aug. 1 in dry lot	One half a grain ration during winter	Grazed without grain until Aug. 1 then full fed in dry lot. No grain during winter	Full fed in summer on pasture	Grazed without grain until Aug. 1 then full fed on pasture	Full fed in summer in dry lot	Full fed in summer on pasture
Initial weight	346 lbs.	351 lbs.	353 lbs.	342 lbs.	352 lbs.	506 lbs.	497 lbs.	338 lbs.	336 lbs.	453 lbs.	452 lbs.	394 lbs.	394 lbs.
Av. daily gain winter period	2.18	1.57	1.67*	.83	.87	1.87	1.90	2.09	1.48	2.19	2.10	.85	.80
Av. daily gain 1st summer period		2.09*		2.87*	1.28*	.90	.87	.87	1.29				
Av. daily gain last summer period		2.08*	2.32*	2.38*	2.31*	2.30	2.93	2.70	2.79				
Av. daily gain total summer period		2.03	1.76	2.55	2.00	1.64	1.90	1.83	2.08	2.0	1.85	1.88	2.34
Final weight	752	938	908	906	821	1068	1119	970	932	1140	1100	870	946
Total feed consumed:													
Shelled corn, lbs.	1542	2621	2044	1885	1360	2287	2290	2117	1499	3348	2137	2427	2760
N. conc.	210	364	285	265	188	235	235	236	236	313	222	337	339
Corn silage	1461	1718	1744	2256	2262	3905	3905	2555	3387	3657	3657	4015	3565
Hay	538	623	661	717	719	279	779	905	924	300	300	566	60
Pasture (dollars)		$4.50	$6.00	$4.50	$6.00	$8.00	$6.00	$8.00	$6.00	$8.00	$8.00		$8.00
Total value of feed	$35.56	$65.00	$55.24	$53.82	$45.34	$58.50	$63.40	$59.20	$52.55	$83.72	$57.96	$52.90	$59.90
Value of feed per cwt. gain	$8.72	$11.07	$9.96	$9.54	$9.69	$10.40	$10.20	$9.35	$9.80	$12.20	$8.95	$11.10	$10.85
Pork credit per steer	$2.10	$9.08	$6.79	$6.50	$4.83								
Selling price per cwt.	$11.90	$15.00	$14.35	$15.00	$13.85	$11.00	$11.65	$16.10	$15.85	$11.25	$11.25	$10.75	$11.25
Return above cost of cattle and feed (inc. pork)	$11.77	$36.26	$34.81	$41.31	$27.41	$4.10	$12.15	$52.35	$51.05	$ .22	$21.10	$4.18	$8.04

* Av. of 2 years only.
[2] Kansas Circulars Nos. 117, 128, 143, 151, 152, and Mimeographed Reports of Calf Feeding Experiments.

[1] Mimeographed Reports of Calf Feeding Experiments.

immediately following weaning. Instead of starting with a small amount of protein concentrate and increasing it as the feeding progresses and the calves get older and heavier, it would seem that a more sensible way would be to start with the larger quantity and gradually decrease the amount fed, or at any rate to feed a given amount, e.g., 1½ to 2½ pounds per head, throughout the entire feeding period.

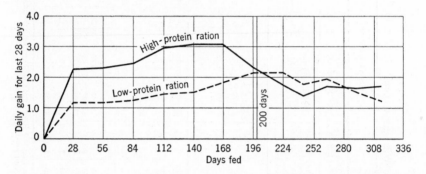

FIG. 69. Effect of amount of protein concentrate upon the gains made by beef calves. These curves suggest that an adequate amount of protein is especially important during the first part of the feeding period. (*Constructed from data of Project 238, Illinois Experiment Station.*)

Protein Supplements for Calves. The comparative value of the various protein supplements used in cattle feeding already has been discussed in Chapter 20. All that needs to be added in this special reference to calf feeding is to emphasize the importance of protein in the ration of young, growing-fattening animals. Care should be taken that at least the minimum protein requirements stated in the rule given on page 324 are met. Usually it will pay to exceed this minimum by ½ pound per head daily, so long as the total protein concentrate fed does not exceed 2 pounds daily for calves fed in the dry lot. Calves fed on good pasture require little or no protein supplement as long as the pasture forage is fresh and green. In six trials covering 6 years at the Ohio Station, calves full-fed shelled corn on bluegrass pasture from about May 10 gained almost as fast as those fed shelled corn and 1 pound of protein supplement until dry weather or a killing frost seriously damaged the pasture. After the pasture was thus damaged the gains of the calves fed no supplement fell off noticeably. The average daily gains for the entire season over the 6-year period were 1.79 pounds for the calves fed the supplement and 1.63 pounds for those that had none. One hundred pounds of protein supplement replaced 143 pounds of shelled corn, on the basis of the feed eaten per hundred pounds of gain.[4]

Silage as a Feed for Fattening Calves. Men who have been accustomed to feeding silage to mature steers often obtain disappointing results from feeding it to calves for the reason that they fail to appreci-

TABLE 233

CORN SILAGE AS A ROUGHAGE FOR FATTENING CALVES*

	1912–13 200 Days		1913–14 238 Days		1928–29 200 Days	
	Corn Silage	No Silage	Corn Silage	No Silage	Corn Silage	No Silage
Average daily gain, lbs..........	2.26	2.01	2.14	2.17	2.37	2.18
Average daily ration:						
Shelled corn, lbs..............	10.4	12.2	10.6	10.9	11.6	11.9
Cottonseed meal...............	2.1	..	2.1	2.2	1.7	1.7
Corn silage...................	7.5	..	12.7	..	8.3	..
Legume hay...................	4.1	6.4	2.6	6.1	2.0	6.7†
Feed per cwt. gain:						
Shelled corn, lbs..............	460	594	498	504	489	547
Cottonseed meal...............	92	..	99	100	72	80
Corn silage...................	332	..	596	..	350	..
Legume hay...................	183	309	121	283	84	307
Cost of gain per cwt..............	$7.60	$8.04	$8.66	$9.07	$10.33	$11.84
Selling price per cwt.............	8.70	8.50	10.00	10.00	15.90	15.65
Return per head above cost of cattle and feed (inc. pork).....	8.85	5.83	12.15	8.86	21.53	10.60

* Illinois Experiment Station: Mimeographed Reports of Calf Feeding Experiment.
† Mixed hay containing approximately 40% red clover.

ate the limited digestive capacity which calves possess. Because of this limited capacity and the fact that calves have growth as well as fattening requirements to meet, any attempt to feed calves large amounts of a bulky roughage such as silage will result in slow gains and relatively little improvement in condition. When forming a part of the fattening ration, silage should be limited to 5 to 12 pounds per head daily, depending upon the amount of hay fed. Excellent results have been secured at the Illinois Station for several years by feeding 8 pounds of silage and 2 pounds of hay daily from the time the calves are on a full feed of grain until they are marketed. As the animals

[4] Ohio Bimonthly Bulletin 205, 1940.

increase in size and gradually attain more capacity for feed, the grain, rather than the roughage, is increased every week or 10 days by approximately 0.5 pound per head per day.

Preparation of Feeds for Calves. Calves because of their relatively small mouthparts are not so able to eat hard, coarse feeds such as ear corn and corn stover as are older cattle. Such feeds, if fed, should be reduced by slicing, grinding, or shredding to pieces of such size as calves can easily handle. However, the necessity of an elaborate preparation of the feeds fed to calves has been greatly exaggerated. Numerous trials conducted at various experiment stations, but especially at Ohio and Minnesota, show that, when the cost of grinding is considered, larger profits are usually secured when both grain and roughage are fed whole. This, of course, does not apply to coarse materials such as ear corn and corn stover but only to shelled corn, oats, and a good grade of palatable hay.

Molasses and Molasses Feeds for Calves. Owing to the fact that a good consumption of grain is essential to make calves improve in condition at a faster rate than they grow in frame, the opinion prevails among feeders that highly palatable materials such as molasses are very desirable in fattening calves for market. Such would indeed seem to be the case, but feeding experiments do not substantiate this opinion. Results secured at both the Iowa and Ohio stations indicate that no advantage is to be had from adding blackstrap molasses to rations composed of sound, wholesome grains and roughages, and trials carried on at the Nebraska Station show no benefits derived from adding a commercial mixed molasses feed to a ration of corn, cottonseed meal, and alfalfa hay, or of corn, alfalfa hay, and corn silage.[5] (See Table 235.)

Time Required to Attain Satisfactory Market Finish. Great variation exists in the time calves are continued on feed before they are sent to market. Feeders who have been accustomed to handling older cattle often underestimate the time required to attain a good finish with young animals and find to their disappointment that market buyers discriminate sharply against their calves because they are only half-fat. On the other hand, there are men who hold that approximately a full year of feeding is necessary if western calves are to be marketed in such condition as will return the most profit. Such men fail to distinguish between the profit which results from the unusually high finish of their steers and that which is due to the favorable prices which usually prevail for fat cattle late in the fall when calves which have been fed nearly a year are, of course, marketed. In all prob-

[5] *Cf.* Table 151.

TABLE 234

NEED FOR PREPARING FEEDS FOR CALVES BY GRINDING, ETC.

	Minnesota Station* 180 Days			Ohio Station† 147 Days					Ohio Station† 154 Days		
	Shelled Corn, Whole Hay	Ground Corn, Whole Hay	Corn and Hay Ground and Mixed	Whole Roughage	Ground Roughage	Chopped Roughage	Steamed Chopped Roughage	Chopped Roughage Mixed with Grain	Long Shock Corn	Cut Shock Corn	Shelled Corn
Daily gain, lbs......	2.31	2.49	2.52	1.82	1.86	1.93	1.76	1.93	1.77	1.93	2.33
Av. daily feed:											
Corn (shelled basis)	15.9	17.0	17.2	5.8	5.8	5.7	5.7	5.8	7.0	7.3	8.7
N. conc...........				2.0	2.0	2.0	2.0	2.0	2.0	2.0	2.0
Corn silage........									6.4	6.7	7.5
Corn stover........				3.0	3.3	3.3	3.4	3.3	6.8	7.0	
Alfalfa hay........	6.6	7.0	6.4	3.7	3.3	3.3	3.4	3.3	1.5	1.6	1.6
Cost of feed per cwt. gain........	$10.08	$10.52	$10.48	$10.26[1]	$9.83[1]	$9.45[1]	$10.39[1]	$9.55[1]	$10.12	$10.17	$7.99
Pork credit per steer lbs........	34	16	16	11	16	12	15	15			
Market value per cwt.	$11.85	$12.00	$12.00	$13.00	$13.25	$13.25	$13.00	$13.50	$10.85	$11.00	$11.50
Return per head over cost of cattle and feed........	$31.80	$30.10	$30.40	$11.95[1]	$14.40[1]	$15.80[1]	$11.40[1]	$17.90[1]	$ .67	$ 1.40	$12.71

* Minnesota Mimeo. Report, 1927.
† Ohio Circular 10, 1928.
‡ Ohio Bimonthly Bulletin 129, 1927.
[1] No charge made for processing roughages in this experiment.

TABLE 235
VALUE OF MOLASSES IN FATTENING CALVES

	Ohio Station* — 252 Days					Iowa Station†			
						1926–27 270 Days		1927–28 240 Days	
	No Molasses	Molasses Replacing Part of Corn	Molasses Hand-fed	Molasses Self-fed	Beet Molasses Hand-fed	No Molasses	Molasses	No Molasses	Molasses
Daily gain, lbs.	2.00	1.92	2.12	2.17	2.14	2.41	2.38	2.32	2.31
Average daily ration:									
Shelled corn	9.7	7.8	9.4	9.0	9.4	11.0	11.0	9.1	8.8
Protein conc.	2.0	2.0	2.0	2.0	2.0	2.7	2.7	2.8	2.8
Molasses		1.9	1.9	4.0	1.9		.4		1.0
Alfalfa hay	1.5	1.5	1.5	1.5	1.5	5.0	4.7	2.2	2.2
Corn silage	6.5	6.5	6.5	6.5	6.5			9.2	9.2
Feed cost per cwt. gain	$12.55	$13.14	$13.19	$14.31	$13.10	$12.09	$12.38	$10.99	$11.48
Market value per cwt.	12.75	12.25	12.20	12.75	12.50	16.50	16.25	16.75	16.75
Pork credits, lbs.	47	40	49	52	51				
Return above cost of cattle and feeds (inc. pork)	−$3.84	−$10.98	−$13.00	−$14.26	−$9.70	$43.91	$39.76	$39.96	$36.52
Water consumption[1]									
Average daily:									
Drunk, lbs.	44.3	44.7	53.9	51.9		54.6	56.8	65.0	59.2
In feed						2.7	2.4	2.4	3.0
Total						57.3	59.2	67.4	62.2

* Ohio Bulletin 463, 1930.

† Iowa Leaflet 27, 1929.

[1] Average April 8 to August 18 for Ohio test; average of a 10-day period in July for Iowa test.

ability even larger profits would have resulted had the calves been full-fed grain during only the 7 or 8 mouths immediately before shipment.

Given choice feeder calves, weighing from 400 to 500 pounds, in average condition, approximately 250 days of good feeding are required to make them sufficiently fat to sell close to the top of the market. Calves fed over such a period will dress from 61 to 63 per cent, which indicates that they are sufficiently fat to meet the requirements of eastern shippers as well as local packers and butchers. Steer calves fed a shorter period are likely to be lacking in finish to a

TABLE 236

EFFECT OF LENGTH OF FEEDING PERIOD UPON MARKET VALUE AND PROFITS

Nebraska Experiment Station* Average of 3 Years			Illinois Experiment Station† 1927–28		
Days Fed	Estimated Value per cwt.	Profit per Head	Days Fed	Estimated Value per cwt. in Home Lots‡	Profit per Head (inc. Pork)
None	$7.58 (cost)	....	None	$10.84 (cost)	....
75 days	8.00	$—.23	112 days	11.25	$10.17
100 "	7.83	—.62	147 "	12.00	16.34
125 "	8.22	2.10	182 "	12.75	24.89
150 "	8.45	3.44	214 "	13.65	33.26
175 "	8.67	4.27			
200 "	9.33	8.89			

* Nebraska Bulletin 229, 1928.
† Illinois Mimeo. Report, 1928.
‡ The market for light yearlings was practically stationary during the period that these calves were fed, so that the increased valuations assigned were due almost entirely to improved finish.

noticeable extent and sell at prices which are less profitable to their owners. However, heifer calves, because of their earlier-maturing qualities, often may be marketed to advantage after 180 to 200 days of full feeding. Indeed, it occasionally happens that heifers which weigh around 450 pounds when started on feed will be discriminated against if fed more than 200 days because they are too fat and heavy to meet the requirements for choice heifer carcasses.

Although steer calves are improved in market desirability by a long, extended feed, the gains made are relatively slow and costly after the cattle have been full-fed for 7 or 8 months. Particularly are small gains made during the heat of July and August by calves that have been on full feed since the previous fall. Except in the case of those men who obtain more satisfaction from "topping the market" than

Fig. 70. The effect of length of feeding period upon the daily gains of beef calves. Note that the gains are high for the first 200 days but relatively low thereafter. (Constructed from gains made by two lots of steer calves fed for 267 days at the Illinois Station in 1926–1927 and one lot fed for 315 days in 1927–1928.) (*Courtesy Illinois Experiment Station.*)

from realizing the most dollars of profit, better results, in the long run, will be secured by full-feeding calves that are to be marketed in the fall only from about April 1 rather than from the beginning of the previous winter.

Seldom does a farmer with cattle to sell experience any difficulty in disposing of them at a price near their actual cash value. If their number is such as to make a carload, they may be shipped to a large central market, where, on every day of the year except Sundays and holidays, every animal received is ordinarily sold before the day is over at a price determined by the supply and demand of the market. Should the number be less than a carload, they may be marketed as part of a cooperative shipment through a local shipping association; or sold to a local livestock buyer; or sold to a local butcher for slaughter. Occasionally, one encounters a feeder who prefers to sell at home even though he has a carload, foregoing his chance to obtain more profit in order to avoid the risks incident to shipping on his own account. Such men, however, are becoming rarer and rarer with the increased attention paid by the market to the small shipper.

Cooperative Shipping Associations. Cooperative livestock shipping associations have been organized in nearly every community throughout the Corn Belt, to provide a way for the man who has less than a carload of animals to market them on his own account. Although such associations usually handle many more hogs than cattle, owing to the custom of cattle feeders to buy and feed cattle in carload lots, they perform a real service for those men who have a cow or two to sell or who feed out a few calves of their own raising. Formerly such men were at the mercy of the local buyers, who were often termed "scalpers" because of the excessive profits they frequently made when trading with farmers unfamiliar with market conditions.

Each local shipping association maintains a local stockyards, where livestock is assembled for shipment, and operates a fleet of trucks for bringing the animals in from the farms and transporting them to nearby central markets. If the central market is more than a night's drive away, shipments are usually made by rail. A manager and other necessary personnel are employed to look after the details of weighing, sorting, loading, and billing of animals and to distribute the receipts of the shipment to the several consignors on the basis of what their stock actually brought at the market. The expense of running the association, including the salary of the manager and an insurance fund to cover all losses sustained en route, is usually met by a flat charge of 5 to 15 cents per hundredweight on all stock handled. Any surplus

TABLE 237

TOTAL CATTLE RECEIPTS AT PRINCIPAL MARKETS*

	1949 (000)	1950 (000)
Chicago	1850	1780
Omaha	1692	1638
Kansas City	1673	1438
Sioux City	1332	1292
South St. Paul	1172	1111
East St. Louis	940	863
Denver	838	872
South St. Joseph	620	566
Ft. Worth	578	540
Total 9 markets	10,695	10,100
Total 65 markets	18,828	17,917

* U.S.D.A., Agricultural Statistics, 1951.

funds remaining at the end of the year are distributed to the patrons on the basis of the weight of livestock shipped.

When to Market. Various rules for marketing have been stated by successful feeders, but it is doubtful that they are taken very seriously,

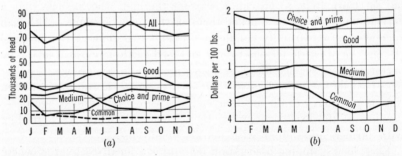

FIG. 71. Receipts and relative prices by grades of beef steers sold at Chicago, 1932–1941. (a) Monthly average receipts; (b) monthly average price differentials. (*Farm Science, December, 1950, Iowa State College.*)

even by their own authors. Perhaps the one most frequently heard is, "Ship when the cattle are ready, regardless of the condition of the market." However, it would seem, from the appearance of many animals received at the yards, that a rule as frequently followed is, "Ship when the market seems right, regardless of the condition of the cattle."

Neither rule is a good one if blindly followed, though each expresses an element of truth which should not be overlooked if satisfactory returns are to be realized.

The approximate time of marketing should be decided at the time the cattle are placed on feed. Only by knowing the length of the feeding period in advance can the method of feeding be planned intelligently. As the cattle begin to approach the degree of finish desired, the market should be studied in an effort to obtain as favorable a price as possible. However, there is no way of knowing definitely which way the market will go. Even the commission men and large buyers, who have had

TABLE 238

MONTHLY DISTRIBUTION OF CATTLE RECEIPTS
AT 67 PUBLIC MARKETS*

	Per Cent of Year's Total Cattle Receipts			
Month	1925	1938	1946	1949
January	7.9	8.2	7.3	7.5
February	6.2	6.3	7.4	6.3
March	7.4	7.8	7.0	7.7
April	7.0	6.9	7.8	7.0
May	6.7	8.0	6.2	7.3
June	6.8	7.7	5.9	7.7
July	8.2	8.0	11.2	7.5
August	9.5	9.6	9.1	10.3
September	9.3	10.0	6.5	10.4
October	12.4	11.2	12.7	12.4
November	10.0	9.2	10.0	9.0
December	8.6	7.1	8.9	6.9

* Swift & Co., Agricultural Research Bulletin 15.

long years of experience, occasionally make serious errors in predicting future price tendencies. Nevertheless, the judgment of such men deserves respect, and their advice regarding shipping should be given careful consideration. They have at hand much information, regarding total supplies, expected loadings, religious holidays affecting consumption, and conditions of the dressed beef trade, that is not available to the individual shipper.

Where to Market. Previous to 1925 nearly all load lots of fat cattle were shipped to terminal markets for sale to packers, order buyers,[1] and large city butchers. However, since that date there has been a gradual decentralization of cattle slaughtering from the large cities to intermediate points closer to sources of supply. Also packers buy more

[1] An order buyer is one who purchases cattle on order for packers and butchers in distant cities, especially in the East.

of their cattle directly from large feeders, on intermediate markets and at concentration yards. Likewise, order buyers fill more of their orders at such locations. (See Table 239.) Nevertheless, the large central markets remain the principal market for the majority of the cattle fattened in the Corn Belt. This is especially true of carload lots of fed steers, a high percentage of which are shipped to Chicago. Cows, heifers, and odd lots of steers frequently can be sold to advantage on smaller markets, through auction sales or to local packers and butchers.

TABLE 239

CHANGES IN PERCENTAGE OF CATTLE PURCHASED THROUGH TERMINAL
MARKETS BY FEDERALLY INSPECTED SLAUGHTERERS*

Year	Through Terminal Markets	Elsewhere
1925	90.7	9.3
1930	88.3	11.7
1935	83.6	16.4
1940	75.1	24.9
1945	76.8	24.2
1950	74.9	25.1

* Compiled by W. J. Wills from Reports of Bureau of Economics, U. S. D. A.

Preparing Cattle for Shipment. Considerable difference of opinion exists in regard to the advisability of attempting to reduce shrinkage by changing the ration before shipping. Some feeders remove all laxative feeds like protein concentrates and legume hay a day or two before shipment and supply non-laxative feeds in their stead. Others withhold both feed and water on the day of shipment in the belief that the cattle will fill better at the market if they arrive very hungry and thirsty. Occasionally, an unscrupulous shipper salts his cattle heavily on the day of shipment to obtain a heavier consumption of water at the market. However, seldom is anything gained from abnormally large "fills," as buyers easily detect such cattle and refuse to bid on them until late in the day, when the excessive weight has largely disappeared.

Unfortunately little information is available regarding the control of shrinkage in cattle. Yet it is an extremely important subject, particularly when cattle prices are high. When cattle are worth $30 a hundred the 40 pounds lost during transit amounts to $12 a steer. Anything the shipper can do to reduce the loss by 5 to 10 pounds a head without noticeably impairing the slaughter merit of the cattle will be highly profitable.

Preliminary studies made at the Illinois Station indicate that withholding feed and water on the day of shipment increases rather than reduces shrinkage. (See Table 240.) Apparently cattle thus handled are greatly disturbed by the abrupt change in their feeding schedule and spend the day on their feet vainly waiting for feed and water instead of lying quietly at rest. As a result they are tired and nervous when loaded and arrive at market in a fatigued condition. Though shrinkage based on loading weights may be in their favor, they have actually lost considerable weight before they were loaded. This loss

FIG. 72. A section of the cattle pens, Union Stock Yards, Chicago.

may well be from 20 to 30 pounds, or the weight of the feed and water that would have been consumed if the regular schedule of feeding had been followed.

Other studies made at the Illinois Station indicate that the substitution of oats for part of the shelled corn ration, and timothy or mixed hay for alfalfa or clover hay, is a sound practice, inasmuch as these changes resulted in less shrinkage. (See Table 240.) However, these non-laxative feeds should be introduced into the ration 4 or 5 days before shipment in order that the undigested portions may have time to affect the nature of the content of the large bowel.

Rail vs. Truck Shipment. Before the advent of the motor truck, cattle were almost always driven from the feed lot to the loading point, but now they are usually hauled. Trucks have replaced rail transportation to a large extent within 200 miles from the central markets, and some of the large trailer trucks holding 15 to 20 fat cattle operate over even longer distances.

The comparative merit of rail and truck transportation for fat cattle

TABLE 240

EFFECT OF CHANGING FEED UPON SHRINKAGE OF FAT CATTLE DURING SHIPMENT*

	Withholding Feed and Water on Day of Shipment		Replacing Laxative Feeds			
			Heifer Calves		Yearling Steers	
	Fed as Usual	Feed and Water Withheld	Shelled Corn, Clover Hay	Sh. Corn 50%, Oats 50%, Timothy Hay	Shelled Corn, L. S. M., Clover Hay	Sh. Corn 50%, Oats 50%, Timothy Hay
Weight out of experiment....	999	998	649	649	1070	1095
Length of change period.....	10 hr.	10 hr.	6 days	6 days	4 days	4 days
Shipping weight.............	999	982	666	665	1069	1104
Market weight..............	963	952	616	624	1011	1052.5
Shrinkage, lb.						
On final experiment weight.	36	46	33	25	59	42.5
On shipping weights.......	36	30	50	41	58	51.5
Shrinkage, percentage						
On final experiment weights	3.6	4.6	5.1	3.9	5.5	3.9
On shipping weights.......	3.6	3.1	7.5	6.2	5.4	4.7
Dressing percentage........	60.6	59.6	57.9	56.0	59.7	58.1

* Illinois Mimeo. Report, 1951.

TABLE 241

RELATIVE USE MADE OF RAILROADS AND TRUCKS IN TRANSPORTING CATTLE TO MARKET

	Per Cent of Cattle Received by Truck	
Market	1935*	1949†
Chicago	35.3	78.9
East St. Louis	46.9	72.6
Indianapolis	84.0	92.0
Kansas City	32.4	50.6
Omaha	54.2	78.9
Peoria, Ill.	86.9	86.7
Sioux City	72.9	78.0
South St. Paul	49.9	73.0
62 public markets	51.0	71.7

* U. S. D. A., Livestock and Wool Statistics and Related Data, June, 1936.
† U. S. D. A., Livestock Market News, August, 1950.

is a disputed point. Cattle undoubtedly ride more comfortably and safely on the rails than in the average truck. However, the greater convenience afforded by the truck in loading the cattle at the farm, at the hour most agreeable to the owner, the somewhat lower charge, and the greatly reduced time during which the cattle are en route have made the truck the favorite method of most feeders who are within easy trucking distance of the market. Since the presence of automobiles on main highways and the poor condition of fences along secondary roads make the driving of cattle to the rail head impractical in most communities, they must be transported by truck from the farm to the loading point, even though they are shipped to market by rail. Usually when they are once in the truck they can be taken directly to market in much less time and at little more expense than would be incurred if they were trucked only to the local station and reshipped by rail. (See Table 242.)

TABLE 242

COMPARISON OF TRUCK AND RAIL SHIPMENT OF FAT STEERS

	Colorado Bulletin 422, 1936 (3-Year Average)		Illinois Unpublished Data (Average of 3 Shipments)	
	Truck	Rail	Truck	Rail
Number of cattle	100	100	69[a]	70[a]
Shipping weight, lb.	835	833	1044	1052
Market weight	806	805	1009	1009
Shrinkage	29	28	35	43
Shrinkage (percentage)	3.6	3.4	3.4	4.1
Bruised carcasses	5.5	4.0	10[b]	10[b]
Freight rate	0.17	0.16	25	22
Hours in transit	3.17	7.0	7.1[b]	13.0[b]
Distance shipped, miles	70	70	135	135

[a] Total cattle in three shipments.
[b] Average of two shipments.

Cattle per Car. The standard stock car is 8 feet 6 inches wide and either 36 or 40 feet long. The shorter car is billed with a minimum weight of 22,000 pounds, and the longer one with 24,400 pounds. That is, the shipper must pay freight on this weight whether his load weighs that much or not. In computing freight charges, market weights are taken, less 800 pounds deducted for "fill." No maximum weights are specified, and the shipper may crowd as many cattle into the car as he can. As an average, about 22 fat 2-year-old steers or 28 fat yearlings constitute a load for a 40-foot car. Cattle ship better if the car is comfortably filled, though overcrowding is more objectionable than underloading. If fewer than 15 mature cattle are to be shipped, they had better be partitioned off in one end of the car and the remainder of the space used for some other class of livestock. Such a plan will result in a saving in freight, and the cattle will not be jolted about so severely by the sudden starting and stopping of the train.

TABLE 243

AVERAGE CAPACITY OF RAIL CARS AND STOCK TRUCKS
FOR TRANSPORTING CATTLE AND CALVES

	Rail Cars*		Stock Trucks†				
Length	36′	40′	10′	12′	14′	18′	30′
Calves							
350 lb.	55	62	12	15	18	24	42
450 lb.	46	51	10	13	15	20	34
Cattle							
600 lb.	36	40	8	10	12	16	27
800 lb.	30	33	7	8	10	13	22
1000 lb.	26	28	6	7	8	11	19
1200 lb.	22	24	5	6	7	9	16
1400 lb.	19	21	4	5	6	8	14

* Western Weighing and Inspection Bureau, Chicago, Illinois, Feb. 1, 1943.
† International Harvester Co.

Billing. Cattle shipped to market should be billed to a reliable commission firm, of which there are 50 or more at large markets like Omaha, Kansas City, and Chicago. It is not necessary to inform the firm in advance of the shipment, though it is good business practice to do so. Neither is it necessary for the shipper to accompany the cattle to market. In all probability they will sell for just as much whether he is present or not. However, it is highly instructive for him to be at the market to compare his cattle with others that sell for higher and lower prices. In this way he will be better able to estimate the probable market value of cattle that he handles in the future.

If the distance from market or unfavorable weather conditions make it at all likely that the cattle will be en route more than 28 hours, a so-called "release" should be signed by the shipper at the time the car is billed. Otherwise the cattle must be unloaded at the end of 28 hours to be fed, watered, and rested. When a release accompanies the waybill, unloading need not take place until the elapse of 36 hours.

Shrinkage. Shrinkage is the loss in weight between feed lot and market. It may be expressed either in pounds per head or in percentage of the weight before shipment. The percentage method is to be preferred, inasmuch as the amount of weight lost usually bears a direct ratio to the size of the cattle.

Shrinkage during shipment is due to excretions from the alimentary tract and the urinary organs, and from moisture given off by the lungs in breathing. A portion of this loss is regained at the market from the feed and water consumed between the time of arrival and the time the cattle are sold and weighed. The amount of shrinkage expressed in percentage of the home or loading weight varies considerably between different loads of cattle. The principal factors responsible for this wide variation are:

1. *The Length of the Journey.* The longer the journey, the greater the shrinkage. The loss in weight, however, does not bear a direct ratio to the distance traveled, since the greatest loss occurs during the first few miles, often between the feed lot and the loading point. (See Table 244.)

TABLE 244

EFFECT OF LENGTH OF HAUL UPON THE SHRINKAGE OF
GRAIN-FED CATTLE TRANSPORTED BY TRUCKS*

Weight Classes	Number of Head	Average Full Weight Out of Lot	After 25 Miles	After 50 Miles	After 100 Miles	After 200 Miles
			Cumulative Percentage of Shrinkage			
Under 1000 lb.	11	954	1.5	2.2	3.1	3.9
1000–1099 lb.	10	1056	2.1	3.0	3.8	4.1
1100–1199 lb.	24	1139	1.8	2.6	3.4	4.1
Over 1200 lb.	15	1263	1.9	2.4	3.1	3.6
Group average	60	1122	1.8	2.5	3.3	3.9

* Unnumbered report, Chicago Union Stock Yards and Transit Co., December 1951.

Note: The cattle in this study were hauled in groups of 5 head in a truck which had a scales in one end, on which they were weighed individually after covering the respective distances. No opportunity to fill was allowed before weighing. Initial weights taken in morning before the cattle were fed.

2. *The Degree of Comfort Experienced en Route.* During extremely hot or very cold weather, shrinkage runs unusually high. Badly crowded cars or trucks and slow, rough runs on trains that make frequent stops are certain to result in considerable loss in weight.

3. *The Condition of the Cattle at the Time of Loading.* As far as possible, the condition of the cattle should be normal at the time they are loaded. Tired, hungry, or thirsty animals will be in poor physical condition to stand the trip, and will be slow to recover upon reaching the market. Likewise, cattle that have consumed large quantities of green grass or have taken too great a fill of water just previous to loading will be in poor condition for the journey.

4. *The Kind of Feeds Used in Fattening.* Cattle that have been fed large quantities of roughage, such as grass and silage, commonly lose more weight than those that have received a full feed of grain. Also cattle that have been fed laxative feeds like linseed meal and alfalfa hay will suffer a larger shrinkage than cattle fed feeds of a less laxative nature.

5. *The Condition of the Cattle.* Since shrinkage is due principally to the loss of excrement from the bladder and bowels, it bears a much closer relation to the size of the animal than to its condition of flesh. In other words, thin 2-year-old steers will lose about as much weight per head during shipment as fat 2-year-olds that are 200 or 300 pounds heavier. However, the shrinkage per 100 pounds live weight is much higher for the thin cattle. Grass-fattened cattle are likely to have a much higher shrink, expressed as a percentage of the loading weight, than grain-fed cattle because they have had a more laxative ration and because they are in lower condition.

6. *The Fill at Market.* The consumption of feed and water after arrival at market is the most important factor in determining the net amount of shrinkage suffered. This in turn is influenced by several factors, of which the more important are: (*a*) weather conditions at the market on the day of sale; (*b*) the length of time the cattle are in the pens before they are sold and weighed; (*c*) the condition of the cattle upon arrival.

Smaller fills are obtained during cold, damp weather than on bright, warm days. Cattle drink little at such a time and have but little appetite for hay after it becomes wet.

The most satisfactory fills are obtained when the cattle reach the market about daylight, thus permitting them to be penned and fed at about their usual feeding time. As a rule, the market is not under way until nine o'clock, so that the cattle have at least 2 or 3 hours in which to eat and drink. Cattle that arrive after the market has opened may be in the pen but a few minutes before being sold and are weighed almost empty. While the price paid for such cattle is often somewhat higher than would have been bid had the cattle taken on the usual fill, the buyer rather than the seller is most likely to profit from the late arrival. After cattle have been in the pens for 4 or 5 hours they cease eating and drinking and begin to lose rather than gain in weight. Hence, good fills are associated with brisk, active markets, rather than with slow, long-drawn-out trading that runs into the afternoon session.

Cattle that arrive at the market tired and worn out from a long, hard journey, or weakened by insufficient water and feed immediately before

TABLE 245

SHRINKAGE OF CATTLE DURING TRANSIT*

Class of Cattle	Hours in Transit	Number of Shipments	Number of Cattle	Average Weight at Origin (lbs.)	Gross Shrinkage		Fill at Market		Net Shrinkage		
					Range (lbs.)	Average (lbs.)	Range (lbs.)	Average (lbs.)	Range (lbs.)	Average (lbs)	Per cent of Live Weight at Origin
Grain-fed											
Non-silage............	Less than 24	4	164	1303	59–95	67	4–48	16	20–64	51	3.91
Non-silage............	24–36	59	1853	1167	47–128	85	19–52	37	18–88	48	4.11
Silage-fed............	Less than 24	14	666	1168	46–128	76	6–97	52	+7‡–67	24	2.05
Silage-fed............	24–36	4	169	1204	84–121	101	50–64	58	27–75	43	3.57
Grass-fattened											
Mixed-range.........	Less than 24	21	1511	700	19–84	37	1–56	22	+12‡–71	15	2.14
Mixed-range.........	24–36	17	872	848	27–118	72	−8†–55	18	19–114	54	6.37

Average shrinkage of grain-fed cattle in transit less than 36 hours, 3.62%.
Average shrinkage of grass-fattened cattle in transit less than 36 hours, 3.88%

* U. S. D. A. Bulletin No. 25.
† Abnormal load, market weight exceeding loading weight.
‡ Abnormal load, sale weight less than unloading weight.

or during shipment, frequently lie down upon being unloaded and will not eat or drink to any extent until they have obtained some rest. If sold on the day of their arrival, their shrinkage will be much above the average because of their small fill. If given time to recover, or if they are suffering only from hunger and thirst, they will probably take on such a large fill that buyers will have nothing to do with them until the effects of the fill have largely disappeared. Best results are secured when the cattle are but moderately hungry and thirsty when received. In such condition they will fill to a moderate extent, but not to the point where they will invite unfavorable criticism.

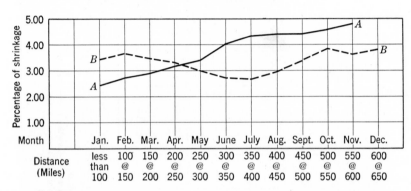

Fig. 73. Effect of *A*, length of haul, and *B*, season of the year, upon the net shrinkage of cattle in transit. (*Constructed from data in U.S.D.A. Yearbook, 1923, p. 942.*)

Losses Sustained during Shipment. Losses resulting from the injury or death of cattle while in transit are of infrequent occurrence. Cattle, because of their size and strength, are less likely to be injured by the rough handling of cars by careless train crews than are hogs and sheep. They are also much better able to withstand unfavorable weather conditions encountered en route than are the other two classes of meat animals. Although occasionally a heavy loss will result from a bad wreck or the use of a defective car or loading chute, probably fully 99 per cent of all cattle shipments arrive at the market with no dead or crippled animals.

Statistics kept by the United States Department of Agriculture of all dead and crippled livestock received at the public stockyards of the United States show that a much smaller percentage of cattle are injured during shipment than of calves, hogs, or sheep. (See Fig. 74.) No data are at hand regarding the relative losses of cattle by truck and by rail. However, the fact that the number of dead hogs arriving by truck at 20 large markets was about 30 per cent larger than those arriving by rail for each year from 1946 to 1950, inclusive, indicates that truck losses are probably greater than rail losses for all classes of livestock.   That these losses are due mainly to carelessness and can to a large extent be prevented by careful loading and handling is shown by a reduction in the number of dead hogs arriving by truck from 1.48 per 1000 in 1946 to 1.26 per 1000 in 1950.   Dead hogs arriving by rail were reduced from 1.21 to 0.95 per 1000 head during the same period.[2]

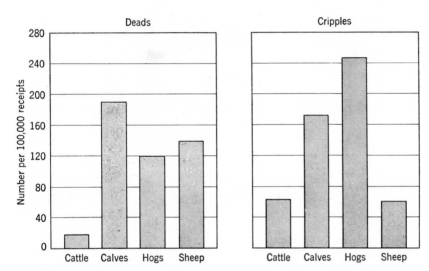

Fɪɢ. 74. Number of dead and crippled animals encountered in receipts of the different classes of livestock, as reported by Bureau of Agricultural Economics for 1950. (*Courtesy Livestock Conservation, Inc., Chicago, Illinois.*)

Unfortunately the relatively few dead and crippled cattle which arrive at the market are not the most serious losses that occur during shipment and for which shippers must make restitution through lower prices than otherwise would be paid for their cattle.   While the 2860 dead and the 12,875 crippled cattle received at public stockyards during 1950 represented a loss of probably less than $2,000,000, the total loss due to bruises was estimated at $27,500,000.[3]   Unfortunately, bruised animals cannot be detected by the buyer at the time of purchase; consequently, he must buy all cattle on the basis that a loss of $1.50 to $2.00 a head will be encountered during slaughter as the result of

2 Livestock Conservation, Inc., Annual Report, 1950–1951, p. 7.
3 Livestock Conservation, Inc., Annual Report, 1950–1951, p. 3.

bruises that must be trimmed out of the carcass beef.	This loss represents 15–20 cents per 100 pounds live weight, or $30–$45 a carload.	An individual shipper can avoid losses from dead and crippled cattle by careful loading and handling, but he cannot escape the losses resulting from bruising so long as other shippers handle their cattle roughly during shipment.	Consequently, every cattle feeder should give his wholehearted support to the program of Livestock Conservation, Inc., an organization representing railroads, commission firms, packers, and stockyard companies, whose principal objective is to reduce losses in marketing livestock.

TABLE 246

CAUSES OF LOSS AND DAMAGE CLAIMS PAID ON LIVESTOCK BY 27 RAILROADS IN 1914*

Classification of Loss	Percentage of Total Livestock Claims	Classification of Loss	Percentage of Total Livestock Claims
Delays	38.76	Defective Equipment	1.88
Unlocated Damage	21.14	Fire	1.57
Rough Handling of Cars	19.28	Concealed Damage	0.11
Wrecks	8.70	Robbery	0.08
Errors of Employees	3.54	Improper Ventilation	0.02
Unlocated Loss	2.74	Concealed Loss	0.01
Improper Handling and Loading	2.17	Total	100.00

* U.S.D.A. Report 113, 1916.

Claims for Loss and Damage.	Loss or damage resulting from the fault of the railroad company or its employees may be recovered by the presentation of a formal claim to the responsible company.	In the case of cattle, the majority of claims are based upon the contention that the shipments were unduly delayed, resulting in abnormal shrinkage or the sale of the cattle upon a lower market than they would have encountered had they arrived on time.	Delays due wholly to unfavorable weather conditions are not a basis for claims, since the railroad is in no wise responsible.	Neither is a loss resulting from defects existing in a car at the time of loading, since the shipper has the right to reject a car that he considers to be unsatisfactory.	Therefore, it is highly important that the shipper carefully inspect each car before loading, to see that there are no holes in the floor, no projecting nails or bolts on which the animals may be injured, or other defects that may render the car unserviceable.

LOCATION OF CATTLE BRUISES

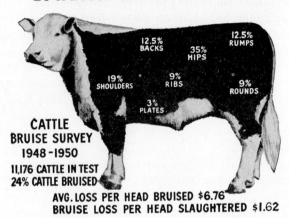

CAUSES OF CATTLE BRUISES

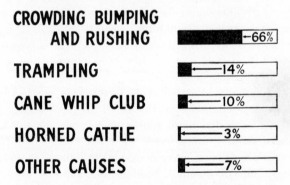

FIG. 75. Location and estimated causes of bruises observed on carcasses of beef cattle during slaughter tests conducted by Wilson and Company. (*Courtesy Livestock Conservation, Inc., Chicago, Illinois.*)

Marketing Costs. A knowledge of the items that go to make up the total marketing expense is highly desirable to enable the individual feeder to estimate accurately the value of his cattle in the feed lot on the basis of current market quotations. Frequently he will be called upon to choose between selling his cattle to a local dealer at a certain price and shipping them to the market on his own account. It is evident that he must know the approximate cost of marketing per hundredweight before he can arrive at an intelligent decision.

Marketing costs are of two kinds, direct and indirect. The direct costs include those cash charges made by the transportation companies and marketing agencies. Indirect costs refer to the loss of weight or shrinkage suffered by the animals between feed lot or shipping point and the market. To the feeder who ships his own cattle, only the direct costs are of interest in computing the cost of marketing per head or per hundredweight. But the man who contemplates selling to a local butcher or dealer must give due consideration to both direct and indirect marketing costs before he is in a position to evaluate his cattle at the loading point on the basis of what they would probably bring at the central market.

Only the direct costs are considered in computing the average marketing expense per steer in Table 247. These costs are made up of the following items:

1. *Freight.* Freight constitutes by far the largest item of expense in the marketing of cattle. The freight charge varies, of course, with the distance and the weight of the load. It is figured on the sale weight of the cattle less 800 pounds per car allowed for the "fill" taken on at the yards. Should this weight be less than 24,400 pounds for a 40-foot car or 22,000 pounds for a 36-foot car, charges are made on the basis of these so-called "minimum" weights.

2. *Terminal Charge.* A charge of $2 to $3 a car is usually made for switching from the tracks of the incoming railroad over the belt line tracks to the unloading chutes.

3. *Yardage.* A nominal fee of 75 to 90 cents per head is charged by the stock yards company for the use of the pens, watering facilities, scales, etc. This is the main source of revenue for the stock yards company and from it must come all money expended for cleaning the pens, repairing fences, pavement, and buildings, as well as for interest, taxes, and dividends. Yardage is paid but once, regardless of the length of time the cattle are held before slaughter or reshipment.

4. *Feed.* Cattle, after being unloaded, are fed hay at the rate of about 10 pounds per head, or 200 pounds per car. This hay is purchased from the stock yards company at approximately twice the price of hay on the farm. It should be kept in mind, however, that this price includes the delivery of the hay to the pens and placing it in the mangers before the cattle.

If, for any reason, corn-fed cattle are held overnight before being sold, they are given a feed of shelled corn. The usual feed of corn is 5 bushels per car. Other feed materials are usually available if the owner of the cattle wishes to use them.

5. *Insurance.* At all large markets, a charge of 5 to 15 cents per car is made against both shipper and buyer to provide for insurance of the cattle against fire while they are in the yards. In this way a fund is maintained which is adequate to reimburse owners for the full market value of any animals destroyed. The wisdom of making provision for such a fund was fully justified in October, 1917, when a fire in the Kansas City Yards destroyed nearly 10,000 head of cattle and calves. Fortunately, the insurance fund that had been built up in the preceding years was sufficient to reimburse fully every owner involved. Checks to the amount of $1,733,779.99 were mailed out the day after accredited appraisals had been made.

6. *Commission.* Cattle shipped to a central market must be consigned to a livestock commission firm, of which there are from 50 to 75 at each of the four or five large markets adjacent to the Corn Belt states. Employees of the firm receive the animals from the stock yards company, drive them to the pens, and see that they have access to plenty of feed and water. Upon the opening of the market, a salesman, frequently one of the members of the firm, shows the cattle to prospective buyers, and finally sells them, unless otherwise instructed by the owner, for the highest offer he has received.

Immediately after the cattle are sold they are driven to the scales, where they are weighed and locked in holding pens to await the orders of the purchaser. The weigh ticket is sent by messenger to the office of the commission firm, where the marketing expenses are computed and a draft drawn upon the firm's account for the net proceeds of the sale. The draft, together with a statement of the sale, is delivered to the owner, if present, or is mailed to his home address or to his local bank. All settlements for freight, yardage, feed, etc., and the collection of the money from the purchaser of the cattle are made by the commission firm without any trouble whatever to the owner.

For all these services a regular charge is made, based upon the number and, on some markets, the weight of cattle sold. The commission for selling varies slightly between different markets and is changed from time to time to meet new business conditions. On January 1, 1952, the selling commission at Chicago was as follows: [4]

Consignments of only one head	$1.50 per head
First 5 head in each consignment	1.20 per head
Next 10 head in each consignment	1.15 per head
Each head over 15 in each consignment	1.10 per head

[4] Formerly buying charges for feeder cattle were considerably lower than selling charges, but currently they are the same on most markets.

However in no instance could the selling charge for a rail consignment of cattle exceed \$38 for each car, nor could the charges for a truck consignment exceed \$38 for the first 24,400 pounds plus 14½ cents for each additional 100 pounds or fraction thereof.

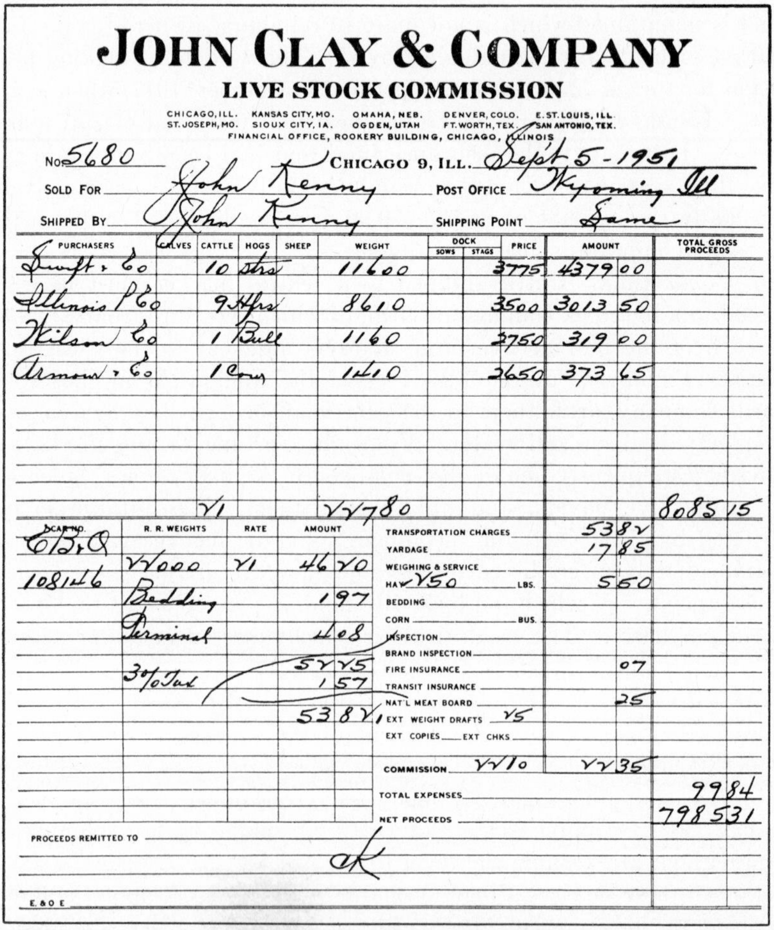

JOHN CLAY & COMPANY

LIVE STOCK COMMISSION

CHICAGO, ILL. KANSAS CITY, MO. OMAHA, NEB. DENVER, COLO. E. ST. LOUIS, ILL.
ST. JOSEPH, MO. SIOUX CITY, IA. OGDEN, UTAH FT. WORTH, TEX. SAN ANTONIO, TEX.
FINANCIAL OFFICE, ROOKERY BUILDING, CHICAGO, ILLINOIS

No. 5680 CHICAGO 9, ILL. Sept 5-1951

SOLD FOR John Kenny POST OFFICE Wyoming Ill

SHIPPED BY John Kenny SHIPPING POINT Same

PURCHASERS	CALVES	CATTLE	HOGS	SHEEP	WEIGHT	DOCK SOWS	DOCK STAGS	PRICE	AMOUNT	TOTAL GROSS PROCEEDS
Swift & Co		10 Strs			11600			3775	4379 00	
Illinois P Co		9 Hfrs			8610			3500	3013 50	
Wilson Co		1 Bull			1160			2750	319 00	
Armour & Co		1 Cow			1410			2650	373 65	
		21			22780					8085 15

CAR NO.	R. R. WEIGHTS	RATE	AMOUNT
CB&Q 108126	22000	21	4620
	Bedding		197
	Terminal		208
			5225
	3% Tax		157
			5382

TRANSPORTATION CHARGES		5382
YARDAGE		1785
WEIGHING & SERVICE		
HAY 250 LBS.		550
BEDDING		
CORN BUS.		
INSPECTION		
BRAND INSPECTION		
FIRE INSURANCE		07
TRANSIT INSURANCE		
NAT'L MEAT BOARD		25
EXT WEIGHT DRAFTS 25		
EXT COPIES EXT CHKS		
COMMISSION 2210		2235
TOTAL EXPENSES		9984
NET PROCEEDS		798531

PROCEEDS REMITTED TO

E. & O. E.

FIG. 76. An "account sales" for a rail shipment of cattle. (*Courtesy John Clay and Company, Chicago, Illinois.*)

Shipments consisting of animals which are owned by more than one shipper and which therefore must be weighed and billed separately are charged slightly higher rates.

Considering the multiplicity of details attended to, the value of the product sold, and the amount of responsibility assumed by the salesman individually, and by the firm collectively, the present commission charges are remarkably low, averaging less than ½ of 1 per cent of the gross value of fat cattle. It is highly doubtful that farmers take home as high a percentage of the sale value of any other major agricultural product as they do in the case of beef cattle. (See Table 247.)

TABLE 247

DISTRIBUTION OF MARKETING COSTS PER HUNDREDWEIGHT

	Per Hundredweight			Per Dollar of Sales		
	1932	1939	1947	1932	1939	1947
Average sale price of beef steers[a]	$6.75	$9.80	$26.25	$1.00	$1.00	$1.00
Average marketing costs[b]						
Transportation	0.31	0.33	0.44	0.046	0.034	0.017
Expenses at market	0.17	0.20	0.24	0.025	0.020	0.009
Net proceeds remitted to shipper	6.27	9.27	25.57	0.929	0.946	0.974

[a] Year Book of Figures, Chicago Daily Drovers Journal.
[b] U. S. D. A., Margins for Marketing Livestock, July, 1949.

Effect of Shrinkage on Marketing Costs. The loss in weight suffered by cattle between the farm and market is as important a factor in determining their home value per hundredweight as the actual marketing charges that must be paid in cash. The monetary loss suffered from shrinkage depends upon two factors, viz., the amount of weight actually lost and the value per hundredweight of the cattle. Both these items may vary considerably between different shipments. Because of these variations, it is impossible to name a figure that will represent, with any degree of accuracy, the "margin" a local dealer must have in order to "break even." With steers shrinking 3 per cent while in transit and selling for $30 at the market, a shipping margin of 90 cents per hundredweight would be necessary to cover the loss due to shrinkage. But with cows shrinking 4 per cent and selling for but $15 per hundredweight, a margin of but 60 cents would suffice. To this margin must be added the approximate fixed charges per hundredweight to obtain the total difference that should exist between feed-lot and market values. This difference will lie between $1 and $2 per hundredweight for most of the cattle in the Corn Belt.

The Financial
31 ———————————— Aspect of
Beef Production

Up to this point, little has been said about the cost of keeping a
herd of beef cattle or the profit that may be expected from fattening
a carload of steers. Mention of financial accounts has intentionally
been omitted in discussing various rations for fear that differences in
"profit made" might distract the mind of the reader from more fundamental differences on which the relative value of the rations really
rests.

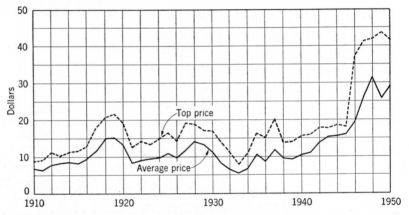

FIG. 77. Fluctuations in top price and average price per cwt. of beef steers at
Chicago, 1910–1950. (*a*) Top price of steers per cwt.; (*b*) average price of all
beef steers. (*Chicago Daily Drovers Journal Year Book,* 1950.)

After all, the amount of profit made on a particular drove of cattle
is the result of such a combination of circumstances and prices that it
is, of itself, a rather poor index of the value of a given method of
feeding and management when carried on over a series of years.
Profits are determined by feed prices, labor costs, market prices of thin
and fat steers, interest rates, death losses, etc. An appreciable change
in any one of these items may affect the financial statement so much
as to turn a reasonable profit into a discouraging loss. Small changes

546

of this nature are of daily occurrence and in a large measure are beyond the control of the feeder. Feed per pound gain and rapidity of gain are inherent qualities of the ration. Changes in price levels have no effect upon them whatever. Hence, it is these items, rather than the profits, that should be given most attention in studying the results of feeding experiments.

Prices of beef cattle, along with prices of nearly all other commodities, fluctuated widely during the first h: lf of the present century, in which period all the feeding experiments to which reference has been made were conducted. (See Fig. **77.**) The financial returns realized from any particular ration used in a feeding experiment might have been much different had the test been made a year or two earlier or later. Consequently, the profits listed in the published results are of value only to the degree that they combine in a single figure the economy with which the gains have been made and the slaughter merit of the finished cattle.

Items of Cost in Beef Production. The principal items of cost in producing beef cattle are the following:

1. Feed.
2. Labor, man, horse, and truck.
3. Interest on animals and equipment.
4. Depreciation on cattle and equipment.
5. Taxes on cattle.
6. Marketing cost.
7. Death risk.
8. Incidentals—insurance, veterinary fees, etc.

It is customary to include all these items, except interest and marketing costs, under the heading, "operating costs." Thus, the total cost of an animal arriving at the market is the sum of the operating costs, interest charges, marketing expenses, and its original cost, if purchased.

Cost of Keeping a Beef Cow. Several studies have been made of the cost of maintaining a cow that is kept primarily for the purpose of raising beef calves. One of the most comprehensive reports on this subject is found in Report 111 of the United States Department of Agriculture, entitled, "Methods and Cost of Growing Beef Cattle in the Corn Belt States." (See Table **248.**) Since these data were obtained from a survey of beef cattle farms made in 1916 they are now very much out of date. However, they appear to be the only detailed cost figures available on commercial beef cow herds. Since the feed cost in this study is approximately the same percentage of the total

TABLE 248

ITEMS IN EXPENSE OF KEEPING A BEEF COW ONE YEAR*

	Number of Farms	Average Number Cows per Farm	Average Value of Cows	Average Cost per Cow											Manure Credit	Net Cost
				Feed Charges			Labor	Equipment	Interest on Cattle	Risk	Taxes	Insurance	Veterinary	Total		
				Summer	Winter	Entire Year										
General Beef Group..	230	31.5	$63.82	$8.20	$16.49	$24.69	$3.88	$1.75	$3.83	$0.43	$0.34	$0.06	$0.14	$35.12	$4.77	$30.35
Per cent of total...						70.3	11.0	5.0	10.9	1.2	1.0	0.2	0.4	100.0		
Baby Beef Group....	66	34.5	69.50	9.11	17.19	26.30	3.11	2.25	4.16	0.43	0.1	0.10	0.11	36.77	5.30	31.38
Per cent of total...						71.8	8.5	6.1	11.3	1.1	0.8	0.3	0.3	100.0		

* U. S. D. A. Report 111, 1916.

cow costs as in studies made by the Kansas Station during the period 1946–1950, viz., 70 per cent,[1] it may be assumed that the other items now bear about the same relation to the total annual cost as they did in 1916. Consequently, if the feed cost is known or can be closely estimated, the total annual cost, as well as the detailed cost items, may be readily calculated.

TABLE 249

ANNUAL COST OF KEEPING A BEEF BULL

	Number of Bulls*			Average Value†	Maintenance Cost‡	Depreciation§	Manure Credits‖	Net Annual Cost
	Total	Average per Herd	Cows per Bull					
General beef group (feeder calves)..	266	4	30	$500	$50.20	$60.00	$ 9.00	$110.20
Baby beef group..	17	1.3	29	665	72.50	93.00	10.60	165.60

* Compiled from Kansas Extension Service Mimeo. Reports, Beef Demonstration Results, 1946–1950.
† Average price of all Hereford bulls sold at auction in 1950, $663. Value of bulls in general beef group was 76 per cent of value of those in baby beef group in U. S. D. A. Report 111.
‡ Calculated from Table 251 and Tables 7, 8, and 15, U. S. D. A. Report 111, 1916.
§ Estimated salvage value, $200; useful life, 5 years.
‖ Double the values of 1916.

Cost of Keeping a Beef Bull. The yearly cost of keeping a bull depends greatly upon the way the bull is handled. If he is allowed to run with the herd and is given little or no extra feed, his cost will but little exceed the average cost for the cows. With the proper care and management, however, both feed and labor costs will be considerably higher for the bull. Moreover, depreciation, almost a negligible item in the case of grade cows, must be considered, especially if the bull is purebred, which, of course, he should be. Interest and risk are considerably greater for bulls than for cows, principally because of their higher valuation. (See Table 249.)

Cost of Producing a Feeder Calf. The cost of raising beef calves to weaning age has varied widely since the 1920's. Feed costs for the breeding herd constitute by far the largest item of cost, with labor and interest on money invested in cattle and equipment being the second and third items of importance. However, the principal difference between high-cost herds and low-cost herds is in the number

[1] *Cf.* Table 251.

of calves weaned per 100 cows of breeding age or in the per cent "calf crop" obtained. Usually changes in feeding and management which will result in more calves raised will reduce the cost per calf very much more than reducing the feed in amount or quality. Of the 66 herd records included in the reports of the Kansas Beef Demonstration for the period 1946–1950 only 7 disclosed calf crops below 90 per cent, and 4 herds weaned a calf for every cow during 1 year of the period. That it is not impossible by good care and management to raise a calf from almost every cow is shown by the record of Briggs and Bailey, Mullinville, Kansas, given in Table 250.

TABLE 250

Calving Record of Briggs and Bailey, Mullinville, Kansas*

Year	Number of Cows in Herd	Number of Bulls	Number of Calves Sold	Calf Crop (per cent)	Average Selling Weight (lb.)	Average Age (days)	Sale Price (per cwt.)	Net Return per Calf†
1946	214	5	207	96.7	431	199	$16.00	$41.62
1947	210	5	203	95.2	452	207	19.50	55.21
1948	219	5	201	91.3	457	202	30.75	100.47
1949	202	5	192	95.5	449	203	23.10	68.51
1950	175	6	164	93.0	518	201	27.75	104.17

* Compiled from Kansas Extension Service Mimeo. Reports, Beef Demonstration Results, 1946–1950.
† After deducting all costs except labor, interest, and equipment costs.

Feed, taxes, and other cash costs were unusually high during the 5-year period 1946–1950, yet the cost of producing feeder calves by the 10 to 16 Kansas farmers and ranchers whose records were compiled by the Kansas Extension Service during that period averaged a little less than 10 cents a pound. Without doubt the principal factor contributing to this low cost was the high calf crop which they obtained. Even in 1950, when the total cow costs were $60 a calf, the feed and cash costs of the feeder calves averaged only $12.58 a hundredweight. (See Table 251.)

It should, of course, be noted that the costs listed in Table 251 do not include labor or interest, each of which is an item that cannot be neglected. If it be assumed that the labor and interest costs are 31.2 per cent of the feed cost of the cows, as they were in 1916,[2] and apply this factor to the averages in Table 251, we get a total cost of $55.64

[2] Cf. Table 248.

for a 465-pound feeder calf, or $11.95 a hundredweight. This is still slightly less than half the average sale price of the Kansas calves during the period covered.

TABLE 251

COST OF PRODUCING BEEF CALVES*

Year	Number of Herds	Total Number of Cows	Percentage of Calf Crop	Winter Feed Cost per Cow	Summer Feed Cost per Cow	Other Costs per Cow†	Total Costs per Cow	Cow Costs per Calf	Weaning Weight of Calves, pounds	Cost of Calves per Cwt.	Sale Value of Calves per Cwt.
1946	10	1540	94.5	$16.50	$ 8.75	$ 6.78	$30.36	$32.13	462	$ 6.95	$16.20
1947	13	940	93	18.70	9.21	7.92	34.43	37.02	467	7.93	22.65
1948	16	2059	93	24.27	10.34	10.25	44.99	48.24	474	10.18	28.80
1949	14	2086	95	19.38	10.81	13.52	43.75	46.67	443	10.54	23.95
1950	13	1288	93	26.45	11.62	17.65	55.72	60.00	477	12.58	30.45
Average‡			93.7	21.05	10.15	11.20	41.85	44.80	465	9.65	24.40

* Compiled from Kansas Extension Service Mimeo. Reports, Beef Demonstration Results, 1946–1950.
† Includes bull costs, taxes, and all other cash costs, but not labor or interest costs.
‡ All averages are simple averages.

The figures in Table 251 were gathered during the period 1946–1950, during which time beef cattle prices were unusually high. Consequently, it should not be inferred that the production of calves has been always as profitable as it appears to be from that table. Neither should it be assumed that production costs in the Corn Belt are as low as they are in central and western Kansas, where the cost-of-production studies were made. Higher land values which result in higher hay and pasture costs, more rain and mud which necessitate better shelter and more bedding, smaller herds which require more labor per cow, and higher taxes result in higher total costs per calf raised in the Corn Belt than on the Western Range. However, this does not mean that beef calves cannot be raised on many Corn Belt farms at a much lower cost than they can be purchased on the Range or at the market. The fact that the number of beef cows on Corn Belt farms increased rapidly from 1938 to 1950 is evidence that beef cow herds were highly profitable during that period. (See Fig. 11.) Whether the cost of production was higher or lower in the Corn Belt than on the Range is beside the point. The important fact is that calves could be raised for less than they could be bought. This situation is likely to continue

as long as the demand for beef is sufficiently greater than the supply to
return satisfactory profits to both breeders and feeders.

Cost of Producing a Yearling Steer. Beef calves, when weaned,
may be carried for a time as stockers, or they may be put into the feed
lot to be fattened as quickly as possible and sold for slaughter. The
former plan of management usually is more profitable for the farmer

TABLE 252

FINANCIAL RETURNS REALIZED FROM ILLINOIS BEEF COW HERDS*

	1949			1950		
	Low-Return Herds	High-Return Herds	All Herds	Low-Return Herds	High-Return Herds	All Herds
Number of farm	42	37	168	78	74	402
Number of cows in herd	16	18.3	15.6	14.9	18.0	16.6
Live cattle produced per cow, lb.	742	785	755	800	813	809
Total return per cow	$158.62	$202.73	$169.81	$210.26	$260.83	$242.05
Feed fed all cattle per cow	136.50	110.86	128.27	167.21	125.90	142.83
Difference (labor, interest, etc.)	22.12	91.87	41.54	43.05	134.93	99.22
Return per $100 feed fed	116	183	132	126	207	169
Price received per cwt. for cattle sold	$22.72	$23.54	$23.28	$25.22	$26.31	$26.22

* Department of Agricultural Economics, University of Illinois, Annual Report Farm Bureau Farm
Management Service, 1949, 1950.

with plenty of roughage and pasture; the latter is more satisfactory
for the farmer who feeds cattle principally to market his grain.
Usually in the Corn Belt, where corn is available, more profit is made
if the stocker phase is followed by at least a short period of grain
feeding than would be made by selling the cattle as feeders directly
off pasture or roughage in the fall or spring. (See Table 253.) However, for the farmer who has no grain but who has excellent pastures,
hay, and silage, the production of yearling feeders may be highly
profitable because of the very cheap gains obtained.

The Financial Aspect of Steer Feeding. The financial problems of
steer feeding as ordinarily practiced are somewhat different from those
of the breeding herd. The principal difference lies in the fact that the
profits from steers usually are made, not by selling the gain put on for
a sum greater than the farm value of the feeds eaten to produce that

TABLE 253

COMPARISON OF PROFITS MADE BY SELLING YEARLING CATTLE
AS FEEDERS AND BY SELLING THEM AFTER A SHORT FEED*

(3-Year Average, 1944–1946)

	Sold as Feeders	Full Fed on Pasture Last 90 Days	Full Fed in Dry Lot for 120 Days
Date removed from pasture	Oct. 9	Nov. 13	Oct. 19
Date marketed	Oct. 10	Nov. 13	Feb. 15
Average final weight, lb.	704	863	1011
Total gain from weaning	305	456	589
Total feed fed after weaning			
Corn, bu.	. . .	23.6	30.8
Protein conc., lb.	141	267	358
Corn silage	3466	3327	3854
Hay	350	397	1205
Cost of feed per cwt. gain (not including pasture)	$7.07	$12.02	$14.60
Pasture days per steer	181	219	191
Weaning value of steer	$51.72	$52.86	$54.72
Cost of feed (not including pasture)	21.57	54.79	85.97
Cost of feed and steer	73.29	107.65	140.69
Selling price at market	14.83	17.80	18.72
Net farm value	94.73	141.22	174.43
Pasture credit per steer	21.44	33.57	33.74
Pasture credit per acre (1.7 acres)	12.61	19.75	19.85

* Illinois Mimeo. Report, Steer Management at the Dixon Springs Experiment Station, February, 1950.

gain, but by selling the weight purchased in the feeder steer for a higher price than was paid for it.

However, it sometimes happens, especially with calves, that the gains cost less than the price at which the cattle are sold. In that case the profit realized is from two sources: (1) that made from selling the purchased weight for a higher price than was paid for it, and (2) that made from selling the gain for more than it cost. Lastly there is also the situation in which the profit comes entirely from that made on the gains. This occurs when the price paid for feeder cattle proves to be higher than the price at which the fattened cattle are sold. Obviously a loss is incurred on the purchased weight. However, the price of fat cattle may be high enough to return a profit on the gain that will wipe out this loss and still leave a net profit on the feeding enterprise. Under normal price conditions this situation is encountered occasionally with calves, because of their low cost of gains, but almost never with yearling or 2-year-old steers. However, gains were frequently the only source of profits made on all ages of cattle during the feeding seasons of 1950–1951 and 1951–1952 when, because of the government price rollback, many droves of cattle sold for less than their cost price per hundredweight. Profits are possible under such price relationship only when cattle prices are very high relative to prices of feed, labor, interest, selling charges, and other items of cost incurred in fattening cattle.

TABLE 254

SOURCE OF PROFITS MADE FROM FATTENING CATTLE*

	1946–1947 Average 17 Droves		1947–1948 Average 10 Droves		1948–1949 Average 15 Droves	
	Per Cwt.	Per Head	Per Cwt.	Per Head	Per Cwt.	Per Head
Purchased weight, lb..		414		654		624
Cost of cattle per cwt.	$17.12		$21.25		$28.86	
Total gain, lb........		513		372		450
Feed cost of gain.....	21.94		32.53		21.16	
Selling price of fat cattle..........	28.91		29.15		26.51	
Gain or loss†						
On purchased weight	+11.79	+$48.81	+7.90	+$51.67	−2.35	−$14.66
On gain..........	+6.97	+35.76	−3.38	−12.57	+5.35	+24.08
Net Return over Cost of Cattle and Feed		84.57		39.10		9.42

* Compiled from Illinois Annual Reports of Feeder Cattle fed by cooperators in Farm Bureau Farm Management Service.
† Plus sign denotes profit; minus sign denotes loss.

It is obvious that under such conditions market fluctuations, over which the individual feeder has no control, exercise a tremendous effect upon the financial outcome of a cattle-feeding venture. For this reason, steer feeding is commonly regarded as containing a larger element of speculative risk than the breeding and raising of calves. Opportunities for making larger profits, as well as the risk of suffering heavier losses, lie with the former.

Are Beef Cattle a Hazardous Risk? When beef cattle prices decline sharply over a period of 6 to 9 months, most feeders suffer severe financial losses as a result of selling their finished cattle at but little more than was paid for the feeder steers. If two or three unfavorable years should come close together, some large feeders, who have borrowed heavily to finance their operation, may lose not only the equity they have in their cattle and feeds but that which they have in their farms as well. Such unfortunate incidents usually are given wide publicity and have fostered the belief that cattle feeding is a highly speculative undertaking, in which one is about as likely to suffer bad losses as to make large profits. Nothing could be farther from the

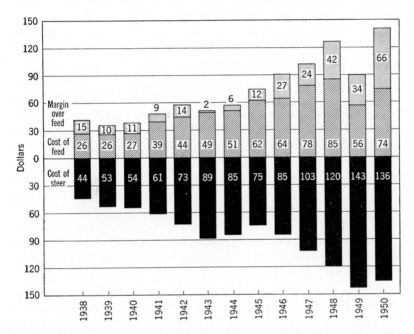

FIG. 78. Average returns realized per head from cattle feeding on Iowa Farm Business Association Farms, 1938–1950. (*The Iowa Farm Outlook Letter, Oct. 25, 1951, Iowa State College.*)

truth. As a matter of fact, the feeding of beef cattle probably has been the most profitable major enterprise during the past 25 years for farmers of the Corn Belt, where cattle have been fed year after year principally to consume home-grown feeds and to facilitate sound methods of soil management. This statement is substantiated by the profits made on cattle fed by farmers keeping cost account records and on those fed by experiment stations during that period. For example, the Indiana Experiment Station has fed from five to eight lots of cattle each year since 1905, or for a total of 46 years during the period 1905–1951. During only 3 of these years were losses incurred

on all lots of cattle fed.   During 8 years a profit[3] was made on some
lots of cattle and losses were incurred on others.   And during 35 years,
or 76 per cent of the total, a profit was made on all lots.   It is very
doubtful that any other major farm enterprise can show as good a
financial record over this same period, which includes the severe depressions of 1907, 1920–1924, and 1930–1936.

It is true that the feeding of purchased cattle involves some speculative risk, inasmuch as one buys the cattle in the expectation of selling
them at a higher price.   But, by feeding, the quality of the meat has
been greatly improved, so that the steer is now much more satisfactory
to the butcher and hence is worth more per pound.   Consequently, the
feeding of cattle should be regarded as a manufacturing process in
which raw materials, in this case thin cattle and feeds, are combined
in such a way that the finished product is much more valuable than
the materials used in making it.   All business and industry encounter
some financial risks, because of economic changes that cannot be
foreseen.   Beef cattle feeding is no different from other businesses in
this respect.   Perhaps the fact that it usually involves a larger investment and can be expanded or contracted more quickly than most
other farm enterprises is largely responsible for its being looked upon
by some as a highly speculative venture.

The Feeder's "Margin."   As stated above, profits from cattle feeding normally result from selling the original weight of the steer for more
than it cost.   The algebraic difference between the sale and cost prices
per hundredweight is referred to as "the margin."   Since the gains
made in the feed lot commonly cost more per pound than the finished
cattle sell for at the market, a positive margin of sufficient size to cover
the loss sustained on the sale of the gain must be had before a profit is
possible.   This margin is commonly referred to as the "necessary
margin" and may be defined as the advance per hundredweight over
cost price that must be secured in order to "break even" on the feeding
operations.   If more than this margin is secured, a profit is realized;
if less, a loss is sustained.

As has been explained, it is sometimes possible, especially with
calves, to put gain on cattle for less per hundred than the cost price
of the cattle.   Then, of course, the cattle may be sold for less than
the purchase price to break even, and the necessary margin is negative.

Much discussion has taken place between cattle feeders as to how
much margin is needed to recover the cost of the feeder cattle and the

[3] The term "profit" as here used refers to the money remaining after the cost of
the cattle and the farm price of all feeds fed have been subtracted from the net
receipts obtained from the sale of the cattle plus the value of the hog gains.

market price of all feeds used in fattening. The most commonly mentioned figure is $2 between the cost of feeders at Kansas City or Omaha and the selling price of the fattened cattle at Chicago. However, there are far too many factors, which affect the amount of margin needed, to permit the naming of a single figure that will apply to all conditions.

Factors Determining Necessary Margin. The amount of margin that must be had to cover all costs is determined by a combination of four factors, each of which exercises its particular influence. These factors are as follows:

1. The initial weight of the cattle. The greater the weight of the cattle when purchased, the smaller the margin that must be had in order to cover the loss sustained from selling the increase in weight for less than it cost.

2. The cost per hundredweight of the cattle. The more the cattle cost per hundredweight, the smaller the necessary margin. This results from the fact that the higher the cost price the less the loss suffered on the increased weight with no margin at all.

3. The cost of the gains made. The high cost of gains is the main reason why a margin is necessary. Hence, the more expensive the gains, the greater the margin needed to obtain reimbursement for the loss they occasion.

4. The amount of gains made. Since the increase in weight made during the fattening period is commonly sold at a loss, it naturally follows that the larger the gains the greater the loss, and hence the greater the margin needed. However, if the gains should cost less than the cattle per hundred, the more gain made the lower the price at which the cattle can be sold and still break even. This means that the more gain put on the less advance in price is needed, but since in this case the necessary selling price declines with the amount of gain, we may say the more gain made the greater the *negative* necessary margin.

While the size of the necessary margin will be determined by the above factors, it must not be supposed that the margin that must be had on a particular lot of cattle can be accurately foretold at the beginning of the feeding period. Although the first two factors are known at the time, the latter two will not be available until the cattle are nearly ready for market.

Mature steers carrying considerable flesh when purchased ordinarily require a smaller margin than thin yearlings, because of their greater initial weight, higher cost price, and the smaller increase in weight needed to make them finished—this in spite of the fact that their age, high condition, and concentrated ration make their gains very expensive. Calves commonly require the smallest margin of all. Their low cost of gains and relatively high cost per hundredweight more than make up the handicap resulting from their light initial weight and the large amount of gain put on before they are marketed.

TABLE 255

PRINCIPAL ITEMS OF COST OF FATTENING CATTLE*

	Average per Steer	Average per Cwt.	Average per Cwt. Gain	Per Cent of Total Operating Costs
Initial weight, lb.	750			
Average gain	300			
Average weight at market	1050			
Cost of cattle on farm	$174.90	$23.32		
Operating costs:				
Feed:	58.65		$19.55	69.0
Other capital charges:				
Power and machinery	2.70		0.90	
Cattle equipment	0.63		0.21	
Buildings	2.40		0.80	
Cash and other expense	3.27		1.09	
Interest on cattle	5.67		1.89	
General farm expense	2.22		0.74	
Total other capital charges	16.89		5.63	19.9
Labor	5.85		1.95	6.9
Management	3.63		1.21	4.2
Total operating costs	85.02		28.34	100.0
Death loss	2.51		0.84	
Total costs	$262.43		29.18	
Recipts and credits				
Sale of cattle at market	271.75	$25.88		
Value of hog gains made behind cattle	3.60		1.20⎫	
Manure credits	2.82		0.94⎭	7.5
	278.17		2.14	
Net profit	15.74			

* Compiled from Table 22, Detailed Cost Report for Northwestern and Western Illinois 1949, Department of Agricultural Economics, University of Illinois, June, 1951.

Items of Cost in Fattening Cattle. Practically the same items of cost are found in steer feeding as in maintaining the breeding herd, but in somewhat different order of importance. The principal differences that should be noted are the absence of any depreciation charge and the inclusion of marketing expenses and hog gains and manure credits in the financial statement.

The Labor Cost of Fattening Cattle.   Next to feed, labor constitutes the largest single item of expense in fattening cattle.   However, on well-managed farms, the farmsteads of which have been planned with a view to having things arranged as conveniently as possible, the labor charge for feeding a drove of steers amounts to only a small percentage of the total cost of fattening.   On other farms where the feed supply and the cattle are far apart, the cost of both man and horse labor is considerable.

On the 15 farms included in the detailed cost studies summarized in Table 255 the cost of labor averaged approximately 7 per cent of the total operating costs, or 10 per cent of the total feed cost.   In similar studies made in DeKalb County, Illinois, during the period 1919–1923 both horse and man labor equaled 8.6 per cent of the total operating costs.   Thus, it appears that the labor used in feeding cattle was reduced but little during the intervening 25 years.   On the DeKalb County farms 4.75 hours of man labor and 2.7 hours of horse labor were expended per 100 pounds of gain made by the cattle.[4]

Wide variations are observed in the amount of labor expended by different farmers in caring for the same number of cattle.   While farm labor is usually plentiful during the winter months, no more time should be spent on the cattle than can be efficiently employed.   To be continually "puttering" around the feed lot at all hours of the day will add unnecessary expense to the cost of fattening and will also needlessly disturb the cattle.

Miscellaneous Farm Costs.   Under miscellaneous or *other costs* are included various items of expense that are encountered only on certain farms or on a given farm only during certain feeding seasons; also a proportionate share of the general overhead expenses of the farm as a whole, such as the cost of maintaining and operating a water supply system, telephone rental, use of tools, and other equipment used by the farm as a whole.   As a rule, the total amount of these miscellaneous expenses is below $2 per head, though it occasionally reaches a much higher figure.   Death risk is an item that, though often absent, sometimes amounts to several dollars a head as a result of the death of one or two animals in a carload when they are nearly ready for market.

Another item of miscellaneous costs that shows considerable variation is taxes.   If cattle are marketed before the date fixed by law as the basis of personal property assessments, usually April 1, no taxes are, of course, paid.   If, however, the cattle are still on hand, the taxes may amount to $1 to $2 per head.   The attempt of feeders to escape this item of expense can often be seen in the increased

[4] U. S. D. A. Technical Bulletin 23, 1927.

receipts of fed cattle at the large market centers during the latter part
of March.

TABLE 256

MISCELLANEOUS COSTS OF FATTENING CATTLE*

	Average per Steer			
	1919	1920	1921	1922
Number of Droves.........	69	108	96	106
Number of Cattle..........	2590	4607	3652	4202
Total Farm or Feed Lot Costs...............	$97.82	$94.68	$47.24	$32.50
Miscellaneous Feed Lot Costs				
Death Loss..............	.33	.41	.30	.26
Veterinary..............	.09	.07	.07	.06
Insurance...............	.04	.03	.01	.01
Taxes....................	1.00	.78	.54	.36
Incidentals..............	.63	.64	.44	.30
Total Miscellaneous Costs...............	$2.09	$1.93	$1.36	$ .99
Per cent Miscellaneous Costs are of Total Feed Lot Costs.................	2.1	2.0	2.9	3.0

* De Kalb County, Illinois, U. S. D. A. Preliminary Report, 1923.

Marketing Costs.   Since marketing costs have been considered in detail in the preceding chapter, little need be said about that subject here.[5]
In cost account studies made by the United States Department of
Agriculture during the period 1919–1923 of many cattle-feeding enterprises in the Corn Belt, marketing costs ranked fourth in importance,
being exceeded by feed, labor, and interest. Even so the cost of
marketing an average steer was only $2.38, or 1.6 per cent of the total
cost, including the initial cost of the animal in the feed lot. Since the
average sale weight was 1075 pounds, the marketing cost was only
22 cents a hundred pounds.[6]   While the cost of marketing per head
and per hundredweight is considerably higher now than it was in
1919–1923, it is even lower than it was then relative to other costs and

[5] Cf. p. 541.

[6] Calculated from data obtained by the U. S. D. A. and the Illinois Experiment
Station, working cooperatively in DeKalb County, Illinois, 1918–1923.

relative to the market value of fat cattle. For example, marketing costs are only about 50 per cent higher than they were at that time, but prices of feeds, labor, and cattle have more than doubled during the period. Although cattle are a highly perishable product of great value and, consequently, require careful and rapid handling by transportation and selling agencies, the expense of marketing them constitutes a smaller percentage of their gross sale value than almost any other important item of commerce. (See Table **247**.)

TABLE 257

IMPORTANCE OF BY-PRODUCTS OF CATTLE FEEDING — HOG GAINS AND MANURE*

	Production per cwt. Gain of Steers		Total Value of By-products per Steer	Value of By-products Expressed in per cent of			Value of By-products less all Fattening Costs Except Feed and Marketing (per Steer)
	Hog Gains (lb.)	Manure, loads		Total Feed Cost	Total Fattening and Marketing Cost	All Fattening Costs Except Feed and Marketing	
1918–19.........	....	....	$22.29	26	21	118	$3.48
1919–20.........	19.7	2.3	19.16	23	19	129	4.27
1920–21.........	13.1	2.0	7.89	21	14	58	−5.64
1921–22.........	16.0	2.0	7.04	26	19	82	−1.59
1922–23.........	16.2	1.6	7.06	18	14	80	−1.79
5-Year Average (Not weighted).	16.25	2.0	12.69	23	17.5	93	−0.25

* U. S. D. A. and Ill. Exp. Sta., Coöperating; Preliminary Reports, U. S. D. A. 1923.

Pork and Manure Credits. The statement is often made that the profits made by the big packers from the slaughter of cattle come from the efficient utilization of the by-products. A similar statement could well be made concerning the fattening of cattle, pork and manure being the by-products which usually add materially to the feeders' profits. Such being the case, proper steps should be taken to recover as much pork and manure as possible.

The amounts of these by-products obtained from cattle feeding vary considerably with the kinds of feed used, the preparation given the corn, the size and surface of the feed lot, the method of feeding, etc. All these points are discussed in some detail in other chapters. The figures in Table **257** are based on data gathered from many feeders and may be considered as the average that may be expected under ordinary feed-lot conditions. With the exception of the year 1920–1921, an abnormal year financially, the value of the two by-products, pork and manure, closely approximated all fattening costs less feed and marketing. In other words, the return from these two items was sufficient to cover all interest, labor, and equipment charges, and all miscellaneous costs such as taxes, death risk, etc. Many practical feeders recognize this relationship and consider that they have "broken even" on their feeding operations if the net returns from their cattle are sufficient to cover the original cost of the steers laid down at the farm and current prices for all feeds eaten. Some men go even further and state that they would be willing to feed cattle year after year if they could be assured of the hog gains and manure to cover the above-mentioned expenses and to return a small profit. While such an arrangement would hardly be satisfactory to the average feeder, who exercises only ordinary care in recovering these two by-products, it does emphasize the fact that the fattened cattle are not the sole source of revenue derived from the feeding enterprise.

Profits Made in Feeding Cattle. Statements are sometimes made that the feeding of purchased cattle is a gamble; that profits made during good years are wiped out by losses suffered in years when prices are low; and that men who stay in the business very long are almost sure to "go broke." It is true that the buying of a drove of cattle to feed involves some speculative risk, inasmuch as they are bought in the expectation that they will be sold at a higher price. It also is true that occasionally prices for fat cattle are so low that nearly all cattle marketed lose money for their owners no matter how skillfully they have been fed. And it is true that in almost every livestock community there lives at least one man who expanded his feeding operations at the wrong time and lost all his savings as a result of his bad judgment. However, such misfortunes are much more likely to occur to the "in-and-outer" who feeds only when he sees a chance to make unusually large profits than tô the man who each year feeds the number and kind of cattle that fit into his farm program most satisfactorily.

That an intelligently planned cattle-feeding enterprise will yield good profits over a period of years is well substantiated by the long-time records of both practical feeders and experiment stations. Since the records of the latter are more available and more appropriate for public scrutiny, they have been used in selecting material for Table 258. It should be kept in mind while studying this table that the period 1921–1941 covered the great agricultural "depression," during which the producers of many agricultural products were constantly imploring for government aid in one form and another. It is significant that beef cattlemen, especially Corn Belt feeders, did not ask any special favors

TABLE 258

FINANCIAL RESULTS OF FEEDING CATTLE DURING THE PERIOD 1921–1941

Year	Kansas Experiment Station, Light-weight Cattle		Illinois Experiment Station, Calves					
	Local Price of Corn per Bushel	Return per Bushel of Corn Fed*	Cost of Cattle in Lots per Cwt.	Selling Price in Chicago, per Cwt.		Local Price Corn per Bushel	Return per Bushel of Corn Fed*	
				Lowest Price	Highest Price		Lowest Return	Highest Return
1921–22	$0.70	$1.40	......	......	......	.....	.....	.....
1922–23	0.70	0.93	......	......	......	.....	.....	.....
1923–24	0.70	0.92	......	......	......	.....	.....	.....
1924–25	1.12	1.47	......	......	......	.....	.....	.....
1925–26	0.70	0.85	......	......	......	.....	.....	.....
1926–27	0.77	1.31	$ 9.90	$11.85	$12.85	$0.70	$1.19	$1.46
1927–28	0.84	1.54	10.84	13.60	14.65	0.84	1.17	1.95
1928–29	0.77	1.42	15.43	15.35	15.90	0.75	0.94	1.19
1929–30	0.84	0.71	13.77	10.00	10.60	0.70	0.19	0.38
1930–31	0.60	0.45	10.68	9.25	9.25	0.45	0.52	0.52
1931–32	No light cattle fed		7.34	7.85	8.35	0.24	0.65	0.76
1932–33	0.21	0.54	7.05	5.85	6.30	0.25	0.17	0.26
1933–34	0.42	0.65	5.47	8.25	9.25	0.42	0.74	0.90
1934–35	....	....	6.10	11.20	12.00	0.80	1.13	1.49
1935–36	....	....	9.38	8.50	8.90	0.50	0.47	0.58
1936–37	....	....	No light cattle fed					
1937–38	....	....	10.00	10.75	11.15	0.50	0.79	0.93
1938–39	....	....	9.65	9.15	9.60	0.42	0.59	0.65
1939–40	....	....	10.65	11.75	12.25	0.53	0.88	1.07
1940–41	....	....	11.50	11.75	12.35	0.65	0.89	1.30
Average	0.70	1.02	9.85	10.36	10.95	0.55	0.74	0.96

* Corn credited with all returns after deducting cost of cattle and market price of all feeds except corn. Hog gains excluded.

and rejected almost unanimously a plan for the payment of subsidies proposed by the federal government early in 1934. (See Fig. 78.)

Calculating Profits from Feeding. Three methods of figuring profits made from cattle feeding are more or less widely used by Corn Belt feeders.   The most common is to state the gross *profit per head,* which is derived by subtracting the cost of the cattle and the farm value of all feeds from the market value per head less marketing costs. Another method is to determine the *return per bushel of corn fed.* This is determined by deducting from the net proceeds the value of all feeds fed except corn.   The remainder is then divided by the number

Fig. 79. An example of how foresight, good judgment, and good luck sometimes combine to make large profits. These steers were contracted in June, 1947, for $18 per cwt. When delivered Oct. 20 they weighed 470 pounds. They were sold in Chicago Aug. 4, 1948, for $39.25 per cwt., at an average weight of 1001 pounds. (*Courtesy F. D. Hartman, Plainfield, Illinois.*)

of bushels of corn eaten to obtain the return realized per bushel.   If this value is greater than the market price of corn, a profit has been made; if not, a loss has been suffered.   (See Table 258.)   Return per acre of pasture grazed or per ton of hay or silage fed may be determined in the same way.   However, a choice must be made between the different components of the ration, as the return per unit of only one item can be determined.   All others must be assigned their respective values on the local market.

The third method of expressing the profit made from a cattle-feeding project is to calculate the *return realized per $100 value of feeds fed.* In this method only the cost of the cattle is subtracted from the net proceeds received at the market, and this remainder is divided by the total value of the feeds fed.   (See Table 259.)   In none of the three methods is any allowance made for labor, interest, and other operating costs.   It is assumed that these expenses are offset by the value of the manure and hog gains obtained from the cattle.

Relative Importance of Feeding and Margins upon Profits.   It is frequently stated that profits from cattle feeding come for the most part from clever buying and selling rather than from skillful feeding and management. Although this statement contains an element of truth, in that it emphasizes the importance of careful buying and selling, it unjustly depreciates the importance of intelligent feeding, which, after all, is the principal factor entirely under the feeder's control. That the kinds and quantities of feed used have as much or more

TABLE 259

RETURNS OBTAINED PER $100 OF FEED FED
BEEF CATTLE, 1933–1950*

Year	From Beef Cow Herds	From Purchased Feeder Cattle	Year	From Beef Cow Herds	From Purchased Feeder Cattle
1933	$ 90	$ 97	1943	$108	$105
1934	84	125	1944	94	107
1935	110	152	1945	110	119
1936	85	96	1946	130	135
1937	99	106	1947	130	138
1938	119	142	1948	143	137
1939	146	131	1949	132	136
1940	134	136	1950	169	170
1941	136	124	18-year average	119	127
1942	127	136			

* Department of Agricultural Economics, University of Illinois, Annual Report Farm Bureau Farm Management Service, 1950.

effect upon the profit as the spread between buying and selling prices per hundred is well shown by the data in Table 260. From the data here presented it appears that costs of gains have a much greater effect than do margins upon the "return realized per $100 of feed fed" for cattle of all ages. However, from the standpoint of "returns above feed costs per head," the size of the margin has a greater effect than the cost of the gain for heavy cattle, while for yearlings both factors appear to have about the same value.

That the kinds and amounts of feeds used affect the profits greatly is strikingly shown by the Illinois results in Table 258. If we assume that each calf consumed 50 bushels of corn, the average difference between the profits derived from the best and the poorest ration was $10.10 a head. If 100 calves were fattened each year, the annual difference would be $1010, and the total for the 14-year period $14,140, which was half the cost of a good 240-acre farm during the period covered by the table.

The Financial Aspect of Purebred Cattle. The breeder of purebreds has financial problems quite different from those of the man who handles only commercial cattle. In the first place, the size of his in-

TABLE 260

RELATIVE IMPORTANCE OF COST OF GAINS AND MARGIN UPON
PROFITS MADE FROM CATTLE FEEDING*

	Feed Cost per Cwt. Gain			Margin (Priced Spread)		
	High $\frac{1}{3}$	Middle $\frac{1}{3}$	Low $\frac{1}{3}$	Low $\frac{1}{3}$	Middle $\frac{1}{3}$	High $\frac{1}{3}$
1. Good to choice calves						
Margin or price spread	$ 5.23	$ 4.64	$ 4.17	$ 2.38	$ 4.90	$ 6.41
Feed cost per cwt. gain	22.42	18.26	15.81	19.33	18.63	18.85
Returns above feed cost per head	61.44	78.02	88.56	60.04	76.23	84.53
Returns per $100 feed fed	152	179	205	162	178	179
2. Common to choice yearlings						
Margin on price spread	7.23	6.35	6.67	5.33	6.76	8.19
Feed cost per cwt. gain	24.91	20.32	17.51	21.14	20.72	20.90
Returns above feed cost per head	77.31	90.37	103.94	73.45	88.62	109.44
Returns per $100 feed fed	155	184	212	167	179	192
3. Good to choice heavy steers						
Margin or price spread	5.83	6.01	4.51	3.64	5.21	7.58
Feed cost per cwt. gain	28.11	22.98	17.92	20.22	25.32	23.25
Returns above feed cost per head	50.28	65.94	57.67	43.49	48.25	83.76
Returns per $100 feed fed	162	186	203	180	168	193

* Illinois Experiment Station, Mimeo. 12th Annual Report of Feeder Cattle Fed in Farm Bureau Farm Management Service, 1951.

vestment in animals is largely a matter of his own choosing, with "the sky as the limit." This is true even though he maintains but an average-sized herd, for what he lacks in numbers can easily be made up in quality and breeding if he is willing to pay the price.

Purebred cattle values vary greatly from herd to herd, as there are wide differences in individual merit and in the popularity of the blood lines represented. They also vary greatly from one period to another, largely because of the degree of prosperity enjoyed by the men handling market cattle. When prices of commercial cattle are high there is a strong demand for purebred bulls to produce steers and heifers for the market. This demand results in increased prices for purebred cattle. The very close correlation usually existing between fat steer prices and prices for purebred cattle may be seen in Fig. 80. During the 21-year period 1900–1920, purebred prices, as determined from the published reports of all important public sales of Shorthorn, Hereford, and Aberdeen-Angus cattle, averaged approximately 3¼ times the average

value per head of native beef steers on the Chicago markets.[7]   During
the early years of this period, some sales were held where but little
better than beef prices were realized.   Later on, however, there were

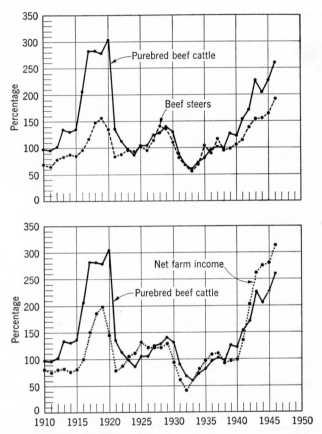

FIG. 80.   The relation of prices of purebred beef cattle to: (a) prices of beef
steers at Chicago; (b) net income of farm operators of the United States.
Index number 1935–1939 = 100. (*Courtesy University of Minnesota.*)

literally scores of sales with averages around $500, while the offerings
from the more noted herds averaged $1000 and upwards.
   As will be seen from Fig. 80, purebred cattle prices skyrocketed during World War I but declined immediately after the war to about the
same level they had occupied before 1914.   A similar rise in prices

[7] Armour's Live Stock Bureau, Monthly Letter to Animal Husbandmen, April 1,
1921.

occurred during World War II, but instead of receding after the war they continued to climb higher and higher, with each of the three major breeds registering each year from 1947 to 1950 successively higher prices than had been reported previously. Sales of both bulls and females in five figures were common during this period, and averages from $1000 to $3000 were realized in scores of public auction sales of purebred cattle.

TABLE 261

PRICES PAID FOR PUREBRED HEREFORD CATTLE
AT PUBLIC AUCTION SALES*

	1950	1940	1930	1920
Number of auction sales	573	220	60	283
Number of cattle sold	38,744	17,893	3,732	15,432
Average price	$604	$195	$217	$416
Average of top sale	$5,160	$1,023	$1,068	$4,050
Top price for bull	$70,500	$7,900	$2,500	$22,000
Top price for female	$17,300	$5,350	$7,600	$8,000
Bulls sold for $10,000 or more	46	33[a]	5[a]	3
Cows sold for $5000 or more	31	6[a]	3[a]	13

* Compiled from Hereford Journal.
[a] Number sold for $2000 or more.

Despite the record prices paid for outstanding animals representing the most popular lines of breeding, the rank and file of purebred cattle continued to sell at conservative prices. In fact, they advanced little more over pre-World War II prices than other agricultural commodities. (See Fig. 80.)

Importance of Depreciation Charge in Purebred Herds. The relatively large amount of money invested in purebred cattle exerts a considerable influence upon the financial situation. Particularly are interest and depreciation charges and death risks affected. Depreciation is an item that may be almost disregarded in the financial aspect of a herd of grade cows, since the cows are usually sold before age affects their market value. In a herd of purebreds, however, depreciation is of considerable importance, as animals bought at high prices are eventually sold for beef. Occasionally the loss suffered from the depreciation on a single animal is sufficiently large to wipe out the profits accruing from the rest of the herd for a full year. The author calls to mind an excellent purebred bull which was purchased for $5000 and was sold at beef prices two years later because he developed into a non-breeder.

Losses from depreciation are particularly heavy during periods of financial depression when prices are falling rapidly. These, however, are to a certain extent covered by the appreciation or increase in values enjoyed during periods of prosperity when prices are advancing. Unfortunately, comparatively few breeders have many cattle on hand when prices are rising, whereas barns and pastures are likely to be full when values are falling. Moreover, there is a pronounced tendency for new men to enter the purebred business after prices have reached a high level, a majority of whom have nothing to sell until the arrival of a period of depression which inevitably follows inflation and overexpansion. The losses suffered on herds so founded are sometimes very large, occasionally necessitating the sale of the cattle for but a fraction of their initial cost.

Operating Costs in Purebred Herds. Operating expenses per animal are somewhat larger for purebred than for grade cattle. The breeder of purebreds, if he is to make progress and succeed, must keep his herd in fairly good condition to insure the maximum development of the young stock and to make a favorable impression on prospective purchasers. This means a larger outlay for feed and labor. Further calls for additional labor result from the general practice of hand mating, from the necessity of keeping the bull and heifer calves separated, from the need for more or less individual feeding and care in order to give each animal the best possible chance to develop, and from the desire of most breeders of purebred cattle to keep the barns and farmstead sufficiently neat and clean to bear inspection by visitors at any time.

As a rule, the building and equipment charge per animal is considerably higher in purebred herds than in grade. Although a certain amount of extra equipment beyond that needed for ordinary cattle is highly desirable, elaborate barns and costly equipment are by no means essential to the raising of animals good enough to meet any requirement. A sufficient number of fairly large, roomy box stalls and well-drained paddocks to permit the proper separation of animals on the basis of age and sex constitutes the principal item of equipment needed for the proper handling of a herd of purebred beef cattle.

Cost of Selling Purebred Cattle. The marketing or selling cost of purebred cattle is materially higher than that of grades. There being no established market for breeding cattle, each breeder is forced to find his own market, which he proceeds to do through various kinds of advertising. Newspapers, livestock journals, signboards, and letterheads announce to the reading public that he has stock for sale, while reproduced photographs, exhibition herds, and public displays of prize ribbons and trophies attest the excellence of his herd as a whole. Even a certain percentage of the cost of an imposing barn, the expense of painting the paddock fences, and the cost of keeping the breeding animals in somewhat higher condition than that necessary to insure their maximum usefulness should properly be charged to advertising. Returns on money thus expended will come from a more ready sale or higher prices for surplus stock rather than from lower operating costs.

Care should be exercised by the beginning breeder lest his selling costs be out of proportion to the prices received. To consign a $300 animal to a sale, the expenses of which, including advertising, catalogs, auctioneer, stall rent, freight, expenses of attendant, etc., are $50 or more per head, is obviously poor policy. It is likely that the net return would be greater if the sale were made at home at little more than beef prices. Unless one is willing to consider a part of the expense of present-day sales as legitimate advertising for future offerings, the total cost of selling should not exceed 8 to 10 per cent of the expected sale price.

Receipts from Purebred Cattle. Receipts from a herd of purebred beef cattle are very irregular regarding both size and time. During periods of prosperity, every surplus animal is taken by eager buyers who show little tendency to haggle over prices. During periods of financial depression, even the more noted breeders have to resort to peddling tactics in order to make sufficient sales to keep their herds down to the required size. At such times it is not unusual for a large percentage of bull calves to be castrated, fattened, and sent to market along with the plainer heifers and those cows that have shown only mediocre breeding ability. Although such sales are trying to the individual breeder, they may be of considerable benefit to the breed as a whole, inasmuch as they cause the elimination of the poorer animals from the lists of registered stock.

Price fluctuations have been the downfall of a great many cattle speculators who attempted to get into the purebred business by buying a "ready-made" herd at peak values. But for the man who builds his own herd from the progeny of a few carefully selected cows of proved merit, price fluctuations, although by no means welcome, are not likely to prove disastrous. Such a situation is well illustrated in the record of the additions to and sales from the herd of J. W. Coder, Elwood, Nebraska, from the founding of his Hereford herd in 1909 down to 1924. This period covers the spectacular rise in purebred cattle values during and immediately after World War I and also the terrific slump in prices that began during the late summer of 1920. It will be noted that most of Mr. Coder's sales were made during this period of depression.

TABLE 262

PURCHASES AND SALES OF HEREFORD CATTLE MADE BY MR. J. W. CODER, ELWOOD, NEBRASKA, OVER SIXTEEN-YEAR PERIOD*

	Purchases			Sales		
Date	Number Bought	Total Cost	Average Price	Number Sold	Total Amount Received	Average Price
1909.....................	5	$835	$167	....	....	....
1910.....................	....	....	....	1	$150	$150
1911.....................	3	440	146	3	300	100
1912.....................	....	....	....	....	....	....
1913.:...................	....	. ..	....	5	600	120
1914.....................	7	1,785	255	3	600	200
1915.....................	2	640	320	2	200	100
1916.....................	4	2,025	506	15	5,165	344
1917.....................	1	830	830	35	10,610	303
1918.....................	2	550	275	17	6,965	409
1919.....................	13	15,025	1155	11	14,070	1279
1920.....................	2	6,500	3250	26	12,015	462
1921.....................	....	....	....	25	7,095	283
1922.....................	....	....	....	27	6,725	249
1923.....................	1	375	375	35	8,675	247
1924..................... (1st 5 months)	....	....	....	23	3,505	152
Total...............	40	29,005	725	228	76,615	336
Cattle on hand June 1, 1924 (including calves).....	....	....	....	73	10,000 (estimated value)	137
Grand Total...........	40	$29,005	....	301	$86,615	

* American Hereford Journal, Vol. 15, No. 4, June 15, 1924.

32 —————— Fitting Cattle for Show and Sale

The exhibition of cattle at public fairs and shows is engaging the attention of an increasing number of breeders with the passing of each year. Such contests afford the exhibitor an opportunity to compare his cattle with those of his fellow breeders and to advertise his stock to the public by displaying them in their most attractive form. However, neither of these purposes will be accomplished satisfactorily unless the animals are brought out in the proper condition with nothing undone that would add to their merit or enhance their appearance in the show ring. "Attention to details" should be the slogan of every prospective exhibitor. Showyard competition is usually keen, and the decision is arrived at only after careful and painstaking examination. In such cases the well-groomed animal that is properly shown by its herdsman has a marked advantage over one lacking somewhat in the completeness of its "toilet" or in showyard etiquette.

Selecting the Show Herd. The selection of the animals that are to compose the show herd should be made as early as possible. For most breeders, the show season begins about August 10 and continues throughout the fall. Inasmuch as from 4 to 8 months are required to bring an animal from good breeding to show condition, the candidates for the show herd should be chosen in late winter or early spring. If more than one candidate is available, two should be fitted, so that a substitute may be on hand should an accident, sickness, or unsatisfactory development disqualify the more promising individual. Especially are substitute animals desirable in the younger classes, where the rate of growth is rapid and marked changes in form and in quality of flesh are of common occurrence.

No one factor is of more importance in selecting animals for exhibition purposes than uniformity among the animals themselves. If all the individuals that compose the herd are of the same general type and show a uniform gradation in size from the youngest to the oldest, they will present the best possible appearance when exhibited for the group prizes. Uniformity of color, although of minor importance, is not without value in the group classes.

General Care and Management. In fitting cattle for show, every reasonable precaution should be taken to insure their comfort and well-being, for it is only when they are quiet and contented that they will make maximum gains. Comfort implies protection from extreme weather conditions, from annoying parasitic insects, and from possible disturbance by other animals. Upon the arrival of hot weather, the cattle should be kept in the barn during the day to prevent their hair from being sunburned and becoming dry and stiff. Moreover, the cattle will be more comfortable in the barn and will fatten more rapidly than if left out in the pasture. If possible, roomy box-stalls, well supplied with clean bedding, should be provided, so that the cattle may be induced to lie down and rest except when they are eating. With the arrival of June or July, the barn should be sprayed to control flies. If the flies become numerous and it is impractical to darken the stalls, the cattle should be covered with light canvas or muslin blankets.

A reasonable amount of exercise is needed by show cattle to maintain a good, active circulation, without which they are likely to get stiff in their feet and legs. Exercise also tends to stimulate the appetite, thus making for a larger consumption of feed and a higher degree of finish. Young animals will usually take sufficient exercise if turned together at night in a small pasture or paddock. Older cattle are often disposed to stand around or to lie down, especially if their feet are somewhat tender. Such animals should be made to exercise by leading them about a mile each day.

The Feeding of Show Cattle. The outstanding difference between the animals in the show and breeding herds is a difference in condition. Cattle entered in an exhibition are presumed to be as nearly perfect as they can be made to appear. Hence, they are expected to show the thickness and wealth of flesh that are associated with early maturity, easy fattening qualities, and an ability to make good use of all feeds eaten. Should they be lacking in finish, they will be open to the criticism that they probably are so lacking in feeding ability that they could not be made any fatter; or that, if made fatter, they probably would have become rough and patchy. That extreme condition is detrimental to breeding animals few will deny. Nevertheless, custom has decreed that condition be given much credit in the show ring. Hence, cattle that are being made ready for show should be fed a liberal amount of concentrates and a relatively small allowance of roughage.

In general, the feeding of show cattle is much like the fattening of steers for market. However, the economy of the ration is of relatively small importance compared with the degree of finish attained. For this reason, considerable use is made of highly palatable feeds, such as molasses and feeds containing molasses, which will tend to sustain a large consumption of concentrates throughout the show season. Mention should also be made of the fact that the quality of flesh is of paramount importance in animals intended for show. Hence, there is a noticeable tendency for fitters of show cattle to feed barley and roots instead of corn and silage. Bran also is usually fed in rather generous amounts, not only for the protein that it contains, but also for the regulatory effect it has upon the digestive tract.

The grain ration of show cattle is almost always ground, particularly during the latter part of the feeding period. Grinding is desirable (1) because of its effect upon the consumption of grain, and (2) because of the ease with which ground feed may be mixed with other materials.

Show cattle are commonly fed three or even four times a day, particularly if they are rather thin and rapid improvement in condition is desired. Supplying a relatively small amount of feed at frequent intervals is much better than feeding a larger quantity at one time. Feed left in the feed-box soon becomes unpalatable from the breath and saliva of the animal and should be removed promptly. In so far as possible, the amount fed should be no more than will be eaten in approximately 1 hour.

The following grain mixtures are recommended for cattle that are being fitted for show:

I. Ground corn	50 lb.	Moisten each feed with
Crushed oats	25 lb.	½ pint of molasses
Wheat bran	15 lb.	diluted with an equal
Linseed meal	10 lb.	volume of water
II. Crushed barley	40 lb.	
Crushed oats	25 lb.	
Wheat bran	10 lb.	
Molasses feed	25 lb.	
III. Shelled corn	50 lb.	
Whole oats	20 lb.	
Linseed meal	10 lb.	
Molasses feed	20 lb.	

All cattle, except those that show a sluggish appetite for grain, should be turned into a field of short grass every night. Besides being a nutritious, laxative feed, grass, especially when laden with dew, tends to keep the feet of the cattle clean. Animals that have the run of a clean pasture are likely to experience little trouble from foul feet. In addition to the pasture, show cattle should be fed a limited amount of bright legume or mixed hay.

Training and Preparation for Show. It should be the ambition of every exhibitor to bring his cattle into the show ring in the best possible condition. This implies that the animals are not only fat and well finished, but also well trained and thoroughly cleaned and groomed.

Training. Judges find it exceedingly difficult to examine restless, fidgety cattle, and are likely to give them scant consideration in distributing the prizes. Instances can be cited where animals have failed to get into the prize lists solely because they were not sufficiently trained to permit their careful examination by the judge. This training should be begun as soon as there is any possibility of the animal's being shown, and continued until the close of the show season.

The first step in training is to teach the animal to lead. This is a small task with a calf, but much more difficult with an older animal. Breeders of purebred cattle usually have occasion to teach most of their calves to lead in connection with the routine management of the herd. In such cases, no training in leading is needed when the age for showing arrives.

The next step is to teach the animal to stand properly while it is being examined by the judge. This step in training is really a difficult process, and the lesson must be repeated over and over again. The animal should be taught to stand perfectly still for several minutes at a time with each foot so placed that each leg is perpendicular and bearing its full share of weight. The back should be carried perfectly straight and the head held at the height of the back. Every day, especially near the opening of the show season, the animal should be led from its stall and "posed" for 15 or 20 minutes with the same care that would be taken in a judging ring.

Washing and Curling. The number of washings an animal should be given before being shown depends upon the condition of its hair and skin. Frequent washings with cold water tend to promote a heavy growth of soft, fluffy hair and to make the hide smooth and pliable. At least one washing a week should be given during the month before the opening of the first show. Soft water and tar soap are desirable, although not absolutely necessary. After the hair and skin have been wetted thoroughly, plenty of soap should be applied and the lather worked in by the vigorous use of a stiff brush. By adding a little water from time to time, the dirt and dandruff are gradually loosened and washed out. Finally, the animal should be rinsed thoroughly with clean water to remove all traces of soap. As much of the rinse water as possible should be scraped and wiped off, and the animal allowed to stand in a place that is free from drafts while it is being

Fig. 81. Marking or lining the coat in preparation for curling. The hair must first be thoroughly wetted either by washing or by spraying. The entire side of a Shorthorn is "lined" from the outer edge of the back down to the level of the knee and hock. Angus, however, usually are lined only on the shoulder and thigh, the hair on the back and ribs being brushed smooth. (*Courtesy The Sunbeam Corporation, Chicago, Illinois.*)

"curled." After this, it should be covered with a warm blanket if the weather is at all cool.

Cattle with long, fluffy hair are usually "curled" before being taken into the show ring. Short-haired animals, on the other hand, are brushed down smooth, the brushing being followed by a brisk rubbing with a woolen cloth slightly dampened with a mixture of equal parts of denatured alcohol and sweet oil.

Curling consists in using the long, fluffy hair, frequently possessed by animals of the Shorthorn and Hereford breeds, for the purpose of improving the general outline and shape of the body. The operation is performed as follows:

An hour or two before the animal is to be shown, the hair should be made moderately wet by being brushed down smooth against the sides of the body with a stiff brush which is dipped frequently into water containing a little creolin and soap.   With a coarse comb, the wet hair is then parted down the center of the back from the neck to the tail, and combed straight out from the median line to the extreme edge of

FIG. 82. The round comb is usually used to curl the hair of the Hereford.
(*Courtesy U.S.D.A.*)

the flat portion of the back.   Parallel lines about an inch apart are next drawn along the sides of the body from the rear edge of the thighs to the front of the shoulders.   These lines can be made by using an ordinary curry comb with every other row of teeth pounded down flat against the back surface.   After all the lines have been made, the hair is lightly combed or brushed up to make it stand out from the sides of the body.   The upper line of hair is curled up even with the level portion of the back, the hair of which is brushed down flat and smooth.   Thus, the long hair when properly combed and curled tends to emphasize the width of the animal and to soften and minimize any undue roughness of conformation, such as is sometimes caused by prominent shoulders, narrow crops, hollow flanks, or a narrow rump.

Clipping Heads and Tails. Aberdeen-Angus and Red Polled calves make a better appearance if their heads are clipped in front of a line drawn around the neck about 3 inches back of the ears. When the long hair is thus removed, the head appears cleaner-cut and more shapely and the poll more sharply defined. The ears are seldom

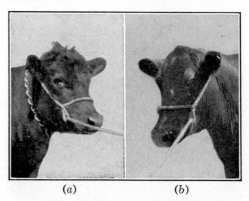

(a)   (b)

Fig. 83. The effect of clipping upon appearance of the head. (a) Unclipped head; (b) same head 10 days after being clipped.

clipped. In all breeds except the Shorthorn, the tail should be clipped from a little above the switch to the tail head, which is gradually tapered off so that it appears to blend nicely with the rump. This clipping should be done a week or 10 days before the animal is shown in order that the clipped hair may lose its stubby appearance.

Care of Horns. In the case of horned cattle, some attention should be given to the horns as well as to the coat. Often the horns will assume a bad direction unless steps are taken early to shape them properly. In general, horns should curve forward, inward, and slightly downward. If they tend to grow in an upward direction, they should be weighted to bring them down. Care should be taken that the weights are not so heavy as to break the horns close to the head. If the horns are rather large and stiff, rasping lightly on the outer border of the desired curve will cause them to change shape more quickly. Obviously, little can be done to improve the shape of the horns of mature animals. If they are too long or have a badly shaped tip, they can often be cut back as much as 2 or even 3 inches by taking off ½ inch or so at a time at intervals of a month or 6 weeks. After each amputation, the end of the horn should be tapered down to make it appear as much like a natural tip as possible.

A week or two before the show, the horns should be scraped and polished. The amount of scraping will depend upon the roughness and size of the horn. In the case of calves much scraping will seldom be necessary. Usually, any roughness can be removed by rasping the

FIG. 84. Clipping the tail from the crotch to the tail head is an important step in preparing both Aberdeen-Angus and Hereford cattle for the show ring. The tails of Shorthorn breeding animals are not clipped. (*Courtesy The Sunbeam Corporation, Chicago, Illinois.*)

horn with a coarse file or rubbing it with coarse sandpaper. Care must be taken that the horn shell is not made too thin. The final smoothing should be done with a fine grade of emery paper or a flannel cloth and emery dust. After the horn has been properly smoothed, it can be polished by rubbing it briskly with a woolen cloth moistened with sweet or linseed oil on which has been dusted a little tripoli. Fairly good success may be attained by polishing with any good metal or silver polish.

Care of Feet. As a rule, the feet of show cattle will require some attention. Animals with long toes or unevenly worn hoofs are less

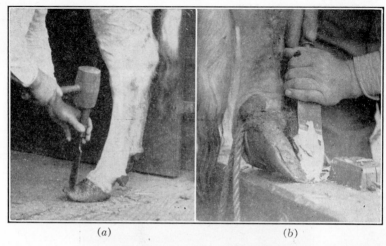

(a)   (b)

FIG. 85. The wrong and right way to trim a foot. (a) The wrong way, which
does not relieve the strain on the pastern; (b) the right way, which levels the
foot and restores the leg to its proper position. (*Courtesy University of Illinois.*)

FIG. 86. A top view of the neck and back of a correctly fitted Shorthorn heifer.
(*Courtesy U.S.D.A.*)

pleasing in appearance and walk less satisfactorily than those that have
had their feet shaped up and their toes properly trimmed. Work on the
feet can best be done while the animal is in a set of stocks. The sills of
the stocks are built at such a height as will permit the tying of the
shank and pastern of the leg in a horizontal position, thus exposing the

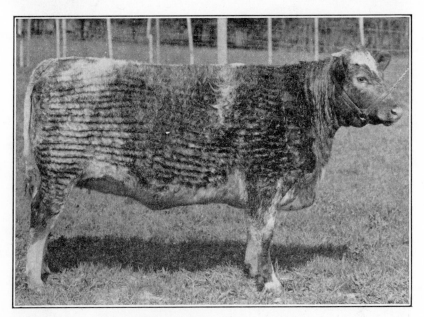

FIG. 87. A properly curled Shorthorn heifer. Although the hair has been
brushed and combed upward until it is thoroughly dry, the horizontal lines of
the marking comb are still plainly visible. (*Courtesy U.S.D.A.*)

underside of the foot for trimming.[1] The practice sometimes followed
of shortening the toes by standing the animal on a hard floor and cutting them off from above with a hammer and chisel cannot be too
strongly condemned. While this method may prevent for a time the
overlapping or rubbing of toes, it leaves the bearing surface of the foot
unchanged, so that the trouble speedily returns. Ill-shapen feet throw
an undue strain upon the bones and ligaments of the lower leg. If they
are allowed to go untrimmed, broken-down pasterns will result.

Feet that are badly in need of trimming should not be leveled up all
at once, but should be trimmed in two or three installments at intervals
of a week or 10 days. In this way an opportunity is afforded for
studying the foot to see what effect the last trimming has had and to

[1] *Cf.* p. 592.

determine what additional work is necessary. It also renders unnecessary the cutting away of so much horn at one operation as to make the foot tender or to cause bleeding.

Fig. 88. Another type of "hair-do." Some herdsmen comb and brush the hair until each hair stands nearly perpendicular to the hide except over the neck and shoulders and on the rear of the thighs. Usually animals with fairly short hair are dressed in this manner. (*Courtesy The Sunbeam Corporation, Chicago, Illinois.*)

Equipment for Showing. Little equipment is needed for the showing of beef cattle, beyond a neat, russet leather halter and a slender cane or pointer to be used in posing the animals. Rope halters will be found satisfactory for tying the cattle in the stalls but do not appear to advantage in the judging ring. Most herdsmen take a Scotch comb or fiber brush into the ring, to use in touching up their animals when the judge is examining entries at the other end of the line. While occasionally these tools are needed to straighten out hair that has been disarranged by contact with the animals on either side, the general tendency is to use them altogether too much. Too much fussing around in the show ring on the part of the attendant betrays a nervousness that may be communicated to the animal. Hence, all actions should be as deliberate and natural as possible.

33 —————————— Buildings and Equipment for Beef Cattle

In the handling of beef cattle, comparatively little equipment is needed. Especially is this true of cattle that are raised and fattened for the open market. Purebred animals, on the other hand, usually are afforded shelter and equipment somewhat more pretentious, though even here the investment in equipment need not be large. However, on the farms of the larger, wealthier breeders it often totals several

Fig. 89. A popular type of beef cattle shelter on Corn Belt farms. (*Courtesy U.S.D.A.*)

thousand dollars. Much of this extra investment is in the form of buildings, apparatus, and devices that make for a more efficient management of the herd and reduce the amount of labor required for its proper feeding and care. A brief discussion of the more important articles of equipment found useful on beef cattle farms will be attempted for the benefit of the reader who is unfamiliar with their use.

Shelter. A satisfactory shelter for beef cattle is one that furnishes adequate protection from wind and rain. Protection against cold is

584

not necessary in Corn Belt latitudes, except for young calves. Numerous experiments carried on with mature, full-fed steers indicate that such cattle do better in open sheds than in closed barns. Apparently, the heat generated by the digestion and assimilation of heavy grain rations is more than sufficient to keep the animals warm. Although breeding cows and stocker steers, on but little more than maintenance rations, undoubtedly are more sensitive to extremely low temperatures, it is not likely that any great advantage is to be derived from housing them in closed barns.

TABLE 263

IMPORTANCE OF SHELTER FOR FULL-FED STEERS

Kind of Shelter	Missouri Circular* (unnumbered)			Pennsylvania Bull. 83, 1907†	
	Barn	Open Shed	Open Lot	Barn	Open Shed
	(lb.)	(lb.)	(lb.)	(lb.)	(lb.)
Daily gain per head	1.78	1.99	2.05	1.93	1.95
Grain per lb. gain	11.02	10.37	10.22	9.49	9.51
Dry roughage per lb. gain	4.32	3.74	4.22	6.16	6.04
Digestible matter per lb. gain	10.77	10.25	10.22	....	....
Daily ration					
Shelled corn	21.47	22.83	23.11	....	....
Dry roughage	8.42	8.24	9.55	....	....

* Average of three trials, 1897–1900.
† Average of five trials.

Paved Feed Lots. Muddy feed lots impose a severe handicap on winter-fed steers. Many a man has ordered a car and shipped his half-fat steers to market for no other reason than to get them out of muddy lots in which they were standing up to their knees. Others have permanently abandoned late winter and spring feeding, thereby acknowledging their defeat in the annual battle against slush and mud.

In the early days of cattle feeding, large amounts of corn fodder were fed, the refuse of which formed a thick covering around the feed troughs, sufficiently deep to bear the weight of the cattle. In former years it was also the custom to feed in large lots or on bluegrass pastures. With such large areas available, it was usually possible to avoid excessive mud by feeding first in one place and then in another. The feeder of the present day, however, has no such relief. His corn stalks are made into silage and are wholly consumed by the cattle, and the high price of land compels him to use no larger lot than necessary for dry-lot feeding.

The best insurance so far devised against possible loss in cattle feed-

Fig. 90. An inexpensive cattle shelter with paved feed lot. A shed 20 feet wide has been built on the west, south, and east sides of a hay barn which provides ground-to-roof storage for baled, loose, or chopped hay. (*Courtesy Burdette Griffith, Fisher, Illinois.*)

ing from bad weather conditions is the paved feed lot. The advantages of pavement are four-fold and may be stated briefly as follows:

1. It adds greatly to the comfort of the cattle, thereby promoting greater gains.
2. It reduces the labor involved in feeding.
3. It makes possible the saving of more manure.
4. It results in a larger production of pork from the droppings of the cattle.

The open lot used by fattening steers need not be large. No greater area is required than that necessary to permit the cattle to move about freely without unduly disturbing each other. Sixty square feet of floor space per mature animal, 50 for yearlings, and 40 for calves is sufficient, especially if the lot adjoins an open shed affording an equal area per head. Two to three thousand square feet of pavement, one-half of which is roofed, will furnish ideal conditions for a carload of cattle. The cost of a 5-inch concrete pavement is not excessive and will soon pay for itself in the increased pork and manure credits secured, to say nothing of the greater gains made by the cattle or the saving of labor in feeding.

Feed Bunks. Feed bunks used by beef cattle should be made of 2-inch material, preferably undressed cypress. The legs should be cut from 4 by 4-inch material and should be both bolted and braced to the body of the bunk. A good method of bracing the legs is shown in

Fig. 91. An elaborate barn designed for housing a large purebred herd. Although desirable from the standpoint of convenience and advertising value, buildings of this type are by no means essential for raising good cattle.

Fig. 92. Bunks that are to be placed in the open, where the cattle can eat from both sides, should be at least 30 inches wide. Thirty-six inches is a more satisfactory width for mature cattle. The floor of the bunk should be 20 inches from the ground and should carry 6- to 10-inch sides, depending on the age of the cattle. Bunks built for mature animals can be used by calves if holes are dug for the legs. Feed troughs that are built inside a barn or shed should be made adjustable as to height, to accommodate cattle of various ages. It will also be necessary to raise the troughs from time to time if the manure is allowed to accumulate in the shed.

Self-Feeders. Figure 93 on the next page illustrates a good type of self-feeder which is satisfactory for feeding either ground or shelled corn. It is mounted on the running gears of an old, low-wheeled wagon and can be easily moved from one place to another. Figure 64 shows

FIG. 92. A good movable type of feed bunk. Its width and depth make it suitable for feeding grain, silage, or hay.

FIG. 93. A portable self-feeder. A feeder of this type is especially useful in feeding on pasture, as its frequent movement insures an even distribution of manure over the field.

a feeder of much the same type, mounted on runners. A self-feeder 8 feet long, with feed troughs along both sides, will hold sufficient feed to last a carload of cattle approximately 2 weeks.

Hay Racks. Various types of racks and mangers are used for the feeding of hay and other roughages. Racks such as are shown in

Fig. 94. An excellent stationary bunk for feeding both grain and roughage. (*Courtesy Colorado Experiment Station.*)

Fig. 95. A satisfactory rack for feeding dry roughage out of doors. The advantages of this type of rack are: (1) the wastage is small, and (2) it is easily filled and cleaned. (*Courtesy Colorado Experiment Station.*)

Fig. 96 are in wide use, but are open to the objections that the wastage of hay is considerable and that they are hard to clean out. In general,

low mangers are superior to overhead racks, since they necessitate the
cattle's working down over the top of the hay in such a way as to cause

Fig. 96. Wastage of hay is high in racks of this type. They are unsatisfactory
for straw or stover because they are difficult to fill and clean out.

Fig. 97. An excellent hay bunk for a barn with overhead hay storage. A false
wall 18 inches from the side of the barn provides a chute through which the hay
is supplied from the mow. If hay is full-fed this chute will hold a week's supply.
(*Courtesy Sam Larimore, Tuscola, Illinois.*)

little wastage of the finer particles and chaff. Should the cattle show
a tendency to "nose" the hay out, a slatted door, through which the

animals must pass their heads, may be hinged to the wall, to be opened when the manger is filled. Low mangers have the additional advantage of being satisfactory for the feeding of corn stover and other coarse roughages.

Fig. 98. Close-up view of head gate. The chute leading to the head gate should be only 24 inches wide to prevent small animals from turning around. (*Courtesy Livestock Conservation, Inc., Chicago, Illinois.*)

Restraint Equipment. All livestock farms where many beef cattle are kept should possess some kind of restraint equipment by which animals may be secured while being dehorned, tested for tuberculosis, given medicines, or subjected to minor surgical operations. The lack of such equipment usually occasions a great deal of labor in catching and throwing the animal to be treated, and often results in making it wild and nervous from the rough handling it has received.

The most common kind of restraint equipment is the dehorning chute, such as is shown in Fig. 98. The "pinch gate" and the "squeeze gate" are built on essentially the same plan as the chute, except that one side is hinged to permit a more thorough restraint of the animal than could be effected by the use of the stanchion alone. All such devices should combine ease of operation with strength of construction, inasmuch as it frequently is necessary, in confining an animal, to close and fasten a gate in the fraction of a second. Dehorning chutes and pinch gates should be built in connection with two or three small lots or corrals in which cattle can be held while being sorted and put through the chute.

Cattle Stocks. Cattle stocks, or bull stocks as they are often called, are essentially an item of equipment for the purebred herd. While their important features may be so combined with those of an ordinary de-horning chute as to make their use possible with unbroken cattle, the

FIG. 99. Cattle stock, showing bull in proper position for trimming the right front foot. The heavy canvas sling under the belly will prevent his lying down. (*Courtesy University of Illinois.*)

more common practice is to build them as a separate or detached unit into which cattle must be led rather than driven. This fact alone would limit their use to animals that are rather easily handled.

The characteristic features of cattle stocks are: (1) rollers on either side at a height of about 4 feet above the floor, made of 5-inch cedar posts or 4-inch steel pipe, for supporting a canvas sling that is placed under the animal to prevent its lying down while in the stocks; and (2) wooden sills, 6 by 8 inches, that extend along either side at a height of 15 inches from the floor, on which the feet may be rested and tied while undergoing treatment. Cattle stocks are exceedingly useful for the restraint of animals during the performance of such minor operations as the ringing of bulls, the removal of ties, the surgical treatment of lump jaw, and the trimming of feet. Figure 99 shows an animal secured in the stocks with a foot in position for trimming. The adjustment of the canvas surcingle is such that a part of the weight of the body is taken off the legs, making it practically impossible for the animal to throw itself or lie down.

Breeding Crates. As stated on page 100, breeding crates are useful in safeguarding the breeding of young heifers to old, heavy bulls. A very satisfactory type of breeding crate is shown in Fig. 100. The rear portion of each side of the stall is surmounted by a 2- by 12-inch plank, across the face of which are nailed cleats to prevent the front feet of the

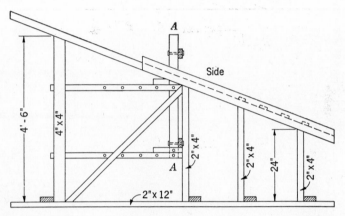

Fig. 100. Diagram of a breeding crate, showing details of construction. (*Courtesy University of Illinois.*)

bull from slipping. The gate or stanchion labeled *A* in the diagram is adjustable to accommodate cows varying in height and length of body.

Dipping Vats. Dipping vats are useful in ridding cattle of lice and other parasites and diseases that affect the skin. They are not common in the Corn Belt, and are, as a rule, found only in connection with extensive feeding plants where large numbers of cattle are handled. Inasmuch as the erection of a modern dipping vat entails considerable expense, one might very properly be built as a community enterprise to serve an entire school district or township. This was the plan commonly followed in the South, when dipping to eradicate the Texas fever tick was for many years compulsory. Power sprayers have largely supplanted dipping vats for the control of lice and flies. Usually, on Corn Belt farms, the same sprayer is used for spraying cattle, disinfecting buildings, spraying the farm orchard, and killing obnoxious weeds.

Loading Chutes. A well-designed loading chute is a necessary item of equipment on every beef cattle farm. Stationary chutes should be located in reference to both roads and holding pens in order that they will be accessible to heavy trucks during rainy weather and in order that cattle may be quickly loaded and unloaded after the truck has been set. Tests carried out at the Union Stock Yards, Chicago, Illinois, indicate that livestock prefer low stair-step risers to a cleated ramp. Whether the advantages of such a chute are sufficient to justify the extra materials and labor required may well be questioned by the farmer who handles only a car or two of cattle a year.

FIG. 101. Excellent equipment for sorting, loading, and dehorning cattle. Note head gate beyond loading chute. (*Courtesy Livestock Conservation, Inc., Chicago, Illinois.*)

A portable loading chute which may be towed behind a truck is often useful in loading or unloading cattle at a distance from the farm-stead where the stationary chute is built. A sketch of a portable truck with a stair-step ramp is shown in Fig. 102.

Labor-Saving Equipment. The shortage of labor on livestock farms has caused a wide interest in labor-saving devices which will shorten the time and lighten the labor required to care for the animals. Such equipment consists of (1) blowers and conveyors for moving feed, (2) storage of feed and stabling arrangements for animals that will require as little movement of the feed as possible, and (3) equipment for cleaning the sheds and yards. Equipment of the first class is fairly expensive and, consequently, is better suited for the large feeder who handles 100 or more cattle than for the farmer who feeds but a car-load. On the other hand, the small feeder will usually be able to store his feeds nearer the cattle than the large operator will. Often by remodeling his barns and carefully planning the location of his grain bins and silo, the small feeder is able to feed and care for his cattle entirely under cover and with a minimum of hand labor.

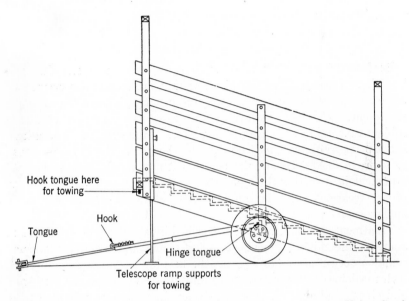

FIG. 102. A portable step-ramp loading chute developed by the Union Stock Yards and Transit Company. (*Courtesy Livestock Conservation, Inc., Chicago, Illinois.*)

Cleaning cattle sheds and lots and hauling and spreading the manure have always been regarded as among the hardest and most disagreeable jobs on the farm. In all probability they have caused many good farm boys to become grain farmers or even leave the farm entirely instead of following in the steps of their cattle-feeding fathers. However, the presence of tractors with hydraulic manure loaders on practically every farm has now eliminated most of the hand labor formerly required in cleaning sheds and feed yards on livestock farms.

Beef cattle are subject to comparatively few serious disorders and infectious diseases. The few ailments that are of common occurrence are for the most part minor troubles and usually yield readily to simple treatment. There are, however, a few diseases to which beef cattle are subject that are of a dangerous character. Moreover, minor ailments, if not properly treated, may quickly develop into serious disorders that may prove fatal. Hence, the beef cattleman should seek to become proficient in detecting the symptoms of the common diseases, so that proper treatment may be administered before the disease has made much progress.

Treatment should usually be prescribed by a competent veterinarian. Some of the minor ailments, such as scours and bloat, are of such common occurrence as to warrant the keeping on hand of a supply of such medicines as the veterinarian may prescribe, which the herdsman himself may administer. Cattlemen, for the most part, rely altogether too much on home-made remedies and "quack" prescriptions, which are likely to do more harm than good. Even in the case of a disease that has little likelihood of causing death, the expense of calling in a veterinarian is usually justified by a much more rapid recovery of the animal than otherwise would occur.

DISEASES COMMON TO BEEF CATTLE

Anaplasmosis. Anaplasmosis is a serious blood disease of cattle which has not yet been encountered in many sections of the United States. However, it is now believed that the disease has been present in the southern states for many years but was not distinguished from Texas fever until that disease had been definitely eradicated. It resembles Texas fever in that it is caused by a blood parasite which is carried from animal to animal by ticks. However, whereas Texas fever is transmitted by only one species of tick, the parasite that causes anaplasmosis may be transmitted by more than a dozen species. This makes the control and eradication of the disease very difficult. While the disease has been encountered in nearly all the southern states, the few outbreaks that have occurred in the North have been confined principally to shipped-in cattle which presumably were infected when purchased.

The disease is especially severe in mature cattle, among which death may claim from 30 to 50 per cent of the animals infected. Calves and yearlings seldom are visibly affected, or else they have the disease in mild form and make a complete recovery. Animals that have the disease and recover, regardless of age, are immune to future infection but usually remain carriers of the disease throughout life, and when introduced into clean herds they are a source of infection for other cattle.

The symptoms of the disease may be either chronic or acute. In the acute form the first symptom noted is a high temperature of 103° to 107° F. After 2 or 3 days the temperature falls to normal, breathing becomes difficult, and the mucous membranes are pale and yellowish and the muzzle dry. Urination is frequent, but the urine seldom is bloody. The patient usually is constipated, and either blood or mucous or both are voided with the feces. In the acute form of the disease death usually occurs in 1 to 5 days after the first symptoms are observed. In the chronic form the infected animals live longer and a greater percentage recover. Recovery of mature animals is usually very slow.

No specific treatment for the cure of anaplasmosis has been perfected; consequently treatment varies widely among veterinarians. Good nursing and care, of course, are vital to recovery. A test has been proposed to detect cattle that are carriers of the disease as well as to determine whether sick animals are in reality suffering from anaplasmosis. If the test proves to be satisfactory, an important step will have been taken in the control of this disease.

Anthrax. Anthrax, also called charbon and splenic fever, is a highly infectious disease and is extremely fatal. Not only is it transmissible from one animal to another, but it may spread rapidly to all species of livestock, and even to man. It is one of the worst scourges of animal life. This disease has existed among European cattle since the early part of the seventeenth century and has caused enormous losses. Its presence in the United States is, in general, confined to certain local areas of rather low, moist land of a more or less mucky character. In such soil the spores of anthrax remain potent for years although no animals whatever graze thereon. Hay grown upon such land may carry the germs of the disease far and wide. The importation of hides has been responsible for outbreaks of anthrax among the cattle in the vicinity of tanneries.

Death from anthrax is very sudden, the finding of a dead animal commonly being the first sign of the presence of the disease. In all cases of sudden death not preceded by symptoms of illness, anthrax should be suspected and the carcass handled with extreme caution until the death can be attributed to some other cause. The characteristic lesions in an animal dead from anthrax are (1) a tarry consistency of the blood, which is of a blackish color and fails to clot firmly, and (2) an enlargement of the spleen to two to five times its normal size. A positive diagnosis, however, can be made only by examining a sample of the blood under a microscope for the presence of the specific bacillus. Where anthrax is suspected, a veterinarian should be called without delay. Burning or deeply burying the carcass of the dead animal, and the prompt vaccination of all other animals of the herd with anti-anthrax serum, constitute the best known methods of preventing the spread of the disease. Animals showing high temperatures should be separated from the others and given serum alone, while others in the herd may be given the simultaneous treatment, consisting of serum and spore vaccine. Those receiving only the serum should be revaccinated after several weeks with both serum and vaccine.

Blackleg. Blackleg is an acute, infectious disease, attacking principally cattle between 6 and 24 months of age. It is characterized by marked lameness and pronounced swellings over the shoulders and thighs, due to the formation of gas in the subcutaneous tissues. When pressure is applied to these swellings, a peculiar crackling sound is heard, which is the characteristic symptom of blackleg. The disease runs a rapid course and almost always terminates fatally in 12 to 36 hours. Like anthrax, it is more or less restricted to certain regions and even to individual fields where the soil is infected with the spores of the disease and where outbreaks commonly occur annually unless prevented by vaccination. Blackleg is of common occurrence in the western half of the United States, but is especially prevalent throughout the Southwest and on the eastern slopes of the Rocky Mountains. Outbreaks have been reported in practically all the Corn Belt states, but in this section the disease is confined to certain areas.

Prevention rather than treatment is the practical method of combatting the disease. All young cattle brought into a region known to be infected with blackleg should be immediately vaccinated with blackleg aggressin, filtrate, or bacterin. The bacterin is made by treating cultures of the blackleg organism with formalin to destroy their poisonous properties but not their antigenic value. It is produced more cheaply than the aggressin or filtrate and is believed to confer a more certain and lasting immunity. Consequently it has largely replaced these immunizing agents in the control of the disease.

Calves born in a region in which blackleg has occurred even infrequently during the past 10 years should be vaccinated with blackleg bacterin at approximately 6 months of age. Usually vaccination is performed when the calves are weaned. If the disease has been more

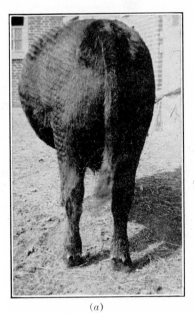

(a)

(b)

FIG. 103. (a) A badly bloated steer. (b) Trocar and cannula for tapping dangerously bloated animals. (*Courtesy O. M. Franklin Serum Company, Denver, Colorado.*)

or less prevalent in the region, vaccination should be performed at 3 to 4 months of age. Vaccination is usually done on the range at the time the calves are castrated and branded.

Bloat. Bloat is caused by the production of an excessive amount of gas in the paunch, brought about by some digestive disorder. The immediate cause is often the eating of a large quantity of easily fermentable feed, such as fresh clover, alfalfa pasture, green corn, or even alfalfa or clover hay. If legume crops are pastured when wet with dew or rain, bloat is especially likely to occur.

Many theories have been advanced to explain why the animal does not get rid of the gas by belching, as is done with the gas formed by the fermentation of ordinary feeds in the paunch. One of the most plausible explanations is that given by Professor Cole of the University of California, who believes that bloat is caused by "the lack of sufficient irritating or scratchy material in the rumen to induce the reflex act of belching."[1]   The fact that cattle in grazing legume forage eat only the tender tips of the plants, which contain little fiber, lends much credence to this point of view.   This theory also helps to explain why the feeding of ground ear corn, straw, and other dry roughages lessens the incidence of bloat in cattle on legume pasture.   However, it does not explain why cattle sometimes bloat seriously when fed alfalfa hay in the dry lot.

The presence of bloat is easily recognized by a pronounced swelling of the left flank.   So long as the distention causes the animal no great discomfort, no alarm need be left, as recovery will usually occur without treatment.   However, the bloated animal should be kept under observation, as occasionally the condition becomes worse very rapidly.   Treatment consists in administering medicines that will arrest the formation of more gas in the paunch and provoke the belching up of that already there.   One pint of mineral oil or 2 ounces of aromatic spirits of ammonia or 2 ounces of turpentine diluted with a pint of cold water will often bring about relief.   Oftentimes, good results may be obtained by tying a stick in the mouth in the form of a bit or gag, to cause the animal to champ its jaws and belch up the gas.

Should the formation of gas proceed despite the medicines administered, it will be necessary to tap the paunch to permit the gas to escape. The paunch is tapped by means of a trocar, which is a sharp-pointed instrument encased in a sheath called the cannula.   The point of the trocar is placed at a spot equidistant from the last rib, the hip bone, and the transverse processes of the lumbar vertebræ, and the handle struck sharply with the palm of the hand in the direction of the right knee of the animal.   Then, while the cannula is kept in place, the trocar is withdrawn and the gas permitted to escape slowly.

Probably the most desirable way of relieving acute bloat is to permit the escape of the gas through a 6-foot piece of smooth ½- or ⅝-inch rubber hose, one end of which is inserted far back in the mouth and carefully pushed down the throat and into the paunch.   With a little practice no difficulty should be encountered in getting the end of the hose over the trachea and into the œsophagus.

Upon recovering from a bad case of bloat, an animal should be given a good purgative, such as 1½ to 2 pounds of Epsom salts dissolved in a half gallon of water.   Moreover, the feed should be materially reduced for 3 or 4 days.

[1] Journal of Animal Science, November, 1943.

Cancer Eye. Cancer eye or epitheomia is a malignant tumor on the eyeball or eyelid of cattle. The disease is found principally on the ranges of the Southwest, where intense sunlight and irritating dust are believed to be at least indirect causes of the malady. Hereford cattle are much more susceptible to eye trouble than Shorthorns; Angus appear to be wholly immune. Apparently the lack of pigment in the eyelid and eyelashes to shield the eye from intense sunlight contributes to the prevalence of the disease. For that reason Hereford cows with a fringe of red hairs around their eyes are highly regarded by many ranchers of the Southwest.

In all probability cancer eye results from an injury to the eye which from lack of treatment develops into a badly infected sore. Usually by the time it is observed it has affected the eyeball or the eyelids to such an extent that treatment, other than surgical, is of little avail. At any rate, if the cow or bull is of considerable value, it should be treated by a veterinarian. If not, it should be sold for beef.

Contagious Abortion. Abortion of the infectious type is one of the worst diseases with which cattle breeders have to contend. It is caused, as a rule, by a specific organism known as the *Bacillus abortus* Bang,[2] though other uterine infections of a more general character may likewise bring about a number of abortions in a herd of cows.[3] Apparently, infection, especially in the case of the Bang organism, gains access to a new victim through the mouth, having been scattered in the uterine discharge of an aborting animal over grass, hay, and other feed materials. Hence, all aborting cows should be segregated from the herd, and kept in quarantine until at least 3 weeks after all uterine discharge has ceased. Their return to the herd at this time does not signify that they are free from the disease, but only that there is little possibility of their communicating it to other animals until the time of their next delivery. Some authorities hold that an infected cow never rids herself of the organisms, though she herself may eventually become sufficiently immune to make possible her calving at the normal time. Bulls, as well as cows, may contract the disease, but here, too, the avenue of infection is thought to be through the digestive tract. The prudent breeder, however, will refrain from mating a bull that he knows is clean with cows that are suspected aborters.

Two tests for contagious abortion are now recognized by most state and federal health authorities, viz., the *agglutination* test and the *plate* test. Both consist in subjecting a small sample of blood drawn from the jugular vein to a definite laboratory procedure and observing

[2] The name now assigned to this organism is *Brucella abortus*.
[3] *Cf.* pp. 625–626.

the reaction. In the agglutination test various dilutions of the blood serum are mixed in small test tubes with specially prepared cultures of the *Brucella* bacillus, and the mixture is allowed to stand for **24** to **48** hours. If the animal is "negative," the bacteria remain in suspension, keeping the solution cloudy, but if it is "positive," the bacteria are precipitated to the bottom of the tube, leaving the fluid above them perfectly clear.

FIG. 104. Collecting blood samples for a Bang's test. A pinch or squeeze gate is very useful in restraining the cattle while the blood samples are drawn.

The plate test consists in putting 0.08, 0.04, 0.02, and 0.01 cubic centimeter of undiluted blood serum in separate squares marked off on a glass plate and treating each of them immediately with one droplet of a concentrated solution of *Brucella abortus* stained with a violet-green dye to permit the test to be more easily read. Positive "reactors" are identified by a flocculating of the bacteria into groups, leaving the liquid between the groups more or less clear, whereas in negatives the entire area covered by the drop of serum remains uniformly cloudy. A modification of the plate test, in which whole blood instead of serum is used, is sometimes employed to permit the culling of reactors while they are still in the squeeze gate or sorting chute. However, the presence of the blood cells reduces the accuracy of reading to a considerable extent.

Each state of the Union has its own laws and regulations for the control of Bang's disease. One method of control widely employed in herds known to be mildly infected is the vaccination of calves at 4 to 8 months of age with attenuated cultures of special strains of *Brucella* bacilli, such as strain No. 19, developed in the laboratories of the Bureau of Animal Industry. Vaccinated calves usually react positively to the blood test for 3 to 5 months, after which period they "clear up" and are negative. Whether they may spread the disease during the clearing-up period and the degree of permanence of their immunity are disputed points among veterinarians. It is for this reason that in most states calfhood vaccination is not recommended for "accredited herds."[4]

Dwarf Calves. The occasional appearance of dwarf or "midget" calves in some families or blood-lines of cattle has been observed by both beef and dairy breeders for many years. However, only recently have such calves occurred in sufficient numbers of purebred herds to awaken breeders and breed associations to a realization of the enormous loss which such calves threaten to cause the beef cattle industry. Since a high percentage of such calves die at birth or shortly thereafter and almost none attain sufficient size to be of value for slaughter, each dwarf calf causes the loss of considerable money income. Usually dwarfs are destroyed as soon as their condition is definitely established. This may not be for 4 or 5 weeks, since dwarf calves when born often appear to be nearly perfect specimens from the standpoint of shape of head and body, especially to the breeder who has had no previous experience with them. However, they soon show the sharply dished face, undershot jaw, extremely paunchy belly, and incoordinated gait which are characteristic of typical dwarf calves. Being weak at birth, they have little resistance to infections and other maladies, which normal calves easily ward off. Particularly are they susceptible to respiratory disorders which render breathing difficult and which frequently terminate in death from pneumonia.

Dwarfism is now believed to be due to imperfect development or improper functioning of the endocrine system, probably chiefly the pituitary and thyroid glands. The condition is believed to be inherited as a simple recessive character; consequently, its occurrence follows the well-known pattern described by Mendel's law.[5] In other words, the birth of a dwarf calf is proof that the factor for dwarfism is present in the germ plasm of both the sire and the dam. Both of them, of course, should be eliminated from the herd. However, not all their

[4] An *accredited herd* is one that is tested annually by a state or federal veterinarian and in which no reactors have been found for at least 2 years.

[5] J. L. Lush and L. N. Hazel. The Inheritance of Dwarfism, *Amer. Hereford Journal*, March 1, 1952, pp. 32–34.

(a)

(b)

FIG. 105. Dwarf calves which show the sharply dished face and paunchy belly characteristic of thyrotropic hormone-deficient dwarfs. (a) Angus dwarf, 11 months of age. (*Courtesy P. W. Gregory, California Experiment Station.*) (b) Hereford dwarf and normal calf, both 10 months of age. (*Courtesy Illinois Experiment Station.*)

offspring need be sold, for only a part of them will carry the factor for dwarfism and some will be entirely free of it, according to the operation of Mendel's law.

For example, a bull or cow which carries the dwarf factor will transmit it to only half of his or her calves, none of which will be dwarfs, if the other parent does not carry it. However, the offspring which do inherit the factor from one parent will in turn transmit it to half of their calves, and thus the character will continue to be in the herd in latent form generation after generation. Dwarf calves will appear in disturbing numbers when a bull carrying the factor is used in a herd in which a high percentage of the cows also carry it, for if both parents carry the factor, 25 per cent of the offspring will inherit it from both parents and will therefore be dwarfs. Fifty per cent of the offspring will inherit it from only one parent and, hence, will be normal in appearance but will transmit the factor to half their offspring. The remaining 25 per cent of the offspring of a bull and cows, all of which carry the factor, will be wholly free from dwarfism both in respect to appearance and in their germ plasm; consequently, they can never transmit it to their descendants.

These facts make the elimination of dwarfism from a herd in which it has become established a long and expensive procedure. However, to retain in the breeding herd animals, especially bulls, that have demonstrated that they carry the dwarf factor will result in a high percentage of the heifers retained in the herd being carriers, and the unwitting use of a carrier bull will result in the birth of a considerable number of dwarf calves. Theoretically, if half the cows are carriers, 12.5 per cent of the calves they produce by a carrier bull will be dwarfs. In practice the incidence of dwarf calves, even in unselected herds, seldom approaches this figure, because cows which have produced one or more of such calves are culled more rigorously than cows with normal offspring.

Foot-and-Mouth Disease. Foot-and-mouth disease is not prevalent in either the United States or Canada. It has gained access to the United States on nine different occasions since 1870, but in each instance it has been promptly stamped out by the slaughter of all infected and exposed animals. The wisdom of such measures is amply justified when one considers the terrible handicap imposed by this plague upon the livestock industry of the countries of Europe and South America where the disease is ever present.

The disease was introduced into Mexico in 1947 by the smuggling of a shipment of Brahman bulls into the country from Brazil, and only through heroic efforts and the expenditure of more than $100 million by the Mexican and American governments working cooperatively was the disease brought under control.   At first an attempt was made to eradicate the disease by the slaughter of all infected and exposed animals.   However, it soon was apparent that this plan was impractical; consequently a program of vaccination and rigid quarantine and inspection was inaugurated.   This method of control has given excellent results, and it now appears that the disease may be entirely eradicated from that country.

Foot-and-mouth disease is seldom fatal, but it causes enormous losses through the loss of flesh suffered during the time the mouths of the animals are so sore that they practically refuse to eat.   Recovery is very slow, and many of the animals are hopelessly ruined from the standpoint of the feed lot.

Foot-and-mouth disease is sometimes suspected in connection with an outbreak of mycotic stomatitis.   The most characteristic differences are that the latter disease affects at most no more than 50 per cent of the herd, and that it is not communicated to either sheep or hogs.[6]

Foul Foot.   Foul foot is most likely to be encountered in calves and show cattle that are shut up in dirty stables during the summer.   Occasionally, cinders or stones may become lodged between the toes of the feet in such a way as to set up inflammation of the skin in the interdigital spaces.   Inasmuch as this part of the foot is very sensitive, severe lameness results.   If prompt attention is not given, the inflammation and swelling may extend well above the hoof and around to the heel.

Treatment consists in cleaning the foot thoroughly and applying a strong antiseptic that will destroy the causative organisms (bacilli necrophorus),[7] which have gained access through the skin.   In mild cases undiluted creolin or iodine will suffice, but if the infection is well advanced a 20 per cent solution of blue vitriol or potassium permanganate is to be preferred.   Bandaging the foot and keeping the bandage well saturated with one or the other of these solutions will usually effect a cure within 3 or 4 days.   Intravenous injections of sodium sulfapyradine are recommended for unbroken cattle that cannot easily be handled.

Foot rot can be largely prevented by keeping the feet properly trimmed and by turning the cattle into dew-laden pastures at night throughout the summer and fall.   A shallow box containing air-slaked lime, through which the animals must walk as they enter and leave the barn, is also an effective method of preventing the disease.

[6] Mycotic stomatitis is caused by a fungus on pasture plants, usually clovers.

[7] The name now assigned to this organism is *Actinomyces necrophorus*.

Founder or Laminitis. Founder or laminitis in beef cattle is usually the result of overeating. Its most frequent occurrence is among steers which are put on a full feed of grain too quickly to allow them to become accustomed gradually to their new ration. The intake of absorbable nutrients is much greater than can be utilized by the body, necessitating the oxidation of the surplus in the tissues. In the destruction of this excess amount of nutrients much heat is produced. Also, the amount of blood and its rate of circulation are considerably increased in the effort of the blood to dispose of the heavy load of nutrients received from the lymphatic system as quickly as possible. As a result the capillaries, especially those near the surface of the body and in the extremities are gorged with blood nearly to the limit of their capacity. The capillaries of the feet, surrounded as they are by the inelastic hoofs, are unable to expand to an appreciable extent. Moreover, the animal after its heavy meal is prone to remain quiet for a considerable time, thereby depriving the feet of the alternate expansion and contraction of the foot structures which accompany movement and which are so essential to a vigorous circulation of the foot. Thus, there comes about a congestion of the blood vessels of the feet, followed by inflammation of the tissues which is manifested by severe lameness.

Treatment of badly foundered cattle is seldom satisfactory for the reason that, as a rule, it is not observed until the damage to the feet has been done. If it is detected in its early stages some relief may be had by applying cold packs to the feet or compelling the animal to stand in a pond or stream of cold water. Owing to the intense pain experienced by badly foundered animals in standing and walking, they spend a large amount of time lying down and go for feed and water only when driven by the pangs of hunger and thirst. As a result they frequently lose rather than gain in weight, especially if they were carrying considerable flesh when the attack occurred. Animals only mildly affected need occasion little concern, but those badly afflicted should be disposed of as soon as it is determined that their condition is chronic. If possible, they should be sold to a local butcher since they are likely to lie down and be trampled if shipped to a distant market. Moreover, such cattle do not command satisfactory prices at terminal markets because of their poor appearance.

Hemorrhagic Septicemia or "Shipping Fever." Hemorrhagic septicemia is a disease caused by bacilli of the same group to which the organisms of chicken cholera and swine plague belong. Veterinarians are inclined to believe that the infection is commonly harbored by cattle as well as by other classes of livestock, but that it produces little or no serious effects unless the vitality of the animals is seriously lowered by undue exposure, exhaustion, injury, or an insufficient allowance of feed.   Calves and thin yearlings are highly susceptible to this disease, especially after a long rail journey during which they have endured much exposure in open cars and experienced great irregularity in the routine of feeding, watering, and resting.   Because of its prevalence among cattle that have recently been shipped from central markets or the range to the Corn Belt for further feeding it is often referred to as "shipping fever."

Inasmuch as the disease is a septicemia, or poisoning of the blood, the entire body is more or less affected; hence, no specific symptoms by which the disease may be diagnosed definitely can be enumerated. The more common manifestations of this disease are a high body temperature, soft, doughy swellings beneath the skin of the throat and neck, extensive swellings of the tongue, and a mucous discharge from the nose and mouth.   A post-mortem examination usually reveals hemorrhages or blood spots of various sizes on the lungs, on the walls of the intestines, and in the fatty tissues surrounding the kidneys.   This disease is sometimes mistaken for blackleg or anthrax.   However, the absence of gas beneath the skin will serve to distinguish it from the former, while the normal condition of the spleen should prevent confusing it with the latter.

Since it appears that septicemia is brought about by an impaired condition of the animal, preventive measures rather than a specific cure should be practiced.   Hard driving; overcrowding in cars; insufficient bedding; irregularity in feeding and watering en route; insufficient time to eat, drink, and rest at unloading points; and improper handling and rations upon the completion of the journey should be avoided.   If the cattle arrive during cold weather, especially if it is wet and stormy, adequate shelter should be provided.   Sufficient time should be given the cattle to recover from their journey and become accustomed to their new surroundings before they are dehorned or subjected to detailed sorting and so forth.   The ration for the first few days should be of good quality, preferably a choice grade of mixed hay with perhaps a little silage after the third or fourth day.   During favorable weather the cattle may have the run of a rather short pasture.

Losses among cattle received for feeding purposes have been so large during some years that considerable study has been made to determine how the disease may be best controlled.   Vaccination with preventive bacterins and aggressins at central markets before shipment or immediately upon the receipt of the cattle at the farm is often practiced as a precautionary measure.   However, extensive investigations made by the United States Department of Agriculture indicate that the vaccination with aggressins, bacterins, and other immunizing agents while in transit or within a few days after arriving at the farm should be discouraged.   Unusually good success has been had in the treatment of sick animals by administering sulfa drugs and penicillin directly into the jugular vein.   In numerous instances calves with high temperatures and other symptoms of beginning pneumonia have appeared to be al-

Fig. 106. A case of shipping fever, showing characteristic attitude of weakness and dejection. (*Courtesy U.S.D.A.*)

most completely recovered within 24 to 48 hours after receiving this treatment.

Although the disease is seldom communicated by incoming animals to cattle already on the farm, a strict quarantine is advisable until it is fairly certain that no sickness is to be encountered.   If death losses are suffered, the carcasses and all bedding materials should be buried deeply or burned and the premises disinfected.

Impaction, Constipation, and Indigestion. Because of the large amount of coarse, dry roughage consumed by cattle, they are somewhat disposed to develop certain digestive disorders during the fall and winter months.   Impaction is the term applied to an abnormal accummulation of material in the paunch.   Constipation, on the other hand, implies a clogging of the large intestine with hard, dry feces.   Indigestion is a more general term, referring to both these conditions, as well as to other digestive disturbances.

The first symptoms of indigestion are usually a loss of appetite and a rise of body temperature. When such conditions are noted, an examination should be made of the bedding material for the amount and character of the recently voided feces. If they are scanty in amount or hard and dry, the patient should be given a strong purgative, such as 2 pounds of Epsom or Glaubers' salts dissolved in a half gallon of water. In the case of impaction, as much as 2 or 3 gallons of water should be given and the left side of the patient powerfully kneaded with the fist to bring about a breaking up and softening of the impacted mass. Constipation ordinarily calls for less drastic treatment. Drench-ing with 1½ pints of castor oil, 2 quarts of raw linseed oil, or 1½ to 2 pounds of Epsom salts will usually bring relief. For calves these doses should be reduced by approximately one-half.

Lumpy Jaw, or Actinomycosis. Lumpy jaw is a non-contagious disease caused by the entrance into the animal tissues of a fungus which attacks the tissues of the throat, the parotid salivary gland, and the bones of the upper and lower jaws. Its presence is indicated by a round swelling, usually quite hard and generally firmly adherent to the sur-rounding parts. The swelling gradually increases in size until it finally breaks open in the form of an abscess, which discharges thick, creamy pus and becomes filled with raw, easily bleeding tissue. If not properly treated, the fungus invades the interior of the jaw bones, causing a loosening of the teeth. Also, growths may be formed in the mouth and pharynx, of such a size as to interfere greatly with eating and breathing.

Not all swellings appearing in the region of the neck are necessarily due to lumpy jaw. A diagnosis can easily be made by examining a little of the abnormal growth beneath a microscope, where the fungus appears to be made up of club-shaped bodies, all radiating from the center of the mass to form a rosette. For this reason the fungus is often called "ray fungus."

Cattle affected with lumpy jaw should be separated from the rest of the herd, as there is danger of spreading the disease through the scatter-ing of the fungus on feed that other animals will consume. Animals of no more than market value should be promptly marketed where they will be slaughtered under proper inspection. Only in advanced cases of the disease are the carcasses likely to be condemned as unfit for food. Valuable breeding animals that are suspected of having lumpy jaw should be examined by a veterinarian and, if found diseased, should be placed under his care. The most satisfactory treatment consists in the complete removal of the growth by surgery. This is easily accom-plished where the growth is not too firmly adherent to the surrounding parts. In such a case, the growth may be cut open, the pus washed out, and the cavity packed with gauze saturated with tincture of iodine. If surgical aid is not available, or if the position of the growth is such as to render an operation extremely hazardous, the internal administration of potassium iodide over an extended period may bring about recovery. However, where surgical treatment is possible, it is much to be preferred.

Mad Itch. Mad itch or pseudo-rabies occurs sporadically throughout the Corn Belt among both cattle and hogs. There is some evidence to support the belief that "swine represent the natural reservoir of the disease and that cattle infections occur incidentally, probably through minor wounds of the skin which become contaminated with nasal secretions of swine which usually are not recognized to be sick."[8] It is not transmitted to man. The presence of the disease is manifest by an intense itching of the skin, which causes the animal to lick, rub, bite, and even chew certain areas of its body in a vain effort to gain relief. Frequently these areas are made raw and bloody by the constant licking and rubbing. The affection of the brain and nervous system is indicated by loud bellowing, aimless charging about the feed lot, and violent stamping of the feet. Usually the animal becomes exhausted and falls down within 24 hours, and is unable to rise because of paralysis. Death usually results within 48 hours from the time the first symptoms are observed.

The disease is believed to be caused by a filterable virus which has not yet been identified. Since the disease does not appear to be transmitted from one steer to another through contact, it is believed that it gains access to the body through small wounds and scratches. "No specific treatment is known and cattle rarely or never recover."[9]

Pink Eye. Pink eye is the term commonly applied to an infectious inflammation of the eye, technically called *infectious catarrhal conjunctivitis*. It is usually encountered only during the summer months, and is more prevalent in cattle on pasture than in those kept in dry lots. Frequently the disease will persist in a herd for several months, during which time nearly all animals will be affected in one or both eyes.

The disease is characterized by an intense inflammation of the mucous membrane of the eye and tears mixed with pus which flow down the side of the face. In its most aggravated form a large grayish yellow ulcer appears on the cornea, which renders the eye temporarily blind.

All animals in a herd in which pink eye is present should be examined carefully every day, and those which show symptoms of the disease

[8] Hagan, W. A., The Infectious Diseases of Domestic Animals, 2nd edition, 1951, p. 729, Comstock Publishing Associates, Ithaca, N. Y.
[9] Diseases of Cattle, U. S. D. A., 1942, p. 363.

should be segregated in a darkened barn and supplied with plenty of fresh water and succulent feed. Their eyes should be thoroughly cleaned of all dirt and pus by washing them with a boric acid solution made by dissolving 1 ounce of boric acid crystals in 2 quarts of boiling water. After the eyes have been thoroughly washed a thin coating of 5 per cent sulfathiazole eye ointment should be applied to the affected parts. This ointment comes in a metal tube and can be squeezed directly on and under the eyelids. Another excellent product for the treatment of pink eye is "Bacatracin," manufactured by Commercial Solvents Corporation. This material is a fine powder which can be "puffed" into the eye by squeezing the container. Mild cases should be treated daily, and those of more severity at least twice a day, until all discharges cease. Eyes on which ulcers have formed sometimes require treatment over several weeks before the return to normal condition.

Pneumonia. Pneumonia is one of the most common diseases affecting young cattle during the winter months. It is especially prevalent during cold, damp weather and among calves that are subjected to considerable exposure because of poor stabling facilities. The characteristic symptoms are a high temperature of 105° to 107° F.; quick, shallow breathing, with dilated nostrils; and a hard, pounding pulse. By applying the ear to the chest, the rasping sound made by the affected lung can be heard. The diseased lung can also be determined by observing on which side the animal habitually lies, remembering that the diseased lung is uppermost. In advanced cases and when both lungs are affected, the animal shows little disposition to lie down. Instead, it takes an unsteady position with head down and fore legs wide apart to make for as much ease in breathing as possible.

Treatment for pneumonia usually consists in the administration of sulfa drugs either alone or with penicillin. Whereas formerly a high percentage of pneumonia cases resulted in death, a large number are now saved by the judicious use of these wonder drugs. Obviously they must be prescribed by a veterinarian. Pending his arrival, the patient should be kept warm by covering with heavy blankets, or, if a young calf, by removal to a heated building. The animal should be kept as quiet as possible, as any exercise or excitement tends to aggravate the condition by increasing the pulse and the rate of respiration.

Scours, or Diarrhea. An abnormal looseness of the bowels is a common disorder among young calves kept under insanitary surroundings or fed improper rations. Calves ranging in age from a few days to 3 months are most likely to be affected, though older animals are by no means immune. The condition in reality is not a disease in itself, but is the result of a diseased condition of a portion of the digestive tract, because of which the food is improperly digested. Prompt treatment should be administered, as a calf affected with a bad case of scours derives little nourishment from the milk and feed eaten, and, hence, loses flesh rapidly, becoming weak and thin.

Most cases of scours are caused by the presence in the digestive tract of harmful bacteria which bring about the formation of toxic products. Hence, the first step in the treatment of scours is the administration of an internal antiseptic that will tend to destroy these harmful organisms. In conjunction with this treatment, a mild purgative should be given to rid the system of the objectionable toxins as soon as possible. Many biological supply houses now manufacture internal antiseptics that give very good results when used for scours. By administering them according to the directions on the printed label, along with 4 to 8 ounces of castor oil, depending upon the size of the calf, the trouble will usually be checked. In the absence of such a preparation, from $\frac{1}{2}$ to 1 teaspoonful of formalin, diluted with a pint of water, may be given. In order that these medicines may bring about the desired result as quickly as possible, the feed of the calf should be somewhat reduced for 3 or 4 days.

A particularly virulent form of scours, which is highly contagious among the calves of a herd, is indicated by grayish yellow or dirty white feces, having a highly offensive odor. Whenever such symptoms are observed, a veterinarian should be consulted immediately, as "white scours" is one of the most serious ailments affecting young calves. In diagnosing white scours, it should be kept in mind that this disease appears within 3 days after birth, whereas other diarrheas seldom develop before the calf is a week or 10 days old.

Tuberculosis. Tuberculosis is one of the most serious diseases affecting domestic cattle. It is caused by a specific organism which attacks all parts of the body, but particularly the glands of the lymphatic system. The glands of the neck, chest, and mesentery are most likely to be affected. In advanced cases the disease spreads to all parts of the body, forming huge masses of tubercles, which interfere greatly with the normal functions of the vital organs. The serious nature of this disease is disclosed by the fact that in 1918, of the 11,000,000 cattle slaughtered in federally inspected establishments, nearly 225,000 were found to be affected with tuberculosis, 40,500 of which were condemned as being unfit for food. Not only is the disease highly contagious from one cow to another, but it may be transmitted from cattle to hogs through the manure, and from cattle to man through the milk.

Indications of the presence of tuberculosis are seldom manifest in the live animal. In advanced cases, the hair becomes harsh and dry, and the animal shows a general run-down appearance. Such symptoms, however, may be brought about by a variety of diseases; hence, they cannot be regarded as conclusive.

The correct method of examining an animal for the presence of tuberculosis is by the so-called "tuberculin test." There are three authorized ways of administering the test, which, in the order of their popularity at the present time, are (1) the intradermal or skin test; (2) the subcutaneous or temperature test; and (3) the ophthalmic or eye test. All these are based on the principle that the introduction of the toxic products of tuberculous bacilli into a diseased animal will produce certain reactions, whereby the presence of the disease can be detected. The reaction to the first test consists in a noticeable swelling of the skin at the point of injection, most in evidence 72 hours later. In the second test, the reaction is a pronounced rise of body temperature lasting from about the eighth to the eighteenth hour after the injection. In the third, it is an inflamed and swollen condition around the eye followed by a yellowish discharge from the inner angle of the eye, in 3 to 10 hours after the application of the tuberculin. All these tests, to be authentic, must be performed by a licensed veterinarian.

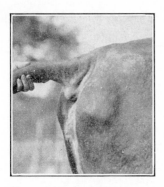

Fig. 107. A TB reactor. Note the swelling under the tail at the point where the interdermal test is made.

As no method of treating tubercular cattle has been devised, all animals reacting to the test are sold for slaughter. Since in most animals the disease has not progressed far enough to affect seriously the value of the carcass for meat, "reactors" should be shipped to markets where they may be slaughtered under federal inspection. The law forbids the sale to local butchers of animals that are known to be tubercular. Under a plan long in force, farmers must submit all their cattle to periodic tests, and must add no untested animals to their herds. The testing is done free of charge by a federal veterinarian. Any reactors that are found must be promptly disposed of after being appraised by a disinterested party. The difference between the appraised value and the amount for which they are sold at the market is shared equally by the owner, the federal government, and the state. However, in no case can the owner recover more than $100 indemnity for any grade animal or more than $200 for a purebred.

Since about 1920, an extensive campaign has been waged by the federal government for the ultimate eradication of tuberculosis from the farms of the country. The effectiveness of the program is evident from the fact that, whereas 9.25 per cent of all cattle tested in the United States from 1893 to 1908 reacted to the test, only 0.19 per cent of the 8,737,500 tested during 1949 were reactors. Nevertheless, the testing program is still being carried on in every county of the nation in the hope that the disease may be completely eradicated. Present plans require the testing of all herds within every county at least once every 3 years, and the immediate sale for slaughter of all reactors. All breeding cattle sold at auction or privately must be tested within 30 days of delivery and a health certificate furnished to the buyer.

Urinary Calculi. Considerable trouble sometimes results from the formation of stone-like mineral deposits in the bladder of male cattle, particularly of steers which are fattened on grain sorghum in the Southwest. The calculi cause no noticeable discomfort to the animal unless they enter or block the entrance to the uretha and prevent the normal discharge of urine. When this condition occurs the animal is extremely nervous, refuses to eat, lies down and gets up at frequent intervals, and shows other signs of acute distress. Should the bladder become ruptured, temporary relief may be obtained, but the peritonitis caused by the urine in the abdomen soon results in death. If the bladder does not rupture, death results from uremic poisoning brought about by the continued absorption of urine by the blood. The cause of urinary calculi is not known. There is some evidence that it is associated with mineral metabolism, since the feeding of bonemeal tends to reduce its occurrence. There is also some evidence that it may be induced by a deficiency of vitamin A. The fact that many steers fed threshed grain sorghum and unground sorghum heads at the Texas Station developed urinary calculi, whereas those fed ground yellow shelled corn had none, lends credence to this explanation of the disease.[10]

Since no effective treatment for urinary calculi has been worked out, feeders living in areas where it occurs should attempt to avoid it by paying close attention to the mineral and vitamin content of the ration and providing an adequate water supply. Frequent salting to induce the drinking of considerable water is recommended.

Warts. Warts are small skin tumors which frequently appear on young cattle, especially on the neck, shoulders, and head. They are more often encountered during the late winter and early spring, when the skin is in poor condition because of the low sterilizing effect of winter sunlight and perhaps faulty nutrition which lowers the natural resistance of young cattle. It has been demonstrated that warts are

[10] U. S. D. A. Technical Bulletin 945, 1947.

caused by a filterable virus which may be transmitted from one animal to another and possibly to other species, including man.

As a rule warts are a temporary condition which will eventually disappear. However, their disappearance can be hastened by the daily application of Vaseline or castor oil, which will favor their absorption. Their absorption can also be accelerated and their spread to other cattle

rendered less probable by the use of a vaccine consisting of finely ground fresh wart tissue suspended in a salt solution to which formalin has been added to destroy the virus. The feeding of Fowler's solution under the direction of a veterinarian is recommended as an indirect treatment to give tone to the skin.

POISONOUS MATERIALS AND PLANTS

Fig. 108.   A bad case of warts.

The sickness and loss of cattle resulting from the eating of poisonous plants and other harmful materials are not of frequent occurrence in the Corn Belt states. In this section of the country the number of plants that are poisonous to livestock is small compared with the number found in the range area. Also the feed supply is usually sufficient to cause animals to pass by poisonous plants, nearly all of which are quite unpalatable compared with good, wholesome forage. However, it occasionally happens, especially in early spring and during prolonged periods of dry weather, that pastures are so short and bare that cattle begin to eat any vegetation available, especially weeds and shrubs that are still green and succulent.

The majority of poisonous plants are found principally in moist, shaded regions, especially in the areas adjacent to ponds and streams. Hence, the forage of timbered and marshy pastures should be examined closely each year to see if perchance there are plants therein which are poisonous to livestock. If any are found, careful watch should be made to detect the first tendency of the cattle to eat them.

Treatment of animals that have eaten poisonous plants should be prescribed by a veterinarian. Remedies given by the mouth are often of little value in overcoming the toxic effect of poisons, owing to the huge volume of the digestive tract and the great mass of stomach and intestine contents that must be reached by the drugs administered. "Reliance must be mainly on prevention and upon such remedies as will increase elimination. A laxative or purgative is always helpful and for this purpose Epsom salts may be given in pound doses, or raw linseed oil in doses of 1 or 2 pints."[11]

Common Crowfoot. This is a common weedy wild flower of the buttercup family that is found in meadows and pastures. The juices of the plant are extremely acrid, and cattle as a rule will not eat it except in the early spring when first turned onto pasture. Several varieties of crowfoot are found in the Central states, nearly all of which are more or less poisonous in the green state but harmless after being cut and dried. The stems, which vary greatly in height according to species, are smooth, hollow, and very much branched. The flowers are small, with pale yellow petals surrounding a very prominent seed head.

Symptoms of crowfoot plant poisoning are gastral enteritis, diarrhea, with excretions of black, foul-smelling feces; together with nervous symptoms, such as difficult respiration, slow chewing of cud, and jerky movements of ears and lips which are sometimes followed by convulsions and death in a few hours.

Ergot. Poison from ergot occurs chiefly during the winter and spring, when considerable amounts of grain and cured roughages are being fed. On the plant ergot affects the seeds, which are hard, black, somewhat curved in shape, and several times larger than the natural seeds. Of the grains, rye is most likely to be affected, while bluegrass and redtop hays are highly susceptible to ergot.

Symptoms of ergotism in cattle are of two types, viz., the spasmodic and the gangrenous. In the former type there are muscular trembling, convulsions, and delirium. Abortion is often brought about by this form of ergot poisoning. In the gangrenous type of the disease there is a mummification and sloughing off of the extremities such as ears, tail, feet, etc., through a degeneration of the small arteries supplying blood to those parts. Treatment of animals showing marked symptoms of ergotism is of little avail. Destruction, except in the case of valuable breeding animals, is recommended.

Fern or Bracken. The common fern or bracken which grows in moist shaded spots in woods and along streams is often the cause of poisoning in cattle. The early symptoms are unsteady gait, loss of appetite, constipation, nervousness, and congestion of the eyes. These symptoms are followed by a spreading apart of the legs in an effort to maintain balance, extreme nervousness and a general loss of muscular control.

[11] Diseases of Cattle, U. S. D. A., revised edition, 1942. Free use has been made of this excellent book in describing the symptoms produced by the poisonous plants which are listed.

Jack-in-the-Pulpit or Indian Turnip. This is a plant of the arum family found growing in wooded areas. It is easily recognized by its peculiar purple-striped, vase-shaped flowers with large erect stamens and pistils. The poisonous nature of this plant has been observed only recently, and few data are available concerning the specific symptoms exhibited by cattle which have been poisoned from this source. However, there appear ample reasons for classifying it among the plants dangerous to cattle.

Nightshades; Henbane and Jimson. These weeds, which belong to the Solanaceae or nightshade family, are coarse, smooth-stemmed, ill-scented plants that inhabit neglected fields and waste places. They prefer a rich soil and are often found in old feed lots and in fields which have been heavily manured. Poisoning is most likely to occur when good grazing is scarce or when hungry feeder cattle are turned into infested lots upon their arrival at the farm.

The common symptoms of nightshade poisoning are unsteady gait, cramps, convulsions, and loss of consciousness. Respiration is difficult, and the pulse very rapid. Fortunately cattle seldom eat these weeds except when forced to do so by extreme hunger.

Water Hemlock. This is one of the most deadly of plants that may be eaten by cattle. The root is the harmful part, and losses are most severe during the early spring when the ground along streams is badly eroded by high water. Also, at this season the roots may be pulled up by cattle grazing the green tops of the plants. Symptoms of hemlock poisoning are intense nervousness, frothing at the mouth and nose, and violent convulsions. Death frequently occurs within an hour after the root of a single plant is eaten.

White Snakeroot. White snakeroot is a rather large coarse perennial weed which is found in many woodland pastures throughout the central states. It can be identified rather easily by its leaves, "which are opposite each other, from 3 to 5 inches long, broadly ovate, with sharply toothed, or serrated edges. Each leaf stalk has three main veins which extend from the base of the leaf and which give off many branches. These veins are prominent on the under surface. In the late summer the white flowers of the plant appear as compound clusters having 8 to 30 flowers."[12]

Poisoning from white snakeroot occurs usually during the late summer and autumn when pastures are dry and brown. Affected cattle show a peculiar trembling of the muscles, which accounts for the name "trembles," applied to the disease in certain localities. This trembling is most pronounced after exercise and tends to disappear following rest.

[12] Illinois Circular 295.

Constipation, general weakness, loss of weight, and incoordination of the voluntary muscles are associated with the disease.

Cows affected with snakeroot poisoning secrete the toxic principle of the plant in the milk. Hence, there is great danger that the disease

FIG. 109. White snakeroot (*Eupatorium urticæfolium*). (*Courtesy Illinois Experiment Station.*)

may be transmitted to human beings, calves, and other animals that are fed milk from cows running in pastures infested with snakeroot plants.

Sorghum Poisoning. Under certain conditions growing sorghum becomes a dangerous feed for cattle, owing to its high content of hydrocyanic acid. Severe drought and frost appear to promote the formation of this poisonous material in sorghums, especially in the second growth that springs up after the main crop has been cut and shocked or harvested for silage. Hence, the grazing of sorghum stubble should be done with extreme caution so that the first signs of illness will be detected and the animals removed from the field.   No trouble is had from feeding the harvested fodder or silage even in the case of frosted sorghum or sorghum badly fired from lack of moisture.

Corn-Stalk Disease.   Numerous losses have occurred among cattle pastured upon corn fields in the fall after the corn is husked.   Occasionally animals are discovered dead in the field, though more often they are found down in a more or less paralyzed condition.   When assisted to their feet, they walk with a staggering gait, indicating general weakness and a lack of coordination of the voluntary muscles.

The exact cause of this disease is a matter of controversy.   Formerly it was attributed to a specific bacteria occurring in the stalk of Indian corn.   Later it was regarded as merely a form of broncho-pneumonia contracted by cattle running in stalk fields during the chilly autumn days without adequate shelter.   More recently this disease has been regarded as a type of hemorrhagic septicemia.   This opinion is supported by the fact that the disease is usually observed only in undernourished cattle that are in a generally run-down condition.

Sweet Clover Poisoning.   Losses among cattle have been reported that apparently were caused by moldy sweet clover hay.   Efforts to extract the poisonous principle from such hay have been unsuccessful, but the poisonous nature of the hay has been clearly demonstrated by feeding it to experimental animals.   However, not all moldy hay produces the disease, and as yet no way has been discovered whereby hay that is dangerous may be detected by physical examination.   In a few instances trouble has been encountered in feeding hay that showed no outward sign of mold, but the experience of the majority of feeders indicates that clean, wholesome hay is a safe feed, at least in moderate amounts.   Even moldy hay that has caused death when fed alone has been fed with apparent safety when combined with other good wholesome feeds and when alternated with other hays or roughage for periods of 10 or 15 days.

The symptoms of sweet clover hay poisoning are general weakness and a loss in the clotting power of the blood.   Autopsy of dead animals reveal large internal hemorrhages as well as hemorrhages immediately beneath the skin.   Animals only mildly affected with the disease are in great danger of bleeding to death from injuries or from surgical operations such as dehorning or castration.   The opinion prevails among many cattlemen that even good sweet clover hay, as well as sweet clover pasture, decreases the power of the blood to coagulate, but this idea is not generally accepted.

Lead Poisoning. Cattle appear to have a liking for fresh paint, and numerous losses have occurred from their licking freshly painted buildings and fences. Instances have occurred where a single old paint bucket thrown on a rubbish pile has been responsible for the death of several valuable animals. Cattle have also been poisoned from eating silage from a silo that was filled before the paint on the inside walls was dry. The symptoms of lead poisoning are general dullness, convulsive movements of the limbs, champing of the jaws, and violent bellowing, followed by prolonged stupor and death.

PARASITES AFFECTING BEEF CATTLE

Flies. Two kinds of flies affecting cattle are common in the Corn Belt, viz., horn flies and stable flies. The horn fly is so called because of its habit of congregating about the base of the horn to rest. Both kinds of flies do great damage to cattle by sucking their blood, as well as by causing them much annoyance, thereby interfering with their feeding or grazing. Horn flies may be practically eliminated by spraying all cattle thoroughly with a fly control spray at the beginning of the grazing season and about once a month throughout the summer. Spray made from either the liquid or powder form of DDT is very effective against horn flies. Stable flies are much more difficult to control, as they appear to become resistant to many fly spray materials after a few years. This species of fly is most troublesome around barns and feed lots, where it breeds in wet straw, manure, spoiled feed, and other kinds of filth. Stable flies can be greatly reduced by frequently cleaning lots and sheds and by piling manure that cannot be plowed under at least a half mile from the barns. New materials for the control of flies are being tested constantly by experiment stations; consequently, inquiry should be made of farm advisers and livestock extension specialists annually to ascertain the best control material available.

Lice. Cattle are subject to three species of lice: the long- and the short-nosed blue sucking lice, and the red biting louse. Inasmuch as the biting lice feed principally on the particles of hair and dead skin, they are not especially troublesome. The sucking lice, however, cause the cattle much annoyance and, if numerous, sap large quantities of blood. Cattle infested with lice spend much time rubbing themselves against posts, trees, and so forth, in an effort to allay the intense itching. Frequently large patches of hair are worn off and the hide rendered hard and calloused.

Lice are most numerous during the late winter and spring. Cattle on pasture are seldom troubled with them. Treatment should be begun in the fall by dipping or thoroughly spraying all cattle with DDT, pyrenone, or some other insecticide that will remain on the hide and hair long enough to kill the lice that hatch out from the eggs.

Treating cattle against lice is extremely difficult during cold weather, inasmuch as spraying or dipping may cause colds and pneumonia. Temporary relief can be obtained by the application of raw linseed oil about the necks, shoulders, and rumps of the affected animals or by dusting the back and shoulders, but especially the areas around the eyes and anus, with 5 per cent wettable DDT powder.

Mange or Itch. Mange of cattle is caused by small mites which attack the skin, causing it to become thickened, covered with crusts, and devoid of hair. As a rule, the rump is the part of the body most likely to be affected, though the back and shoulders may also be included. In many respects mange of cattle resembles the disease known as "scab" in sheep, though it is by no means regarded as being so serious. Treatment consists in liberal applications of a solution of lime-sulfur or a nicotine dip. In mild cases where but a small portion of the body is affected, an ointment made of flowers of sulfur and lard will often effect a cure.

Ox Warbles. Ox warbles, or grubs, are a very serious cattle parasite in practically all countries of the northern hemisphere. It has long been present in every state of the United States, although in many localities it is of little economic importance. The degree of infestation appears to vary from year to year even in heavily infested areas, which leads to the belief that the population is affected by climatic conditions, particularly severe cold weather, while the insect is in the pupa stage, which is spent in the ground. The heaviest infestations are found in the Southwest, and it is possible that it is principally from feeder cattle from that region that most of the severe outbreaks of this parasite in the Corn Belt occur.

The adult fly, commonly known as the heel fly and somewhat resembling a small black bee, appears on the first hot days of summer, usually during the month of June. Immediately upon its arrival, it proceeds to deposit clusters of eggs on the skin of the host, fastening them to the hairs about the feet and legs, especially to those just above the heel. Although the flies can neither bite nor sting, cattle show a natural dread of them and will often run frantically from one end of the pasture to the other, holding their tails high in the air, attempting to escape. Yearlings are more likely to be attacked than calves, and calves more than adults. The insects will not fly over water, and cattle frequently protect themselves by retreating into ponds and streams.

Besides being greatly harassed by the adult flies, cattle experience much annoyance from the presence of the grubs under the skin along their backs. Moreover, the numerous holes greatly lessen the value of their hides, and the beef in the vicinity of the grubby lesions often is slimy and has a bad color. Such beef is commonly referred to as "licked beef." Altogether the total loss to the country occasioned by the warble fly is estimated at nearly $100,000,000 a year.

The larvæ, which hatch out in 4 to 6 days, immediately penetrate the skin at the base of the hairs to which they were attached. Thence

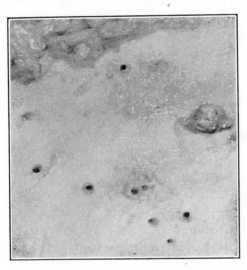

Fig. 110. A badly damaged hide caused by ox warble larvæ. Note encysted larva at right. (*Courtesy Livestock Conservation, Inc., Chicago, Illinois.*)

they proceed, by no well-defined route, to the region of the neck, where they gather about the œsophagus. Here they are found from October until about the first of February. As yet no plausible reason has been advanced for their congregating near the œsophagus. Formerly it was believed that the maggots gained entrance to the body of the host through the mouth and that they punctured the œsophagus on their way to the back. This theory is now disproved, and the presence of a few larvæ in the gullet is thought to be wholly accidental. During late winter, probably in February and March in the Corn Belt, the larvæ leave the region of the neck and migrate to the back, where they form the characteristic swellings beneath the skin. Here an orifice is made through the hide, toward which the larva directs its posterior end. In this position the larva increases rapidly in size. The pus and mucus caused by its presence constitute the food material from which this growth is effected. During this time at least two metamorphoses are known to occur by means of which the larva becomes larger and stouter. Finally, upon the arrival of spring, the grub, now fully grown, works its way through the hole in the skin and falls to the ground, where it pupates previous to its transformation into a mature fly. Pupation lasts from 4 to 6 weeks, the time decreasing as the season advances.

Protection against ox warbles consists in killing the grubs by introducing poisonous substances into the holes in the hide during the late winter months. If such treatment is postponed too long, the maggots will become so large as to cause serious ulcers if killed and not removed. In a small number of gentle cattle, which harbor only a few grubs each, the larvæ can be killed one at a time by removing the scabs over the openings in the hide and dusting the backs with 1 to 1.65 per cent rotenone powder, working the dust into the hide with the fingertips. Large grubs which are nearly full grown should be squeezed out and destroyed. However, the treatment of a large herd, especially of unbroken cattle, must be made by spraying with a power sprayer. Treatment should be begun about 25 days after the first bumps appear on the back and should be repeated at 30-day intervals. Rotenone, which is the trade name given to powdered derris root, is the recommended agent. Directions for diluting and applying the material should be obtained from the distributor.

Ringworm. Ringworm is a diseased condition of the skin caused by a fungus or vegetable parasite. It is mildly contagious and may spread from one animal to another unless properly treated. The disease is quite easily detected by the appearance of gray, crusty, circular patches about the head, shoulders, and neck, accompanied by a harsh, brittle condition of the hair surrounding the affected area. It is of rather frequent occurrence among young cattle during the winter and early spring. Treatment consists in removing all crusts from the affected parts by washing with soap and water, after which the areas should be treated frequently with tincture of iodine or sulfur ointment until the skin again becomes smooth.

Screw Worms. Screw worms are the maggots of the so-called greenish "blowfly" that is observed about dead animals and those suffering from neglected wounds during the summer months. Attracted by the odors of decaying flesh or decomposed blood, these flies deposit their eggs in cuts, wounds, and open sores, where they hatch within 2 or 3 days into the so-called screw-worm larvæ. These maggots burrow deep into the surrounding flesh, greatly aggravating the seriousness of the sore. Freshly cut horn stubs, castration wounds, and neglected injuries are especially likely places of attack.   However, screw worms are not especially troublesome in the Corn Belt.   It is in the South and Southwest that they cause the greatest injury.

Treatment for screw worms consists first in applying an antiseptic and fly repellent which will prevent the deposit of eggs in the wound. "EQ335," which was developed by the United States Department of Agriculture, is the preparation now recommended for this purpose. This remedy contains 3 parts lindane, 35 parts pine oil, 42 parts mineral oil, 10 parts emulsifier, and 10 parts of a silica gelatin.   When applied to wounds with a brush, it kills maggots deep in the wound, young maggots as they hatch from eggs, and flies attracted to the wound to feed and lay more eggs.   Wounds should be watched carefully and retreated at 7-day intervals until they are healed.[13]   The prevalence of screw-worm infestation may be reduced greatly by burning or burying deeply all carcasses of animals, as they are practically the only media in which breeding occurs.

Trichomoniasis.   Trichomoniasis is a venereal disease of cattle caused by an amoeba-like organism which infects the reproductive tract of both cows and bulls.   The disease may be diagnosed readily by a veterinarian from the presence of the flagellate organisms in vaginal or cervical smears examined under a low-power microscope.   The organism is more difficult to obtain from the sheath of the bull; consequently his infection is more readily confirmed by mating him with a virgin heifer and checking her uterine and cervical smears for the organism at her next heat period.

Infection of cows results in a mild inflammation of the vagina and uterus with an accompanying discharge which lowers the likelihood of conception, or which may cause abortion, especially during the second to fourth month of gestation.   Frequently, however, the dead, macerated fœtus remains in the uterus, which becomes filled with a thin, grayish white, almost odorless fluid.   When this condition occurs the cow seldom exhibits any symptoms of illness but behaves in a normal manner except that she fails to show the usual signs of approaching parturition.   Should abortion occur, she may come in heat in a few days, which fact is a basis for distinguishing this type of abortion from that caused by the brucellosis bacillus.

Bulls infected with trichomoniasis frequently show no visible signs of the disease, although usually there is a mild inflammation of the prepuce and penis during its early stages.   The disease is often transitory in cows, but it usually is chronic in bulls, which reinfect the cows

[13] American Meat Institute, Meaty News, May, 1951.

each time they are bred.   If infected bulls are sold for slaughter and breeding operations discontinued for at least 3 months, the disease usually will disappear from the herd.

Vibrionic Abortion.   This is an infectious type of abortion caused by a small, comma-shaped protozoan that attacks the capillaries of the maternal and fœtal placentæ, interfering with the nutrition of the fœtus, thereby causing its death and expulsion.   This type of abortion differs from brucellosis in that it tends to be more prevalent in older cows than in young cows and heifers and often causes abortions through three or four successive pregnancies in contrast with the immunity frequently acquired after one or two abortions from brucellosis. Another difference usually noted between the two diseases is that the fœtus is more or less decomposed when the abortion has been caused by vibrio organisms.   However, the only certain method of diagnosing the disease is to identify the vibrios under the microscope.   These usually can be found in cultures made from the liver, stomach contents, and heart blood of the aborted fœtus, but especially in cultures made from the kidneys.   The disease also may be diagnosed by an agglutination test similar to that for diagnosing brucellosis.

Vibrionic abortion of cattle is comparatively rare in the United States, having been reported in only a few areas.   It is, however, rather common in sheep and frequently is the cause of large numbers of dead lambs.   No effective treatment for the disease is known. Control measures, therefore, consist in the isolation of all suspected cows, pending the completion of microscopic and agglutination tests, and their sale for slaughter if the findings are positive.

35 ——————————————— Sterility

By Harry Hardenbrook Jr., D.V.M., M.S.,

Assistant Professor of Veterinary Clinical Medicine

University of Illinois

Sterility may be defined as the inability to produce sex cells with enough viability to effect fertilization and develop to the stage where a positive diagnosis of pregnancy may be made. Sterility may be designated as relative or absolute, temporary or permanent. Comparatively few bulls and cows are absolutely and permanently sterile. When such a condition is believed to exist, the animal is held to be valueless as a breeder and is sold for slaughter to save further expense. Most of the barren cows and infertile bulls encountered in beef herds are temporarily sterile and will regain their breeding abilities with appropriate treatment and good care and management.

Sterility in Cows. The temporary and relative form of sterility in cows may manifest itself merely by the failure of pregnancy to result from what appeared to be a normal service; or by the failure of the cow to come in heat at the usual age or at the normal period after calving. Often the condition will correct itself, after a time, without treatment but may recur after the termination of pregnancy. This is the form of sterility that is usually responsible for the so-called "irregular" breeding cows. Its incidence varies greatly from herd to herd and in the same herd from year to year. However, the economic loss which it produces in the form of late-born calves and abnormally small calf crops is enormous. Consequently, the constant observation of all breeding females to detect symptoms of breeding irregularities as soon as they occur and their immediate referral to experienced veterinarians for treatment are highly important.

Causes of Sterility in Cows. Breeding failures in cows usually are due to one or more of the following causes:

(a) Non-specific infections of the genital tract.
(b) Specific diseases, such as brucellosis, trichomoniasis, and vibriosis.

(c) Endocrine disturbances.

(d) Anatomical defects and abnormalities.

(e) Genetic and physiologic failures of a functional type.

Most veterinarians agree that the first cause listed is the one encountered most frequently. In the typical beef herd where the bull is known to be fertile, the most usual cause of sterility is some surgical infection of the cervix or uterus. It is estimated that approximately 50 per cent of all cases of temporary sterility in cows are due to infections of the uterus, and 25 per cent are the result of infections of the cervix. More rarely the Fallopian tubes or the vagina are involved in the pathological condition which develops as a result of a bacterial invasion of the tissues.

Observations made of the reproductive tracts of cows during the first 2 months after calving have disclosed that a certain amount of bacterial invasion of the cervix and uterus normally occurs during this period but that by 40 or 50 days after parturition the uterus has usually regained the healthy, non-pregnant state. The reinstitution of œstral cycles of normal length and duration is a reasonably reliable indication that the reproductive tract has returned to normal. A good general rule to follow is that cows should not be rebred within 50 days after calving, since bacteria are likely to be present in the reproductive tract at an earlier date and breeding may interfere with the normal healing processes and extend the period of infertility. On the other hand, if breeding is delayed for several months after calving, a decrease in fertility may be encountered, probably as a result of the impaired functioning of the accessory sex glands through disuse. In general, then, a reasonable period should elapse after calving before rebreeding is attempted, but the period should not be greater than necessary. Usually the more fertile herds are those in which the cows are bred on a schedule which will result in the spacing of calves by approximately 12 months.

Brucellosis, trichomoniasis, and vibriosis are three breeding diseases which should always be borne in mind when a considerable number of cows in the herd fail to conceive, especially if abortions have occurred recently. Specific tests for brucellosis and vibriosis can be performed on blood samples obtained from the suspected animals, and the presence of trichomonad organisms in the herd may be verified or ruled out by the microscopic examination of a semen sample obtained from the herd sire or by mating him with a virgin heifer and checking her cervical and uterine smears for the organism as she approaches her next heat period. Veterinary assistance and laboratory facilities are, of course, required for an accurate diagnosis of these diseases and an appraisal of the extent of infection. These diseases, if present, usually affect a considerable percentage of the cows and are seldom the direct cause of the occasional breeding failures encountered in beef herds.

Endocrine disturbances, such as are seen when cows fail to come in œstrum or when cows show evidence of nymphomania or almost constant œstrum, are not very common and are responsible for only about 10 per cent of all breeding failures. Often cases suspected of being caused by the malfunctioning of the endocrine glands are found upon examination to be due to infection. If infections have been ruled out, the judicious and careful use of appropriate hormones may restore the endocrine balance, which, in turn, will condition the reproductive system for œstrum, conception, and pregnancy.

A long list of genetic, physiologic, and anatomic causes are responsible for another 10 per cent of the breeding failures observed in beef cows. Sometimes the presence of an excessive amount of fat in the pelvic region may lead to partial protrusion of the vagina with eventual inflammation of that region. Usually such a cow breeds poorly and, if she becomes pregnant, is likely to develop an everted vagina or uterus at calving time. Some strains of beef cattle appear to have a genetic character which is reflected in the development and efficient functioning of only one ovary; or both ovaries may be abnormally small. Though this condition in a mild form is sometimes encountered, it usually does not lead to a complete inability to conceive but only a decrease in the efficiency of the cow as a breeder. Sometimes heifers will have a rudimentary hymen-like membrane in front of the cervix, which will prevent the complete elimination of the normal cervical and uterine secretions. These secretions are ideal media for the growth of local bacteria, the toxic products of which decrease the likelihood of conception. Although there are many causes of sterility which may result from genetic, physiologic, and anatomic abnormalities, the total number of cows so affected is small compared with those which are sterile as a result of bacterial invasion of the genital tract.

Treatment of Barren Cows. Information gleaned over the years indicates that the probability of restoring a barren cow to breeding condition and eventual pregnancy is sufficiently good to warrant the time and expense involved, if the cow is of outstanding value and cannot be replaced easily in the herd. When each sterile animal is diagnosed and treated on an individual basis by a qualified veterinarian, the short-term recovery rate for those cases where the infertility is of a temporary or relative nature is approximately 7 out of 10. Much better results, of course, are secured if treatment is begun as soon as breeding irregularities are noted than if action is delayed until the condition is of long standing. Usually the failure of a female to have a heat period before 18 months of age or within 4 months after calving or her failure to conceive after three matings is sufficient basis for suspecting that an abnormal condition exists and requesting a veterinarian to diagnose the condition and prescribe treatment.

When cows fail to come into œstrum, they should first be checked for pregnancy. Approximately 1 cow in 20 that are thought to be sterile will be found to be with calf. Frequently the sire of the calf will be a source of conjecture, since there is no record of the cow's having been bred.

Treatment for infections will, of course, depend upon their nature and the extent to which they have invaded the genital tract. Whether antiseptics, antibiotics, or other drugs are used locally, or whether hormone products are used systematically, will depend upon what is found when the individual animal is examined.

Occasionally a cow or heifer will be encountered which requires some stimulation of the endocrine system in order to bring about ovulation at the time most favorable for conception. Invariably the use of hormones should be preceded by a careful examination of the genital tract to check the possibility of a bacterial infection and by a rectal examination of the ovaries to determine their functional state. When only minor disturbances of the ovaries are found upon examination, the manual expression of the corpus luteum will frequently result in the occurrence of œstrum a few days later and make possible a successful mating. If neither infection of the genital tract nor any unusual condition is observed, the administration of hormones should be seriously considered. A wide variety of both natural and synthetic hormones is available to the practitioner, and the temptation is strong to administer a mixture of several in the hope that one of them will correct the trouble. However, a better plan is to administer the hormone believed most likely to produce the results desired. The stage of the œstral cycle should be taken into consideration in choosing the hormone preparation. If no corpus luteum is present, or if it has been expressed manually, an anterior pituitary derivative should be given to stimulate the development of the Graafican follicles. If, however, the corpus luteum is near its peak and is not to be disturbed, the hormone of choice would be a pituitary extract high in lutenizing ability to overstimulate temporarily the corpus luteum and thus, indirectly, hasten its disappearance. Thus, favorable conditions are brought about for follicular development and eventually œstrum and conception.

The effect produced by the administration of hormones is sometimes very prompt but in other instances is delayed for several days. If no response is obtained after a reasonable time, the hypothesis upon which the treatment was based should be carefully reviewed, and if it is still considered sound, the treatment should be continued, possibly with increased dosages, until the desired results are obtained or the futility of the treatment is demonstrated.

Sterility in Bulls. At times breeding failures will be so widespread in a herd that the bull will be suspected of being the major cause of the trouble. When the bull is considered to be the principal cause of breeding failures in the beef herd, the owner should have the act of breeding checked by his veterinarian. This requires that the examination be performed at a time when a cow in heat is available. Often a careful physical examination will reveal a broken penis, an hematoma, or an adhesion which must be corrected before a successful service can be performed. It is always wise to obtain a sample of semen to permit a laboratory examination of the number and condition of the sperms to be made.

Causes of Sterility in Bulls. The failure of a bull to settle his cows may be due to any one of several reasons, the more important of which are the following:

(a) Inadequate sex drive or insufficient *libido*.
(b) Abnormal production of spermatozoa, resulting in too few sperms, or in too high a percentage of defective sperm cells.
(c) Poor transportation of sperm cells from the testicles of the bull to the reproductive tract of the cow.
(d) Inability to breed the cow because of abnormal conformation or of a diseased condition of the hind legs and feet.
(e) The presence of bacteria in the semen as a result of an infection of some part of the reproductive tract.

Inadequate sex drive or desire may be due to a variety of causes. Sometimes it is due to the attempt to use a young bull on a cow too large for him to mount successfully. The result of his failure to copulate is the development of a mild sense of frustration. Frequently giving him assistance and trying him only on females selected for their small size and willingness to stand quietly will restore such a bull to a high state of breeding efficiency. It is possible that the apparent lack of sexual desire is due to an unwillingness of the bull to mount the cow because of the bad condition of his rear legs or feet. This possibility should always be considered in the case of old bulls which have become "slower" and "slower" over a period of several weeks. In other cases, a lack of *libido* may be due to a hormone deficiency, in which event the oral administration of synthetic thyroid is the usual treatment.

Treatment of Sterile Bulls. The checking of the semen for number, motility, form, and structure of the spermatozoa should be the first examination made of bulls which have been serving their cows satisfactorily but have gotten only a low percentage with calf. Frequently, evidence of testicular degeneration is disclosed by such examination, or perhaps evidence is found of failure of sperm production. Such failures are not uncommon in bulls which have been transported long distances by rail or truck or in overfat bulls which have been subjected to long periods of unusually hot weather. Treatment of sperm failures consists principally in good feeding, care, and moderate exercise to encourage nature to repair the damaged tissue. A series of hormone treatments with appropriate pituitary extracts is often of great value in stimulating the germ-producing cells and the cells which produce the male sex hormones. Breeding should be limited during treatment to a single service at monthly intervals to obtain a normal semen sample for laboratory examination.

The failure of transportation of the spermatozoa from the testicles to the genital tract of the cow may be due to an inflammatory condition in the vas deferens, the prostate gland, or the seminal vesicles, which results in the reflex inhibition of sperm discharge; or it may be due to defects of the penis, such as the adhesion of the glans to the prepuce; or the organ may have been injured or even broken during a previous copulation. If an adhesion exists, surgery is required; if an injury has occurred, appropriate treatment to reduce the swelling and promote healing of the tissues is recommended. If an inflammatory process is found which involves the seminal vesicles or prostate, the systematic use of the appropriate antibiotic or sulfa drugs may materially decrease the recovery time. Occasionally rectal massage of an infected prostate or seminal vesicle will aid the passage of the purulent exudate into the urethra and thus hasten recovery.

Inability to serve cows is often encountered in very short-legged, compact bulls, especially when they are in show condition and are somewhat awkward and clumsy. Usually the inability is temporary and may be corrected by reducing the ration and forcing the bull to exercise daily to get rid of his excess fat. Inability to serve also may be due to defects or infections of the feet, which make the bull unstable on his hind legs or which cause severe pain when he shifts much of his weight onto them when attempting service. Abnormalities of conformation, such as extreme paunchiness and bad sickle-hocks, may handicap a bull so badly that he frequently will not be able to serve cows which also are abnormal in respect to certain details of conformation.   In old bulls arthritis and rheumatism may so limit their activity as to render them almost useless.

The presence of bacteria in the semen of bulls will not only tend to decrease the viability of the sperm cells but may very easily infect the cows to which they are mated and thus prevent their conceiving even when they are bred to other bulls.   Consequently, bulls having bacteria in their semen should not be used until the infection has disappeared. Since the reproductive tract of the male can be examined more easily than that of the female, the seat of infection and the extent of damage suffered by the affected tissues can usually be determined by a careful physical examination.   Treatment, however, presents more of a problem.   Usually it consists in the parenteral injection of one of the sulfonamids or one of the antibiotics rather than the irrigation of the genital tract with antiseptics.   Response to such treatment may be rapid, but more often it is rather slow.   Consequently, a bull showing bacterial infection in his semen will not, as a rule, be available for breeding for several months.   If his fertility is not impaired and his use is desired, the collection of semen by means of an artificial vagina and its treatment with appropriate antibiotics to destroy the bacteria may pave the way for artificial insemination.   Though such a procedure can be followed with relative safety, it is not recommended for the average beef herd.

Index

Abortion, contagious, 601–03, 625–26
"Accredited" herds, 80, 603
Actinomycosis, 610–11
Afterbirth, expulsion of, 117–18
  removal of, 119–20
  retention of, 118–19
Age, at which to breed, 90–94
  correction for, in calves, 69–70
  culling for, 77–79
  effect upon investment, 235
    economy of gain, 230–31
    feed consumed, 232–33
    gain required to finish, 232
    hog gains, 235–36
    length of feeding period, 231–32
    quality of feeds fed, 233–34
    rate of gain, 228–29
    utilization of pasture, 234–35
  of breeding cattle, 75–79
    effect on weight of calves, 71
  of cattle to fatten for market, 236
Agglutination test, 601
Aims of the breeder, 52–54
Alfalfa hay, for fattening cattle, 366–69
  for stocker cattle, 195
  meal, 348–50
  vs. clover hay, 368–69
Allantois, 102–04
Alsike clover hay, 371
Amnion, 102–04
Anaplamosis, 596–97
Anthrax, 597–98
Antibiotics, 468–69
Areas of beef production, 10–17
Artificial insemination, 99–100
Auscultation of fœtal heart beats, 109
Atlas sorgo silage 197–98, 407–08

Baby beef, production of, 7–8, 509–26
  economics of, 509–12
Ballottement, 109
Barley, for breeding animals, 292
  for fattening cattle, 289–92
  for feeding show animals, 292
  grinding of, 290, 484–85
Bedding materials required by cattle, 34–35

Bedding materials required by cattle, water-holding capacity of, 36
Beef cattle cycle, 17–18
  production, areas of, 10–17
  in Corn Belt, 11–14
  in Cotton Belt, 16–17
  in Eastern and Lake states, 15
  in Western Range area, 11
  phases of, 3–10
Beet molasses, 300
Beet pulp, for fattening cattle, 298–300, 421–22
Blackleg, 598–99
Blackstrap, 300
Bloat, 599–600
Blood test for abortion, 601–02
Bluegrass, for breeding cattle, 129–32
  for fattening cattle, 431–33, 437
  for stocker cattle, 211–14, 449
Bran, wheat, for fattening cattle, 342–43
  for young calves, 125–26
Branding, 185
  horn, 187
Breed, selection of, 54–55
Breeding animals, cost of, 81–82
  selection of, 52–82
  effect on growth, 90
  methods of, 97–100
Breeding crate, 100, 593
Breeding herd, buildings and equipment for, 150–52
  summer management of, 127–48
  winter feeding of, 149–69
Breeding record, importance of, 62–65
Breeding season, 94–95
Breeding stocks, *see* Breeding crate
Brewer's grains, 344–45
Broad ligament, 84
Buildings and equipment, 26, 150–52, 584–95
Bulls, conditioning of, 172–73
  cost of, 81–82
  cost of maintaining, 549
  production testing of, 65–68
  progeny testing of, 68–69
  ratio of cows to, 101
  selection of, 62

Bulls, winter feeding and management of, 172–73, 210–11
Burdizzo pincers, 183–85

Calcium requirements of cattle, 463–64
Calf crop, factors affecting, 120–24
Calves, breeding and rearing of, 3–4, 512–13
  cost of raising, 549–52
  creep feeding of, 142–46, 513–17
  feeding, of home-bred, 512–13
    of western-bred, 517–19
  feeds for nursing, 124
  junior and senior, 96–97
  new-born, care of, 116–17
  preparation of feeds for, 522–23
  protein supplements for, 520–21
  separation from cows, 137
  spring vs. fall, 95–96
  summer care of, 142–46
  time required to finish, 522–26
  value of silage for, 521
  weaning of, 174
  winter care of, 170–72
Calving, in pasture, 136
  signs of, 112–13
Cancer eye, 601
Castration of calves, 181–84
Cattle, death losses of, 29, 559
  dual-purpose, 8–9
  effect on soil fertility, 30–42
  fattening for market, 217–27
    profits from, 562–65
  feed consumption of, 263–67
  getting on feed, 268–69
  labor requirements of, 26–29
  losses from shipment, 538–40
  marketing of, 527–45
  number per car and truck, 533–34
  percentage of corn consumed by, 25
  preparation for shipment, 530–31
  purebred, production of, 9–10
  relation to general farming, 19–29
  scrub, feeding of, 258–59
  shrinkage in transit, 534–38
  stocks, construction of, 592
  tick, 16
"Cattling down" corn, 474–75
Chaffing hay, 490–91
Chorion, 102–04
Chutes, dehorning, 591
  loading, 593–95
Clipping of show cattle, 578
Clover hay, 366
Commercial feeds, see Mixed feeds
Commission charges, 543–44

Concentrates, carbonaceous, 278–309
  for breeding cattle, 161–62
  for fattening cattle, 278–309
  for stocker cattle, 204–05
  protein, see Protein concentrates
Constipation, 609–10
Contagious abortion, 601–02
Contract feeding, 226–27
Cooking of feeds, 488–89
Cooperative shipping associations, 527
Cord, umbilical, 104–05
Corn cobs, for breeding cattle, 159
  for fattening cattle, 380–83
  for stocker cattle, 201–04
Corn, ear, 477
  fodder for beef cows, 153–56
  for breeding cattle, 287
  for fattening cattle, 278–287
  ground, 478–84
  new vs. old, 280–82
  preparation of, 474–84
  shelled, 477–78
  shock, 475–76
  silage, see Silage
  snapped, 476–77
  variety, importance of, 285–86
Corpus luteum, 85–86
Cost, of beef production, 547–59
  of breeding animals, 81–82
  of fattening cattle, 552–60
  of keeping beef bulls, 549
  of keeping beef cows, 547–49
  of producing calves, 549–52
  of yearling steers, 510–11, 552
Cotton Belt, beef production in, 16–17
Cottonseed, feeds, 331–32
  hulls, for fattening cattle, 383–85
  meal, 329–31
    as substitute for corn, 332
    cold-pressed, 331
    poisoning from, 332
    vs. linseed meal, 334–36
Cotyledons, uterine, 104
Cows, computing rations for, 162–67
  cost of maintaining, 547–49
  fattening for market, 246–47
  gains during summer, 135–36
  gains during winter, 167–70
  pregnant, care of, 110–11
  selection of, 59–62
  summer feeding without pasture, 146–47
  winter rations for, 152–67
Creep-feeding calves, 142–46, 513–17
Crossbreeding, 56–58
Curling cattle for show, 575–77

Cystic ovary, 86

Death risk, 29
Deferred grazing, 453
Dehorning, 174–80
  effects of, 175, 179–80
  equipment for, 178
  methods of, 175–79
Depreciation, importance of, in purebred cattle, 568–69
Dipping vats, 593
Direct shipments of feeder cattle, 218–21
Diseases of cattle, 596–616
  importance of, in buying breeding cattle, 79–81
Distillers' grains, 344–45
Dixon Springs, plan of using pasture, 456–58
Dried beet pulp, 298–300
Drugs, effect on cattle, 466
Dual-purpose cattle, 8–9
  methods of managing, 8–9
Dwarf calves, 603–05

Ear corn, 477
  silage, 284–85
Ear marking, 185–86
  tags, 186–87
  tattooing, 186
Eastern states, beef production in, 15
Elastator, castration by, 184–85
Ensiloing, chemical changes due to, 386–87
  losses from, 387–89
  physical changes due to, 389–90
Equipment, for beef cattle, 584–95
  for showing cattle, 582–83
  labor-saving, 594–95
  restraint, 591–92
Ergot, 617

Fallopian tubes, 102
Fattening cattle, for market, 5–6, 217–27
  on grain, 262–77
  on pasture, 441
  reasons for, 217–18
  risk encountered in, 554–56
Feed, amount consumed by cattle, 263–67
  cooked, 488–89
  full, 262–63
  full vs. limited, for fattening cattle, 269–77
Feed bunks, 587–89
Feeder cattle, for limited grain rations, 276–77

Feeder cattle, for summer feeding, 430–31
  importance of age of, 228–36
  importance of sex of, 238–47
  importance of type of, 247–51
  numbers fed, 217–18
  sources of, 218–21
Feeding, contract, 226–27
  free-choice method of, 500–01
  hand, details of, 502–05
  in transit, 226
  methods of, 221–23, 497–505
  show cattle, 573
  nursing calves, 124–26, 142–46, 171–72, 513–15
Feeds, number per day, 502–03
  preparation of, 474–96
Feet, care of, 579–82
  foul, 606
Fern poisoning, 617
Fertilizing constituents, excreted by cattle, 32
  losses of, in manure, 37
Financial aspect, of breeding herd, 547–50
  of purebred cattle, 565–71
  of steer feeding, 552–65
  of young cattle, 549–52
Fitting cattle for show and sale, 572–83
Flies, control of, 621
  protection from, 140–41, 573
Fodder, corn, for breeding cattle, 153–55
  for fattening cattle, 475–76
Fœtal heart, auscultation of, 109
  membranes, 102–04
  movements, 109–10
Fœtus, position in uterus, 105
Foot-and-mouth disease, 605–06
Foul foot, 606
Founder, 607
Fowlers' solution, 466
Free-choice method of feeding, 500–01
Free-martin, 106
Freight, charges on cattle, 542
Full feed, definition of, 263

Gains, of beef cows, during summer, 135–36
  during winter, 167–70
  of heifers in feed lot, 238–39
  of steers, on full feed, 230
  on pasture, 444–46
  of young stocker cattle, 189–91, 212–14
General farming, relation of beef cattle to, 19–29
Generative organs of cow, 83–85

Gestation period, 110
Gluten feed and meal, 336
Grade, effect on time to finish, 257–58
    importance of, in feeder cattle, 251–54
Grades, of feeder cattle, 252–53
Grain, mixtures for fattening cattle, 293
    rations, for the breeding herd, 161–62
        for calves, 124–26, 146
        for steers on pasture, 437–40
        rolled vs. ground, for beef cattle, 486–87
    sorghum, fodder and stover, 159
        for fattening cattle, 295–98
        for silage, 407–08
        grinding of, 485–86
        varieties of, 295
    use of, in fattening cattle, 262–77
Grass, see Pasture
    silage, see Silage, hay-crop
Grazing, deferred, 453
    night vs. day, 436–37
    rotation, 451–53
    season, length of, 133–34
Ground corn, 478–80
Group vs. stall feeding, 501–02
Guarantee of breeding animals, 80–81

Hand feeding, details of, 502–05
Hay-crop silage, see Silage
    early vs. late cut, 375
    grinding and chaffing, 490–91
    legume, see Legume hay
    racks, types of, 589–91
    utilization of, by cattle, 24–26
Heifers, age to breed, 90–94
    for feeding purposes, 238–42
    gain, in feed lot, 239–40
        on pasture, 212–14
    market requirements of, 238, 241
    spayed, advantages of, 245–46
    winter feeding of, 209–11
Hemorrhagic septicemia, 607–09
Hog credits, 561–62
Hogs, gains from undigested feed, 235–36
    ratio to steers, 475
Hominy feed, 293
Hormones, effect on fattening, 466–68
    of reproduction, 86
Horns, branding, 187
    polishing of, 578–79
    removal of, 174–80
    training of, 180–81

Impaction, 609–10
Inbreeding, 73–75
    coefficient of, 74–75

Indian turnip poisoning, 618
Indigestion, 609–10
Individuality, importance in selection, 59–62
Insurance, of cattle at market, 543
Intradermal test for tuberculosis, 614
Investment, in buildings and equipment, 26
    in purebred cattle, 566

Kafir corn, 295
    stover, 379–80
Kansas plan of deferred feeding, 453–55

Labor cost, of fattening cattle, 559
Labor pains, 113–14
Labor requirements of beef cattle, 26–29
Lactation, effect on growth, 90
Laminitis, 607
Lead poisoning, 621
Legume hay, as a source of protein, 313, 358
    energy equivalent, 163–64
    for breeding cattle, 160
    for fattening cattle, 366–72
    pasture, see Pasture, legume vs. grass
        silage, see Silage, hay-crop
Lespedeza hay, 371
    pasture, 456–57
Lice, treatment for, 621–22
Limited grain rations, 269–77
    effect on cost of gains, 269–70
    effect on profits, 271
    effect on rate of gain, 270
    for cattle on pasture, 442–43
    practical use of, 276–77
Linseed meal, 333–35
    old and new process, 334
    vs. cottonseed meal, 334–35
Lumpy jaw, 610–11

Mad itch, 611
Mammoth clover, 371
Mange, 622
Manure credits, 561–62
    importance of saving, 33–34
    losses from, 33–34, 37–39
    preservation of, 38–39
    production of, 39–42
Margin, effect on profits, 564–65
    feeder's, defined, 556–57
    necessary, 556
        factors determining, 557
Market, when to, 528
Marketing cattle, 527–45
    cost of, 541–45, 560–61

Marketing cattle, cost of, effect of shrinkage on, 545
Marking cattle, 185–87
Master breeders, 53–54
Mating, methods of, 97–100
Meconium, 117
Membranes, fœtal, 102–04
Milo maize, 295
Mineral-deficient areas, 464
Mineral supplements, 463–64
Minerals, required by cattle, 463–66
  trace, 464–66
Missouri plan of utilizing pastures, 456
Mixed feeds, for fattening cattle, 351–56, 574
  hay, 374–75
Molasses, ammoniated, 350–51
  for fattening cattle, 300–02
  for feeding show cattle, 574
  for supplementing corn cobs, 202–04
  for supplementing urea, 347
Molasses feeds, 303–04, 354–56
  for calves, 522–25
Mycotic stomatitis, 606

Necessary margin, see Margin
Neck chains, 185–86
Nightshade poisoning, 618
Nitrogenous concentrates, see Protein concentrates

Oats, for breeding cattle, 289
  for fattening cattle, 287–89
  grinding of, 287, 484–85
  vs. rolling, 486–487
Œstrum, occurrence and duration, 86–88
  after parturition, 121
  signs of, 88
Ophthalmic test for tuberculosis, 614
Os uteri, 83
Ova, 85
Ovaries, 85–86
Oviducts, 85
Ox warbles, 622–24

Parturition, 112–21
  causes of, 112
  rendering assistance in, 115–16
  signs of, 112–13
Pasture, advantages of feeding on, 426–27
  area per animal, 134–35, 446–49
  creep feeding calves on, 142–46
  for breeding animals, 127–34
  for fattening cattle, 426–58
  for show cattle, 574

Pasture, gains made on, 135–36, 444–46, 449–50
  grain rations to use on, 437–40
  legume vs. grass, 130, 432–34
  methods of utilizing, 450–58
  permanent vs. temporary, 129–32
  selecting cattle for, 430–31, 441
  turning cattle onto, 434–35, 440–41
  utilization by beef cattle, 21–24
    better methods of, 450–58
  varieties of, 431–34
  vs. dry lot for summer feeding, 429–30
  winter, for beef cows, 160–61
Paved feed lots, 585–87
Pavilion of oviduct, 85
Peanut meal, 350
Pedigree, importance of, 71–75
Phases of beef production, 3–10
Phosphorus, required by cattle, 463–64
Pinch gate, 591
Pink eye, 611–12
Placenta, 103–04
  expulsion of, 117–18
  removal of, 119–20
  retention of, 118–19
Pneumonia, 612
Poisonous plants, 616–21
Pork credits, 235–36
  value of, 561–62
Potatoes, dehydrated, 308–09
  for fattening cattle, 304–06
Prairie hay, for fattening cattle, 373–74
  for stocker cattle, 194
"Predigested" feeds, 496–97
Pregnancy, 102–11
  discrimination against, in market cattle, 242–43
  duration of, 110
  effect on fattening, 242–45
    on growth, 244
  examination for, 108–10
  multiple, 105–06
  signs of, 106–08
Prices, market cattle, fluctuation of, 546
  purebred cattle, 566–67
Production records, importance of, 65–71
  testing of bulls, 65–68
Profits, from breeding cattle, 549–51
  from fattening cattle, 562–65
    method of calculation, 563–64
  from stocker cattle, 5, 552–54
Progeny testing of bulls, 68–71
Protein concentrates, amount to feed, 319–26
  as conditioners and appetizers, 319
    substitute for corn, 326–28

Protein concentrates, fed to beef cattle, 329–56
  for cattle on pasture, 437–40, 443–44
  requirements, of fattening cattle, 312
    of pregnant cows, 163
    of stocker cattle, 194–96
  rules for feeding, 324–28
Protein feeds, mixed, 351–56
  supply of, 330
Purebred cattle, advantages of, 9–11
  financial aspects of, 565–71
  importance in Corn Belt states, 14
  operating costs of, 569
  prices of, 566–68
  production of, 9–10
  receipts from, 570–71
  selling costs of, 569

Quarantine of breeding cattle, 80

Rail shipment of cattle, 531–32
Rations, computing, for beef cows, 162–67
  for stocker cattle, 205–09
Red clover hay, 366
  pasture, 432
Release, thirty-six-hour, 225–26
Restraint equipment, 591–93
Ringworm, 624
Rolled vs. ground grain, 486–87
Root crops, for fattening cattle, 304
  in Great Britain, 306–07
Roughage, amount to feed, 363–64
  classification of, 358
  composition of, 357
  digestion, theory of, 362–63
  fattening cattle without, 364–65
  function in fattening ration, 357–62
  preparation of, 489–95
  replacement value of, 267
  utilization of, by beef cattle, 19–21
Rye for fattening cattle, 293

Salt, consumption of, 460–63
  forced feeding of, 462
Scours, 612–13
Screw worms, 624–25
Scrub cattle, feeding of, 258–60
Selection of breed, 54–55
  of breeding animals, 52–82
  of feeder cattle, 260–61
  of show animals, 572
Self-feeders, construction of, 587
  use in summer feeding, 427
  value in fattening cattle, 497–98
Self-feeding, 497–500

Sex of feeder cattle, importance of, 238–41
Shade, value of, 140
Shelled corn, 477–78
Shelter, for beef cows, 150–51
  importance for full-fed cattle, 584–85
Shipment, billing of, 224–26, 534
  direct, 218–19
  feed-in-transit, 226–27
  losses sustained during, 538–40
  preparing animals for, 530–32
Shipping associations, cooperative, 527–28
Shipping fever, 607–09
Shock corn, for breeding cows, 153–55
  for fattening cattle, 475–76
  grinding of, for cattle, 491–95
Show cattle, feeding of, 573
  fitting of, 575–81
  selection of, 572
Shrinkage, effect upon marketing costs, 545
  factors affecting amount of, 535–36
  of cattle in transit, 534–38
Silage, A.I.V., 422
  alfalfa, see Silage, hay-crop
  amount to feed, 392–93
  beet-pulp, 421–22
  canning refuse, 420–21
  chemical changes occurring in, 386–87
  corn content per ton, 402
    for beef cows, 152–53
    for fattening calves, 396–98, 521
    for fattening cattle, 386–406
    for stocker cattle, 197
    frosted corn for, 402–03
    proper stage to harvest, 400–01
    varieties of corn for, 401–02
    vs. shock corn, 396–98
  corn stover, for breeding cows, 156–57
    for stocker cattle, 197–98
    method of making, 156–57
  ear-corn, 284–85
  effect, upon grain consumption, 392
    upon hog gains, 403–04
    upon shipping and sale, 404–05
  frozen, value of, 403
  hay-crop, cost of making, 492
    for breeding cows, 153
    for fattening cattle, 417–18, 493
    for stocker cattle, 200
    method of making, 413–15
  legume, see Silage, hay-crop
  millet, 419–20
  moldy, value of, 403
  oat, 420

Silage, oat, and pea, 419
  physical changes occurring in, 389–90
  preservatives, use of, 414–15, 422
  replacement value of, 398–99
  shrinkage of, 388–89, 424–25
  sorghum, 159, 407
  soybean, 410–12
  Sudan grass, 418–19
  sunflower, 408–10
  value of dry roughage with, 399–400
  vs. dry roughage, for fattening cattle,
    394–96
Silos, kinds and types, 422–24
  sealing of, 424–25
Snakeroot poisoning, 618–19
Snapped corn, 476–77
Soaking of feed, 487–88
Soil fertility, relation of cattle to, 30–42
Sorghum, grain, *see* Grain sorghum
  poisoning, 619–20
Southern states, beef production in, 16–
  17
Soybean hay, 369–71
Soybean oil meal, 337–42
  old *vs.* new process, 337
Soybean silage, 410–12
Soybean straw, 195, 370
Soybeans, value for fattening cattle, 337,
  340
Squeeze gate, 591
Stalk fields, for beef cows, 157–58
  for stocker cattle, 200–01
Stall *vs.* group feeding, 501–02
Sterility, 627–33
  treatment for, 629–31, 632–33
Stock foods, 469–70
Stockers, computing rations for, 205–09
  growing of, 4–5, 188, 211–12
  methods of wintering, 191–93
  winter gains of, 189–91
  winter rations for, 191–97
    effect of, on summer gains, 190–91
Stover, corn, for breeding animals, 153–
  54
  for fattening cattle, 376–79
  for stocker cattle, 196–97
  grain sorghum, 379–80
  silage, *see* Silage
  value of grinding and shredding, 196–
    97, 491–93
Straw, for bedding, 34–36
  for beef cows, 158–59
  for fattening cattle, 380
  for stocker cattle, 196
  utilization of, by cattle, 20–21
Sudan grass pasture, 132

Sudan grass silage, 418–19
Sunflower silage, 408–10
Sweet clover hay, 372
  pasture, for beef cows, 135
    for fattening cattle, 432
  poisoning, 620

Tankage, 343–44
Tattooing, 187
Terminal charge, 542
Texas fever, 16
Through billing of cattle, 224–25
Timothy hay, 372–73
Trocar, 599
Tuberculosis, 613–15
  prevalence of, 79
  tests for, 614
Trichomoniasis, 625–26, 628
Type, importance of, in breeding cattle
  60–62
  importance of, in feeder cattle, 247–51

Umbilical cord, 104–05
Urachus, 104
Urea, 345–48
Urinary calculi, 615
Uterus, 84
  examination of, 108–09
  irrigation of, 120–21

Vaccination, for abortion, 79, 187, 602–
  03
  for blackleg, 187, 598–99
Vagina, 83
Velvet beans, 350
Vibrionic abortion, 626, 628
Vitamins, 470–73
Vulva, 83

Warbles, 622–24
Warts, 615–16
Water, daily consumption of, 459–60
Water bag, 115
Water hemlock poisoning, 618
Weaning calves, 174
Western Range area, beef production in,
  11
Whartonian gelatin, 104
Wheat, for fattening cattle, 292–93
  preparation of, 292–93, 486–87
Wheat bran, for fattening cattle, 342–43
  for nursing calves, 125–26
White snakeroot poisoning, 618

Yardage, 542
Yeast, value for cattle, 469